PERMAFROST

Engineering Design and Construction

PERMAFROST
Engineering Design and Construction

Associate Committee on Geotechnical Research,
National Research Council of Canada

EDITED BY
G. H. Johnston

John Wiley & Sons
Toronto   New York   Chichester   Brisbane

Canadian Cataloguing in Publication Data

National Research Council of Canada. Associate
Committee on Geotechnical Research.
   Permafrost

Bibliography: p. 483.
Includes index.
ISBN 0-471-79918-1

1. Civil engineering—Cold weather conditions.
2. Permafrost.   3. Frozen ground research.
I. Johnston, G. H.   II. Title.

TA713.N37   624.1′5136   C80-094785-1

Printed and bound in Canada by Hunter Rose Company Ltd.

10 9 8 7 6 5 4 3 2 1

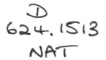

Table of Contents

TABLE OF CONTENTS
Chapter 7   FOUNDATIONS (cont'd)

Foreword

The Associate Committee on Geotechnical Research of the National Research Council of Canada was established in 1945 to coordinate and stimulate research on the engineering and physical aspects of the terrain in Canada. In 1958, the Associate Committee sponsored a permafrost research conference on the special problems posed by the terrain in northern Canada and, as a result, a Permafrost Subcommittee was formed in 1960. This subcommittee has sponsored several research conferences, seminars and workshops on special topics. A conference held in 1969 dealt with permafrost problems related to the mining and petroleum industries and led to the formation of the Subcommittee on Pipeline and Land Use Technology in Northern Terrain. The new subcommittee (disbanded in 1973) was very active and was instrumental in arranging a successful Canadian Northern Pipeline Research Conference in 1972.

Engineering activity in the Canadian North has grown steadily but increased greatly in recent years, due mainly to the search for and development of petroleum and mineral resources and the desire to improve the standard of living for northern residents. The need to make available the most recent technology on northern construction was emphasized not only at the Canadian Northern Pipeline Research Conference but also at a seminar on Guidelines for Scientific Activities in Northern Canada, sponsored by the Canadian Government Advisory Committee on Northern Development and held shortly after the Pipeline Conference. The Associate Committee on Geotechnical Research therefore undertook to prepare a manual of practice for construction on permafrost, the need for which was strongly endorsed by both industry and government.

A Task Force was established to develop an outline for the manual and make suggestions concerning its preparation and content. This group consisted of F. E. Crory, U.S. Army, Cold Regions Research and Engineering Laboratory; K. L. Hall, Trans-Mountain Pipe Line Company; Dr. R. M. Hardy, R. M. Hardy and Associates Limited; G. H. Johnston, Division of Building Research, National Research Council (Chairman); N. A. Lawrence, Associated Engineering Services Limited; and L. Samson, Terratech Limited. All have extensive experience in northern engineering and construction practice. The terms of reference for the manual were that it should cover all aspects of construction on permafrost, including the nature and distribution of permafrost in Canada, site and route selection and investigation, excavation and placement of earth materials in the North, and design and construction principles for engineering works, including foundations, utilities, transportation facilities, dams and reservoirs. The basic objective was to provide information and guidance to those involved with engineering design and construction in permafrost areas.

Many people contributed their expertise in permafrost engineering to the preparation of this volume. Financial support was received from the Division of Building Research, National Research Council of Canada and the Department of Indian and Northern Affairs. It is a special pleasure for me to express, on behalf of the Associate Committee, sincere thanks and appreciation to all individuals and organizations who contributed both materially and financially to the preparation of this volume, which describes the state of the art in permafrost engineering.

L. W. Gold
Chairman
Associate Committee on
Geotechnical Research

Preface

About one-half the land area of Canada and the Soviet Union, more than 60% of Alaska, about 22% of the People's Republic of China and extensive areas in northern Eurasia as well as Greenland and Antarctica are underlain by perennially frozen ground, more commonly known as permafrost. Permafrost may also underlie rivers, lakes and the ocean and is found at high elevations in mountainous areas. Because the nature and distribution of frozen ground can be rather unpredictable, and because it frequently contains large quantities of ice, many difficult engineering problems are encountered. As much as possible of the information and experience gained in past years has been summarized in this book to provide guidance to those engaged in engineering design and construction on permafrost.

All aspects of permafrost engineering could not be treated comprehensively in a book such as this. What has been attempted, however, is to outline the major factors that influence and must be considered in the design and construction of engineering works, and to suggest principles and methods that can be applied, together with sound engineering judgment, to satisfactorily construct on permafrost. It is hoped that the subject has been covered in sufficient detail so that the information given in this volume, which contains an extensive list of references, will achieve this objective.

Although the information presented is applicable in general to most permafrost engineering problems, special or novel investigations and design and construction methods, which are beyond the scope of this book, may be required when unusual structures or facilities are to be designed and constructed or when unusual or complex subsurface conditions are encountered. In such cases, the work should be conducted by those having experience and competence in the field of permafrost engineering.

The book is divided essentially into two parts. The first four chapters are introductory in nature and are meant to acquaint the reader with the main factors, such as the climate, terrain features and permafrost conditions, that affect engineering operations in the North and to describe the properties and behaviour of frozen ground. Chapters five to ten deal with methods for site and route investigations, the excavation and placement of earth materials and the design and construction of engineering works in permafrost. The last chapter emphasizes the need to monitor performance and to keep detailed site, construction and inspection records and the importance of carrying out regular maintenance work if a structure or facility is to perform satisfactorily.

Much is known about permafrost but much remains to be learned if safe and sound engineering works are to be constructed economically. All those engaged in northern engineering are encouraged to record their experience so that design and construction practices can be improved and construction and maintenance costs reduced.

G. H. Johnston

Acknowledgements

Sincere appreciation is expressed to all contributors for their willing cooperation and assistance in preparing material for this book. The wide scope of the subject could not have been covered without the benefit of their expert knowledge and experience in northern engineering and allied topics. The guidance provided by the Task Force is gratefully acknowledged. In addition to preparing some of the material, Mr. F. L. Peckover and Dr. J. F. Nixon reviewed most of the manuscript and made many constructive suggestions, which were greatly appreciated. Special and most sincere thanks must be expressed to Dr. R. F. Legget, former Director of the Division of Building Research and former Chairman of the Associate Committee on Geotechnical Research, who reviewed the complete manuscript. The benefit of his comments, advice and experience so willingly given was invaluable in the final preparation of the book.

The assistance and cooperation received from the Graphics Unit, Division of Building Research, and especially from Mr. F. Crupi and Mr. L. R. Smith, in preparing the illustrations is gratefully recognized. Sincere thanks and appreciation must be recorded for the many hours and special effort given by Mrs. N. E. Hardy in typing the several drafts and the final manuscript of the book.

Sincere thanks must also be expressed to Mr. C. B. Crawford, Director, Division of Building Research and Past Chairman, Associate Committee on Geotechnical Research and Dr. L. W. Gold, Chairman, Associate Committee on Geotechnical Research, for their encouragement, understanding and never-failing support in the preparation of the book.

The continued interest and expert assistance given by Mrs. Trudy L. Rising, Mr. Greg Ioannou and Ms. Francine Geraci of John Wiley & Sons Canada Limited is gratefully acknowledged.

List of Contributors

G. H. ARGUE
  Airport Facilities Branch, Airports and
Construction Services, Ministry of Transport,
Ottawa, Ontario.

T. H. W. BAKER
  Geotechnical Section, Division of Building
Research, National Research Council of Canada,
Ottawa, Ontario.

D. W. BOYD
  Atmospheric Environment Service, Department of
Fisheries and Environment—seconded to Division
of Building Research, National Research Council
of Canada, Ottawa, Ontario. (Retired)

R. J. E. BROWN
  Geotechnical Section, Division of Building
Research, National Research Council of Canada,
Ottawa, Ontario. (Deceased)

E. I. CAREFOOT
  Associated Engineering Services Limited,
Edmonton, Alberta.

A. L. DAVIES
  Montreal Engineering Company Limited,
Montreal, Quebec.

D. M. DAVISON
  Klohn, Leonoff Consultants Limited, Calgary,
Alberta.

J. A. FULLERTON
  Transportation Directorate, Design and
Construction, Department of Public Works,
Ottawa, Ontario.

L. W. GOLD
  Associate Director, Division of Building Research,
National Research Council of Canada, Ottawa,
Ontario.

L. E. GOODRICH
  Geotechnical Section, Division of Building
Research, National Research Council of Canada,
Ottawa, Ontario.

M. C. HARRIS
  Thurber Consultants Limited, Edmonton, Alberta
(Formerly with R. M. Hardy and Associates
Limited, Edmonton, Alberta).

D. W. HAYLEY
  EBA Engineering Consultants Limited,
Edmonton, Alberta.

xv

J. A. HEGINBOTTOM   Terrain Sciences Division, Geological Survey of
                         Canada, Department of Energy, Mines and
                         Resources, Ottawa, Ontario.

J. M. HUNTER   Resource Geophysics and Geochemistry Division,
                         Geological Survey of Canada, Department of
                         Energy, Mines and Resources, Ottawa, Ontario.

G. H. JOHNSTON   Geotechnical Section, Division of Building
                         Research, National Research Council of Canada,
                         Ottawa, Ontario.

B. LADANYI   Department of Civil Engineering, Ecole
                         Polytechnique, Montreal, Quebec.

N. A. LAWRENCE   Consultant, Associated Engineering Services
                         Limited, Edmonton, Alberta.

P. LUKOMSKYJ   Associated Engineering Services Limited,
                         Edmonton, Alberta.

J. R. MACKAY   Department of Geography, University of British
                         Columbia, Vancouver, British Columbia.

J. G. MACPHERSON   Acres Consulting Services Limited, Winnipeg,
                         Manitoba.

G. McCORMICK   R. M. Hardy and Associates Limited, Edmonton,
                         Alberta.

J. D. MOLLARD   J. D. Mollard and Associates Limited, Regina,
                         Saskatchewan.

N. R. MORGENSTERN   Department of Civil Engineering, University of
                         Alberta, Edmonton, Alberta.

J. F. NIXON   R. M. Hardy and Associates Limited, Calgary,
                         Alberta.

F. L. PECKOVER   Geotechnical Consultant, Vaudreuil, Quebec
                         (Formerly engineer of Geotechnical Services,
                         Canadian National Railways, Montreal, Quebec).

E. PENNER   Geotechnical Section, Division of Building
                         Research, National Research Council of Canada,
                         Ottawa, Ontario.

W. J. SCOTT   Resource Geophysics and Geochemistry Division,
                         Geological Survey of Canada, Department of
                         Energy, Mines and Resources, Ottawa, Ontario.

W. W. SHILTS   Terrain Sciences Division, Geological Survey of
                               Canada, Department of Energy, Mines and
                               Resources, Ottawa, Ontario.

R. M. STRANG   Department of Plant Science, University of
                               British Columbia, Vancouver, British Columbia
                               (Formerly with Department of Indian and
                               Northern Affairs, Ottawa, Ontario).

D. E. THORNTON   Environmental Protection Service, Department of
                               Fisheries and Environment, Edmonton, Alberta.

G. P. WILLIAMS   Information Services Group, Division of Building
                               Research, National Research Council of Canada,
                               Ottawa, Ontario.

Glossary of Permafrost Terms

Although many terms used in permafrost engineering are defined in the text, the following list of selected permafrost terms has been compiled for easy reference. The terms listed have been taken almost verbatim from the booklet *Permafrost Terminology*, prepared by Brown and Kupsch (1974). In each case, the definition only is given and it is recommended that the reader consult the booklet for further details and explanatory notes concerning each term.

For a list of terms and definitions pertaining to muskeg (peatlands), a feature of the northern terrain that is intimately associated with permafrost, the reader is directed to lists compiled by MacFarlane (1969) and Stanek (1977). Similarly, for terms related to patterned ground and periglacial features, the reader should consult publications by Washburn (1956, 1973). Geological, geomorphological, geotechnical and foundation engineering terms and definitions will be found in standard reference texts on those subjects.

active layer—the top layer of ground above the permafrost table that thaws each summer and refreezes each fall.

alass—a circular to irregular lowland (varies from less than 1 km^2 to many times that area) from which the originally large ice content (up to 80% by volume) has essentially disappeared, resulting in a lowering of the ground surface by 5 to 20 m.

beaded stream—a drainage pattern of individual streams in which pools or small lakes are connected by short stream reaches.

cryosphere—that part of the Earth's crust and the atmosphere subject, for at least a part of each year, to temperatures below 0°C.

cryoturbation—a collective term to describe all soil movements due to frost action.

depth of thaw—the distance from the ground surface downward to frozen ground at any time during the thawing season.

depth of zero annual amplitude—the distance from the ground surface downward to the point beneath which there is virtually no annual fluctuation in ground temperature.

drunken forest—a group of trees leaning in a random orientation; usually associated with thermokarst topography.

freezing index—the number of degree-days (the difference between the mean temperature each day and 0°C, either positive or negative) between the highest point in the autumn and the lowest point the next spring on the cumulative degree-day time curve for one freezing season. The air freezing index is determined from temperatures measured about 1.4 m above the ground surface, while that determined from temperatures measured at or immediately below a surface is known as the surface freezing index.

frost cracking—fracturing of the ground by thermal contraction at temperatures below 0°C.

frost-susceptible soil—soil in which significant detrimental ice segregation occurs when the requisite moisture and freezing conditions are present.

frost table—any frozen surface in the active layer that is moving downward towards the permafrost table due to thawing.

frozen ground—soil or rock having a temperature below 0°C.

geocryology—the study of earth materials having a temperature below 0°C.

ground—earth materials, including all types of soil and rock and their constituents.

ground heave—upward movement of the ground causing a raising of the ground surface as a result of the formation of ground ice in excess of pore fillings.

ground settlement—downward movement of the ground causing a lowering of the ground surface resulting from the melting of ground ice in excess of pore fillings.

ice, aggradational—the additional newly formed or incorporated ground ice resulting from a raising of the permafrost table or a lowering of the permafrost base.

ice, buried—ice formed at the surface and later covered with soil.

ice, epigenetic—ground ice that formed after the deposition of the earth material in which it occurs.

ice, excess—the ice in the ground that exceeds the total pore volume that the ground would have under natural unfrozen conditions.

ice, ground—ice in pores, cavities, voids or other openings in soil or rock, including massive ice.

ice, intrusive—ice formed from water intruded or injected under pressure into a porous earth material.

ice, massive—a comprehensive term used to describe large (with dimensions measuring at least 10-100 cm) masses of underground ice, including ice wedges, pingo ice and ice lenses.

ice, pore—ice occurring in the pores of soils and rocks.

ice, reticulate—network of horizontal and vertical ice veins forming a three-dimensional rectangular or square lattice commonly found in frozen glaciolacustrine sediments.

ice, segregated—ice formed by the migration of pore water to the freezing plane where it forms into discrete lenses, layers, or seams ranging in thickness from hairline to greater than 10 m.

ice, sill—ice in a concordant, tabular mass formed by water intruded or injected under pressure into a porous earth material.

ice, syngenetic—ground ice that formed more or less simultaneously with the deposition of the earth material in which it occurs.

ice, tension-crack—ice, banded or layered, which forms in cracks produced by tension or mechanical rupture of the ground, resulting mainly from the growth of segregated or intrusive ice.

ice, thermal contraction—ice formed in cracks in the ground caused by thermal contraction of the ground surface.

ice, vein—a comprehensive term for ice in cracks where it occurs in bodies of various shapes, including tabular forms and wedges.

ice content—the ratio, expressed as a percentage, of the weight of the ice phase to the weight of dry soil.

ice lens—1. a dominantly horizontal lens-shaped body of ice of any dimension.
2. commonly used for layers of segregated ice that are parallel to the ground surface. The lenses may range in thickness from hairline to as much as about 10 m.

ice segregation—the process of formation of segregated ice by freezing of water in mineral or organic soil.

ice vein—a seam or vein of ice occupying a crack that cuts across rock or soil layers.

ice wedge—a massive, generally wedge-shaped body with its apex pointing downward, composed of foliated or layered, vertically oriented, commonly white ice; from less than 10 cm to 3 m or more wide at the top, tapering to a feather edge at the apex at a depth of 1 to 10 m or more. Some ice wedges may extend downward as far as 25 m and may have shapes dissimilar from wedges. They may be "active" or "inactive," depending on whether they are or are not growing by repeated, but not necessarily annual (winter), cracking.

ice wedge cast—an infilling of soil or sediment into the space formerly occupied by an ice wedge.

icing—a sheet-like mass of ice, either on the ground surface or on the surface of river ice.

intrapermafrost water—free water occurring in unfrozen zones within the permafrost.

non-frost-susceptible soil—a soil that does not display significant detrimental ice segregation during freezing.

palsa—a Fennoscandian term for a round or elongated hillock or mound, maximum height about 10 m, composed of a peat layer overlying mineral soil. It has a perennially frozen core that extends from within the covering peat layer downward into or toward the underlying mineral soil.

patterned ground—a general term for any ground surface of surficial soil materials exhibiting a discernible, more or less ordered and symmetrical, micro-physiographic pattern.

peat—an unconsolidated, compressible soil consisting of partially decomposed, semi-carbonized remains of plants (such as mosses, sedges and trees), some animal residues and commonly some mineral soil.

peatland—any terrain covered by a layer of peat.

peat plateau (see also palsa)—a low, generally flat-topped expanse of peat, rising one or more metres above the general surface of a peatland. A layer of permafrost exists in the peat plateau, which may extend into the peat below the general peatland surface and even into the underlying mineral soil.

perennially frozen ground—see *permafrost*.

periglacial—1. the area, geomorphological processes and deposits characteristic of the frost-affected immediate margins of existing and former glaciers and ice sheets.
2. the environment of cold regions in which frost action is important; the features resulting from frost action.

permafrost—the thermal condition in soil or rock of temperatures below 0°C persisting over at least two consecutive winters and the intervening summer; moisture in the form of water and ground ice may or may not be present. Earth materials in this thermal condition may be described as perennially frozen, irrespective of their water and ice content.

permafrost, contemporary—1. permafrost in thermal equilibrium with current mean annual surface temperature and ground heat flux.
2. newly formed permafrost in an area where surface temperatures have fallen below 0°C.

permafrost, continuous—permafrost occurring everywhere beneath the exposed land surface throughout a geographic regional zone, with the exception of widely scattered sites (such as newly deposited unconsolidated sediments) where the climate has just begun to impose its influence on the ground thermal regime and will cause the formation of continuous permafrost.

permafrost, discontinuous—permafrost occurring in some areas beneath the ground surface throughout a geographic regional zone where other areas are free of permafrost.

permafrost, dry—perennially frozen soil or rock without ice or with an ice content lower than the pore volume, so that it does not yield excess water on thawing.

permafrost, epigenetic—permafrost that formed after the deposition of the earth material in which it occurs.

permafrost, ice-rich—perennially frozen ground that contains ice in excess of that required to fill pore spaces.

permafrost, marginal—permafrost that is very close in space, temperature or time to thawing; i.e.,
    (a) permafrost at or near the southern limit of the permafrost region, or
    (b) permafrost of which the temperature is very close to 0°C (a few tenths of a degree) anywhere in the permafrost region or
    (c) permafrost that lasts for only a few years and then dissipates.

permafrost, relic—occurrences of permafrost that reflect past climatic conditions differing from those of today, and which must have formed when the ground surface temperature was different (usually lower) than it is now, as they are not in thermal equilibrium with the present mean annual ground surface temperature.

permafrost, sporadic—permafrost occurring in the form of scattered permafrost islands in the more discontinuous permafrost zone.

permafrost, submarine—permafrost occurring beneath the sea or ocean bottom.

permafrost, syngenetic—permafrost that formed more or less simultaneously with the deposition of the ground in which it occurs.

permafrost, thaw stable—perennially frozen soils that do not, on thawing, show loss of strength below normal, long-time thawed values nor produce ground settlement.

permafrost, thaw unstable—perennially frozen soils that show, on thawing, a significant loss of strength below normal, long-time thawed values and/or significant settlement, as a direct result of the melting of the excess ice in the soil.

permafrost, widespread—permafrost that is widely distributed but not continuous beneath the land surface.

permafrost aggradation—an increase in thickness and/or areal extent of permafrost because of natural or artificial causes as a result of climatic cooling and/or change of terrain conditions such as vegetation succession, infilling of lake basins or human activity.

permafrost base—the lower boundary surface of permafrost above which temperatures are negative (below 0°C) and below which temperatures are positive (above 0°C).

permafrost degradation—a decrease in thickness and/or areal extent of permafrost because of natural or artificial causes as a result of climatic warming and/or change of terrain conditions such as disturbance or removal of an insulating vegetation layer by fire or human means.

permafrost limit—the geographical distal boundaries of the circumpolar continuous and discontinuous permafrost zones.

permafrost table—the upper boundary of permafrost.

permafrost thickness—the vertical distance between the permafrost table and the permafrost base.

pingo—an Eskimo term for a conical, commonly more or less asymmetrical, mound or hill, with a circular or oval base and commonly fissured summit, occurring in the continuous and discontinuous permafrost zones, which has a core of massive ground ice covered with soil and vegetation, and which exists for at least two winters. They may be either "open" or "closed" system pingos depending on their mode of formation.

polygon—a type of patterned ground consisting of a closed, roughly equidimensional figure bounded by several sides, commonly more or less straight but some, or all, of which may be irregularly curved. A polygon may be either "low centre" or "high centre," depending on whether its centre is lower or higher than its margins.

polygon, ice wedge—any polygon surrounded by troughs underlain by ice wedges.

polygon, tundra—ice wedge polygon covered entirely with tundra vegetation.

residual thaw layer—the layer of thawed or unfrozen ground between the seasonally frozen ground and the permafrost table.

retrogressive thaw or "bi-modal" flow slide—a slide that consists of a steep headwall, containing ice or ice-rich sediment, which retreats in a retrogressive fashion through melting, and a debris flow formed from the mixture of thawed sediment and ice, which slides down the face of the headwall to its base.

seasonal frost—seasonal temperatures causing frost (below 0°C temperatures) that affect earth materials and keep them frozen only during the winter.

seasonally frozen ground—ground affected by seasonal frost.

seasonally thawed ground—ground affected by seasonal thaw during the summer and seasonal frost during the winter.

soil wedge—a generally wedge-shaped, downward tapering body of soil different in structure (and possible texture) from the surrounding soil, which may be an ice wedge cast or produced by repeated frost cracking and infilling with soil where no ice wedge was ever present.

solifluction—the process of slow, gravitational, down slope movement of saturated, nonfrozen earth material behaving apparently as a viscous mass over a surface of frozen material. Solifluction features include lobes, stripes, sheets and terraces.

string bog—boggy area marked by serpentine ridges of peat and vegetation, interspersed with depressions, many of which contain shallow ponds.

subpermafrost water—free water in the ground below the permafrost base.

suprapermafrost water—free water in the ground above the permafrost.

talik—a layer or body of unfrozen ground within the permafrost. It may be either a "closed" or an "open" talik, depending on whether it is or it is not entirely surrounded by permafrost.

thaw basin—a depression of the permafrost table created by natural or artificial thawing.

thaw consolidation—1. the process by which a reduction in volume and increase in density of a soil mass occurs, following thaw, in response to the escape of water under the weight of the soil itself and/or an applied load.
    2. the process by which settlement due to thaw (thaw settlement) is impeded by the flow of water from the soil.
Thaw consolidation is a time-dependent phenomenon that is not governed exclusively by the rate of thaw or position of the thaw front. It may proceed for many years.

thaw settlement—the generally differential downward movement of the ground surface resulting from escape of water on melting of excess ice in the soil and the thaw consolidation of the soil mass.

thaw slumping—a type of mass movement caused by the conversion of ice into water in a soil by ground thaw, creating the kind of landslide that most closely resembles the more temperate climate earth flow, with a well-developed breakaway scarp front.

thawing index—the number of degree-days (the difference between the mean temperature each day and 0°C, either positive or negative) between the lowest point in the spring and the highest point the next autumn on the cumulative degree-day time curve for one thawing season. The air thawing index is determined from temperatures measured about 1.4 m above the ground surface, while that determined from temperatures measured at or immediately below a surface is known as the surface thawing index.

thermokarst (topography)—the irregular topography resulting from the process of differential thaw settlement or caving of the ground because of the melting of ground ice in thaw unstable permafrost.

tundra—a treeless, generally level to undulating region of lichens, mosses, sedges, grasses and some low shrubs, including dwarf willows and birches, which is characteristic of both the Arctic and higher alpine regions outside of the Arctic.

unfrozen water content—the ratio, expressed as a percentage, of the weight of unfrozen water to the weight of dry soil.

zero curtain—the zone immediately above the permafrost table where zero temperature (0°C) lasts a considerable period of time during freezing and thawing of the overlying ground.

Symbols and Units

The symbols used in this book are defined where they appear in the text. They conform, wherever possible, to standard engineering notation in use in Canada. Geotechnical symbols are based primarily on those recommended for use in Canada by the Canadian Geotechnical Society and closely follow the recommendations of the International Society of Soil Mechanics and Foundation Engineering and the International Society for Rock Mechanics (Barsvary et al. 1980).

Throughout the book the use of the International System of Units (S.I.) has generally been emphasized but in most cases the equivalent Imperial Unit has also been given. Wherever possible, hard conversion has been used. In some cases Imperial Units only have been used. The S.I. Units (commonly referred to as metric units) conform with Canada's National Standard, which is the Canadian Metric Practice Guide CAN 3-Z234.1-76 prepared by the Canadian Standards Association and approved by the Standards Council of Canada.

Some general terms, symbols and S.I. Units and multiples recommended by the Canadian Geotechnical Society are given in the following table:

Term	Symbol	S.I. Unit and Multiple
length	L, l	km, m, cm, mm, μm, nm
breadth	B, b	km, m, cm, mm, μm, nm
height, thickness	H, h	km, m, cm, mm, μm, nm
depth	D, z	km, m, cm, mm, μm, nm
diameter	d, D	km, m, cm, mm, μm, nm
area[a]	A	ha, m^2, cm^2, mm^2
dry volume	V	m^3, cm^3, mm^3
fluid volume	v	kL, L, mL
time[b]	t	d, h, min, s
velocity	v	km/h, m/s
acceleration	a	m/s^2
acceleration due to gravity (g = 9.81 m/s^2)	g	m/s^2
mass	m	t, kg, g
density	ρ	t/m^3, kg/m^3, g/cm^3
unit weight	γ	kN/m^3

Term	Symbol	S.I. Unit and Multiple
pressure, stress	σ, τ	MPa, kPa
temperature	T	°C, K
energy, work quantity of heat[c]	E, W, Q	kJ, J
power, heat transfer rate[d]	P, q	kW, W
moment of force, torque	M, T	MN·m, kN·m, N·m

[a] ha (hectare) = 10,000 m^2

[b] The second (s) is the only S.I. Unit; day (d), hour (h) and minute (m) are permitted units.

[c] J = joule = N·m

[d] W = watt = J/s

The term "mass" in the S.I. System is used to specify the quantity of matter contained in material objects and is independent of their location in the universe [unit = kilogram (kg)].

The term "weight" is used as a measure of the gravitational force acting on a material object at a specified location and generally varies as the object changes location [unit = newton (N)]. Standard gravity at sea level = 9.806 65 m/s^2.

The term "unit weight" in the S.I. System is used when expressing the gravitational force per unit volume (N/m^3).

The term "density" refers to mass per unit volume (kg/m^3).

Stress and pressure are expressed as the force per unit area (N/m^2 = Pa). The pascal (Pa) is the unit used in Canadian practice.

Tables and lists of conversion factors for units used in the Canadian construction industry are contained in the "Manual on Metric Building Drawing Practice," Special Technical Publication No. 3, Division of Building Research, National Research Council of Canada, prepared by C. S. Strelka, L. Loshak and J. S. Torrance. To aid the reader who may be more familiar with Imperial Units, some conversions extracted from this Manual are listed below. Conversion factors are taken to six significant figures where appropriate. Note that the long ton (U.K.) = 2240 lb and the short ton (used in Canadian practice) = 2000 lb.

	Metric to Imperial			Imperial to Metric	
Length					
1 km	=	0.621 371	mile	1 mile = 1.609 344	km
1 m	=	3.280 84	ft	1 ft = 0.304 8	m
1 mm	=	0.039 370	in.	1 in. = 25.4	mm
Area					
1 km^2	=	0.386 102	mile^2	1 mile^2 = 2.589 99	km^2
1 ha	=	2.471 054	acre	1 acre = 0.404 686	ha
1 m^2	=	10.763 9	ft^2	1 ft^2 = 0.092 903	m^2
1 mm^2	=	0.001 550	in.^{2}	1 in.^{2} = 645.16	mm^2
Volume, Capacity, Modulus of Section					
1 m^3	=	1.307 95	yd^3	1 yd^3 = 0.764 555	m^3
	=	35.314 7	ft^3	1 ft^3 = 0.028 317	m^3
1 L	=	0.035 315	ft^3	28.316 8	L
1 mL	=	0.061 024	in.^{3}	1 in.^{3} = 16.387 1	mL
1 L	=	0.219 969	gal	1 gal = 4.546 09	L
Velocity, Speed					
1 m/s	=	3.280 84	ft/s	1 ft/s = 0.304 8	m/s
	=	2.236 94	mile/h	1 mile/h = 0.447 04	m/s
1 km/h	=	0.621 371	mile/h	1 mile/h = 1.609 344	km/h
Acceleration					
1 m/s^2	=	3.280 84	ft/s^2	1 ft/s^2 = 0.304 8	m/s^2
Volume Rate of Flow					
1 m^3/s	=	35.314 7	ft^3/s	1 ft^3/s = 0.028 317	m^3/s
	=	19.005 3	10^6 gal/d	10^6 gal/d = 0.005 262	m^3/s
	=	2.118 88	ft^3/min	1 ft^3/min = 0.471 947	L/s
1 L/s	=	13.198 2	gal/min	1 gal/min = 0.075 768	L/s
	=	791.891	gal/h	1 gal/h = 0.001 263	L/s

Metric to Imperial

Mass

1 tonne (t)	= 0.984 207	long ton
	= 1.102 312	short ton
1 kg	= 2.204 62	lb

Density (Mass/Unit Volume)

1 kg/m³	= 0.062 428	lb/ft³
	= 1.685 56	lb/yd³
1 t/m³	= 0.752 48	long ton/yd³
	= 0.842 777	short ton/yd³

Force

1 MN	= 100.361	tonf
kN	= 0.100 361	tonf
	= 0.112 404	tonf (short ton)
	= 224.809	lbf
1N	= 0.224 809	lbf

Pressure, Stress, Modulus of Elasticity (1 Pa = 1 N/m²)

1 MPa	= 0.064 749	tonf/in.²
	= 0.323 85	tonf/ft²
	= 0.072 519	short tonf/in.²
	= 145.038	lbf/in.²
1 kPa	= 20.885 4	lbf/ft²

Work, Energy, Heat (1 J = 1 W·s)

1 MJ	= 0.277 778	kW hr
1 kJ	= 0.947 817	Btu
1 J	= 0.737 562	ft lbf

Power, Heat Flow Rate

1 kW	= 1.341 02	hp
1 W	= 3.412 14	Btu/h

Imperial to Metric

Mass

1 long ton	= 1.016 05	t
1 short ton	= 0.907 184	t
1 lb	= 0.453 592	kg

Density

1 lb/ft³	= 16.018 5	kg/m³
1 lb/yd³	= 0.593 278	kg/m³
1 long ton/yd³	= 1.328 94	t/m³
1 short ton/yd³	= 1.186 553	t/m³

Force

1 tonf	= 0.009 96	MN
1 tonf	= 9.964 02	kN
1 tonf (short ton)	= 8.896 44	kN
1 lbf	= 0.004 45	kN
1 lbf	= 4.448 22	N

Pressure

1 tonf/in.²	= 15.444 3	MPa
1 tonf/ft²	= 107.252	kPa
1 lbf/in.²	= 6.894 76	kPa
1 lbf/ft²	= 47.880 26	Pa
1 short tonf/in.²	= 13.789	MPa

Work

1 kW hr	= 3.6	MJ
1 Btu	= 1.055 06	kJ
1 ft lbf	= 1.355 82	J

Power

1 hp	= 0.745 700	kW
1 Btu/h	= 0.293 071	W

Intensity of Heat Flow (Heat Loss from Surfaces)

1 W/m²	=	0.316 998	Btu/ft² hr	1 Btu/ft² hr	= 3.154 59	W/m²

Thermal Conductance (Heat Transfer Coefficient)

1 W/(m²·°C)	=	0.176 110	Btu/ft² hr °F	1 Btu/ft² hr °F	= 5.678 26	W/(m²·°C)

Thermal Conductivity

1 W/(m·°C)	=	0.577 789	Btu/ft hr °F	1 Btu/ft hr °F	= 1.730 73	W/(m·°C)
	=	6.933 47	Btu in./ft² hr °F	1 Btu in./ft² hr °F	= 0.144 225	W/(m·°C)

Calorific Value (Mass and Volume Basis)

1 kJ/kg	=	0.429 923	Btu/lb	1 Btu/lb	= 2.326	kJ/kg
(1 J/g)						(J/g)
1 kJ/m³	=	0.026 839 2	Btu/ft³	1 Btu/ft³	= 37.258 9	kJ/m³

Thermal (Heat) Capacity (Mass and Volume Basis)

1 kJ/(kg·°C)	=	0.238 846	Btu/lb °F	1 Btu/lb °F	= 4.186 8	kJ/(kg·°C)
1 kJ/(m³·°C)	=	0.014 910 7	Btu/ft³ °F	1 Btu/ft³ °F	= 67.066 1	kJ/(m³·°C)

Some other conversion factors, based mainly on the centimetre-gram-second (c.g.s.) system of units but also including some Imperial Units, that may be helpful in geothermal work are given below.

c.g.s. to S.I.   S.I. to c.g.s.

Energy, Work

1 calorie	=	4.187	J	1 J	= 0.238 8	calories

Intensity of Heat Flow

1 cal/cm² s	=	41.87	kW/m²	1 W/m²	= 0.023 88	mcal/cm² sec

Thermal Conductivity

1 cal/cm sec °C	=	418.7	W/m·K	1 W/m·K	= 2.388	mcal/cm sec °C
	[=	242 Btu/ft hr °F)]				

	c.g.s. to S.I.			S.I. to c.g.s.	
Heat Capacity (Mass and Volume Basis)					
1 cal/g °C	= 4.187	kJ/kg·K	1 J/kg·K	= 0.238 8	mcal/g °C
1 cal/cm^3 °C	= 4187	kJ/m^3·K	1 J/m^3·K	= 238.8	mcal/cm^3 °C
Latent Heat					
1 cal/g	= 4.187	kJ/kg	1 J/kg	= 0.238 8	mcal/g
1 cal/cm^3	= 4187	kJ/m^3	1 J/m^3	= 238.8	mcal/cm^3

Heat of Fusion of Water

79.7 cal/g = 144 Btu/lb = 334 J/g

Thermal Diffusivity

1 mm^2/s = 0.038 75 ft^2/h

1 ft^2/h = 25.806 mm^2/s

CHAPTER 1

Northern Engineering– Basic Considerations

(Contributors–D. W. Boyd, J. A. Heginbottom, G. H. Johnston, R. M. Strang and G. P. Williams)

1.1 Introduction

In this book, the North is considered to coincide with the permafrost region (Chapter 2), which, in Canada, covers about 50% of the country, including all of the Yukon and Northwest Territories and the northern parts of British Columbia, the Prairie Provinces, Ontario, Quebec and Labrador (Fig. 1.1). The major factors that distinguish building in the North from building in southern, more temperate areas are the climate, the unusual and varied terrain and the relative isolation of most building sites.

The climate is usually not much more severe than that experienced in other cold areas of the northern hemisphere, such as the Prairie Provinces of Canada. It differs mainly in the duration of the winter rather than in the extremes of temperature. Thus the technical problems posed by climate are not significantly different from those encountered in more southern cold regions. Nevertheless, the climate does have several important implications for building in the North. The long winter and hours of darkness mean a very short construction season, which is restricted still further by the periods of freeze-up and break-up during which many areas are completely isolated from each other because of difficulty of movement.

Permafrost or perennially frozen ground is an important feature of the terrain that leads to many of the technical problems associated with northern engineering (Muller 1947, Brown and Johnston 1964, Brown 1970a, Ferrians et al. 1969). Therefore it must be given special attention in the design, construction and operation of all structures and facilities.

The great distances, combined with difficult access and limited transportation facilities in the North, exert an important influence on the economics of northern building. The relative isolation of most construction sites and the attendant problems of lack of local manpower and materials mean that most of the skilled labour, equipment and materials required must be brought in from the south at high cost. Similarly, maintenance and replacement of damaged equipment create further difficulties. All these jointly introduce serious economic and logistic

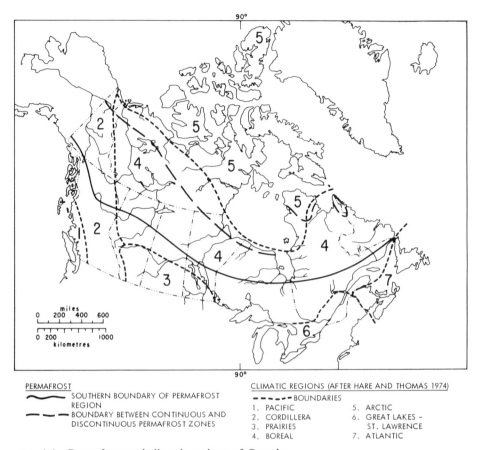

PERMAFROST
SOUTHERN BOUNDARY OF PERMAFROST
REGION
BOUNDARY BETWEEN CONTINUOUS AND
DISCONTINUOUS PERMAFROST ZONES

CLIMATIC REGIONS (AFTER HARE AND THOMAS 1974)
BOUNDARIES
1. PACIFIC   5. ARCTIC
2. CORDILLERA   6. GREAT LAKES –
3. PRAIRIES   ST. LAWRENCE
4. BOREAL   7. ATLANTIC

FIG. 1.1   Permafrost and climatic regions of Canada.

problems, which must be taken into account when planning and carrying out
engineering works in the North.

These factors and other important aspects of northern engineering are discussed in this chapter. Though Canadian examples are used, permafrost conditions in Alaska and Northern Eurasia present similar engineering and construction problems.

1.2 Climate and Weather

There is considerable variation in the climate of the North American permafrost
region, which, in Canada, lies mainly within two broad climatic regions: the Arctic and the Boreal (Fig. 1.1). The Arctic climatic region of Canada covers practically all areas north of the treeline. Contrary to what might be expected,
Canada's record low temperatures have not been observed in this region. The
precipitation varies from desert conditions in the Queen Elizabeth Islands to light
in the eastern part of this region.

The Boreal climatic region of Canada includes a large part of the Northwest Territories west of Hudson Bay, the northern parts of the Prairie Provinces and most of Ontario, Quebec and Labrador. Extremely low temperatures occur every winter throughout most of the northwest section and very high temperatures may occur in summer. Precipitation is light in the northwest, but snowfall is particularly heavy in the central Quebec-Labrador portion of the region. The Yukon lies within the Cordillera climatic region, but it is virtually impossible to map the climate accurately in this complex region because of the very rugged terrain.

General and detailed information on the climate of the Canadian North is available in several publications of the Canadian Atmospheric Environment Service (Thompson 1967, 1969, Burns 1973, Canada Transport 1967a, b, Canada Environment 1971, 1973) and others (Boyd 1975, Fletcher and Young 1976, Hare and Thomas 1974, Hare 1968).

Essentially all the heat at the surface of the earth comes from the sun, but its distribution is affected by several factors, such as the wind. During the summer, the average atmospheric pressure is much the same over the whole permafrost region and winds on the average are light. During the rest of the year, the average pressure over Baffin Bay and Davis Strait is quite low and the highest pressures are over or near the Mackenzie Valley. The resulting north or northwest winds

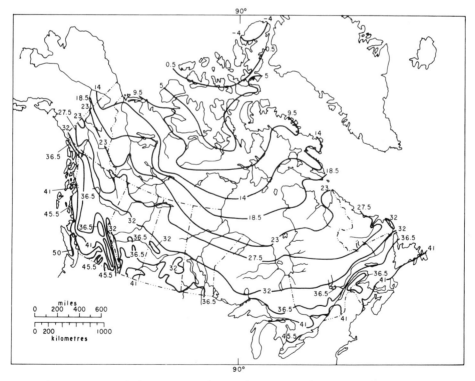

FIG. 1.2   Mean annual air temperature (°F)—based on period 1931-1960.

bring cold dry air from the far north down into the Hudson Bay area and the northern sections of the provinces from Saskatchewan to Quebec, and often further south. As a result, the Hudson Bay area is colder than any other area at the same latitude around the world. Mean annual air temperatures in Canada based on the period 1931-60 are given in Fig. 1.2.

The record low temperature for Canada of −81°F (−63°C) has been observed at Snag and Mayo, Y.T. Other stations in the Yukon and one station in each of British Columbia, Alberta and Ontario have all reported temperatures below −70°F (below −57°C). Temperatures below −60°F (below −51°C) have been reported in all but the four Atlantic provinces. On the other hand, the lowest temperature reported by any station in the N.W.T. was −70°F (−57°C) at Inuvik, and more than half the stations have never been as cold as −60°F (−51°C).

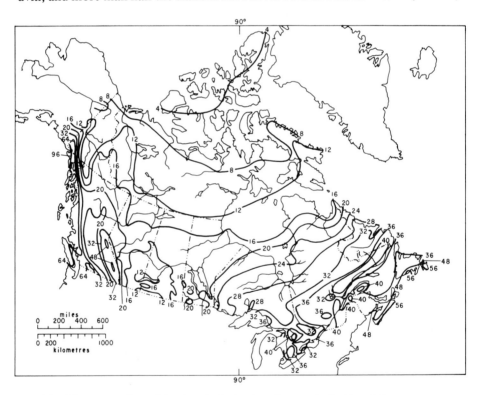

FIG. 1.3 Mean annual precipitation (inches)—based on period 1931-1960.

Precipitation varies appreciably throughout the North but decreases generally from south to north. The mean annual precipitation based on the period 1931-60 is given in Fig. 1.3. The annual total precipitation in the James Bay area is around 25 in. (650 mm), about two thirds of which falls as rain and the rest as snow. In an average winter, there will be snow on the ground for about six months and the maximum depth will be about 30 in. (75 cm).

Around Great Slave Lake the annual total precipitation averages about 12 in. (300 mm), about half as rain. In an average winter, there will be snow on the ground for six or seven months with a maximum depth of 20 to 25 in. (50 to 65 cm). In the Arctic Islands the annual total precipitation is only 2 to 6 in. (50 to 150 mm) and more than half of this falls as snow. The snowfall averages less than 30 in. (75 cm) over the whole area (water equivalent—snow/water = 10:1). In an average winter, there will be snow on the ground for about nine months, with a maximum depth of 10 to 15 in. (25 to 40 cm), but it is seldom evenly distributed. During the long, cold winter the wind blows upland areas nearly bare and piles the snow in huge drifts behind obstructions and in gullies (Fraser 1964).

Climate and permafrost are caused by solar radiation or lack of it. Short wave radiation from the sun is the ultimate source of almost all energy and long wave radiation to outer space is the ultimate sink. Since both ground and air are affected by these radiations, there is a broad relationship between average ground and air temperatures. Thus, average air temperatures measured about 4.5 ft. (1.5 m) above the ground surface can be used to estimate the probable presence or absence of permafrost (see Section 2.3).

Air freezing and thawing indices can be used to compare the climates of different locations and are also used for engineering design purposes (Section 4.2). They are computed by totalling the number of degree days above (thawing index) or below (freezing index) 32°F (0°C) for each year. Values for many locations in northern Canada have been calculated by Thompson (1966) and for some 880 Canadian weather stations by Boyd (1973, 1976).

As shown in Figs. 1.4 and 1.5, the air thawing indices in northern Canada range from about 4,000 Fahrenheit degree days (D.D.F.) in central Manitoba to less than 500 D.D.F. in the northern Arctic Islands and the air freezing indices range from about 4,000 to 12,000 D.D.F. at the same locations. The main reason for these great differences is the range in solar radiation over about 30 degrees of latitude in northern Canada. This corresponds to a difference of 30 degrees in the elevation of the sun at noon at any season and results in large variations not only in the amount of solar radiation received but also in its distribution throughout the year.

The relative number of hours of daylight and darkness at various latitudes during the year are shown in Fig. 1.6. Near the end of June, Moosonee has about 16 hours of daylight, while north of the Arctic Circle the sun remains above the horizon for 24 hours. In the far north, the solar radiation arrives from a much lower angle and therefore the daily total on a horizontal surface is about the same at all these latitudes. In midwinter, however, Moosonee still has about 8 hours of daylight while in the far north there is none.

If winter is defined as the period when the mean air temperature is below 32°F (0°C), then near the 32°F (0°C) isotherm (Fig. 1.2) the winter lasts almost six months. On the same basis, near the 2,000 D.D.F. thawing index line (Fig. 1.4) the winter lasts from early October till mid-May. In the Arctic Islands winter begins about the end of August and continues till after the middle of June. In the

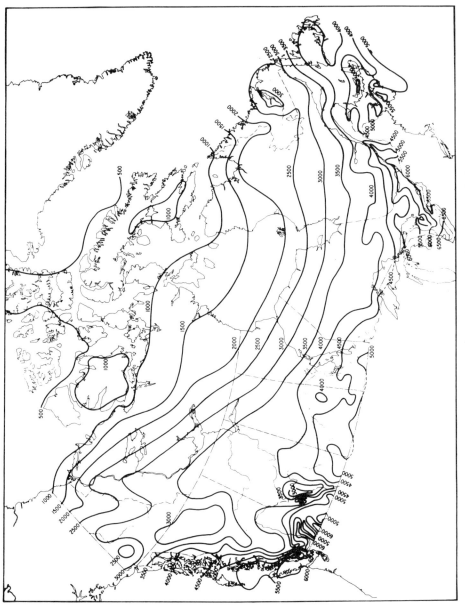

FIG. 1.4 Mean annual thawing index in Fahrenheit degree days—based on period 1931-1960 (After Boyd 1973).

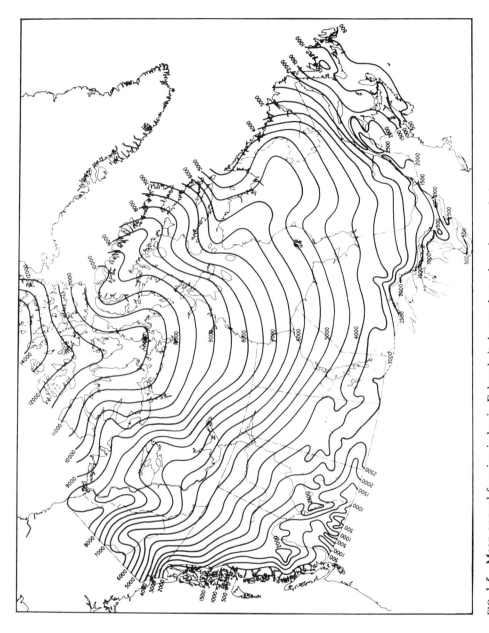

FIG. 1.5 Mean annual freezing index in Fahrenheit degree days—based on period 1931-1960 (After Boyd 1973).

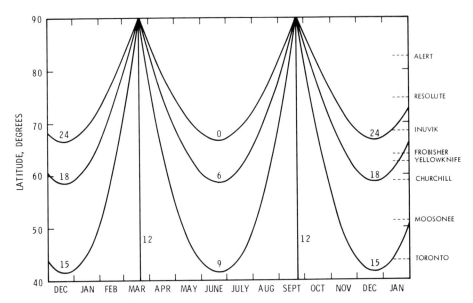

FIG. 1.6   Hours of darkness each day.

six to ten weeks of milder weather the mean temperature is usually around 40°F
(5°C). Record maximum temperatures are mostly between 60 and 70°F (15 to
20°C). It is not, therefore, the extreme cold that makes Arctic winters so severe,
but rather their extreme length, the winds and blowing snow and the continuous
darkness.

   Altitude has a marked effect on the climate. A high elevation regime in the
temperate zone has certain similarities and many anomalies when compared with
a high latitude regime. Annual temperature extremes may be similar in both
regimes but the great difference in insolation has a marked influence on the diurnal temperature cycle. Snowfall volume and distribution patterns also are much
different at high elevations.

   Vertical temperature gradients up mountain slopes are normally steep.
Climatologists commonly use an average rate of change of 3.3F°/1000 ft.
(6C°/km) when estimating temperatures at high elevations from observations
made at lower elevations.

   The combination of low temperature and wind has a pronounced effect on the
comfort and efficiency of men working in a cold environment. Wind chill is a
measure of the degree of coldness or of potential human discomfort. It is a computed index based only on air temperature and surface wind speed and roughly
indicates the cooling rate of exposed flesh (Thomas and Boyd 1957, Siple 1945).
The nomogram in Fig. 1.7 gives wind chill values for different conditions of wind
and temperature in the shade. In bright sunshine the values should be decreased
by about 200.

   A wind chill equivalent temperature is commonly used to describe local
weather conditions. It is the temperature that will produce the same cooling effect

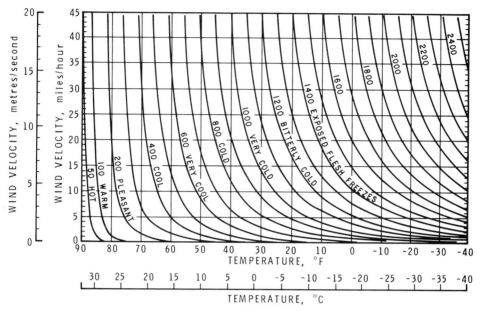

FIG. 1.7 Nomogram of dry-shade atmosphere cooling—wind chill (After Siple 1945). (Cooling is expressed in kilogram calories per square metre per hour for various temperatures and wind velocities. The cooling rate is based upon a body at a neutral skin temperature of 33°C (91.4°F). When dry cooling rate is less than the rate of body heat production, excess heat is removed by vaporization. Under conditions of bright sunshine, cooling is reduced by about 200 calories. Expressions of relative comfort are based upon an individual in a state of inactivity.)

with a wind of 5 mph (8 km/h) as is produced by the actual temperature and wind speed. Table 1.1 can be used to determine the equivalent wind chill temperature from the ambient air temperature and wind speed. Outside working activities are affected at −30°F (−34°C) but work is not severely curtailed until −40°F (−40°C) is reached. In general, the low humidity of the northern environment reduces the discomfort associated with low temperatures. Although Canada's lowest temperatures have been recorded in the Yukon, the strong winds over the flat district of Keewatin and the very low temperatures in the continental interior and the Arctic Islands combine to make the Churchill-Chesterfield Inlet-Resolute Bay area one of the most bitterly cold on earth.

Several weather-related phenomena can drastically reduce visibility and seriously hamper movements in the North. Whiteouts and ice fogs are the result of the frequent and persistent temperature inversions characteristic of cold regions (Gerdel 1969). They are most common during the winter when the required extreme low temperature conditions prevail for several days. Whiteout occurs when the sky is overcast with dense, low stratus clouds, producing a diffuse, shadowless illumination. Where the ground surface is blanketed by unbroken, uniformly mono-coloured expanses of snow, this illumination tends to blot out

TABLE 1.1

Wind Chill Equivalent Temperature

WIND SPEED			LOCAL AIR TEMPERATURE °F (°C)								
mph	32 (0)	23 (−5)	14 (−10)	5 (−15)	−4 (−20)	−13 (−25)	−22 (−30)	−31 (−35)	−40 (−40)
(m/s) [km/h]				EQUIVALENT TEMPERATURE °F (°C)					
5 (2) [8]	32 (0)	23 (−5)	14 (−10)	5 (−15)	−4 (−20)	−13 (−25)	−22 (−30)	−31 (−35)	−40 (−40)
10 (5) [16]	22 (−6)	12 (−11)	1 (−17)	−10 (−23)	−20 (−29)	−30 (−34)	−42 (−41)	−51 (−46)	−62 (−52)
15 (7) [24]	16 (−9)	4 (−16)	−8 (−22)	−19 (−28)	−31 (−35)	−41 (−40)	−53 (−47)	−66 (−54)	
20 (9) [32]	11 (−12)	−1 (−18)	−14 (−26)	−25 (−32)	−37 (−38)	−49 (−45)	−62 (−52)		
25 (11) [40]	7 (−14)	−5 (−21)	−18 (−28)	−30 (−34)	−43 (−42)	−55 (−48)			
30 (13) [48]	5 (−15)	−8 (−22)	−21 (−29)	−34 (−37)	−47 (−44)	−61 (−52)			
35 (16) [56]	3 (−16)	−10 (−23)	−24 (−32)	−37 (−38)	−50 (−45)	−64 (−53)			
40 (18) [64]	2 (−17)	−11 (−24)	−25 (−32)	−38 (−39)	−51 (−46)	−66 (−54)			
45 (20) [72]	1 (−17)	−12 (−24)	−26 (−32)	−39 (−39)	−52 (−46)				
50 (22) [80]	0 (−18)	−13 (−25)	−27 (−33)	−40 (−40)	−54 (−48)				

all traces of surface texture and relief. The erasure of objects subconsciously used to gauge distances results in the loss of depth perception. Ice fogs may vary from a light fallout of minute ice crystals to a dense man-made fog caused by pollution of the atmosphere with water vapour from vehicle exhausts or residential or industrial effluents. Water (steam) fogs occur over open leads in the Arctic sea and other water bodies at all seasons of the year but are most prevalent during the summer and often create a navigation hazard. Sea fogs and low stratus cloud drifting in over coastal areas impede both air and ground transportation in the Arctic during the summer. Radiation and advection fogs may persist at higher elevations for several days, immobilizing all surface and air movements. As low fogs, they further reduce visibility during whiteouts.

Blowing snow, which is common to all parts of the North but particularly in tundra areas, will reduce visibility not only during a snowstorm but also on clear days when fresh loose snow is lifted from the ground surface by high winds. The combination of very strong winds, blowing snow and low temperatures can frequently immobilize all forms of transportation for days.

The length of the spring break-up period (when ice is melting from streams and lakes—accompanied by flooding and ice jamming on larger rivers—and the ground is excessively wet and soft) and the fall freeze-up period (when an ice cover is forming on streams and lakes and the ground is freezing) can vary considerably from one area to another and from year to year depending on regional and/or local weather conditions. Break-up can last from one to six weeks and freeze-up from one to three months. During these periods, all forms of transport, including air, may be restricted. Average dates for the start of the freezing and thawing seasons in northern Canada, based on the period 1949-59, are given by Thompson (1966).

1.3 Terrain

Northern Canada is as structurally and physiographically varied as the rest of the country, as shown in Fig. 1.8. The core is the Canadian Shield, formed mainly of Precambrian crystalline rocks and with altitudes generally less than 2,000 ft. (600 m). To the west and north lie a chain of lowlands, plains and plateaus of generally flat-lying sedimentary rocks. Further west is the rugged terrain of the Cordillera, where deformed sedimentary and intrusive rocks rise to over 7,000 ft. (2000 m). At its eastern edge, along the coast of Labrador and Baffin and Ellesmere Islands, the Shield forms a highland rim with summit elevations between 5,000 and 7,000 ft. (1500 and 2000 m).

With the exception of small areas in the interior Yukon Territory, the entire present land surface has been covered by ice sheets at least once. Glaciation had a profound effect on the landscape of most of the region, producing the alpine landscapes of the eastern highland rim and of parts of the Cordillera. The lowlands are dominated by depositional glacial landforms. In the central and eastern Arctic, marine sediments are found in most of the coastal areas within a few hundred feet of sea level (Prest et al. 1968, Bird 1967).

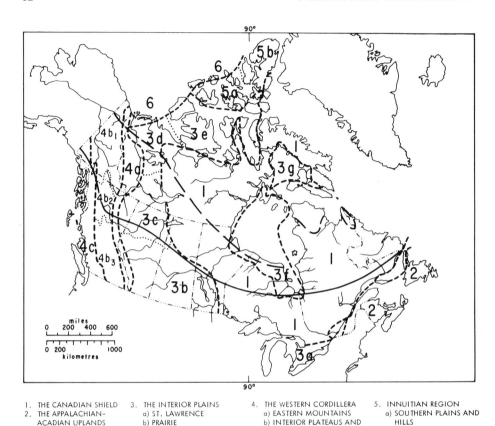

FIG. 1.8   The principal physiographic regions of Canada.

1. THE CANADIAN SHIELD
2. THE APPALACHIAN-
   ACADIAN UPLANDS

3. THE INTERIOR PLAINS
   a) ST. LAWRENCE
   b) PRAIRIE
   c) PEACE-SLAVE LOWLAND
   d) MACKENZIE
   e) ARCTIC
   f) HUDSON BAY
   g) FOXE BASIN

4. THE WESTERN CORDILLERA
   a) EASTERN MOUNTAINS
   b) INTERIOR PLATEAUS AND
      MOUNTAINS
   c) COAST RANGES

5. INNUITIAN REGION
   a) SOUTHERN PLAINS AND
      HILLS
   b) NORTHERN MOUNTAINS
6. ARCTIC COASTAL PLAIN

The results of glaciation are expressed in variations in the degree of bedrock exposure across the region. Considerable areas of exposed bedrock occur in the Cordilleran region and in the eastern highland rim. Bedrock plains or plateaus exist over large areas between Lake Athabasca and Coronation Gulf and most of Nouveau Québec and Labrador. A widespread blanket of unconsolidated materials covers the northern Interior Plains, the Hudson Bay Lowland, Banks Island and Victoria Island. Surface materials of the remainder of northern Canada are a mosaic of unconsolidated deposits and bedrock. Peatland, more commonly known as muskeg, covers more than half of the southern part of the permafrost region in Canada as shown in Fig. 1.9 (MacFarlane 1969, Radforth and Brawner 1977). Much of northern Canada is underlain by perennially frozen ground and ice is a common constituent of the frozen unconsolidated deposits. In areas of fine-grained or organic soils, ground ice may be abundant, and may occur in large tabular sheets or wedges. When large volumes of ice melt, thaw lakes and hummocky or thermokarst terrain can result (Mackay 1972a).

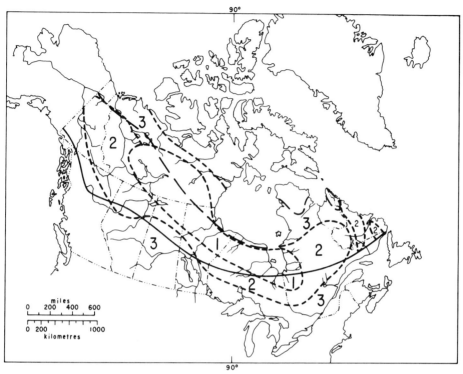

FREQUENCY OF OCCURRENCE
1. HIGH
2. MEDIUM
3. LOW

FIG. 1.9   Distribution of muskeg in Canada (After Radforth 1961).

Glaciers now cover less than 5% of the Canadian North. They are concentrated on the large islands of the eastern Arctic (Baffin, Devon, Ellesmere and Axel Heiberg) and in the St. Elias Mountains in the southwestern Yukon Territory (Prest et al. 1968).

Unconsolidated deposits are being modified by surface processes, particularly those associated with the freeze-thaw cycle, such as frost shattering and solifluction (Bird 1972, Washburn 1973). These processes have resulted in the widespread development of patterned ground and in generally youthful soils, particularly in the northern part of the region. More mature soils are found in the warmer, southern part and in the valleys of the western mountains. The most important characteristics of northern soils are their low temperatures, stoniness, the permafrost substrate with its high ice content and the high water content of the active layer during the summers.

Perennially frozen ground and the long cold winters are major controls on the northern biophysical environment. Apart from the youthful nature of the soils, these factors have major effects on the hydrology and vegetation of the north. Drainage is, in general, poorly developed and a high proportion of the terrain is

occupied by freshwater lakes and rivers or by wetlands (saturated soil or vegetation). All these water areas are ice-free for less than half the year. The ice-free
period on the lakes ranges from less than 180 days along the southern edge of the
permafrost region to less than 30 days in the Queen Elizabeth Islands. Wetlands
are almost completely absent in the Arctic Islands and lakes are fairly rare in both
the Arctic Islands and the western mountains.

Northern rivers typically have very high flows early in the thaw period, followed by low flows with sharp storm peaks throughout the rest of the summer.
Most of the land area drains to the Arctic Ocean or to Hudson Bay; Labrador
and eastern Quebec drain to the Atlantic, while much of the Yukon Territory
drains to the Pacific. The Arctic Islands have very short rivers. The largest
drainage basin in northern Canada is that of the Mackenzie River.

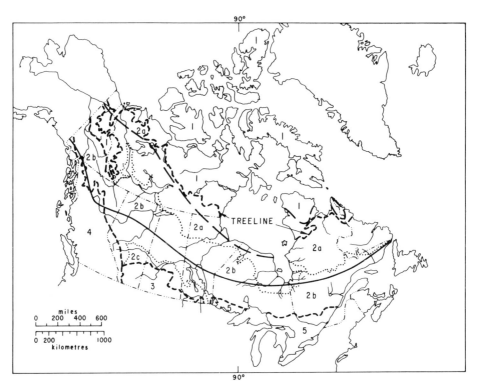

1.   TUNDRA
2.   BOREAL
         a. FOREST AND BARREN
         b. PREDOMINANTLY FOREST
         c. FOREST AND GRASS
3.   GRASSLAND
4.   MONTANE AND SUBALPINE
5.   GREAT LAKES - ST. LAWRENCE

FIG. 1.10   The forest regions of Canada (After Rowe 1972).

The vegetation of the North is dominated by tundra and polar desert to the north of the treeline and by woodland to the south of it (Fig. 1.10). The polar desert occupies all of the Queen Elizabeth Islands and the northern parts of the islands immediately south of Parry Channel. South of the tundra is a transitional zone of open tundra-woodland and south of this is a zone of northern woodland. In the Hudson Bay Lowland these zones are replaced by lowland muskeg-forest vegetation. North of latitude 60°, closed boreal forest occurs only in a narrow tongue along the upper Mackenzie Valley and in the valleys of the southern Yukon.

1.4 Population

It is estimated that only 135,000 people live within the Canadian permafrost region. Approximately 57,000 live in the Yukon and Northwest Territories and 78,000 in the northern parts of the Provinces. More than 50% of the total reside in several communities having populations between 1,000 and 20,000. Most of the remainder live in the many small settlements, with from 10 to 1,000 inhabitants, scattered along the major river systems and the sea coasts.

It is estimated that probably less than 10% of the total population of the Canadian permafrost region is available for work on construction jobs. Not only is the potential local work force small in number, but it is scattered over an extremely large area and few people have technical skills.

1.5 Transportation

Movement of personnel, materials and equipment into the North from southern centres and around construction sites or local areas must be carefully planned. Access can be by land, water and air transport systems. All are affected and limited by the vagaries of weather, short season, limited terminal facilities, communication problems and/or environmental considerations. Various aspects of northern transportation systems and equipment and logistics problems are described in several conference publications (Sater 1969, Canada Transport 1971, Slocum 1972, How 1975).

The principal road and rail routes serving the Canadian North are shown in Figs. 1.11 and 1.12 respectively. None of the six railroads penetrate the area significantly, although their northern terminals connect with major onward transport systems, e.g., Whitehorse (road and air), Hay River (road, air and water) and Churchill (water and air).

The major road network is concentrated primarily in the Yukon, but all-weather roads are being developed in the southern Mackenzie Valley, the northern parts of the Prairie Provinces and the east side of James Bay. No roads exist in the remainder of the Canadian North. Winter (snow and ice) roads, constructed on land and on lakes and rivers, are used extensively by tractor and truck

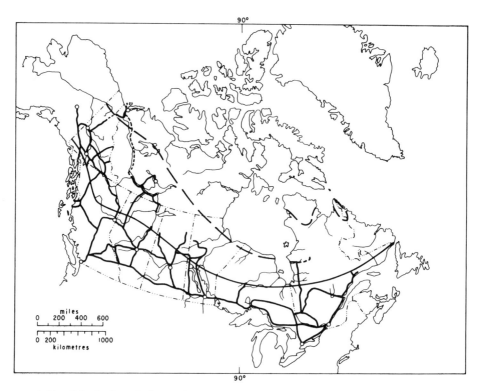

FIG. 1.11   Principal roads in northern Canada.

"swings" to move large quantities of materials and equipment into remote sites. They must be carefully prepared and used, however, for safety over ice and for environmental reasons (Adams 1978).

Various types of tracked, low-pressure wheeled vehicles and air-cushion vehicles are used for off-road travel over relatively short distances. In many areas they are restricted to the winter period because of potential serious damage to the terrain.

Water access to the Canadian North is by two main systems—the Mackenzie River serving the northwest and the eastern sea route serving the Arctic Islands and Hudson Bay region (Fig. 1.13). When ice conditions permit, vessels can travel through Bering Strait and along the north coast of Alaska from the west.

Shallow draft tugs and barges are used on the Mackenzie River system and serve the Arctic coast as far east and west as Spence Bay and Prudhoe Bay respectively. Oceangoing vessels on the eastern sea route move cargo from eastern Canadian and U.S.A. seaboard ports; Montreal is one of the main centres.

The Mackenzie River system is open for about four months, from about early June to early October, while the eastern Arctic sea route is limited to the two month period from mid-July to about mid-September. It is critical, therefore, that purchase and movement of construction materials and equipment be care-

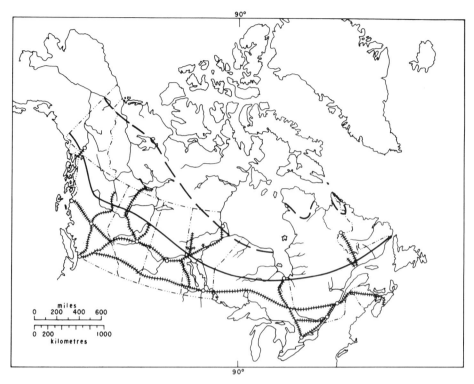

FIG. 1.12   Principal railway routes in northern Canada.

fully scheduled to ensure that they arrive at the southern terminals in time to be moved northward during the very short shipping season.

The lack of year-round ground and water transport systems throughout a large part of the North means that air transportation is the primary method used in many areas. At present, there are 26 civil airports in the Yukon and Northwest Territories operated by the Canadian or Territorial governments. Only eight have paved runways, the remainder having gravel, graded earth or turf runways. In addition, several other airstrips in the North are operated privately or by the Department of National Defence. The locations of principal airfields and scheduled flight routes, including some of the feeder lines, are shown in Fig. 1.14.

Helicopters and small, fixed-wing aircraft equipped with wheels, skis or floats are used extensively to service the smaller communities and also to support construction or exploration parties at isolated locations. All air operations are greatly influenced by weather conditions (such as sudden storms, icing, whiteouts and fogs), the lack of electronic navigational aids in some areas (such as the Arctic Islands), the long period of darkness during the winter months and communication difficulties.

Although the cost of moving materials and equipment into the North by air greatly exceeds that of the other methods, air transport has been and no doubt

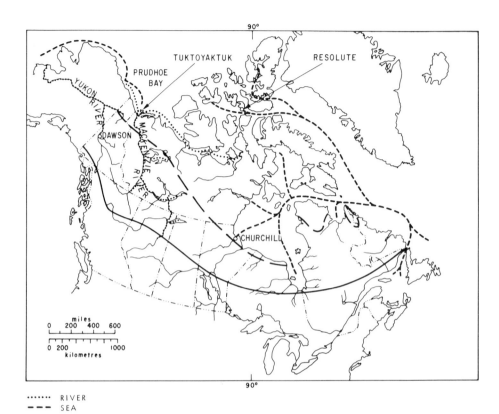

······· RIVER
--- SEA

FIG. 1.13   Principal water transport routes in northern Canada.

will continue to be the primary means for opening up and supporting the development of the North, particularly the more remote areas of the northern mainland and the Arctic Islands; in many cases it is the only form of transport that can provide access.

1.6 Communications

Good communications are essential to the conduct of efficient exploration and construction operations in the North. Most communities have local telephone and radio-telephone systems, which are linked to north-south routes by landlines, microwave or troposcatter systems. Satellite communication provides a better level of service but will probably not be fully utilized for some time because of its high cost and the need for some further technological improvements such as better ground terminals. Present communication systems, particularly radio, will therefore remain in use. Although they may adequately satisfy the limited needs of a private organization, few of these operate with a high degree of reliability because of the far North's ionospheric conditions, which are particularly irregular due to auroral (electrical) and polar (magnetic) effects.

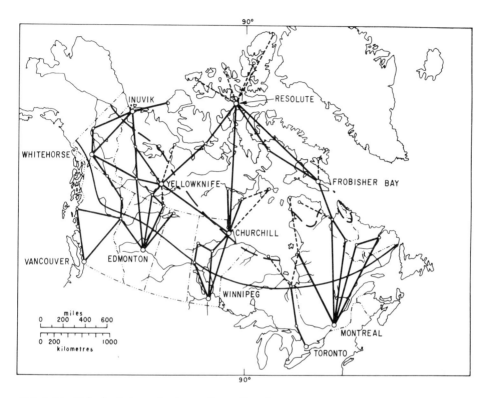

FIG. 1.14   Principal air routes in northern Canada.

1.7 Environmental Concerns

Engineers have always employed economic and social criteria in the design and construction of various works. In recent years, however, public concern for the environment has increased greatly and environmental criteria must be given somewhat higher priority. These involve an assessment of the potential impact that man's activities will have on the quality of the environment as it affects people and wildlife with special emphasis on air, land, water and noise pollution. Major resource, transportation and utility projects in the North may cause environmental damage in many ways over wide areas and may adversely affect other developments (Duffy 1975). Some of the harmful effects of major projects are unknown in their magnitude and ramifications as only limited information is available on the physical and biological environment and natural processes and systems.

All levels of government have taken the position that, for better resource and environmental management, the potential environmental effects of major projects need to be evaluated early in the conceptual, planning and design stages. An impact assessment is required by the authorities to determine whether an activity should proceed from the feasibility study stage and also to guide the subsequent planning and design process after approval to proceed with a project has been given. In northern Canada, federal, provincial and municipal legislation to control pollution and use of the air, land and water is in effect or is being promulgated and guidelines have been or are being prepared to assist in the preparation of environmental impact statements (Naysmith 1971, 1975, Judd 1973). Generally, the project developer is responsible for conducting environmental studies. The impact analysis cannot be limited to the specific facility; the total impact of all activities and environmental changes relating to a project must be considered.

The basic effects of pollution in the North are no different from those elsewhere. The amount or spread of pollutants may be less but several local factors compound the problem. Temperature inversions can, by restricting air movement, result in persistent local concentrations of air-borne pollutants. Frozen soils and frost heaving often make it impossible or difficult to dispose of pollutants by burying them deeply. Streams cannot be used to flush away even small quantities of bio-degradable waste because they are frozen for long periods during the year. Low temperatures inhibit biochemical degradation so that pollutants are likely to persist for long periods. Soil and climatic conditions may limit the kinds of control and clean-up techniques that can be used. Due to the fragile nature of the ground thermal regime in permafrost areas, the effects that natural and man-made changes can have on environmental conditions may be particularly serious. Changes in vegetation, drainage and water quality or temperature will affect not only animal and aquatic life but also human activities which depend on them.

Destruction of or damage to the surface vegetation by fire or by man's activities can have serious consequences. Removal of the ground cover or even a single vehicle pass over the tundra can cause uncontrolled permafrost degradation and erosion. A general but uneven lowering of the ground surface and a marked increase in surface water is usually the result of local thawing, particularly in ice-rich materials. If this occurs on level ground the process may soon stop, although ponding of water, which alters the surface albedo and surface heat exchange, may cause permafrost degradation to continue and result in extensive thermokarst topography. On sloping terrain, drainage of water will result in surface erosion and deposition of soil down the slope. Erosion of ice-rich materials can cause widespread excavation, slumping and flows of soil, in many cases seriously affecting both the land and nearby water bodies.

Pollution effects on wildlife and vegetation are very closely interrelated. Destruction of vegetation, which is slow to become reestablished, is important in that birds and animals are dependent either directly or indirectly on vegetation and cannot survive easily without it. Petroleum products spilled on land may destroy vegetation but usually affect only localized areas unless large quantities of liquids are involved. All seabirds, wildfowl and marine mammals are very susceptible to oil spills into water bodies. The well-known effects experienced in the south will be magnified in the North by the slower breakdown time and compounded by difficulties of clean-up particularly in ice-covered waters.

Threats to fish can be either physical or chemical. Physical threats include structures and activities, such as dams, culverts, mining of borrow materials from water bodies and use of explosives, which hinder fish passage, destroy spawning areas and increase water temperatures. Chemical threats to fish include disposal of toxins in garbage and toxic mine wastes, and disposal or accidental spilling of petroleum products.

Noise can be a serious direct threat to wildlife. It may result in critical losses among the young of breeding herds or flocks, may cause animals to over-exert themselves in winter and may also frighten animals away from preferred winter habitats. At certain times of the year, therefore, construction operations may have to be curtailed or stopped. Similarly, some facilities may have to be designed so that operating noise levels are kept within acceptable limits.

It is important, therefore, that the interaction of man and the environment be given serious consideration in planning all phases of any northern project. Undue disturbance of the various ecosystems may have drastic consequences in time.

1.8 Drainage

Drainage is of special importance in the design, construction and maintenance of engineering structures and facilities in permafrost regions. Permafrost provides an impermeable barrier below the ground surface, thus causing surface water to move and collect in the active layer. This results in much surface water accumulation during the entire summer, even if precipitation is slight.

Moving water is an effective erosive agent of frozen soils. During the very short spring period, the snow melts quickly and relatively large flows of water run off rapidly over the frozen ground surface, eroding channels. During the summer, additional erosion may occur from flows of ground ice melt water resulting from thermal degradation of permafrost caused by ponding of water and removal of the vegetation cover. Subsurface water may also be present in or move through unfrozen zones (taliks) in the permafrost. The frequent occurrence and growth of ice masses (icings) on the ground or river ice during the winter period complicates the problems of drainage control in permafrost terrain.

Disruption of the natural surface and subsurface movement of water by man's activities or structures, such as exploration or winter trails, linear structures (roads or pipelines) and building pads, may have serious consequences if drainage is not considered or inadequate drainage facilities are provided (van Everdingen 1979). The ground thermal regime can be affected to the point where deep thawing and erosion seriously affect structures and the local environment. Ground settlement and stability are major considerations but, in addition, the availability of moisture can introduce or increase the detrimental effects of frost action. Drainage of existing water bodies can also have significant consequences. Freezing of the previously unfrozen, saturated, underlying materials may result in frost heave and thermal contraction cracking and growth of ice wedges or other ground ice forms. A relatively minor disturbance of natural drainage, either surface or subsurface, can cause the formation of extensive icings. These ice deposits frequently block culverts and bridges, inundate or accumulate along roads and even form on building sites (Tolstikhin and Tolstikhin 1974).

Generally, the design of drainage control works or systems can only be based on rather general principles and on an engineering appraisal of local site conditions because reliable information for design rainfall and snow melt calculations is frequently not available for many northern areas. The effects of a specific structure or facility and permafrost degradation and erosion are also difficult to evaluate with confidence. In many cases, natural drainage channels and the vegetation cover should be disturbed as little as possible and drainage ditches not excavated, particularly in the continuous permafrost zone. The degree of success achieved in preventing or controlling icings will depend on the ability to predict the severity of icing at a particular site. Engineers should be familiar with all the factors that determine icing occurrences so that they are in a position to recognize potential problems (Carey 1973).

In the foregoing discussion, emphasis has been placed mainly on the interaction of surface drainage and engineering works. It should be recognized, however, that in general there is little information on hydrological conditions in permafrost areas of northern Canada and, therefore, such studies must be given special attention. Data on streamflows and groundwater movement are particularly important with respect to the design of culverts, bridges and wharves and the provision of water supplies and disposal of liquid wastes for northern communities, in addition to their effect on the occurrence and distribution of permafrost (Owen 1967, Williams and van Everdingen 1973, Demers 1974, Church 1977).

1.9 Construction Materials

Natural construction materials are not readily available or are non-existent in much of the North. It has been suggested that the organic mat of peat and moss, which covers much of the land in forested regions and parts of the tundra, might be used for insulation in embankments or utility lines, or for revegetation purposes, but it is difficult and expensive to harvest, haul and process. Much more important, removal of this insulating ground cover would result in widespread and deep-seated permafrost degradation and would not be permitted, in most cases, for environmental reasons.

In Canada, only a relatively small portion of the Yukon and Northwest Territories is tree covered. Fairly dense stands of merchantable timber occur in places along the Mackenzie and Liard River valleys and some parts of the Yukon, but elsewhere the forest cover is stunted, sparse or non-existent. Timber for foundation piling, saw logs and mine props has been obtained for local use in the Mackenzie District but, in general, wood for construction purposes is not available in any quantity and when available is frequently of an inferior grade. Similar conditions, with some exceptions, prevail in the permafrost region in the northern parts of the Provinces, but construction sites south of 60°N latitude are usually within reach of southern lumber supply centres.

Rock, sand and gravel are the only construction materials available in many areas. Even these materials must be carefully evaluated to ensure that they can be used and will perform satisfactorily in the northern environment. Granular materials and quarry-run or crushed rock are used extensively for fills and embankment construction. Rock excavation is expensive, however, and supplies of sand and gravel are limited. In some cases, the only sources of granular material are stream beds and its removal may be prohibited or restricted because of potential danger to fish and water fowl or unacceptable changes to stream morphology and hydrology. Removal of granular materials from stream beds and other sources such as eskers, moraines, beach ridges and talus slopes may also be restricted or "rationed" because the limited supply cannot meet the demand created by many large construction projects planned or under way in the same locality.

Sedimentary rocks consisting of shales, siltstones, sandstones and similar relatively "soft" rocks occur extensively in the North. Various problems have been encountered with these and partly metamorphosed rocks, and granular materials derived from them, when used in embankments or as concrete aggregates (Deo et al. 1974, Gillott and Swenson 1973, Legget et al. 1966). Shales may be susceptible to post-construction degradation when used in fills or embankments. Problems include disintegration of the quarried material and settlement due to loading, drying, slaking or thawing, heave caused by wetting or freezing, slope instability, and surface and subsurface erosion. Gravel particles derived from sandstones and limestones may be weakly cemented and may disintegrate relatively quickly when subjected to traffic or other loads.

Many gravel deposits are very "dirty" in their natural state, containing large amounts of fines and therefore requiring extensive washing and screening before they are suitable for concrete aggregate. The problems of concrete disintegration due to exposure to freeze-thaw cycles or alkali-aggregate reaction have also been experienced in the North. Cement, of course, must be brought in from the south.

1.10 Construction Season

Although the long, cold winters and periods of darkness in the North may severely curtail or prevent various construction operations, sufficient experience has been accumulated over the years that certain activities can be conducted throughout the year, even during the coldest weather. These include the placement of concrete, earthwork operations such as excavation and the construction of embankments or fills, and the drilling of exploration and production petroleum wells. Precautions must be taken to protect men, equipment and materials under the severe adverse conditions of low temperatures, strong winds

and darkness. The advantages and disadvantages, including the all-important
cost/benefit (economic) aspect of conducting work in the North, must be carefully evaluated.

It is most important that construction work schedules be carefully evaluated
and planned to take advantage of the best weather conditions. Failure to do so
will result in greatly increased costs and delays. Information on winter or cold
regions construction practice and feasibility is given by several authors (Bennett
1975, Havers and Morgan 1972, Fulwider and Stearman 1968, Kaplar and
Metrish 1974, Yoakum 1966, Lovell and Osborne 1968, Crocker 1971, William-
son 1971, Roberts 1976).

1.11 Design and Construction Principles

The approach to be followed in the design and construction of engineering works
on permafrost will be determined by detailed site or route investigations, previous
experience in the area, the type of structure or facility to be built and its ultimate
effect on the local environment. Normally one of two broad principles can be
followed based on whether or not the frozen foundation soils or rock are thaw-
stable or thaw-unstable.

Permafrost conditions can be neglected and conventional designs and construction methods used when foundation materials are stable upon thawing. Such
materials include sound rock, free of ice-filled fissures, or clean, non-frost-
susceptible, well-drained sand and gravel deposits that:

(a) do not contain ice, which would result in settlement upon thawing,

(b) will not settle excessively upon thawing because of their loose structure,
and

(c) are not underlain by unsuitable materials that would be affected by thawing
during the life of the structure.

Some problems may be experienced during the construction period when some
operations such as placement of concrete in and excavation of frozen ground will
be hampered by the presence of permafrost but, in general, conventional procedures that take into account these special conditions can be followed.

Where thaw-unstable foundation materials are present, the most desirable approach for permanent structures is to design and construct them so as to preserve
the frozen ground condition. If preservation of permafrost is not possible, then it
may be advisable to thaw and consolidate the ground or to remove poor (ice-rich,
frost-susceptible) soil and backfill with more acceptable material prior to erection
of the structure. It should be recognized that a significant amount of time is required to apply the "thaw-and-consolidate" procedure and this will significantly
affect the project schedule. Similarly, if permafrost degradation is inevitable during the life of the structure and tolerable settlements are anticipated and can be
accommodated in design, then adjustable foundations or rigid structures with
subsequent remedial maintenance to take care of the movements can be considered. These are special cases, however, and must be carefully evaluated. Nor-

mally, designs that permit degradation of permafrost are used only when foundation materials are thaw-stable, when settlements can be tolerated and are taken into account, or where temporary construction is involved.

Care should be taken to avoid close spacing of structures whose foundations are designed by different methods, particularly when the construction of one may detrimentally affect the thermal condition of the foundation soils of another. This does not necessarily imply that thawing will occur. For example, the construction of a new building, road or utility line immediately adjacent to an existing building may raise the frozen ground temperature under an existing adjacent building above that for which its foundation was designed. The result may be unacceptable movements or even failure of the existing structure. Building sites, irrespective of the construction method, should be thoroughly prepared and graded to ensure drainage of water away from the structure and the site as a whole.

The general principles and considerations just outlined with respect to permafrost are applicable to most northern engineering projects, including development of the mineral and petroleum resources. Permafrost problems are basically the same, no matter what type of project is undertaken. Although mining, petroleum exploration and production and pipelines are not treated as separate topics in this book, pertinent information and references are contained in the following chapters. A few general comments are made here, however, to emphasize some of the more important aspects.

Underground and open pit mining operations are influenced by permafrost in several ways (Dubnie 1972, El'chaninov et al. 1980, Linell and Johnston 1973, Skuba 1974). The occurrence of permafrost (particularly in the discontinuous zone) and ice poses problems in the exploration of ore bodies and the excavation and transport of frozen ground (Chapters 2 and 6). Large masses of ice have been encountered at depth in some cases and the existence of thin lenses of ice throughout various strata is fairly common. Methods to ameliorate permafrost conditions prior to mining have been investigated (Nicholson 1976, 1978). The frozen condition can be an advantage in certain underground situations, e.g., when the ground is hard frozen and well cemented by ice. Large cavities can be excavated with a minimum of support in some materials that are normally difficult to mine. On the other hand, spalling of rock and progressive closure of the workings by creep may occur, particularly in warm-temperature frozen ground (Pettibone 1973, Thompson and Sayles 1972). Control of ventilating and heating procedures and especially of seepage and drilling water in underground mines is most important. Increased air temperatures may cause undesirable thawing of frozen soil or rock. Ice may block ditches, coat tracks, stairways and ladder rungs and interfere with operation of power and communication cables and equipment. Problems of slope instability and moisture infiltration at the mine or tunnel entrance, where seasonal freezing and thawing occurs, must be taken into account in the design and construction of portals (Linell and Lobacz 1978). If the frozen rock is competent, toxic and other wastes sometimes can be stored underground in mined-out areas, but the storage chambers must be kept dry and at a below freezing temperature and must be sealed off by concrete bulkheads. The bulkheads and stopings must be able to withstand the high water pressures that will occur when the mine is abandoned and flooded. The design and construction of dams and dykes to enclose waste disposal ponds on the ground surface are discussed in Chapter 9.

Probably the most difficult problem experienced in open pit mining involves the design of safe and economic slopes in ice-rich overburden and rock. Procedures are not well established for the design and control of thawing of such slopes and require further study. The stability of slopes and measures that can be considered to minimize thawing are discussed in Sections 2.5.2, 3.7, 8.1 and 8.2.2. Garg and Kalia (1975) and Garg and Devon (1978) discuss the design of pit slopes at Schefferville, Quebec. A manual concerned primarily with the investigation, analysis and design techniques required for the optimum layout of open pit mine slopes has been published by Canada Department of Energy, Mines and Resources (1976-77). Although it does not deal specifically with permafrost, it contains much relevant information, with emphasis on mine design for maximum economic return, consistent with operating safety and protection of the environment.

Permafrost problems faced by the petroleum industry in the development of northern oil and gas resources are many and varied. They differ from those experienced in other engineering activities, mainly in degree rather than kind of difficulty. Exploration and production operations are conducted to or at great depth, both on land and offshore, and the problems posed by the areal extent, thickness and lithology of permafrost and the properties and behaviour of perennially frozen, thawing and freezing ground can complicate matters considerably and frequently require the development of special equipment and techniques. In addition, new problems are introduced if gas hydrates are encountered; extremely high pressures can result if the hydrates decompose or "thaw" in a confined system (Davidson et al. 1978).

Drilling operations and the movement of warm oil or gas through permafrost in a production well will result in extensive thawing of the surrounding frozen ground. Cooled drilling fluids and/or insulated casing are normally used to minimize or prevent detrimental thaw settlement and downdrag. Freezeback of the thawed zone around a well may occur when it is shut-in during or after drilling, or after a production period. Significant pressures can be generated, not only around the wellbore but also between casing strings, and may result in collapse or distortion of the casing. Special equipment, techniques and designs are frequently required to cement wells and for casing and wellheads. Attention must also be given to clean-up and restoration operations during and following drilling at a site; mud sumps must be constructed so that escape of toxic fluids and undue thawing and contamination of the surrounding area and water bodies does not occur. Goodman (1977-78) discusses many of these problems in a series of articles dealing with well completions in permafrost.

Although several small diameter pipelines have been constructed in permafrost areas of the world (e.g., the Canol line from Norman Wells to Whitehorse, constructed in 1942-44), it was not until the Prudhoe Bay field in northern Alaska was discovered in 1968 that attention was given to the construction of large diameter pipelines in northern North America. The discovery of gas and oil on the Alaskan North Slope, in the Mackenzie Delta-Beaufort Sea area and the Arctic Islands of Canada, as well as the permafrost region in the Soviet Union, precipitated detailed studies of the environmental and engineering problems involved. The investigation and selection of an appropriate route for a pipeline is most important and the main technical difficulties relate primarily to whether a line can be buried or must be placed above ground in permafrost areas. Prime consideration must be given to thaw settlement in the case of a "hot" pipeline in ice-rich perennially frozen ground and to the effects of frost action (heave) in the case of a chilled pipeline located in unfrozen ground (on land and under rivers and other water bodies) and in permafrost.

To date, the only operating large diameter pipeline in northern North America is the Trans-Alaska oil pipeline. Design and construction aspects of this line, which carries warm oil in a 48 in. (1220 mm) diameter pipe about 800 miles (1290 kilometres) from Prudhoe Bay to Valdez on the south coast of Alaska, are described by Liguori et al. (1979). Slightly less than half the length of the pipeline is installed in a conventional buried mode; the rest of the line is supported above ground on specially designed pile systems to avoid difficulties in areas of ice-rich permafrost (Heuer 1979). The various problems that must be considered in the design, construction and operation of pipelines in permafrost areas are discussed in several chapters of this book.

1.12 Building Codes and Information

Most local authorities throughout Canada, including the North, use the general performance requirements for building foundation systems given in Part 4 of the National Building Code of Canada (Canada National Research Council 1980a, b). Pertinent information to assist the code user in the design, construction and inspection of foundations is given in the Canadian Foundation Engineering Manual (Canadian Geotechnical Society 1978). No code dealing specifically with the design and construction of engineering structures and facilities on permafrost is available for Canada. This book has been prepared, therefore, to provide information and guidance to those involved with permafrost engineering in Canada.

Information relevant to the North on structural loads, including loads due to snow and the effects of wind and earthquakes, are contained in Part 4 of the National Building Code of Canada (Canada National Research Council 1980a) and its Supplement (Canada National Research Council 1980b). Winds can be quite variable and strong at various times and locations in the North and are an important design consideration, especially in tundra areas (Fig. 1.15). Gusts exceeding 100 mph (160 km/h) have been recorded.

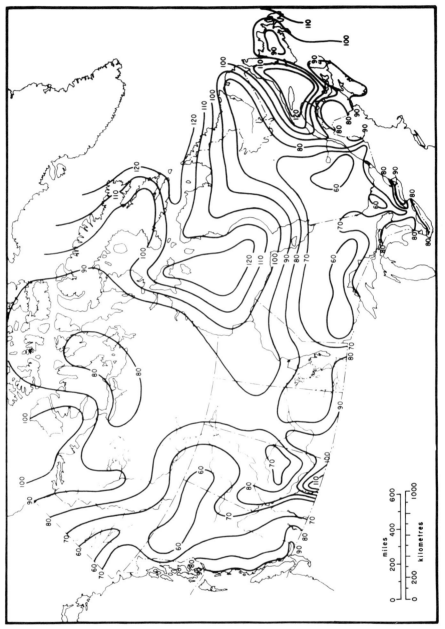

FIG. 1.15   Wind gust speeds in miles per hour based on a 30-year return period (From Canada National Research Council 1965).

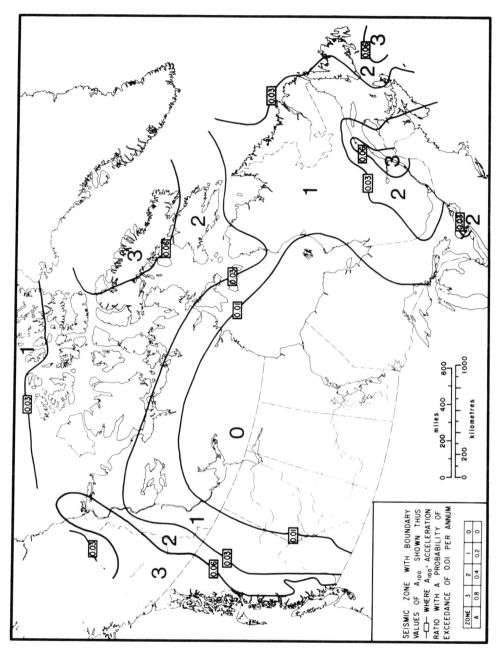

FIG. 1.16   Seismic zones in Canada (From Canada National Research Council 1980b).

Strong ground motions due to earthquakes can have serious effects not only on structures themselves but also in areas of unstable soils where large scale landslides may be initiated. Records, although limited, indicate that the largest earthquakes in northern Canada have occurred in the southwestern and northern parts of the Yukon, Baffin Bay and on Baffin Island. Others have occurred offshore in the Arctic Ocean near the western Arctic Islands and near the northern end of Hudson Bay. The seismic zones delineated in Fig. 1.16 show that much of the Yukon, the Mackenzie Delta area and Baffin Island are within Zone 3, the zone of highest seismic risk. Most of the Arctic Islands, the Boothia and Melville peninsulas, parts of Baffin Island and northern Quebec and the area along the Yukon-Northwest Territories boundary are within Zone 2. The seismicity of northern Canada and the estimation of seismic risk in Canada are discussed by Stevens (1974), Stevens and Milne (1974), Whitham (1975) and Basham et al. (1977).

Monographs prepared by the Cold Regions Research and Engineering Laboratory (CRREL) of the U.S. Army (Gerdel 1969, Stearns 1965, 1966, Wilson 1967, 1969, Scott 1964, 1969, Mellor 1965, Sanger 1969, Alter 1969a, b, Roethlisberger 1972, Carey 1973) and various U.S. Army, Air Force and Navy technical manuals on Arctic and Subarctic construction (U.S. Navy 1955, 1967, U.S. Army 1966, U.S. Army/Air Force 1965, 1966a, b, c, 1967) provide much information and guidance for those engaged in northern engineering. Up-to-date information on geotechnical engineering in cold regions is given by Andersland and Anderson (1978) and on utilities in cold regions by Canada Environment (1979). Many books, codes or "Instructions" dealing with construction on permafrost have been published in the Soviet Union. Several have been translated for the information of North American engineers (U.S.S.R. 1960, 1962, 1964, 1967, 1969, Tsytovich 1973, Kudryavtsev 1977).

Papers dealing with all aspects of permafrost and northern engineering have been published in the proceedings of various conferences and meetings held in recent years. A selected list of conference proceedings is given in the bibliography.

A Bibliography on Cold Regions Science and Technology, prepared by the Science and Technology Division, U.S. Library of Congress, is published by the U.S. Army, Cold Regions Research and Engineering Laboratory, Hanover, N.H. It is recognized as a comprehensive source of worldwide literature on all aspects of snow, ice and frozen ground, the construction of buildings, roads, railways, pipelines and other facilities and the behaviour and operation of materials and equipment in cold regions. The CRREL Bibliography is available through an on-line computer retrieval system and is accessible through most technical libraries.

CHAPTER 2

Permafrost Distribution and Terrain Characteristics

(Contributors–R. J. E. Brown, G. H. Johnston,
J. R. Mackay, N. R. Morgenstern and W. W. Shilts)

2.1 Occurrence and Distribution of Permafrost

Permafrost is defined as "the thermal condition in soil or rock of having temperatures below 32°F (0°C) persist over at least two consecutive winters and the intervening summer" (Brown and Kupsch 1974). Permafrost (also referred to as perennially frozen ground) is defined solely on the basis of temperature; moisture in the form of water and ground ice may or may not be present. The formation and existence of this perennially frozen (thermal) condition in earth materials are controlled primarily by the climate and various terrain factors, but are also greatly influenced by the works of man. Ground thermal regime means the temperature pattern existing in the ground.

About one-fifth of the world, including one-half of Canada's land surface, is underlain by permafrost (Brown 1970a). The permafrost region of North America is divided into two principal zones—the discontinuous in the south and the continuous in the north (Brown and Péwé 1973). Their extent in Canada is shown in Fig. 2.1 and typical profiles of the vertical distribution of permafrost in these zones are shown in Fig. 2.2.

In the discontinuous zone, permafrost exists together with areas of unfrozen ground (Brown, R. J. E. 1964, 1965, 1967a, 1968, 1975, Johnston et al. 1963). Unfrozen layers (taliks) may occur within the permafrost. In the southern fringe area of this zone, permafrost occurs in scattered islands ranging in size from a few square feet (square metres) to several acres (hectares). It is confined mainly to peatlands (Fig. 2.3), but may also be found on north-facing slopes, in shaded locations and areas of thin snow cover. Northward, permafrost becomes increasingly widespread in a greater variety of terrain types. It varies in thickness from a few inches (centimetres) at the southern limit of the discontinuous zone to 200 to 300 ft. (60 to 100 m) at the boundary with the continuous zone. The depth to the permafrost table ranges from 2 to 10 ft. (0.6 to 3 m) or more, depending on local climatic and surface conditions. The active layer does not always extend to the permafrost table. In the discontinuous zone, the permafrost temperature at the depth of zero annual amplitude, where there is virtually no annual fluctuation in

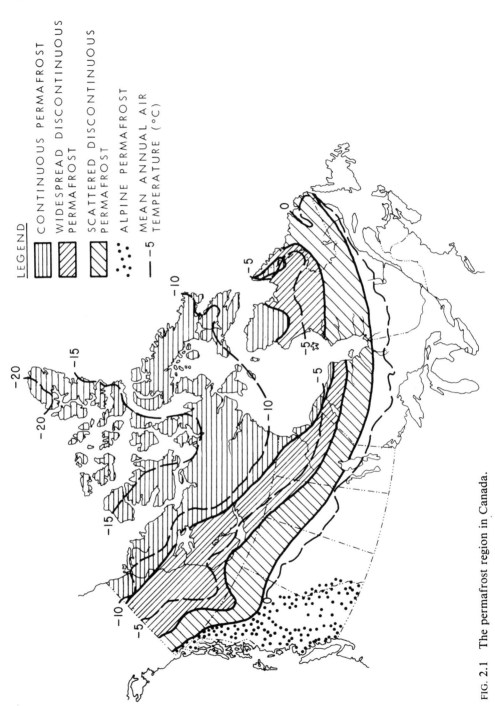

FIG. 2.1   The permafrost region in Canada.

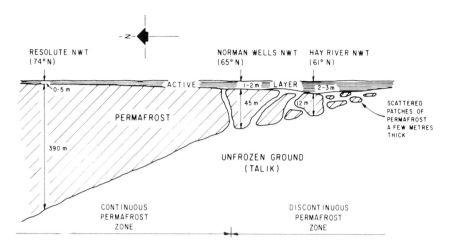

(a) Typical vertical distribution and thickness of permafrost.

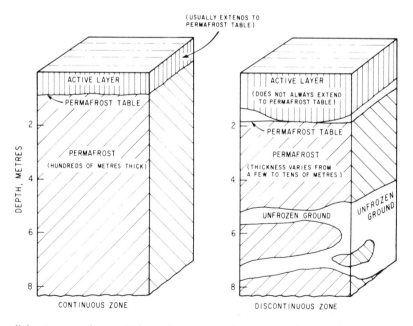

(b) Typical profiles in permafrost region.

FIG. 2.2   Typical profiles of permafrost distribution.

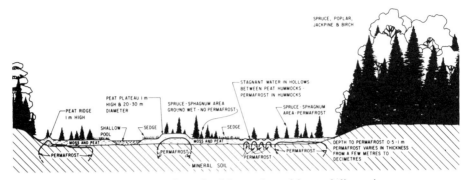

FIG. 2.3   Profile through typical peatland in southern fringe of discontinuous zone showing interaction of permafrost and terrain.

temperature, generally ranges from a few tenths of a degree below 32°F (0°C) at the southern limit to about 23°F (−5°C) at its northern boundary.

In the continuous zone, permafrost exists everywhere beneath the land surface except in newly deposited unconsolidated sediments where the climate has just begun to influence the ground thermal regime (Brown 1967b). In Canada, the thickness of permafrost is 200 to 300 ft. (60 to 100 m) at the southern limit of this zone, increasing to more than 2,000 ft. (600 m) in the northern parts of the Canadian Arctic Archipelago (Brown 1972, Judge 1973a, b, Mackay 1967). The active layer generally varies in thickness from about 1 to 3 ft. (0.3 to 1 m) and commonly extends to the permafrost table except near bodies of water. The permafrost temperature at the depth of zero annual amplitude ranges from about 23°F (−5°C) in the south to about 5°F (−15°C) in the extreme north.

The distribution of alpine permafrost in mountainous regions, such as the Western Cordillera in Canada, varies with altitude (Fig. 2.1) as well as latitude, and is very sensitive to the thickness of the snow cover (Brown 1967b, Harris and Brown 1978). The lower altitudinal limit decreases northward. It is estimated to decrease steadily from an elevation of about 7,000 ft. (2,100 m) above sea level at latitude 49°N to about 4,000 ft. (1,200 m) in northern British Columbia (Brown 1967a, Ogilvie and Baptie 1967). With increasing elevation at any location, the distribution of permafrost changes progressively from scattered islands to widespread occurrences and finally becomes continuous. Usually, permafrost is more widespread and thicker on north-facing slopes but variations in snow cover and vegetation on different slopes complicate the situation.

In a totally different environment, permafrost is known to occur offshore in many northern areas of the world (Vigdorchik 1980a, b) including the eastern Canadian Arctic (Samson and Tordon 1969) and under the Beaufort Sea (Mackay 1972b, Shearer et al. 1971, Judge 1974, Hunter et al. 1976, Osterkamp and Harrison 1976a, b). Investigations to date in the Beaufort Sea indicate that permafrost under the seabed can be either degrading or aggrading and its thickness and areal distribution are quite variable. Temperatures below 32°F (0°C) are almost certain to exist beneath the sea bottom in the channels separating the islands of the Arctic Archipelago.

At present, the thickest permafrost measured in Canada is about 2,375 ft. (720 m) on Cameron Island. Judge (1973b), however, has predicted maximum thicknesses of 3,500 ft. (1,000 m). Very thick permafrost is probably not confined to the Arctic Islands. A thickness of more than 1,300 ft. (400 m) has been projected in northern Quebec based on temperature measurements to depths of 860 ft. (260 m). A thickness of about 2,300 ft. (700 m) has been measured on Richards Island in the Mackenzie Delta (Taylor and Judge 1974, 1975, 1976).

The occurrence and distribution of permafrost are affected principally by various climatic and terrain factors (Brown and Péwé 1973, Mackay and Black 1973, Stearns 1966). Climate is basic to its formation and existence (Brown 1969, 1970b). A broad relationship exists between mean annual air and ground temperatures in the permafrost region as shown in Fig. 2.1 (Brown 1966a). The southern limit of permafrost coincides roughly with the 30°F (-1°C) mean annual air isotherm. Between the 30°F (-1°C) and 25°F (-4°C) mean annual air isotherms, permafrost is restricted mainly to the drier portions of peatlands, some north-facing slopes and local shaded areas. North of the 25°F (-4°C) mean annual air isotherm, permafrost becomes increasingly widespread and thicker. The boundary between the discontinuous and continuous zones appears to be near the 17°F (-8°C) mean annual air isotherm. Northward in the continuous zone, permafrost increases in thickness in response to decreasing mean annual air temperatures.

FIG. 2.4   Relationship of permafrost to relief—Alaska Highway, northern British Columbia. Permafrost occurs in north-facing, tree and moss covered slope (left) but not in deciduous tree covered slope (right).

Permafrost conditions are affected by terrain factors, such as relief, vegetation, hydrology, snow cover, glacier ice and soil and rock type, and by fire (Brown 1969, 1970a). Relief influences the amount of solar radiation received by the ground surface and the snow accumulated on it. The effects of orientation and steepness of slope are particularly evident in mountainous regions (Price 1971) as shown in Fig. 2.4. Variations in snow cover and vegetation may modify the distribution of permafrost on north- and south-facing slopes. Similar differences can occur on a small scale with variations in microrelief.

FIG. 2.5   Relationship of permafrost to vegetation. Permafrost is about 80 ft. (25 m) thick under peat plateau where peat is about 6 ft. (2 m) thick, but does not occur under wet, sedge-covered treeless depression in foreground. Near Gillam, Manitoba.

The main influence of vegetation, particularly the ground surface layer of moss and peat, is its role in insulating the permafrost from thawing during the summer (Figs. 2.3, 2.5, 2.6). It is one of the most important factors determining the thickness of the active layer (Brown 1966b). Removal or even disturbance of the surface organic cover causes deepening of the active layer and degradation of the permafrost (Bliss and Wein 1971). In the discontinuous zone this may result in the disappearance of bodies of permafrost in a number of years, while in the con-

FIG. 2.6 Relationship of permafrost to vegetation. Permafrost is about 20 ft. (6 m) thick under peat bog in foreground, but does not occur under deciduous tree covered area in background. Near Flin Flon, Manitoba.

tinuous zone the permafrost table will be lowered. Although the influence of the ground surface vegetation cover is dominant, trees are also important in that they shade the ground from solar radiation, intercept some of the snowfall and contribute to transpiration.

The snow cover regime and the length of time that snow lies on the ground are important factors (Nicholson and Granberg 1973, Mackay and MacKay 1974, Nicholson 1976). A heavy fall of snow in the late autumn inhibits frost penetration and a thick snow cover that remains until late in the spring delays thawing of the frozen ground. The frequency of occurrences such as these determines the net effect of the snow cover on the ground thermal regime.

Surface and subsurface water greatly influence the distribution and thermal regime of permafrost. In the discontinuous zone permafrost may degrade (or its formation be prevented) in poorly drained areas. A thaw basin always exists beneath lakes and rivers that do not freeze to the bottom in winter (Johnston and Brown 1964, 1966, Brown et al. 1964, Brewer 1958a, b, Shilts and Dean 1975) and shifting stream channels change the permafrost distribution and thermal regime below and adjacent to them (Smith and Hwang 1973, Smith 1976, Scott 1978).

Even small ponds that freeze to the bottom each winter influence and can greatly modify the ground thermal regime. The thermal effect in all cases extends not only below, but also to some distance beyond, the water-land interface due to the much warmer temperature imposed by the water on the underlying ground. In a similar way the sea has an important thermal influence on permafrost, causing it to be thinner at the shoreline than inland. The distribution of offshore per-

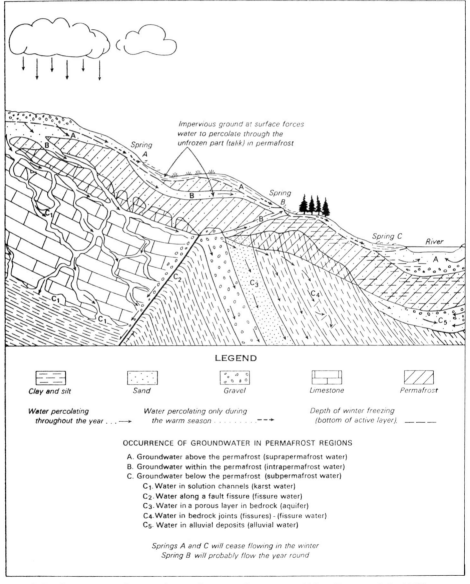

FIG. 2.7   Occurrence of groundwater in permafrost areas (After Brown, I.C. 1967).

mafrost is also greatly affected by the sea—and can be extremely complex because of the large changes and significantly different surface conditions that occur, such as water temperature and salinity, type and rate of deposition of sediments and coastal erosion (Werenskiold 1953, Lachenbruch 1957a, Mackay 1972a, Jenness 1949, Hunter et al. 1976, Judge 1974).

Groundwater movement in permafrost areas is restricted by the presence of both perennially and seasonally frozen ground (Brandon 1965, 1966, Williams 1965, Williams and van Everdingen 1973, van Everdingen 1974, Tolstikhin and Tolstikhin 1974). As shown in Fig. 2.7, free water may occur in the ground above permafrost (suprapermafrost water), in unfrozen zones (taliks) within the permafrost (intrapermafrost water) or below the permafrost base (subpermafrost water). Although permafrost is commonly assumed to be impermeable, it should not be classed indiscriminately as an impermeable material. In many cases it should be treated as a confining bed of low but finite permeability. Groundwater (which in some cases is saline and thus has a lower freezing point) may discharge through unfrozen zones under artesian pressure or gravity from sources below, within or above the permafrost, thus creating complex ground thermal regimes, particularly near lakes and streams.

The destruction of the ground vegetation cover by fire will have varying effects on permafrost, depending on the condition of the vegetation and the rate of burning. Both the thermal and moisture regimes of the ground may undergo considerable alteration. The degree to which these systems are influenced depends upon many factors but primarily on the intensity of the fire and amount of vegetation destroyed (Sykes 1971, Wein 1976, Kane et al. 1975). If it moves rapidly through an area, such that the ground vegetation is charred only, little change may occur in the permafrost provided the energy balance at the surface remains relatively unaltered. If dry conditions have prevailed in the past and the surface vegetation and peat are severely damaged or destroyed, considerable change may occur in areas underlain by ice-rich perennially frozen soils (Fig. 2.8). In such a situation, the depth of the active layer in the Norman Wells area was found to double after a fire (Zoltai and Tarnocai 1974). Water released from melting ground ice may cause extensive erosion, slumping or landslides, and a general lowering of the permafrost table will result (Heginbottom 1973, 1974, Mackay 1977a, Viereck 1973a, b).

Glaciers and ice caps covering the ground surface affect the heat exchange between the atmosphere and permafrost. The bottom temperature of an ice sheet is at or below 32°F (0°C) (Philberth and Federer 1971). Continental glaciation appears to have greatly affected permafrost conditions in the past and evidence of its modification to the ground thermal regime in the North is apparent today (Jessop 1971).

The influence of exposed mineral soil and bedrock on permafrost conditions is controlled by the albedo and thermal properties of these materials. The rate of permafrost aggradation and the thickness of the active layer are directly affected by variations in soil and rock type when the ground is not covered by vegetation,

FIG. 2.8   Results of fire near Inuvik, N.W.T. 1968. (a) widespread thawing of
permafrost and drainage of melting ground ice on slopes denuded of moss cover and
vegetation, (b) hummocks and clay boils exposed—moss cover and peat destroyed,
(c) thawing and erosion along bulldozed firebreak.

water or ice (Brown 1973a). In most areas of the permafrost region it is difficult
to isolate the role of bare soil and rock because of the presence of other environmental factors.

2.2 The Active Layer

The active layer is the top layer of ground above the permafrost table that freezes
and thaws annually as shown in Fig. 2.2 (Brown 1971). Heat and moisture
movements between the permafrost and the atmosphere take place in the active
layer. They are influenced by the same climatic and terrain factors that affect the
permafrost and interact in a complex manner.

In the continuous permafrost zone the bottom of the active layer usually coincides with the permafrost table except near water bodies. In the discontinuous
zone, however, the active layer extends down to the permafrost table in some
locations but not in others. In the latter case the active layer is separated from the
permafrost by a layer of ground, called the residual thaw layer, which remains
unfrozen throughout the year.

In general, the thickness of the active layer decreases in the permafrost region from south to north but it can be extremely variable at any location depending on local conditions. For example, within a small area in the discontinuous zone the thickness may range from about 2 ft. (0.7 m) where there is thick moss and peat to more than 30 ft. (10 m) in exposed bedrock. Similarly, the thickness at one location in the northern part of the continuous permafrost zone may range from 1.5 ft. (0.5 m) in wet silts and clays with no vegetation cover to about 6 ft. (2 m) in exposed granite bedrock. The thickness can also vary from year to year due to varying climatic conditions.

Natural freezing and thawing of the active layer may be retarded by phase change due to the latent heat of fusion of water—known as the zero curtain effect. A temperature of 32°F (0°C) may persist at a particular level for as much as several weeks thus delaying freezing or thawing of the ground. Further complications are caused by the common occurrence of the active layer freezing upward from the permafrost table as well as downward from the ground surface (Mackay 1974a).

Ice may be distributed in three layers within the frozen active layer: an upper layer with small ice inclusions; a middle layer that is desiccated because moisture has been withdrawn towards two freezing fronts, one moving down from the surface, the other up from the permafrost table; and a lower layer with a mixture of thin and thicker ice lenses immediately above the permafrost table. At the end of the thawing season, water in the active layer tends to be concentrated at the permafrost table.

The thickness of the active layer, and hence the position of the permafrost table, can be rapidly and drastically altered as a result of naturally occurring or man-made changes to the environmental conditions in the area. Natural changes include forest fires and landslides; man-made changes include clearing of trees, moss and peat or snow from the ground surface, interruption of drainage, erection of buildings and placement of fills. It is most important that the effects of these changes on the ground thermal regime be known. Methods of assessing and computing them are discussed in Chapter 4.

The active layer often consists of frost-susceptible soils and, in addition, is saturated with water because of the underlying impermeable permafrost and generally poor drainage in many northern areas. Serious engineering problems are caused by frost action during seasonal freezing and thawing of the active layer. The frost action process, the resulting detrimental effects and the methods used to control them are discussed in Sections 3.8, 7.3 and 8.1.

2.3 Ground Temperatures

Permafrost exists as a thermal condition that is reflected in ground temperatures never exceeding 32°F (0°C) (Gold and Lachenbruch 1973). Fluctuations in air temperature during the year produce corresponding fluctuations in ground temperature, although their magnitude is reduced with increasing depth by the effect of the vegetation and snow surface covers as well as by the thermal characteristics of the soil or rock. In addition, a time lag is introduced with increase in depth. The depth of zero annual amplitude is commonly between 30 and 50 ft. (10 to 15 m), as shown in Fig. 2.9. Below this depth, the ground

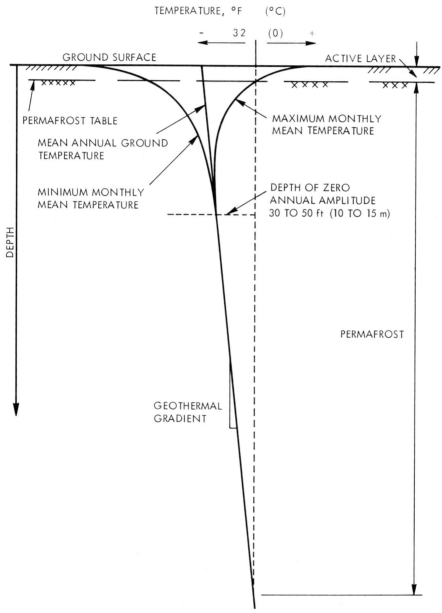

FIG. 2.9   Typical ground temperature regime in permafrost.

temperatures change only in response to the geothermal flux and changes in climatic conditions extending over centuries.

The temperature regime of permafrost depends on present and past climatic and terrain factors (Gold 1967). Snow cover and the complex energy exchange regime at the ground surface cause the mean annual ground temperature, measured at the depth of zero annual amplitude, to be several degrees warmer than the mean annual air temperature. Local microclimates and terrain conditions cause variations ranging from about 2 to 10F° (1 to 5C°) in the difference between the mean annual air and ground temperatures, but an average range of 6F° (3.3C°) can be used (Brown 1966a). Observed temperatures in permafrost at the depth of zero annual amplitude in the discontinuous zone range from a few tenths of a degree below 32°F (0°C) to about 23°F (−5°C), the mean annual air temperature ranging from 30°F (−1°C) to about 17°F (−8°C). In the continuous zone, permafrost temperatures range from about 23°F (−5°C) to 5°F (−15°C) with mean annual air temperature values of about 17°F (−8°C) to −3°F (−19°C).

Geothermal gradients ranging from about 1°F/40 ft. to 1°F/300 ft. (1°C/22 m to 1°C/160 m), depending on the type of soil or rock and the effect of past climatic periods, have been measured in permafrost regions in the northern hemisphere (Jessop 1971, Judge 1973a, b, Taylor and Judge 1974, 1975, 1976, Lachenbruch et al. 1966, Lachenbruch and Marshall 1969). An average value of

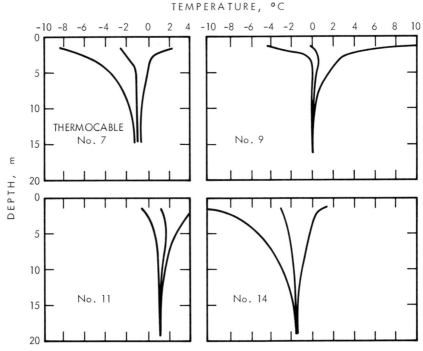

FIG. 2.10 Ground temperature envelopes, Schefferville, P.Q. 1971 (Modified from Nicholson and Thom 1973).

1°F/100 ft. (1°C/54 m) can be used. A change of 1F° (0.5C°) in the mean annual air temperature, for example, would result over a long period of time in a change of 1F° (0.5C°) in the mean annual ground temperature. This could cause a change in permafrost thickness of approximately 40 to 300 ft. (12 to 90 m), depending on local conditions.

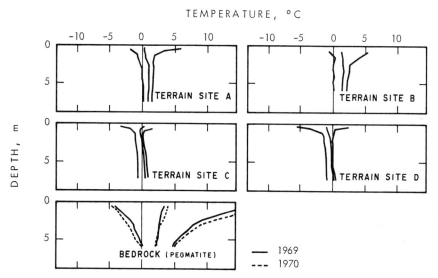

FIG. 2.11   Ground temperature envelopes, Thompson, Manitoba 1969 and 1970 (After Brown 1973a).

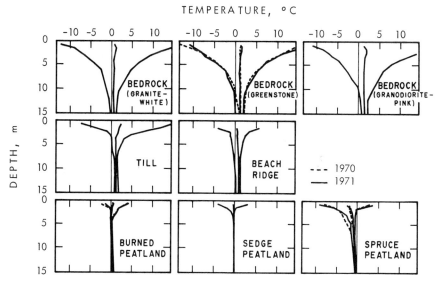

FIG. 2.12   Ground temperature envelopes, Yellowknife, N.W.T. 1970 and 1971 (After Brown 1973a).

For most northern engineering projects, a knowledge of the ground thermal regime is of importance to depths ranging from 20 to 200 ft. (6 to 60 m). In some cases, such as drilling and production of gas, oil and water supply wells and in mines, it must be known to much greater depths, particularly in the continuous permafrost zone. Permafrost temperatures measured at various sites in northern Canada are reported by several authors, including Brown 1967b, 1973a, 1978, Cook 1958, Judge 1973c, Mackay 1967, 1975a, Nicholson and Thom 1973, Taylor and Judge 1974, 1975, 1976. Some typical examples are given in Figs. 2.10 to 2.16.

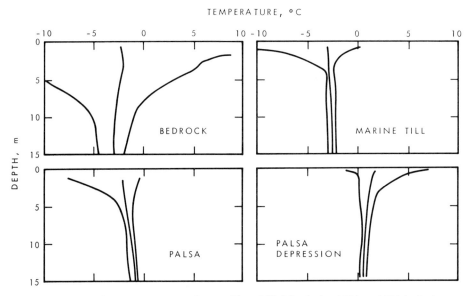

FIG. 2.13   Ground temperature envelopes, Churchill, Manitoba 1974 to 1976 inclusive (After Brown 1978).

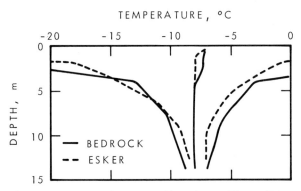

FIG. 2.14   Ground temperature envelopes, Rankin Inlet, N.W.T. 1974 to 1976 inclusive (After Brown 1978).

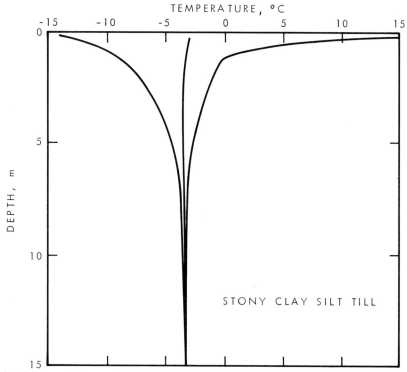

FIG. 2.15   Ground temperature envelope, Inuvik, N.W.T. 1974 to 1977 inclusive.

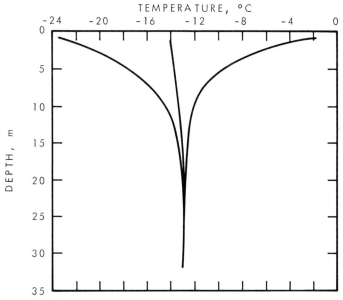

FIG. 2.16   Ground temperature envelope, Resolute Bay, N.W.T. 1955 (After Cook 1958).

As can be seen from some of the examples, the mean annual temperature at the depth of zero annual amplitude may vary by several degrees at different sites at one locality. In addition, the annual fluctuation in temperature can vary appreciably, particularly at shallow depths. These variations, due to differences in local terrain and microclimate conditions (Brown 1973a, Smith 1975a), are most important with regard to the design and construction of engineering works. Methods of determining the influence of these factors on the ground thermal regime are discussed in Chapter 4.

2.4 Ground Ice

Ice can be found in all types of frozen ground including gravels and bedrock (Mackay and Black 1973). It can vary greatly in amount from place to place and with depth below the ground surface, and is an especially critical factor in bearing capacity, settlement and slope stability problems, particularly when the ground thaws. It is therefore one of the most important considerations in the location, design of foundations and construction and performance of engineering struc-

TABLE 2.1
Summary of Ground Ice Descriptive System
(After Pihlainen and Johnston 1963, Linell and Kaplar 1966)

A. ICE NOT VISIBLE[a]

Group Symbol	Subgroup Description	Symbol	Field Identification
N	Poorly bonded or friable	Nf	To determine presence of excess ice, use procedure under note[b] and hand magnifying lens as necessary. For soils not fully saturated, estimate degree of ice saturation: medium, low. Note presence of crystals or of ice coatings around larger particles.
	No excess ice Well-bonded Nb Excess ice	Nbn Nbe	

B. VISIBLE ICE—LESS THAN 1 INCH THICK[a]

Group Symbol	Subgroup Description	Symbol	Field Identification
V	Individual ice crystals or inclusions	Vx	For ice phase, record the following when applicable: Location Size
	Ice coatings on particles	Vc	Orientation Shape Thickness Pattern of

	Random or irregularly oriented ice formations	Vr	Length arrangement
			  Spacing
			  Hardness
			  Structure } per Group C
			  Colour

	Stratified or distinctly oriented ice formations	Vs	Estimate volume of visible segregated ice present as percentage of total sample volume.

tures in permafrost areas. The great variability in the amounts and types of ground ice that can occur even within a small area means that detailed subsurface investigations, described in Section 5.5, must be conducted prior to undertaking any engineering project.

Ground ice is a broad term for all types of underground ice irrespective of age or origin. Thus, it refers not only to ice which has frozen in situ in the ground, but also to surface ice (e.g., lake, river and glacier ice) that has been preserved by burial. Although ice pans or blocks buried by sloughing river and lake banks or in moraines near active glaciers have been encountered, buried surface ice is relatively rare and will be excluded from the following discussion.

2.4.1 Description and Classification of Ground Ice

A description of ground ice should adhere to a recognized standard which is applicable both in the field and in the laboratory. Such a descriptive system, which has been widely used in North America, is given in Pihlainen and Johnston (1963) and Linell and Kaplar (1966) and is summarized in Table 2.1.

C. VISIBLE ICE—GREATER THAN 1 INCH THICK			
Group Symbol	Subgroup Description	Symbol	Field Identification
ICE	Ice with soil inclusions	ICE + soil type	Designate material as ICE[c] and use descriptive terms as follows, usually one item from each group, when applicable:
	Ice without soil inclusions	ICE	

Hardness	*Structure*[d]
HARD	CLEAR
SOFT	CLOUDY
(of mass, not	POROUS
individual	CANDLED
crystals)	GRANULAR
	STRATIFIED
Colour	*Admixtures*
(Examples):	(Examples):
COLOURLESS	CONTAINS
GRAY	FEW THIN
BLUE	SILT INCLUSIONS

(a) Frozen soils in the N group may, on close examination, indicate presence of ice within the voids of the material by crystalline reflections or by a sheen on fractured or trimmed surfaces. The impression received by the unaided eye, however, is that none of the frozen water occupies space in excess of the original voids in the soil. The opposite is true of frozen soils in the V group.

(b) When visual methods are inadequate, a simple field test to aid evaluation of volume of excess ice can be made by placing some frozen soil in a small jar, allowing it to melt, and observing the quantity of supernatant water as a percentage of total volume.

(c) Where special forms of ice such as hoarfrost can be distinguished, more explicit description should be given.

(d) Observer should be careful to avoid being misled by surface scratches or frost coating on the ice.

No standard classification system for ground ice exists. Most classification systems are genetically based upon the thermal, hydrologic and geomorphologic conditions which led to the growth and preservation of ground ice (Katasonov 1961, Mackay 1972a, Shumskiy 1964, Shumskiy and Vtyurin 1966, Vtyurina and Vtyurin 1970). Genetic classification systems are useful for engineering purposes because if the type of ice is known, further inferences can often be made with regard to its three-dimensional distribution.

Identification of the ground ice type should be based upon a number of criteria, such as the nature of the terrain and vegetation cover; the past thermal, hydrologic, and geomorphic history of the site; details of the ice petrofabrics and soil if available in an exposure; and laboratory analyses. If drill cores are available, much can be learned from ice fabric analyses (Shumskiy 1964), the microstratigraphy of the ice and foreign material, and the chemical and isotopic composition of the ice (Mackay and Lavkulich 1975, Michel and Fritz 1978).

2.4.2 Ground Ice Types

The more common ground ice types, discussed below, are shown in Fig. 2.17 along with typical ice descriptions based upon Table 2.1. Pore ice bonds or cements soil grains together. Soils with only pore ice may yield little or no excess water when thawed. If the growth of pore ice was accompanied by water expulsion or water was withdrawn to feed a nearby ice lens, the soil may be unsaturated when thawed.

Segregated ice grows in all types of soil by the addition of water to a stationary, or quasi-stationary, freezing front. The ice lenses range from hairline streaks to masses of nearly pure ice tens of feet (metres) thick (Figs. 2.18 to 2.22). Most lenses probably grow slightly above the base of permafrost as it advances downwards during the freezing stage. They tend to be composed of nearly pure transparent ice interlayered with soil. The crystallographic c-axes and bubble trains may be oriented vertically, i.e., normal to the freezing front. Small stones and soil particles may occur in isolation, as if suspended in clear ice. This distinguishes segregated ice from intrusive ice (water). Most large masses of segregated ice lie at depths exceeding 10 ft. (3 m), the ice is harder than wedge ice and layering is generally horizontal (Mackay and Stager 1966, Mackay 1971, 1973a, Rampton and Mackay 1971). The maximum depth to which segregated ice can occur in permafrost is unknown but Mackay (1976) suggests that it could grow to depths of at least 200 ft. (60 m). All soils with segregated ice yield excess water when thawed, although the soil layers between ice lenses may be unsaturated.

Reticulated vein ice (Mackay 1974b, McRoberts and Nixon 1975) is a variety of segregated ice distinguished by a three-dimensional reticulated ice vein (lens) pattern (Figs. 2.18, 2.19, 2.20). The ice is often found in fine-grained glacial till and lake and marine clays. The reticulate vein ice may grade upwards into aggradational ice and downwards into horizontal ice lenses. The ice is usually pure and

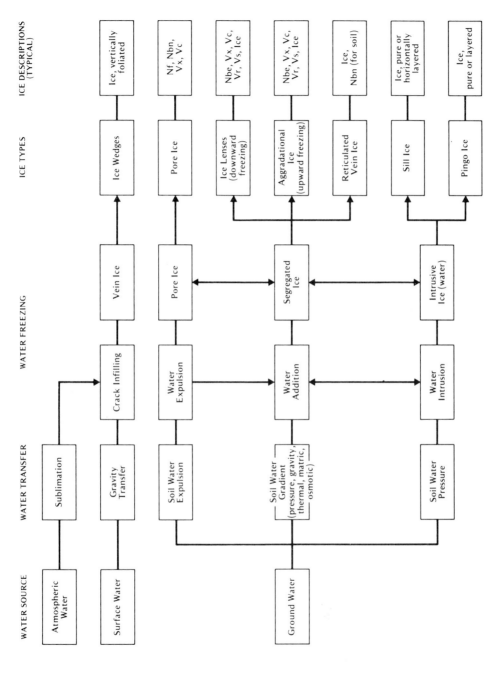

FIG. 2.17 Classification of ground ice based upon the water source and principal transfer processes at the time of freezing (modified from Mackay 1972a). Typical ice descriptions for the ice types are given in the right hand column (see Table 2.1).

sediment free. Thaw of the ice veins yields excess water but thaw of the intervening clay blocks may yield little to no excess water.

Aggradational ice grows in response to a rise of the permafrost table due to a
climatic change, the addition of material to the ground surface (as by soil creep,
sedimentation, or organic accumulation), or by a combination of diverse factors.
Aggradational ice is composed of relatively thin ice lenses frozen at the bottom of
the active layer and later preserved in permafrost; no massive ice sheets will be
formed. The ice lenses are crudely parallel to the undulations of the permafrost
table. In vegetated areas, old roots, weathered soil horizons and other active layer
features may be incorporated into permafrost in the zone of aggradational ice.
The upper 5 to 10 ft. (1.5 to 3 m) of the ground in many Arctic areas with fine-
grained soil may have considerable aggradational ice.

Ice wedges are V-shaped masses of vertically foliated ice that underlie the
troughs of tundra polygons (Black 1954). Ice wedges grow by thermally-induced
winter cracking of the ground, repeated irregularly over a long time, with subsequent infilling of the vertical cracks by melt-water and ice crystals (Lachenbruch

FIG. 2.18   A 25 ft. (8 m) thaw face 15 miles (25 km) southeast of Tuktoyaktuk,
N.W.T. shows a variety of ice types. The age sequence, from youngest to oldest, is: ice
lenses, reticulated vein ice, massive segregated ice, aggradational ice and ice wedge ice
(J. R. Mackay photograph).

FIG. 2.19   Ice layers (black), mainly horizontal up to 0.2 in. (5 mm) thick in grey silty clay.

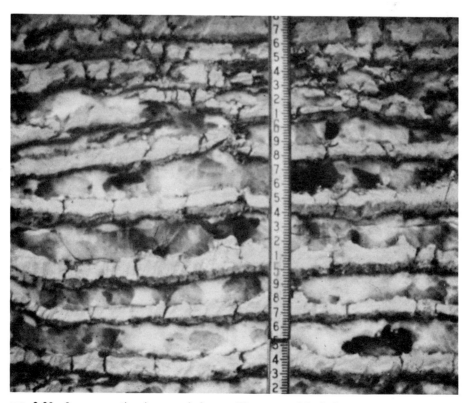

FIG. 2.20   Ice segregation in varved clays at Thompson, Manitoba.

FIG. 2.21   Massive ice deposits in exposure of perennially frozen stony, fine-grained soil
on the west side of the Mackenzie River Delta, N.W.T.

1960a, 1961, 1962, Mackay 1973a, 1975b, c). Some wedges are also vertically
banded with organic matter and soil derived from the trough above the wedge.
The ice usually contains numerous bubbles, which cause it to fracture readily
under a blow, in contrast to most other ice types. Individual wedges may attain a
width of 10 to 15 ft. (3 to 5 m) and reach depths of 15 to 30 ft. (5 to 10 m). Actively growing ice wedges are restricted primarily to areas of continuous permafrost (Péwé 1966). In general, ice wedges are considerably younger than the
permafrost in which they occur. Where the upper permafrost surface is rising,
however, as by sedimentation, accumulation of organic matter or soil creep, ice
wedges of the same age as the surrounding permafrost (often referred to as
syngenetic ice wedges) may grow.

    Sill and pingo ice are formed by the freezing of water intruded under pressure.
Sill ice may form by water intrusion in winter between a downwards freezing active layer and the top of permafrost. The ice tends to be pure and not far below
the ground surface. Pingo ice forms the cores of pingos (ice-cored hills—Fig.
2.23), which are rather localized in distribution (Mackay 1973b). Pingos are
discussed in more detail in Section 2.5.4.

FIG. 2.22   Massive ice in gravel pit at Inuvik, N.W.T.

FIG. 2.23   Pingo ice core exposed by coastal erosion near Tuktoyaktuk, N.W.T.
(J.R. Mackay photograph).

Segregated ice lenses from hairline to 1 or 2 in. (25 or 50 mm) thick are the form of ground ice most frequently encountered in northern Canada. They will inevitably be found in most fine-grained, perennially frozen soil deposits, especially within the top 10 to 20 ft. (3 to 6 m). Massive ice deposits, which include ice wedges and large segregated ice lenses, are also quite common but their distribution tends to be more localized.

It must be emphasized that significant amounts of ice are frequently found in all types of bedrock and may occur to depths of 20 or 30 ft. (6 or 10 m) or more, not only in sedimentary formations but also in igneous or metamorphic rocks that may or may not be covered with overburden. This ice results from the freezing of surface or ground water, which has percolated or been injected along or into joints, fractures, seams, bedding planes and voids or cavities in the rock.

2.5 Terrain Features

Various micro- and macro-landforms, which are mainly the result of the cold climate and/or drainage or water conditions, are found in the permafrost regions of the world. Processes involved in the formation of these features include mass-wasting, frost action, thawing and erosion. Virtually all these features are indicative of potentially troublesome conditions, which may seriously affect structures and therefore must be carefully assessed by the engineer.

Some features are restricted to the active layer only, while others are more deep-seated and involve either the aggradation or degradation of permafrost. The various periglacial features and processes are described in detail by Washburn (1956, 1973). Some of the more distinctive features are briefly discussed in the following sections, with emphasis being placed on ice-related forms and slope movements because of their engineering significance.

2.5.1 Patterned Ground

Various features, such as circles, polygons, nets, steps and stripes, which are more or less symmetrical in form, are referred to as patterned ground (Washburn 1956). They are characteristic of, but not necessarily confined to, the active layer and result primarily from frost action. They may be sorted or unsorted or otherwise modified, depending on whether one or more processes, such as frost creep, solifluction, thermal cracking or vegetation growth, are involved. Circles, polygons and nets usually occur on nearly horizontal surfaces, while all forms of stripes are confined to slopes. Patterns are generally small-scale features with maximum dimensions ranging from about 1 ft. (0.3 m) to as much as 300 ft. (100 m). Some patterns are primarily related to frost heaving or contraction of frozen materials under conditions of extreme cold, while others are caused by mass transfer of thawed material in or on the active layer (solifluction).

One widespread and easily recognized feature is the ice wedge polygon (Figs. 2.24 and 2.25). These occur as a result of repeated thermal contraction cracking

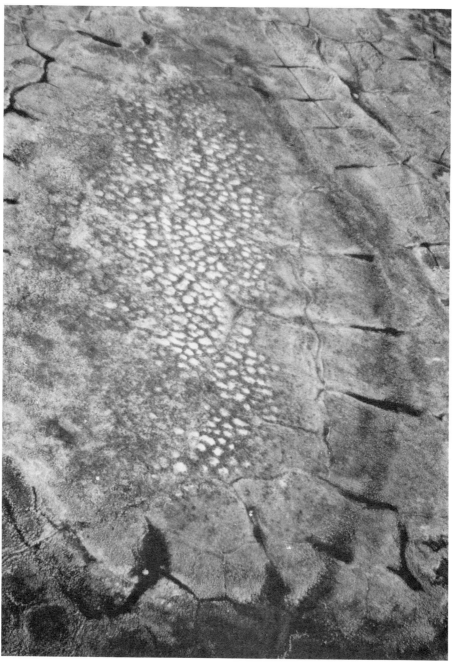

FIG. 2.24   Patterned ground, Kaminak Lake, District of Keewatin, N.W.T. Frost polygons are confined to organic terrain whereas mud boils (white spots) are confined to areas underlain by marine silty clay (Geological Survey of Canada photograph).

FIG. 2.25   Polygonal patterned ground in the tundra south of Tuktoyaktuk, N.W.T.
The polygons are about 45 to 100 ft. (15 to 30 m) in diameter.

of the ground due to extremely low winter temperatures, with the vertical cracks
being infilled with snow meltwater, which freezes and, in time, forms wedge-
shaped ice masses in the permafrost (Mackay 1974c). Although these polygons
are usually well defined in tundra areas, their surface expression may be masked
by vegetation or erased due to movements in the active layer. Actively growing ice
wedges are restricted primarily to the continuous permafrost zone, but inactive
ice wedges may be found in some areas of the discontinuous zone.

Not all polygonal patterns seen on the ground surface are underlain by ice
wedges. In some cases, particularly in the discontinuous zone but also in the continuous zone, the cracks are infilled with soil. In some areas, during a period
when the climate warmed and the ice wedges melted, the ice was replaced by soil
slumping from the sides of the crack when the active layer increased in thickness.
In other areas in the far North that have little or no precipitation, the cracks were
infilled by soil deposited by the wind or from slumping of the walls.

The active layer is a dynamic unit that is continually moving and adjusting on
even the most gentle slopes. The net effect of these movements is mass transfer of
material downslope. The underlying frozen surface adjusts upward or downward

in response to the thickening and thinning of the active layer, caused by the mass movements as well as in response to the heat transfer properties of the various types of soil that move over it on their way downslope. Patterned features associated with mass transfer include solifluction stripes, mud boils (non-sorted circles of frost boils), sorted circles, stone stripes, hummocks and steps.

FIG. 2.26 Typical permafrost landscape, eastern District of Keewatin, N.W.T. Note how till is flowing out as solifluction lobes over bare bedrock at right-centre of photo; till surface is covered by round mud boils, 6 to 10 ft. (2 to 3 m) in diameter and faint solifluction stripes in background. Frost cracks in foreground are in raised gravelly marine beaches (Geological Survey of Canada photograph).

These features are caused by frost action or movements of the thawed layer and generally reflect relatively slow mass transfer downslope (Fig. 2.26). The forms result from surface creep of saturated, muddy or clayey sediments or from arte- sian or freezing pressures built up within the active layer (Washburn 1973, Shilts 1973, 1974, Lundqvist 1969, McRoberts and Morgenstern 1974a, b, Mackay and MacKay 1976). Mass movement of material downslope can also be quite rapid, occurring over periods of a few minutes to a few years and often involve large quantities of material (Fig. 2.27).

2.5.2 Slope Movements and Stability

The following is restricted to the consideration of slope movements peculiar to the presence of frozen ground. Landslides in unfrozen ground have been found in

FIG. 2.27   Active flow slides on Kazan River, District of Keewatin, N.W.T. Materials
are till and marine sediments (Geological Survey of Canada photograph).

northern Canada, particularly in recent sediments adjacent to bodies of water
and in Cretaceous shales. Instability in unfrozen materials is well discussed in the
literature, and for all practical purposes the processes that occur, and the analyses
that can be used in design, are common to unfrozen slopes in both northern and
southern environments (Eckel 1958, Skempton and Hutchinson 1969). In the case
of slope instability when permafrost is present, most problems arise when thawing occurs. Shearing through frozen ground has been noted in some naturally occurring slopes but is relatively rare. Finn et al. (1978) point out the potential for liquefaction of thawed cohesionless soils situated between the frozen active layer
and the underlying permafrost due to dynamic loadings such as those caused by
earthquakes.

   Typical features of landslides and related phenomena of mass-wasting in permafrost are described in the literature (Bird 1967, Mackay 1966a, Mackay and
Mathews 1973, Washburn 1973). The characteristics and distribution of landslides in the Mackenzie Valley have received special attention (Chyurlia 1973,
Isaacs and Code 1972, Code 1973, McRoberts and Morgenstern 1973). A landslide classification system based solely upon descriptive features (Fig. 2.28) has
been suggested by McRoberts and Morgenstern (1973, 1974a). In this classification the term "flow" describes a type of movement that exhibits the characteristics of a viscous fluid in its downslope motion. Mobility is often substantial and

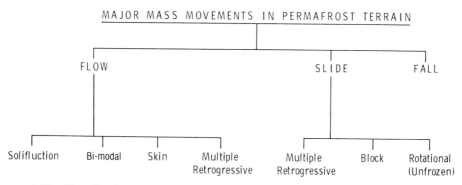

FIG. 2.28   Classification of landslides.

rapid and, as the movements are largely distributed throughout the mass, prefail-
ure relief features are rapidly destroyed. As noted in Fig. 2.28, there are four
recognizable types of flow movements.

Solifluction areas are readily identified by lobate flow features and associated
patterned ground (Washburn 1956, 1973). Active solifluction flows are normally
found at high altitudes and in the far North. If fine-grained materials are present
in the flow, care must be taken to recognize the possibility of sheared material in
place. Areas of active solifluction can usually be avoided during site selection.
Although solifluction movements have not been a serious impediment to northern engineering projects to date, relic solifluction features have been very
troublesome in temperate zones (Weeks 1969, Chandler 1970).

Skin flows involve the detachment of a thin veneer of vegetation and mineral
soil with subsequent movement over a planar inclined surface. The result is long
ribbon-like forms, which may coalesce and cover a wide area. Although skin
flows usually develop on steep slopes, they are also common on flatter slopes.
McRoberts (1973) records the initiation of skin flows on slopes as flat as 6°. Fig.
2.29 illustrates skin flows in weathered shales on a north-facing 25° slope near the
Root River, N.W.T. These flows are commonly found in ice-rich recent
sediments, particularly following a forest fire. Examples are recorded by several
investigators, including Hardy and Morrison (1972), Hughes (1972) and Mackay
and Mathews (1973). Skin flows develop when the pore pressures generated during thaw reduce the shearing resistance to levels below the shear stress induced by
gravity forces. It is possible to predict these pore pressures using thaw
consolidation theory in an infinite slope analysis and so account for instability on
relatively gentle slopes. Details are given by McRoberts and Morgenstern (1974a).

Bi-modal flows have a biangular profile that typically consists of a low angle
tongue and a steep headscarp. The term also indicates that two different modes of
mass movement occur. The movement mechanisms in the headscarp differ from
those in the tongue. In the most active bi-modal flows, the permafrost in the
headscarp is directly exposed to the atmosphere and degrades by ablation. In

FIG. 2.29   Skin flows, Root River, N.W.T. (N.R. Morgenstern photograph).

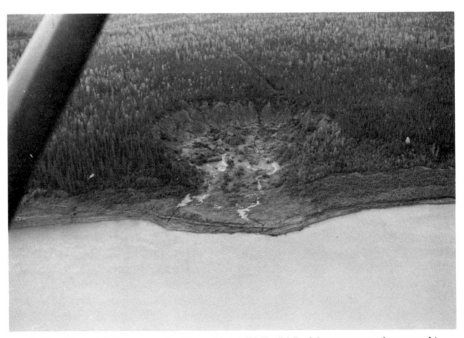

FIG. 2.30   Bi-modal flow near Ft. Norman, N.W.T. (N.R. Morgenstern photograph).

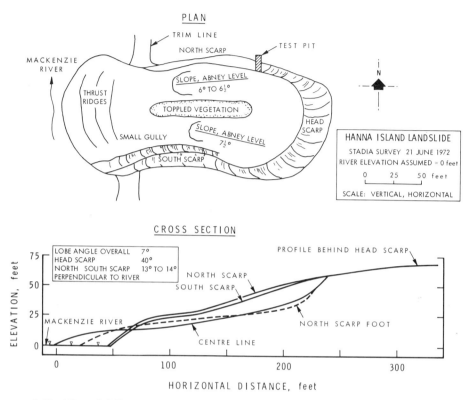

FIG. 2.31   Bi-modal flow near Hanna Island, Mackenzie River, N.W.T.

some instances, the permafrost soils are not sufficiently ice-rich to allow a sustained ablation process and a thawed active layer begins to form on the steeply inclined slope. When this thaws to some critical depth, the headscarp fails by the development of a skin flow in the thawed layer.

The tongues of bi-modal flows are usually inclined at angles ranging from a few degrees to about 14°, depending upon the characteristics of the debris. Active tongues have very little shearing resistance due to the presence of high pore water pressures (McRoberts and Morgenstern 1974a). The water content of the tongue may approach the liquid limit of the soil, thereby increasing its mobility. Fig. 2.30 illustrates a bi-modal flow on the Mackenzie River across from Fort Norman, N.W.T. A plan and section of another on the Mackenzie River is given in Fig. 2.31.

After a bi-modal flow is initiated, ablation can generate substantial rates of mass-wasting. Table 2.2 contains a summary of observations by McRoberts (1973). It is evident that bi-modal flows can seriously affect adjacent structures and facilities. These flows are initiated by some process (or combination of processes) that removes the insulating cover of vegetation and thawed soil, exposing ice-rich material in such a manner that an ablation mechanism can be started and

TABLE 2.2

Summary of the Rate of Movement of Headscarps in Bi-modal Flows
(After McRoberts 1973)

Flow	Movement	Rate cm/day
Hume River (HU1)	21 m in 6 years	3.6*
Hume River (HU2)	76 m in 6 years	12.7*
	150 m in 28 years	5.4*
Fort Simpson landslide	3 m in 6 weeks	7.3
Fort Norman landslide	36 m in 11 years	3.3*
Arctic Red River gravel pit	12 m spring thaw to August 1972	20.0
Isachsen	7 to 10 m/summer	7.0 to 10.0*
Kendall Island	Average 2 m in 41 days	4.8
Garry Island (Site B)	July 10 to August 15	7.8
	August 16 to September 5	5.3

* Assumed thaw season = 100 days

sustained. The most positive procedure for preventing bi-modal flows is to eliminate the initiating processes so that the integrity of the insulating cover is maintained.

Multiple retrogressive flows have an overall flow form, but retain some portion of their pre-failure relief. Although the overall profile of these landslides is biangular, their form suggests that a series of retrogressive failures have occurred at the headscarp. These can be seen in some locations but rotational slides are found in others. Examples are shown in Figs. 2.32 and 2.33.

FIG. 2.32 Multiple retrogressive flow on the Mackenzie River 20 miles (32 kilometres) downstream from Ft. Simpson, N.W.T. (N.R. Morgenstern photograph).

FIG. 2.33   Extensive slides caused by melting of massive ground ice in the tundra near Tuktoyaktuk, N.W.T.

Flow-dominated failures on natural slopes and cut slopes are common in permafrost areas, particularly in fine-grained frozen soils. Pufahl (1976) analyzed the heat balance at the surface of exposed thawing permafrost and verified the theory developed by means of field experiments. The studies indicate that the heat balance components provide an uncommonly large heat source to produce the high rates of ablation noted in the field. Methods of stabilizing both natural and cut slopes are described by Pufahl (1976) and Pufahl and Morgenstern (1979). These utilize surcharge loading and insulation to increase the normal effective stress disproportionately to the shearing stress and to control the rate of thaw and generation of excess pore water pressures.

Slide movements in frozen ground may be classified as block or multiple retrogressive slides. Block slides involve a large single block that has moved down with little or no backtilting. Multiple retrogressive slides are characterized by a series of arcuate, concave-toward-the-toe blocks that step upward toward the headscarp. Block and multiple retrogressive slides are illustrated in Figs. 2.34 and 2.35 respectively. These landslides are large-scale features, about 150 to 200 ft. (45 to 60 m) high, and are associated with shear failure in frozen soil. McRoberts

FIG. 2.34   Block slide, Mackenzie River Valley, N.W.T. (N.R. Morgenstern photograph).

FIG. 2.35   Multiple retrogressive slide, Mountain River, N.W.T. (N.R. Morgenstern photograph).

and Morgenstern (1974b) discuss the mechanics of slides in frozen soil in detail and indicate the likelihood that the base of the failure lies in unfrozen clay, at least under some stratigraphic conditions that occur in the Mackenzie Valley. The occurrence of block and multiple retrogressive slides are readily detected from air photos and these features can be avoided by appropriate site selection.

The final form of failure in natural slopes is the fall, which simply involves the downward movement of detached blocks falling under the influence of gravity. Falls occur commonly along the banks of rivers or lakes, where thawing and erosion undercut the bank and large blocks of frozen material subsequently break off. This facilitates bank recession; lateral migration of about 33 ft./yr. (10m/yr) has been reported in the Colville River area by Walker and Arnborg (1966) and in the Mackenzie Delta by Gill (1972).

2.5.3 Thermokarst

Thermokarst is the term used to describe topographic depressions resulting from the thawing of ground ice (Washburn 1973). The thawing of ice-rich permafrost can result from a variety of causes, including warming of the climate, disturbance or removal of vegetation and changes in ground surface conditions caused by nature or man's activities such as fire, disrupted drainage, ponding of water, flooding, and construction. Thermokarst topography is uneven, consisting of thaw lakes, cemetery mounds, sinkholes, beaded streams and similar features (Brown 1973b).

Thermokarst topography is commonly formed where massive ice, such as ice wedges or thick layers of segregated ice, exists in the ground. Perhaps the most common feature is the thaw lake, which is found throughout the Arctic and Subarctic. They are widespread in northern Alaska and Canada, occurring in the Mackenzie Delta area (Mackay 1963a, 1971, Rampton 1973), on Baffin and Banks Islands (Bird 1967, French and Egginton 1973) and elsewhere in Canada (Cailleux 1971). Beaded streams (Fig. 2.36) and cemetery mounds result from the melting of ice wedges. Cemetery mounds are particularly well expressed in the vicinity of Richmond Gulf and for some distance north of there, where they follow a narrow belt inland from the east coast of Hudson Bay.

A lowering of the permafrost table in areas where much ground ice exists is probably one of the most dangerous of the disruptive human activities in northern engineering projects, and the resulting or potential effects of man-made thermokarst are the subject of much current Arctic research. Examples of man-induced thermokarst resulting from exploration and construction activities on Banks Island are given by French (1975a, b, 1976) and in the Mackenzie Delta area by Watmore (1969) and Kerfoot (1973).

2.5.4 Pingos, Palsas and Peat Plateaus

Pingos are large, ice-cored mounds formed by water under pressure in open or closed systems (Washburn 1973). They are one of the largest and most spectacular permafrost landforms, ranging in size from 20 to 200 ft. (6 to 60 m) high

FIG. 2.36 Typical beaded thermokarst stream in ice wedge polygon area, District of
Keewatin, N.W.T. (Geological Survey of Canada photograph).

and from 60 to 1,200 ft. (20 to 365 m) in diameter and are found in the permafrost region throughout the northern hemisphere.

The closed-system or Mackenzie-type pingos occur mainly in the continuous permafrost zone of northwestern North America and, in Canada, are very common near the Mackenzie Delta and on adjacent portions of the Arctic coastal plain (Mackay 1962, 1963b, 1966b, 1973b, 1979, Pihlainen et al. 1956) where they are almost always associated with drained lakes (Fig. 2.37 and 2.38). They form when the thaw bulb that formerly existed beneath the lake refreezes from the top after the lake or pond drains. Growth of ice lenses and freezing of excess water trapped below the advancing freezing front causes up-doming of the ground surface where the resistance to expansion is the least. The domed ground surface is characterized by radial tension cracks, which result from stretching of the overburden. The rate of formation of pingos is rapid. Based on field measurements, Mackay (1973b) estimates the vertical growth rate to be about 5 ft. (1.5 m) in the first one or two years.

The open-system or East Greenland type pingo (Müller 1959) occurs principally in the discontinuous permafrost zone and is common in the Yukon and western

FIG. 2.37 Pingo about 60 ft. (20 m) high, 60 miles (100 kilometres) north of Inuvik, N.W.T. Note polygonal markings on sides indicating pingo formed in old drained lake basin.

FIG. 2.38 Active pingo near south edge of Eskimo Lakes, Mackenzie District, N.W.T.
This pingo has formed since 1950 in a shoaling bay. Its height is about 20 ft. (6 m)
above water level. Note characteristic radial tension cracks and disruption by thawing
near apex (Geological Survey of Canada photograph).

Alaska, particularly in forested areas (Brown and Péwé 1973, Hughes 1969).
Open-system pingos form in areas of moderate to great relief, where water,
trapped below thin permafrost or in thawed layers within the permafrost, pushes
its way close to the surface, freezing in the perennially frozen ground. As the ice
thickness increases, the ground surface is domed. These pingos are physically
similar to closed-system pingos and are differentiated from them mainly on the
basis of their location and local permafrost conditions.

Pingos are also found in the Canadian Arctic Islands (Balkwill et al. 1974,
French 1975b, Pissart 1967, Pissart and French 1976) and the interior of the
N.W.T. mainland (Craig 1959). A pingo is located in the Simpson Peninsula,
N.W.T. (Tarnocai and Netterville 1976) and a dense field of small pingo-like
features covers about 75 square miles (195 square kilometres) of the coastal plain
near the Maguse River delta on the west side of Hudson Bay. Submerged, pingo-
like features are also found in shallow portions of the Beaufort Sea (Shearer et al.
1971).

Palsas and peat plateaus also result from aggradation of permafrost and are a
characteristic of the Subarctic, commonly occurring in areas of discontinuous

FIG. 2.39   Palsa about 10 ft. (3 m) high near Great Whale River, P.Q.

permafrost throughout the world. Palsas are mounds of peat with a permafrost core usually less than 300 ft. (100 m) in diameter and rising 3 to 25 ft. (1 to 7 m) above the surrounding wet peatland (Fig. 2.39). Peat plateaus are perennially frozen peat deposits occurring as islands in unfrozen bogs or as very thick peat deposits on slightly sloping mineral terrain (Fig. 2.40). Their generally flat surface is about 3 ft. (1 m) above the lowland watertable and they may range in area from a few square yards (few square metres) to one or two square miles (several square kilometres). Polygonal peat plateaus are similar but are divided into a polygonal pattern by trenches underlain by ice wedges 6 to 12 ft. (2 to 4 m) deep (Zoltai and Pettapiece 1973, Tarnocai 1973).

Ice segregation in the thick peat deposits usually consists of thin lenses, but occasionally ice layers from 9 to 12 in. (200 to 300 mm) thick may be found. Ice layers 3 to 6 ft. (1 to 2 m) thick are frequently found at the peat-mineral soil interface or in the underlying frozen mineral soil, which is always fine-grained (i.e. silt or clayey silt). The freezing of these saturated materials and the growth of the segregated ice layers accounts for the formation of these distinctive features.

Palsas and the associated peat plateaus are quite common in central and northern Alaska and are widespread throughout the Canadian discontinuous permafrost zone, being found in all physiographic regions from Labrador to the

FIG. 2.40 Air view of forested peat plateau (top of photograph). Wet, sedge-covered treeless depression with no permafrost in middle of photograph. For ground view of this feature see Figure 2.5.

Yukon (Brown 1967a, 1968, 1975, Railton and Sparling 1973, Hamelin and Cailleux 1969, Zoltai and Tarnocai 1975). Although generally thought to belong to the southern part of the discontinuous zone they, or similar features, have been observed in the lower Mackenzie Valley and in the Arctic Archipelago in the continuous permafrost zone.

Great care must be taken to ensure that engineering operations do not cause detrimental disturbance to the environments in which these various features exist. For example, drainage of small ponds or lakes may result in freezing of underlying thawed ground and the formation of ice lenses or closed-system pingos. Deep thawing under a structure, or disruption of subsurface drainage by creation of a frozen zone (as around a chilled buried pipeline or under an embankment) in a previously unfrozen area could cause artesian water to form segregated ice, small pingos or surface icings. Similarly, disturbance of the ice-rich palsas and peat plateaus will inevitably result in rapid thaw and significant—if not disastrous—settlement of structures built on them.

CHAPTER 3

Engineering Characteristics of Frozen and Thawing Soils

(Contributors–G. H. Johnston, B. Ladanyi,
N. R. Morgenstern and E. Penner)

3.1 Introduction

Earth materials in a frozen, freezing, thawing, thawed and unfrozen state will be encountered on most engineering projects in the permafrost region. Thus the properties and behaviour of foundation soils under load will be more varied than in non-permafrost areas, even though their composition and moisture content may be the same. Problems related to the strength and deformation behaviour of frozen soils, settlement of thawing and thawed soils and heave of freezing soils must be anticipated when engineering works are undertaken. The present state of knowledge of the various phenomena and processes involved and the properties and behaviour of these materials in their different states are reviewed in this chapter.

3.2 Composition and Structure of Frozen Soil

Frozen soil is a complex, multiphase system, usually consisting of four components, each having different physico-mechanical properties: soil particles, ice, water and air. Recognition of the interaction of these components and their distribution in the system under various states of stress is basic to an understanding of the properties and engineering behaviour of frozen ground (Scott 1969, Tsytovich 1973, Anderson and Morgenstern 1973).

The properties of frozen soils are affected not only by the size and shape of the mineral particles, but also by the physico-chemical properties of their surfaces, determined essentially by their mineralogical composition. The role of the soil particles depends on the intensity of chemical bonds between their surfaces and the surrounding medium such as the pore water and the pore ice.

Ice is a most important component of frozen ground. It is a visco-plastic substance with quite specific physico-mechanical properties which differ greatly from those of other natural solid materials. Frozen soils occurring in nature contain varying amounts and many forms of ice. Rarely is it distributed uniformly or homogeneously in the ground (see Section 2.4). When a soil freezes, some of the moisture may accumulate in the form of large crystals and lenses of ice. On the other hand, some moisture freezes in the pores and bonds the mineral particles together to form a monolithic mass. The frozen pore moisture is termed ice-cement.

Based on the type and distribution of ice in the soil, the structure of frozen soil may be massive, layered or reticulate. A massive structure (not to be confused with massive ground ice forms) is characterized by the predominant presence of pore ice and by a relatively low total ice content. On the other hand, frozen soils with a layered or reticulate structure contain segregated ice and their total ice content is relatively high. In soils with a reticulate structure, ice lenses generally form a random net, while in those with a layered structure they occur as well-oriented horizontal lenses alternating with soil layers having a massive structure.

Experimental evidence shows that not all the water in most fine-grained soils (silts and clays) freezes unless the temperature is appreciably below 32°F (0°C), so that there is no specific freezing point, the water freezing progressively as the temperature drops. In some fine-grained soils as much as one-third of the water may remain unfrozen at a temperature several degrees below 32°F (0°C). With changing temperatures the changing proportions of frozen and unfrozen water significantly influence the strength and deformation characteristics of frozen soil and have important effects on its thermal and other properties.

Frozen soils may be described as hard frozen, plastic frozen or dry frozen, depending on their pore ice and unfrozen water contents and their compressibility under load (U.S.S.R. 1969). Hard frozen soils are firmly cemented with ice, are subject to a relatively brittle failure and exhibit practically no consolidation under load. Plastic frozen soils are cemented by ice but have viscous properties due to their high unfrozen water content and therefore will compress under load. Dry or friable frozen soils have a very low moisture content and are not cemented by ice. Their compressibility is the same as for unfrozen soils having the same composition, moisture content and density. A change in temperature of the frozen soil will change the amount of unfrozen water in it. Thus a hard frozen soil may be transformed to a plastic frozen soil if the temperature rises and vice versa.

Water vapour in frozen soils can have an important effect on their properties in certain cases, as it will migrate under a thermal gradient from a warm to a cold point. In unsaturated frozen soils this phenomenon may represent the principal mechanism of moisture redistribution during temperature and phase changes (Tsytovich 1973).

3.3 Physical Properties of Frozen Soil

To define properly the composition of frozen soil in terms of the four principal phases, the following parameters have to be determined:
  (1) total water content of frozen soil, w,
  (2) bulk density of undisturbed frozen soil, γ_f,
  (3) unit weight of solid soil particles, γ_s,
  (4) unfrozen water content, w_u, or, alternatively, the relative ice content of frozen soil, i_r.

The total water content w includes all types of water (frozen and unfrozen) contained in the frozen soil—

$$w = w_u + w_i \tag{3.1}$$

or $$w = w_u + w_v + w_1 \tag{3.1a}$$

where w_u is the unfrozen water content at a given temperature, w_i is the total ice content, w_v is the water content due to pore ice (ice-cement) and w_1 is the water content due to ice inclusions, such as ice lenses, crystals and coatings on soil particles.

The water content of the frozen soil (massive structure) between ice layers w_b is then

$$w_b = w_v + w_u \tag{3.2}$$

All water contents are expressed as a ratio of the weight of water to the weight of dry soil. The values for w, w_b and w_u are determined experimentally, and w_v and w_1 are calculated from Eqs. 3.1 and 3.2. The value of w_u may be found by special experimental procedures, several of which are described by Anderson and Morgenstern (1973). Soviet investigations (U.S.S.R. 1969) have shown it may be estimated from

$$w_u = k_u w_p \tag{3.3}$$

where w_p denotes the water content of soil at the plastic limit expressed as a fraction and k_u is a coefficient depending on the type of soil, the plasticity index and the temperature of the frozen soil. Values for k_u are given in Table 3.1.

TABLE 3.1

Coefficient k_u
(From USSR 1969)

Soil Type	Plasticity index	k_u Temperature °C					
		−0.3	−0.5	−1	−2	−4	−10
1. Sands	<1	0	0	0	0	0	0
2. Silty sands	1-2	0	0	0	0	0	0
3. Sandy silts	2-7	0.6	0.5	0.4	0.35	0.3	0.25
4. Clayey silts	7-13	0.7	0.65	0.6	0.5	0.45	0.4
5. Silty clays	13-17	*	0.75	0.65	0.55	0.5	0.45
6. Clays	>17	*	0.95	0.9	0.65	0.6	0.55

* All pore water is unfrozen

Tice et al. (1976) describe a method by which the unfrozen water content can be predicted from the liquid limit of a soil with sufficient accuracy for general engineering purposes. This technique is useful provided the soil does not contain an excessive amount of soluble salts and the liquid limit does not exceed 100.

The bulk density γ_f of a frozen soil is the weight of a unit volume of frozen soil and is determined by measuring the volume and weight of undisturbed frozen samples taken in the field. The dry density of undisturbed frozen soil γ_{d_f} is the weight of dry soil divided by the total volume of frozen soil. Its relationship with the frozen bulk density γ_f and the total moisture content w is, by definition

$$\gamma_f = \gamma_{d_f} (1 + w) \tag{3.4}$$

Assuming full saturation, which is usually valid in soils with excess ice and no unfrozen water, then

$$\gamma_f = \frac{G_s \gamma_w (1 + w)}{(1 + 1.09 G_s w)} \tag{3.4a}$$

where G_s denotes the specific gravity of soil particles and γ_w is the density of water $= 62.5$ lb./ft.^{3} (1000 kg/m^3).

The unit weight of solid soil particles γ_s is the weight of the particles divided by their volume. It is usually expressed as

$$\gamma_s = G_s \gamma_w \tag{3.5}$$

From γ_s and γ_{d_f}, the void ratio e and the porosity n can be calculated.as

$$e = \gamma_s/\gamma_{d_f} - 1 \tag{3.6}$$

$$n = e/(1 + e) \text{ or } 1 - \gamma_{d_f}/\gamma_s \tag{3.7}$$

The relative ice content i_r is the ratio of the weight of ice to the total weight of water (both frozen and unfrozen) in a frozen soil. For soils having a layered or reticulate structure it is

$$i_r = w_i - w_u/w = (w_v + w_1) - w_u/w \tag{3.8}$$

and for a frozen soil with a massive structure it is

$$i_r = (w_v - w_u)/w \tag{3.9}$$

The corresponding degree of saturation with ice S_i, defined as the ratio between the volume of ice and the volume of pores in frozen soil (massive structure), is given by

$$S_i = w_i G_s \gamma_w/e \gamma_i \tag{3.10}$$

where γ_i is the density of ice $= 57.2$ lb./ft.^{3} (916 kg/m^3).

On the other hand, the degree of saturation with unfrozen water is given by

$$S_u = w_u G_s/e \tag{3.11}$$

Therefore, the total degree of saturation with moisture (ice and unfrozen water) for a frozen soil is

$$S = S_i + S_u = (w_i \gamma_w/\gamma_i + w_u) G_s/e \tag{3.12}$$

It should be noted that $\gamma_w/\gamma_i \approx 1.09$, and $2.6 < G_s \leq 2.8$ for mineral particles and $1.1 \leq G_s \leq 2.5$ for organic matter.

From Eqs. 3.6 and 3.12 one can also derive a useful relationship between the dry density of a frozen soil γ_{d_f}, ice and water contents w_i and w_u, and the degree of saturation S

$$\gamma_{d_f} = \frac{\gamma_w}{1/G_s + (1.09\ w_i + w_u)/S} \tag{3.13}$$

3.3.1 Unfrozen Water in Frozen Soils

Not all the water freezes when fine-grained soils are subjected to freezing temperatures. They may contain significant amounts of unfrozen water, particularly in the range of temperatures that are of practical importance to the engineer. Phase composition curves for several soils and soil constituents are shown in Figs. 3.1 and 3.2. This phenomenon is generally regarded as resulting from surface forces which define the nature and limits of the water that surrounds the particles (Williams 1967, Anderson and Morgenstern 1973). The closer one approaches the particle surface, the higher are the surface forces, which consist essentially of capillary and adsorption forces. The temperature decrease required for freezing of the water held to the soil particles (freezing-point depression) will vary with the intensity of these forces. Furthermore, it has been shown experimentally that unfrozen water can move through frozen soil under electrical and osmotic as well as thermal gradients. This movement is confined

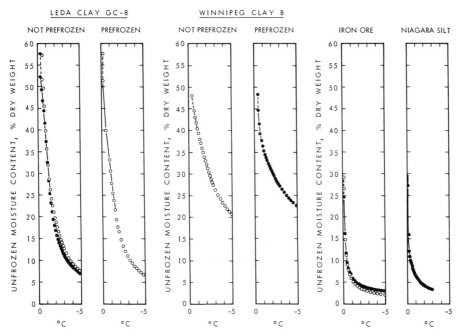

FIG. 3.1   Variation of unfrozen water content with temperature for four different soils (After Williams 1967).

mainly to the unfrozen interfacial films, but can be significant (Dirksen and Miller 1966, Hoekstra 1966, 1969, Anderson and Morgenstern 1973, Harlan 1973).

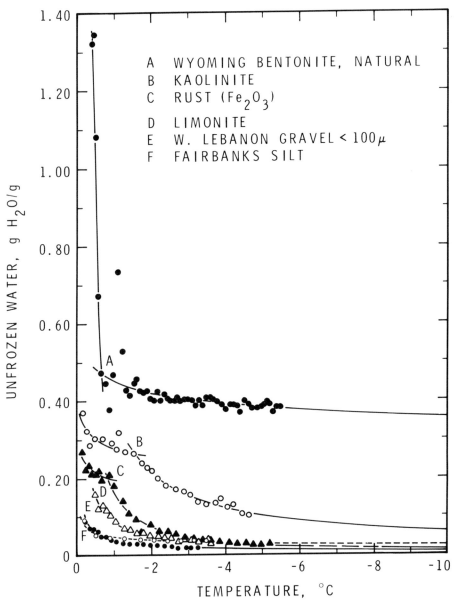

FIG. 3.2 Variation of unfrozen water content with temperature for six representative soils and soil constituents (After Anderson and Morgenstern 1973).

According to experimental evidence obtained by several investigators (Yong and Warkentin 1966, Nersesova and Tsytovich 1966, Dillon and Andersland 1966, Anderson and Tice 1972), the main factors determining the unfrozen water content in saturated frozen soils are temperature, specific surface area of the solid phases, pressure, chemical and mineralogical composition of the soil, other physico-chemical characteristics (especially the nature of exchangeable cations) and solute content and composition. Of all these factors, temperature is the dominant one, followed closely by the specific surface area of the soil matrix and the activity of soil minerals.

Anderson and Tice (1972) indicate that the unfrozen water content of most remoulded frozen soils can be conveniently represented by a simple power law equation

$$w_u = m\theta^n \qquad (3.14)$$

where m and n are characteristic soil parameters and θ is temperature in degrees Celsius below freezing, expressed as a positive number. Some typical values of m and n are given in Table 3.2. Based on experimental data, two prediction equations, giving the unfrozen water content as a function of temperature, have been proposed. That of Dillon and Andersland (1966) incorporates values for the specific surface area, Atterberg limits, freezing-point depression of the pore water, clay mineral type and a defined activity ratio for the soil. On the other hand, the one proposed by Anderson and Tice (1972) requires values for specific surface area only. These two similar equations are discussed by Anderson et al. (1973). The unfrozen water content of a frozen soil increases with an increase of pressure at constant temperature. The application of pressure tends to increase the thickness of the interfacial unfrozen water. This is an important factor in ice segregation and frost heaving (Hoekstra and Keune 1967).

TABLE 3.2

Soil Parameters m and n
(From Anderson and Tice 1972)

Soil	m	n
Limonite	8.82	-0.83
Fairbanks silt	4.81	-0.33
Kaolinite	23.80	-0.36
Wyoming bentonite	55.99	-0.29

Dissolved impurities in the soil water, in addition to adsorptive and capillary forces, act to depress the freezing point temperature (Ayers and Campbell 1951, Williams 1967, Banin and Anderson 1974, Cary and Mayland 1972). Solutes in the soil water shift the unfrozen water content-temperature (phase composition) curve toward lower temperatures. It is generally believed that the magnitude of this shift is comparable with the freezing-point depression of the soil solution corresponding to the osmotic potential of solutes added. If the salt content is low, the freezing-point depression is generally small. If the temperature of the frozen soil is decreased and ice is formed, however, dissolved salts are concentrated by fractionation in the residual unfrozen films and the freezing point of the residual liquid fraction is further depressed. The chemistry of the interstitial fluid is most important, particularly with regard to frozen saline soils encountered both onshore and offshore (subsea), as it will decisively influence material properties and behaviour (Tsytovich et al. 1978).

Soviet investigators (U.S.S.R. 1973a) define the salt content of a frozen soil as the ratio of the weight of salts in the soil to the dry weight of the soil (including the salt) expressed as a percentage. They consider a frozen soil to be salty if the salt content exceeds the following values:

for silty sands	0.05%
for fine, medium, coarse and gravelly sands	0.10%
for ordinary and sandy loams	0.15%
for clay	0.25%

3.4 Mechanical Properties of Frozen Soils

The phenomena that control the mechanical behaviour of frozen soils are complex and not yet fully understood. Much useful work has been carried out in the development of theoretical methods and laboratory studies on artificially prepared soils tested under well-controlled conditions to describe or understand their behaviour. Much caution and judgement must be exercised, however, in applying the results in actual practice, because of the wide variations in soil structure and in loading and thermal boundary conditions that can be encountered in situ (Anderson and Morgenstern 1973).

3.4.1 Deformation and Strength Properties

The behaviour of frozen soils under quasi-static loading is usually very different from that of unfrozen soils because of the presence of ice and unfrozen water films. In particular, frozen soils are much more subject to creep and relaxation effects, and their behaviour is strongly affected by temperature change. In addition to creep, volumetric consolidation may also develop in frozen soils having large unfrozen water contents.

As with unfrozen soils, the strength of frozen soils depends on interparticle friction, particle interlocking and cohesion. In frozen soil, however, bonding of particles by ice is the dominant strength factor. This is complicated by the unfrozen water films surrounding the soil particles which restrict interparticle contact. The strength of ice in frozen soil is dependent on many factors, such as temperature, pressure, strain rate, grain size, crystal orientation and density. At very high ice contents, frozen soil behaviour under load is similar to that of ice.

At low ice contents, however, when interparticle forces begin to contribute, the unfrozen water films play an important role, especially in fine-grained frozen soils.

The transmission of stress through unfrozen water films is not well understood, although other properties of these films have been given considerable attention. It is known, however, that pressure melting occurs in frozen soil when hydrostatic or deviator stresses are applied. It develops from stress concentrations on the ice component between soil particles and from hydrostatic pressure on the ice. As a result, the amount of unfrozen water tends to increase with pressure and the water flows to regions of lower stress where it refreezes (Tsytovich 1960, Vyalov 1966a, Low et al. 1968, Chamberlain et al. 1972).

Movement of water under stress gradients is considered to be an important factor in creep and stress relaxation in low ice content frozen ground. When water migrates under stress, structural and ice-cementation bonds break and mineral particles slip. These processes, which are time-dependent and are accompanied by reorientation of ice crystals and mineral particles parallel to the sliding direction, result in a reduction of the shearing resistance (weakening effect). On the other hand, due to simultaneous consolidation effects, an increase in intermolecular bonds takes place and some new ice-cementation bonds are formed (strengthening effect). If, during creep of these low ice content soils, strengthening exceeds weakening, then the creep rate decelerates. If weakening overcomes strengthening, however, the creep rate will accelerate and failure will eventually result. Between the two extremes, steady-state creep may exist for some period of time. These phenomena result in the typical time-dependent behaviour of low ice content frozen soils under load, discussed in the following section.

3.4.1.1. *Creep of Frozen Soil Under Constant Load*

Several types of tests may be used for determining the basic creep properties of frozen soils under load. To describe the effect of time on the behaviour of frozen soils creep tests on cylindrical specimens subjected to a constant uniaxial stress are frequently run. Data from these tests are used to construct strain-time curves similar to that shown in Fig. 3.3. Three distinct stages of creep are usually evident. The primary stage (I) is characterized by a continuously decreasing slope or creep rate. The secondary or steady-state creep stage (II) is characterized by a constant slope, which is the minimum creep rate reached during the test. Finally, the tertiary stage (III) is characterized by an accelerated creep rate, which normally leads to ultimate failure of the specimen.

The proportion of the total curve each segment represents depends not only on the material but also on the stress level used during the test and, to a certain degree, on the specimen shape. At low stress levels, primary creep appears to dominate in low ice content frozen soils (Sayles 1968). This means that, for a stress condition less than some critical value usually called "long-term strength," the creep rate will always tend to zero. Because these frozen soils when subjected

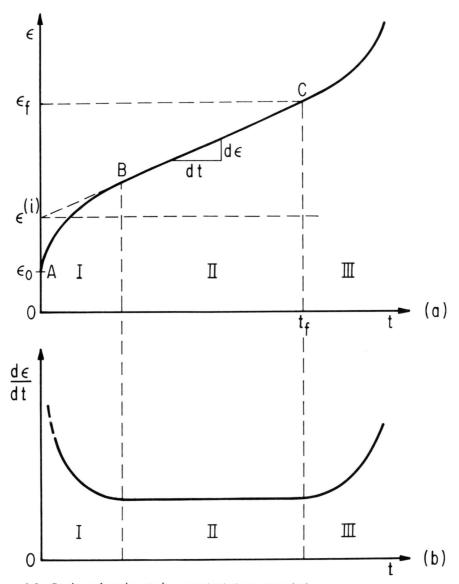

FIG. 3.3 Strain and strain rate in a constant stress creep test.

to such stresses will eventually become stable, it is extremely important to determine if such a stress level exists for a particular material.

For ice-rich soils under moderate stress conditions, steady-state creep is dominant. In this case the primary stage can often be neglected and the entire creep
curve considered as being linear. In many practical frozen soil creep problems,
steady-state creep is found to be dominant (Thompson and Sayles 1972). At high
stress levels, the specimen may appear to go straight into accelerated creep,
without well-defined primary and secondary stages, and fails after a short period

of time. The stress producing such a short-term failure of the specimen is referred to as the "short-term strength" of the material.

If a series of uniaxial compression creep tests are carried out on identical samples, at the same temperature but at various applied loads

$$(\sigma_a < \sigma_b < \sigma_c < \sigma_d < \sigma_e)$$

a set of creep curves as shown in the right lower quadrant of Fig. 3.4 is obtained. Information contained in these creep curves can be represented in various ways, some of which are shown schematically in the figure.

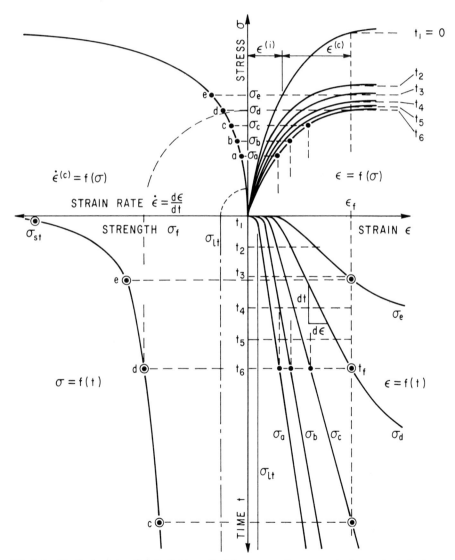

FIG. 3.4 Typical plots of data from uniaxial compression creep tests conducted at a constant temperature and confining pressure (After Ladanyi 1972).

If the creep curves are intersected by constant time lines, for example, and the intersection points projected to the upper right plot, a set of isochronous "stress-strain" curves are obtained, each of them representing the state of strain in the soil after a given time under load. With the exception of the instantaneous curve (t = 0), these curves are different from those obtained in stress-strain tests conducted with a controlled rate of strain. On the other hand, if steady-state strain rates are plotted against stress, as in the upper left quadrant of Fig. 3.4, the basic rheological curve of the soil for the particular test conditions is obtained. For frozen soils in the usual temperature range, the curve frequently has a complex non-linear shape.

Finally, if the points of failure on the creep curves are determined by some conventional method and the failure stresses are plotted against the corresponding times to failure, as in the left lower quadrant, a "delayed strength" curve is obtained. This shows how the strength of the frozen soil decreases with time from its short-term value σ_{st} and tends asymptotically toward its long-term strength σ_{lt}.

The creep behaviour of frozen soils depends also on temperature and normal (or confining) pressure, and therefore different plots of this kind will be obtained for any new combination of these two parameters. Because of this relatively complex rheological behaviour of frozen soils, special methods must be used for processing experimental information so that it can be put into an analytical form useful for engineering design. One such method will be described in the following section.

3.4.1.2 *Effect of Time on Stress-Strain and Strength Behaviour*

(a) Stress-Strain-Time Relations for Creep in Uniaxial Compression

The method for processing test data described here deals with steady-state creep and should be used, therefore, only for creep and failure processes in frozen soils that are under stress beyond the region of primary creep, usually for periods longer than 24 hours. It is similar to that proposed by Vyalov (1962), but is presented in a form originally described by Hult (1966) and Ladanyi (1972).

A set of creep curves obtained in a series of constant temperature creep tests, step-loaded to different uniaxial stress levels ($\sigma_1 < \sigma_2 < \sigma_3 < \sigma_4$) and carried out for time periods sufficiently long so that the steady-state portion of each curve is clearly defined, are approximated by straight lines as indicated in Fig. 3.5. A law that describes these straight lines rather than the actual creep curves is then established. It is evident that the predictions derived from such a law will be in error during the primary creep stage but the error will become negligible when the stress has been applied for several days or more.

Using a straight-line approximation, the strain ϵ in the steady-state creep period is given by

$$\epsilon = \epsilon^{(i)} + \dot{\epsilon}^{(c)}t \tag{3.15}$$

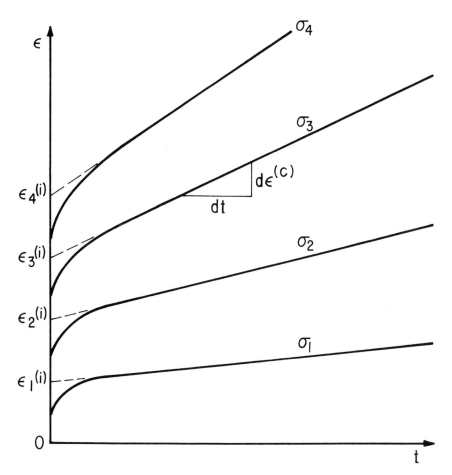

FIG. 3.5   Linearized creep curves (After Hult 1966).

where the pseudo-instantaneous strain $\epsilon^{(i)}$ and the steady-state strain rate $\dot{\epsilon}^{(c)}$ are functions, F and G respectively, of the applied stress σ and temperature T.

As described by Ladanyi (1972), once the functions F and G are determined, the strain in a creep process in which the load is increased in steps (σ and T being constant for each step) can be obtained by a summation procedure, as shown schematically in Fig. 3.6. For a continuous increase of σ with time, the total strain at any given moment is given by

$$\epsilon = F[\sigma(t), T] + \int_{o}^{t} G[\sigma(t), T]\, dt \qquad (3.16)$$

which is analogous to Rabotnov's theory of hereditary creep used by Vyalov (1962) for frozen soils.

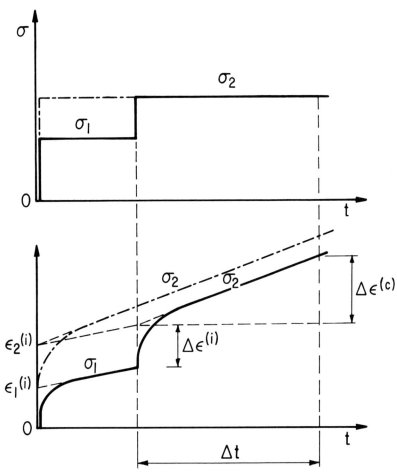

FIG. 3.6   Creep response to stage loading (After Ladanyi 1972).

The pseudo-instantaneous strain $\epsilon^{(i)}$ consists of an elastic (reversible) portion $\epsilon^{(ie)}$ and a plastic (irreversible) portion $\epsilon^{(ip)}$. The elastic portion is related to stress by Hooke's law

$$\epsilon^{(ie)} = \sigma/E \tag{3.17}$$

where E is a temperature-dependent overall Young's modulus, which is smaller than the instantaneous or dynamic elastic modulus because it includes the delayed elasticity effect. The plastic portion $\epsilon^{(ip)}$ may often be approximated by a power law

$$\epsilon^{(ip)} = \epsilon_k(\sigma/\sigma_k)^k \tag{3.18}$$

in which σ_k plays the role of a temperature-dependent deformation modulus. The exponent $k(\geq 1)$ is usually little affected by temperature, while ϵ_k is an arbitrary small strain introduced for normalization purposes.

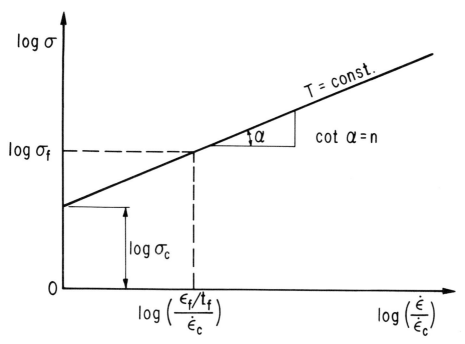

FIG. 3.7   Log-log plot of secondary creep rates vs stress with an example of the determination of creep strength.

When a load is applied, then

$$F(\sigma, T) \approx \epsilon^{(i)} = \epsilon^{(ie)} + \epsilon^{(ip)} \qquad (3.19)$$

$$= \sigma/E + \epsilon_k (\sigma/\sigma_k)^k$$

For the unloading case, the second term should be deleted, because $\epsilon^{(ip)}$ is an irreversible quantity. The creep function, $G(\sigma, T)$, may often be written as a simple power expression (Vyalov 1962, Hult 1966);

$$G(\sigma, T) \approx \dot{\epsilon}^{(c)} = \dot{\epsilon}_c (\sigma/\sigma_c)^n \qquad (3.20)$$

where σ_c and n are creep parameters, both dependent on temperature, but σ_c much more so than n. The quantity $\dot{\epsilon}_c$ is a small arbitrary strain rate introduced only for normalization purposes. The stress quantity σ_c is the uniaxial stress that causes a secondary creep rate equal to $\dot{\epsilon}_c$ and is often called the creep proof stress or creep modulus. Once $\dot{\epsilon}_c$ has been selected, the numerical values of σ_c and n are obtained from a log-log plot of experimental stress vs strain rate curves, shown in Fig. 3.7.

Substituting Eqs. 3.19 and 3.20 in Eq. 3.16, the constitutive creep equation of the frozen soil is obtained. For one single step load this simplifies to

$$\epsilon = \sigma/E + \epsilon_k (\sigma/\sigma_k)^k + \dot{\epsilon}_c (\sigma/\sigma_c)^n t \qquad (3.21)$$

For a constant σ and varying t, Eq. 3.21 represents the secondary portion of creep curves. For a constant t and varying σ, it represents a family of non-linear isochronous stress-strain curves (isocurves). Figure 3.8 shows families of creep and isocurves obtained for a frozen silty sand at three different temperatures (Vyalov 1962).

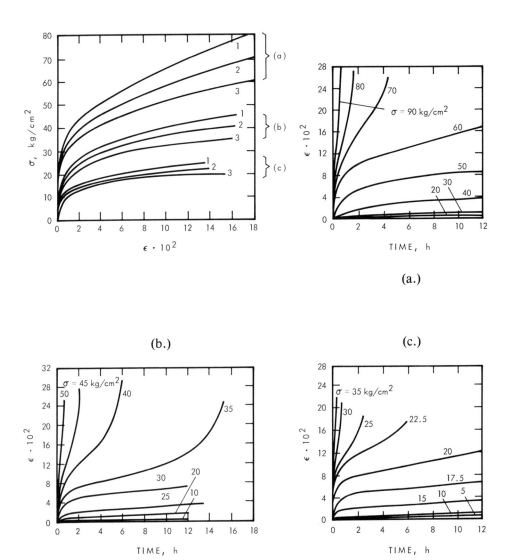

FIG. 3.8   Constant stress creep curves and isocurves for a frozen silty sand at 3 different temperatures: (a) –4°F (–20°C), (b) 14°F (–10°C) and (c) 25°F (–5°C) (After Vyalov 1962).

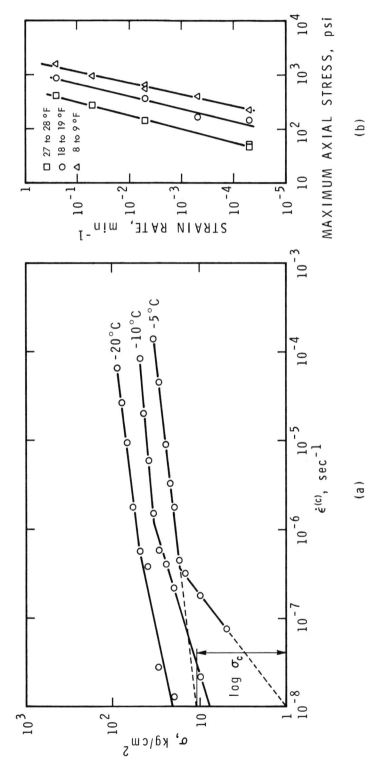

FIG. 3.9 Plots of stress *vs* secondary creep rate obtained in uniaxial compression tests: (a) from constant stress creep tests with a frozen silty sand (After Vyalov 1962) and (b) from constant strain rate tests with a natural permafrost soil—fine sand (After Perkins and Ruedrich 1973).

(b) Creep Strength in Uniaxial Compression

Creep strength is defined as the stress level at which, after a finite time interval, either rupture or instability leading to rupture occurs in the material. In tensile creep testing the creep strength is usually taken as the stress at which actual rupture occurs. In compression creep testing, however, especially of ductile materials such as high temperature metals and frozen soils in which a much less clearly defined plastic type of failure is common, the creep strength is most often identified with the time at which the first sign of instability occurs. In constant stress creep testing this is the time at which steady-state creep changes to accelerating creep (point C in Fig. 3.3). In a constant strain rate test this sign of instability would coincide with the first drop of strength after the peak of the stress-strain curve.

In general terms, the problem of creep strength prediction consists of finding a relationship between the creep strength σ_f and the magnitudes of such factors as time to failure t_f, steady-state or minimum creep rate $\dot{\epsilon}^{(f)}$, strain at failure ϵ_f and temperature T. In compression creep tests on frozen soils it is often found that the amount of permanent strain at the onset of tertiary creep is approximately constant for a given temperature and confining pressure (Vyalov 1962). Physically, the phenomenon may be interpreted by saying that instability in creep occurs when total damage done by straining attains a certain critical value.

Ladanyi (1972) suggests that the creep strength for long time intervals and at a constant temperature can be given by

$$\sigma_f \approx \sigma_c \, (\dot{\epsilon}_f / \dot{\epsilon}_c)^{1/n} \tag{3.22}$$

where $\dot{\epsilon}_f = \epsilon_f / t_f$ is the average creep rate to failure for long time intervals. This equation has the same analytical form as Eq. 3.20 and therefore the creep strength σ_f can be read directly from the plotted creep relationship as shown in Fig. 3.7.

On the other hand, Eq. 3.22 implies that there is a definite relationship between the secondary or minimum creep rate and the strength in frozen soils, and that this relationship should plot as a straight line in a log-log plot of σ_f vs $\dot{\epsilon}_f$. Figure 3.9(a) gives the results of uniaxial compression creep tests with a frozen silty sand at three different temperatures (Vyalov 1962, see also Fig. 3.8) and shows that this may be a reasonable assumption, at least for limited intervals of strain rate. Fig. 3.9(b) shows that the same type of relationship between strength and strain rate may hold also for controlled strain rate tests, which is another way of determining the parameters σ_c and n in Eq. 3.22. This equation also implies that the uniaxial compression strength of frozen soils tends to zero when time tends to infinity. It is expected that this would apply for all frozen soils which have zero strength at the same density when unfrozen.

For cohesive frozen soils, the ultimate long-term strength cannot be less than that in the unfrozen state at the same density and water content. For such soils, therefore, Eq. 3.22 can be written as

$$\sigma_f \approx q_{uu} + \sigma_c \, (\dot{\epsilon}_f/\dot{\epsilon}_c)^{1/n} \tag{3.23}$$

where q_{uu} is the long-term unfrozen unconfined compressive strength of the soil. In cohesionless frozen soils, the ultimate long-term compressive strength is due to intergranular friction and may exist only when there is a confining pressure and direct contact between the grains. It should be noted that the two time-dependent strength equations 3.22 and 3.23 are valid only beyond the primary creep period and should not be used for time-to-failure intervals shorter than about 24 hours.

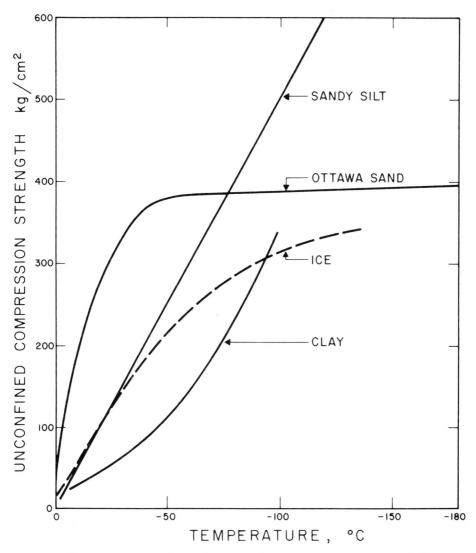

FIG. 3.10 Temperature dependence of uniaxial short-term compressive strength for various frozen materials (After Sayles 1966 and Wolfe and Thieme 1964).

3.4.1.3 *Effect of Temperature on Creep and Strength*

Creep and strength properties of frozen soils are strongly influenced by their
temperature, mainly because of the temperature-dependent behaviour of the pore
ice and the variation with temperature of the unfrozen water content. Figure 3.10
shows the typical increase in short-term uniaxial compression strength of three
soils and of ice for a very large range of decreasing freezing temperatures. It can
be noted that strength variation with temperature depends on the soil type and,
within a considerable range of freezing temperatures, the short-term strength of
some fine-grained frozen soils may be lower than that of ice. Figure 3.11 shows,
for two frozen sands over the usual permafrost temperature range, that while the
variation is non-linear for the short-term strength it is practically linear for intermediate and long-term strengths.

Various functions have been used to describe the dependence of creep rate on
temperature. One such function is the Arrhenius (exponential) equation (Ladanyi
1972)

$$\dot{\epsilon} \alpha \exp (\theta) \tag{3.24}$$

where θ is the number of degrees below 32°F (0°C) with positive sign.

For practical purposes, however, it is convenient to use either a power or a
linear form for expressing the effect of temperature, as proposed by Vyalov
(1962). One such power form is

$$f_1(\theta) = (1 + \theta/\theta_c)^\omega \tag{3.25}$$

where θ_c is an arbitrary temperature, e.g., 1°C. The values of both the exponent ω
and the creep modulus σ_c (Eq. 3.20) can be obtained by plotting $\sigma_c(T)$ values, obtained from several creep tests at different temperatures, vs $(1 + \theta/\theta_c)$ in a log-
log plot as in Fig. 3.12(a).

For limited temperature intervals, a linear form such as

$$f_2(\theta) = 1 + \theta/\theta_0 \tag{3.26}$$

may be sufficient. The corresponding linear plot of $\sigma_c(T)$ vs θ is shown in Fig.
3.12(b).

Table 3.3 gives values of short- and long-term uniaxial compressive and tensile
strengths for some typical frozen soils and ice as reported by Voitkovskiy (1968).

3.4.1.4 *Effect of Ice Content on Strength*

Owing to the very large variation in the ice content of natural permafrost soils,
ranging from a weakly ice-cemented soil to pure ice, their physical and
mechanical properties may vary widely. Considerable interest has been shown,
therefore, from the time of the earliest permafrost investigations, to determine
how the strength of a frozen soil varies with its ice content (Tsytovich and Sumgin
1937). The results usually obtained are similar to that shown for a fine sand in
Fig. 3.13 (Kaplar 1971a).

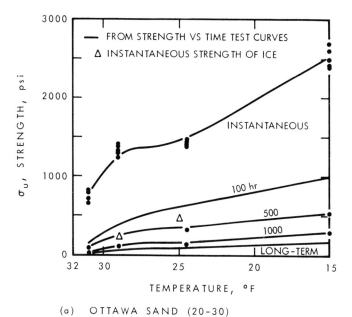

(a)   OTTAWA SAND (20-30)

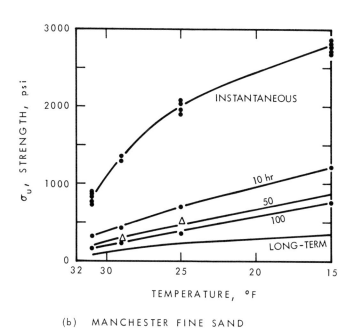

(b)   MANCHESTER FINE SAND

FIG. 3.11   Temperature-time dependence of uniaxial compressive strength for two frozen sands (After Sayles 1968).

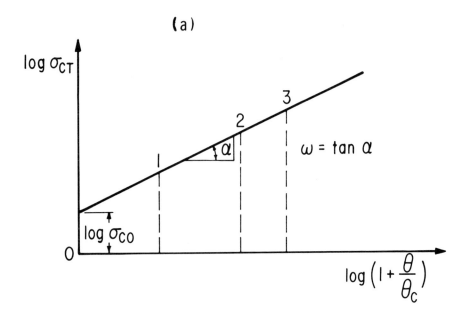

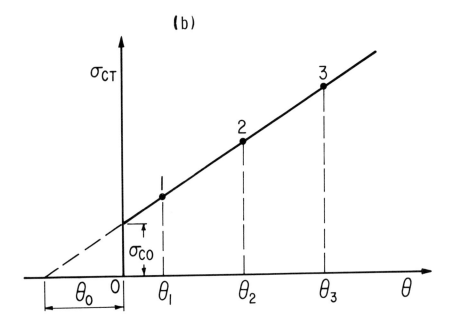

FIG. 3.12   Determination of parameters for temperature dependence of strength according to Eqs. 3.25 and 3.26.

TABLE 3.3
Short-Term and Long-Term Strengths of Some Typical Frozen Soils and Ice
(After Voitkovskiy 1968)

Soil type	Total water content %	Temperature °C	Uniaxial strength, kg/cm²			
			Short-term		Long-term	
			Compressive	Tensile	Compressive	Tensile
Medium and fine sand	17-23	-3	60-70	17	6.5	1.8
Silty sand	20-25	-0.3	10-12	5-8	2-3	1.0-1.5
		-5.0	30-40	20-25	6-10	3-5
		-10.0	60-70	40-50	35	11
		-20.0	120-140	50-60	60	21
Clayey silt	20-25	-5.0	23	20	20	9-12
		-10.0	39	30	25	12-15
		-20.0	66	40	40	16-20
	30-35	-3.0	30-35	12-16	3.6	2.5
	35-40	-0.5	8-10	4-6	2	1-2
Clay	25-35	-1.0	15	5	—	1.6
		-5.0	35	13	—	5.0
Polycrystalline ice	100	-3.0	16-20	10-12	0	0
		-10.0	32-40	17-20	0	0

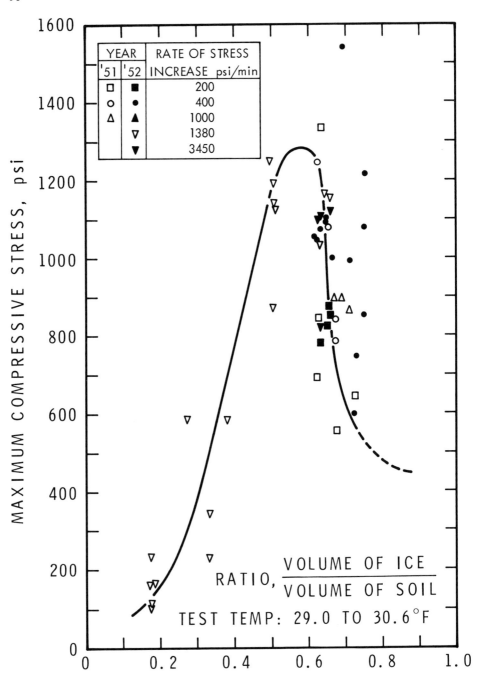

FIG. 3.13 Short-term uniaxial compressive strength vs ice content for Manchester fine sand (After Kaplar 1971a).

For a sand-ice or silt-ice mixture, various studies have shown that as the ice content increases the strength will increase until it reaches a maximum value at a certain optimum ice content. At that point the best possible combination occurs of the simultaneous effects of ice-cement cohesion, intergranular friction and dilatancy. After the peak is reached, the strength decreases rather rapidly with increasing ice content due to a loss of intergranular contacts and interlocking. Eventually, at ice contents greater than about 80%, the strength tends to that of pure polycrystalline ice.

For a sand-ice mixture, Goughnour and Andersland (1968) note a rapid increase in shear strength when the concentration of sand is about 42% by volume. They consider that at this point, friction between sand particles and dilatancy begin to contribute to the shear strength. When a dense sand-ice mixture is sheared, volume increase due to dilatancy tends to produce tensile stresses in the ice matrix, thus creating an effect analogous to an increase in effective confining pressure. Before the ice matrix fails, a large part of the strength of dense frozen sands may be attributed to this. At high confining pressures, however, as in unfrozen sands, the dilatancy effect can be completely suppressed and even reversed because of the fracture of sand grains (Chamberlain et al. 1972).

Although much experimental information is available on the behaviour of mixtures of ice with sand or silt (Kaplar 1971a, Goughnour and Andersland 1968, Hooke et al. 1972) similar information on fine silts and clay soils is still very scarce. Nevertheless, since fine-grained soils at freezing temperatures close to 32°F (0°C) usually contain considerable amounts of unfrozen water, it may be anticipated that the strength of these soils would probably be lower than that of pure polycrystalline ice at the same temperature and strain rate. The results of some recent investigations reported by Tsytovich (1973) seem to support this view.

3.4.1.5 *Effect of Normal Pressure on Creep and Strength*

Experimental evidence shows that in dense frozen soils, in which mineral grains are in direct contact during shear, both the creep behaviour and the creep strength are affected by the normal or confining pressure acting during shear or compression. Usually, when a dense, ice-saturated sand is sheared, it is found that the ice matrix fails at a low strain, and then sliding friction and grain interlocking become active and the sand resistance becomes a function of the normal stress (Sayles 1973, Alkire and Andersland 1973).

Analysis of the effect of normal pressure on strength of frozen soils must, of necessity, be based on total stresses. When the ice saturation approaches 100%, the behaviour of a sand-ice mixture at low strain rates may be analogous to that of water-saturated soils in drained tests. At high strain rates, however, its behaviour may be similar to that of saturated unfrozen soil during an undrained shear test as long as the ice matrix does not fail, and similar to that of a sand-crushed ice mixture in drained tests when the ice matrix fails. As a consequence, apparent friction angles in a sand-ice mixture may vary considerably with its density and the applied strain rate (Vyalov 1962, Sayles 1973, Alkire and Andersland 1973). As shown by Sayles (1973), however, at lower applied stresses and resulting lower strain rates, representing a "drained" frozen soil behaviour, the frictional resistance is dominant and the ultimate angle of friction may be only a few degrees smaller than that of unfrozen sand of the same density. This conclusion is also supported by the results of similar investigations reported by Andersland and Al Noury (1970), Neuber and Wolters (1970), Alkire and Andersland (1973) and Chamberlain et al. (1972).

In addition, according to Chamberlain et al. (1972) who performed triaxial compression tests on a frozen sand and a frozen silt, a strength increase with normal pressure can be expected to occur only up to a confining pressure of about 5000 psi (34.5 MPa). Their data actually show a decrease in strength when the confining pressure became large enough to induce pressure melting of pore ice (thus bringing about an increase of unfrozen water content in the soil and resulting in excess pore water pressures).

In frozen clays at permafrost temperatures, because of the unfrozen water content and the lack of friction and grain interlocking, the effect of normal pressure on strength and creep is usually very low and can be neglected for all practical purposes (Andersland and Al Noury 1970, Neuber and Wolters 1970).

If the same creep-testing procedure as described for uniaxial compression is used for uniaxial tension and triaxial compression tests, a set of failure envelopes of Mohr circles at failure (or at the onset of tertiary creep) can be obtained where each envelope corresponds to a given time to failure or a given applied strain rate. Such experimental failure envelopes of approximately parabolic shape are shown for various frozen coarse-grained soils by Vyalov (1962), Kaplar (1971a) and Sayles (1973). Proposed methods for analyzing data obtained in such tests for the failure (peak strength) and pre-failure (secondary creep) states are given by Ladanyi (1972).

3.4.1.6 *Deformability of Frozen Soils*

The total deformation of a frozen soil under load, as described previously, is usually considered to be composed of an instantaneous portion and a time-dependent portion, both of which contain a reversible and an irreversible component. The reversible component of instantaneous deformation determines the response of frozen soils to very short-term and dynamic loading, which will be discussed in Section 3.4.2. The time-dependent deformation of frozen soils has already been discussed in preceding parts of this Section. The data presented here on the deformability of frozen soils under short-term loads in terms of a static Young's modulus E and Poisson's ratio ν are reported by Tsytovich (1973) and result mainly from cyclic compression tests on 8 in. (200 mm) cubes of three different types of frozen soil.

For the three frozen soils under a pressure of 0.2 MPa, the variation of the modulus E with temperature was found to be approximately represented by the following empirical formulae:

(1) For frozen sand (grain size 93% > 0.25 mm, 1.4% < 0.05 mm, and total moisture content w = 17 − 19%) at temperatures down to −10°C,
$$E = 500 (1 + 4.2\,\theta)$$

(2) For frozen silt (grain size 64.4% > 0.05 mm, 9.2% < 0.005 mm, and w = 26 − 29%) down to −5°C,
$$E = 400 (1 + 3.5\,\theta)$$

(3) For frozen clay (grain size more than 50% < 0.005 mm, and w = 46 − 56%) down to −5°C,
$$E = 500 (1 + 0.46\,\theta)$$

where E is the modulus in MPa and θ the number of degrees Celsius below 0°C (with positive sign). It was also found that the stress-strain behaviour under cyclic loading is much more non-linear at higher than at lower freezing temperatures, where nearly all the pore water is frozen. As a result, E decreases with normal pressure much more at higher than at lower temperatures.

When these values of E are compared with that of ice obtained under similar conditions (Tsytovich, 1973, gives a value of E_{ice} = 2400 MPa at a temperature of −15°C and a pressure of 0.2 MPa), it is found that the modulus for ice is smaller than that of dense frozen sand and silt but is much larger than that of clay (E = 720 MPa), due to the large amount of unfrozen water in the clay.

Poisson's ratio for the three types of frozen soil was found to decrease with decreasing temperature from about 0.40 at high temperature when the behaviour of the soil is plastic to about 0.13 at low temperatures when practically all the pore water is frozen and the soil becomes more rigid.

3.4.1.7 Compressibility of Frozen Soils

Frozen soils are usually considered to be practically incompressible and therefore volume change deformations can be neglected compared with creep deformations. Investigations conducted on various types of frozen soils at different freezing temperatures show, however, that the compressibility of frozen soils can be significant and cannot be neglected in some cases, especially when large areas are loaded (Brodskaya 1962, Tsytovich 1973).

Compressibility and its time dependence in frozen soils is due to several causes, such as instantaneous compression of the gaseous phase, creep of the ice-cement due to shear stresses at the grain contacts, and hydrodynamic consolidation due to the expulsion under stress of unfrozen water, the amount of which varies with pressure.

According to Brodskaya (1962) the shape of the oedometer compression curve varies with the type and temperature of frozen soil. Usually, with soils of low compressibility at temperatures close to 32°F (0°C), its shape is not very different

TABLE 3.4
Coefficient of Compressibility m_v of Frozen Soils
(From Tsytovich 1973)

Soil type	w %	w_u %	T °C	m_v, cm²/kg × 10⁻⁴ Load kg/cm²				
				0-1	1-2	2-4	4-6	6-8
Medium sand	21	0.2	−0.6	12	9	6	4	3
	27	0.0	−4.2	17	13	10	7	5
	27	0.2	−0.4	32	26	14	8	5
Silty sand, massive structure	25	5.2	−3.5	6	14	18	22	23
	27	8.0	−0.4	24	29	26	18	14
Medium silty clay, massive structure	35	12.3	−4.0	8	15	26	28	24
	32	17.7	−0.4	36	42	37	21	14
Medium silty clay, reticulate structure	42	11.6	−3.8	5	10	18	42	32
	38	16.1	−0.4	56	59	39	24	16
Medium silty clay, layered structure	104	11.6	−3.6	54	54	59	44	34
	92	16.1	−0.4	191	137	74	36	18
Varved clay	36	12.9	−3.6	15	22	26	23	19
	34	27.0	−0.4	32	30	25	20	16

from that obtained for the same soil when unfrozen, due mainly to the high unfrozen water content. At lower temperatures, however, the effect of ice-
cementation becomes more pronounced and the compression curve becomes
S-shaped, similar to that usually obtained for unfrozen cemented or pre-
consolidated soils. Some data for the coefficient of total volume compressibility
m_v obtained in oedometer compression tests on various soils at different
temperatures and pressures are given in Table 3.4.

3.4.2 Dynamic Properties of Frozen Ground

Information on the dynamic properties of frozen soils is important with regard to
the behaviour of structures subjected to seismic or vibratory loads, and the
evaluation of results of seismic field surveys in permafrost areas.

Dynamic properties are expressed either in terms of two dynamic elastic
parameters: the dynamic modulus of elasticity E_D and the dynamic Poisson's
ratio v_D; or in terms of the propagation velocities of compressional waves V_p and
shear waves V_s in the material. The two sets of dynamic parameters are uniquely
related by the theory of elasticity.

3.4.2.1 *Body Waves in Isotropic Media*

In an extended homogeneous isotropic solid, considered as a continuous medium,
two types of body waves exist: compressional waves commonly called dilata-
tional, longitudinal, primary or P-waves, and the slower shear waves, also called
transverse, secondary or S-waves. The relationship between the velocity of the
body waves and the corresponding elastic constants of the medium depends on
the mass density of the material and the shape of the body in which they propagate (Roethlisberger 1972, Stevens 1975).

If, for example, the body is a slender circular rod, the longitudinal velocity due
to extensional disturbance is

$$V_L = \sqrt{E_D/\rho} \qquad (3.26)$$

while the shear wave velocity produced by torsional incitation is

$$V_s = \sqrt{G_D/\rho} \qquad (3.27)$$

where ρ is the mass density and the shear modulus G_D is defined by

$$G_D = E_D/2(1 + v_D) \qquad (3.28)$$

It should be noted that E_D and G_D have units of pressure (psi, Pa), while ρ has
units of mass. In the British system of units, ρ is equal to the ratio $\rho = \gamma/g$ where
γ is unit weight (in lb./in.^{3}) and g is the acceleration of gravity equal to 386.2
in./sec.^{2} In the SI system of units, ρ is the mass in kg/m^3, since E_D and G_D are in
Pa.

For propagation of waves in an extended isotropic medium, the following
equations are valid

$$V_p = \sqrt{\frac{E_D}{\rho} \frac{1 - \nu_D}{(1 + \nu_D)(1 - 2\nu_D)}} \qquad (3.29)$$

$$V_s = \sqrt{G_D/\rho} \qquad (3.30)$$

From Eqs. 3.26 and 3.29, the relationship between the velocities of the longitudinal body wave V_P and the one-dimensional longitudinal wave in a slender bar V_L, is given by

$$V_p/V_L = \sqrt{\frac{1 - \nu_D}{(1 + \nu_D)(1 - 2\nu_D)}} \qquad (3.31)$$

The dynamic elastic parameters E_D and ν_D deduced from wave propagation velocities are different from those obtained from any type of static loading tests because the latter contain the additional effects of elastic relaxation and creep.

3.4.2.2 Seismic Velocities

Velocities of various subsurface materials are commonly obtained during field seismic surveys by standard refraction or reflection methods. Interpretation of results can be difficult in many cases, however, because the condition of the materials is not known. On the other hand, laboratory studies on soils or rocks are especially useful in investigating their dynamic properties because the effect of specific parameters including composition, temperature, pressure and water content can be investigated under controlled conditions (Roethlisberger 1972).

Either resonance or pulse transmission techniques are usually used in the laboratory to determine the dynamic properties of frozen soil or rock. The resonance or sonic method consists of inducing vibrations in the samples and determining resonant frequencies, from which the wave velocities are calculated. Circular rods (cores) and rectangular bars are frequently used and longitudinal, torsional or flexural vibrations are applied. The pulse transmission technique is based on measurements of travel-times of sonic or ultrasonic pulses. This method is directly comparable with seismic travel-time determinations, apart from the difference in wave-length. The main advantage of the method is that arbitrarily shaped specimens can be used (Roethlisberger 1972).

Parameters that influence the compressional and shear wave velocities in soils and rocks include grain size and lithology, total moisture content and the nature of interstitial fluid, temperature and degree of freezing of interstitial water, porosity and pore structure, confining pressure and degree of cementation (Garg 1973, Vinson 1978).

Seismic velocities in soils and rocks are affected by cold temperatures only when they contain water (King et al. 1974). Since most soils and rocks contain water, they usually show a different velocity below the freezing point than above it. The change in velocity, however, can occur gradually as temperatures decrease

TABLE 3.5

Compressional Wave Velocities in Permafrost
(After Barnes 1966, Roethlisberger 1972, Garg 1973, King et al. 1974)

Material	Locality and (Reference)	Seismic velocity km/s Frozen	Unfrozen	Approx. temp. °C
Silt and organic matter	Fairbanks, Alaska (Barnes)	1.5-3.0	0.6-1.2	−1
Gravel	Fairbanks, Alaska (Barnes)	4.0-4.6	1.8-2.3	−1
Glacial till	McMurdo Sound, Antarctica (Roethlisberger)	3.0-4.3	0.5-1.5	−20
Shale and sandstone	Alaska (Barnes)	2.5-2.6	1.5-2.1	−9
Limestone	Bedford (King et al.)	6.1	4.8	−8
Limestone	Warminster (King et al.)	5.65	4.3	−5
Sandstone	Berea (King et al.)	5.75	4.0	−9
Sandstone	Boise (King et al.)	5.1	3.3	−1
Iron ore (a) unaltered (b) altered	Schefferville (Garg)	6.1 5.5	3.0 1.4	−1 −1

below 32°F (0°C) if the water is saline or because of the interfacial forces in fine-grained soils.

Velocities are higher in frozen soils or rocks than in the same unfrozen material. The change of velocity that occurs in a given soil or rock type is a function of the degree of saturation and of the ratio of frozen to unfrozen water. Compressional wave velocities V_p for a number of frozen and unfrozen earth materials are given in Table 3.5. It will be seen that the largest increase in V_p from the unfrozen to the frozen state occurs in unconsolidated sediments. Values for coarse-grained materials are generally higher than for fine-grained ones, especially at temperatures close to 32°F (0°C).

For comparison, the velocity of compressional waves in most soil-forming mineral grains (with the possible exception of clay minerals) varies from about 13,000 to 22,000 ft./sec. (4.0 to 6.5 km/s), pure ice has a velocity of about 13,000 ft./sec. (4.0 km/s), water about 4800 to 5300 ft./sec. (1.45 to 1.58 km/s) depending on temperature and salinity, and air at 32°F (0°C) has a seismic velocity of about 1200 ft./sec. (0.36 km/s). The velocity in some types of dry, spongy, organic matter may be even lower (Barnes 1966).

The compressional wave velocities in several earth materials are plotted as a function of temperature in Figs. 3.14 and 3.15. Some information on variation of

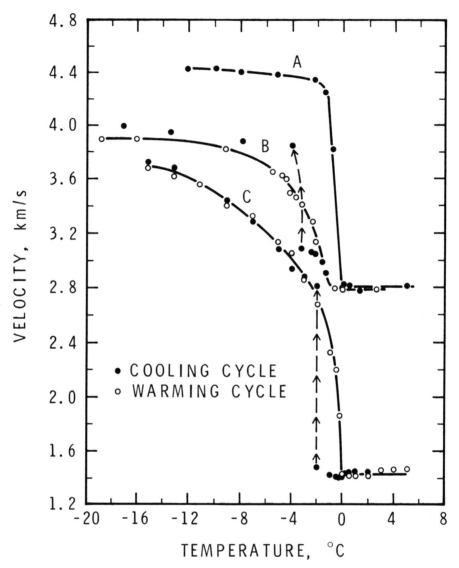

FIG. 3.14 Compressional wave velocity vs temperature for (A) 20-30 Ottawa sand, wet density $\gamma = 2.20$ g/cm^3; (B) Hanover silt, $\gamma = 1.80$ g/cm^3 and (C) Goodrich clay, $\gamma = 1.80$ g/cm^3, under fully saturated conditions (After Nakano and Froula 1973).

compressional and shear wave velocities with temperature for several limestones, sandstones and surficial materials is given by King et al. (1974) and by Kurfurst (1976). Values of V_p for several types of frozen soils (clays to coarse sand) at various temperatures and ice contents, obtained by Soviet investigators, are given by Zarubin and Dzhurik (1975) and Dzhurik and Leshchikov (1978).

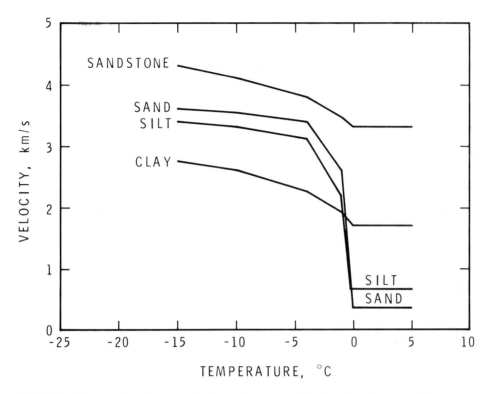

FIG. 3.15   Compressional wave velocity vs temperature for 3 soils and one rock type (After Aptikaev 1964).

In frozen granular soils almost all of the water freezes at 32°F (0°C). The compressional velocity changes suddenly at 32°F (0°C) and no hysteresis is observed in the velocity curve during a freeze-thaw cycle. On the other hand, silt and clay have fine pores in which a significant portion of the water remains unfrozen at subfreezing temperatures. It is evident that a strong correlation exists between compressional wave velocity and unfrozen water content. The observed hysteresis in the velocity curves of both Hanover silt and Goodrich clay (Fig. 3.14) during a freeze-thaw cycle is considered to be caused by the unfrozen water content. In fact, Nakano and Froula (1973) found that if the compressional wave velocities are plotted against the unfrozen water content then a single curve is obtained, regardless of the cycle (Fig. 3.16).

The role of unfrozen water in shear wave propagation is not as pronounced as for compressional waves. As fluid water cannot resist shear, then the soil mineral matrix must play a major role in shear wave propagation. The shear velocities of crystalline rock and polycrystalline ice are about 10,000 and 5,500 ft./sec. (3.0 and 1.6 km/s), respectively. The measured shear velocities of frozen soils fall between these two bounds (Nakano and Froula 1973).

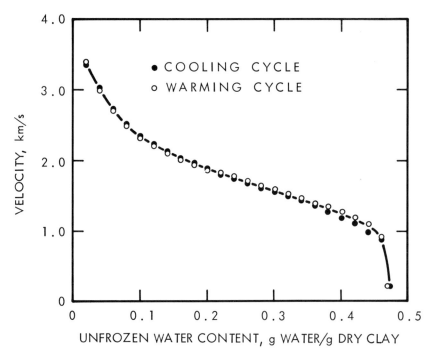

FIG. 3.16 Compressional wave velocity vs unfrozen water content for Kaolinite clay.
The solid circles indicate the cooling cycle and the open circles indicate the heating cycle
(After Nakano and Froula 1973).

3.4.2.3 *Dynamic Parameters*

Vinson (1978) reviewed the results of field and laboratory investigations conducted to date and found them to indicate that:

(1) dynamic stress-strain properties for coarse-grained soils can be nearly an
    order of magnitude greater than for fine-grained soils, and energy absorbing
    properties can vary significantly with soil type and composition,

(2) over a range of void ratios from 0.3 to infinity (ice) dynamic stress-strain
    properties for fully saturated soils can decrease by a factor of 5,

(3) dynamic stress-strain properties of frozen soils increase with increasing de-
    gree of ice saturation,

(4) the same properties decrease and damping properties increase with increasing
    temperature,

(5) the same properties decrease and damping properties increase with increasing
    axial strain amplitude from $10^{-3}\%$ to $10^{-1}\%$,

(6) the frequency of loading has only a minor effect on dynamic stress-strain
    properties, and the effect on damping properties may be important at low fre-
    quencies, and

(7) confining pressure has an important effect on the dynamic properties of coarse-grained soils and a relatively unimportant effect on fine-grained soils.

The complex dynamic moduli (E_D and G_D) calculated from wave transmission velocities in frozen soils have been found to increase with a decrease in temperature; the greatest rate of increase occurring between 32° and 20°F (0° and −6.7°C) (Kaplar 1969). At temperatures lower than 20°F (−6.7°C), the dynamic properties of silts and clays are markedly more temperature-dependent than those of coarse-grained soils, due mainly to their much greater unfrozen water contents. On the other hand, ice and an ice-rich peat with a water content of about 300% by weight, showed only a slight increase in dynamic moduli with decreasing temperature.

TABLE 3.6

Dynamic Elastic Moduli E_D of Frozen Soils and Ice
(After Kaplar 1969)

Material	Modulus of elasticity E_D			
	psi × 10^6		GPa	
	at 32°F	at −10°F	at 0°C	at −23°C
Peabody gravelly sand	5.0	6.0	34.5	41.4
Yukon silt	1.6	3.3	11.0	22.8
Boston blue clay	0.8	2.2	5.5	15.2
Laboratory ice	1.2	1.5	8.3	10.3
Lake ice	0.4	0.5	2.8	3.5

Kaplar (1969) carried out investigations in the temperature range from 32° to −10°F (0° to −23°C), and found that:

(a) the dynamic elastic moduli for coarse-grained soils are more than four times those for fine-grained soils and ice. Some typical values for frozen soils and ice are given in Table 3.6, and

(b) values of dynamic Poisson's ratio for frozen soils range between 0.25 and 0.38 and do not show any well-defined dependence on temperature or soil type. Average values for laboratory-frozen ice and natural lake ice range from 0.32 to 0.40, with a maximum range from 0.28 to 0.47.

Vibratory tests conducted on several selected soils by Stevens (1975) indicate that their stiffness varies with the ratio of volume of ice to volume of soil, that ice is less rigid than frozen saturated soil and that frozen soils are as much as 100 times as stiff as the same soils in the unfrozen state. Stiffness of frozen soil decreases at a relatively low rate with temperature increase, but decreases abruptly as the temperature approaches the freezing point. Values of Poisson's ratio reported by Stevens (1975) for three frozen soils at various temperatures, dynamic stresses and frequencies are given in Table 3.7. Vinson (1978) summarized the effects of various parameters on the dynamic properties of frozen soil and ice. The results of studies conducted in the laboratory and the field on the relationships between the static and dynamic Young's moduli, the modulus of

TABLE 3.7

Poisson's Ratio for Several Frozen Soils
(From Stevens 1975)

Frequency, Hz	Temperature		
	$+25°F$	$+15°F$	$0°F$

20-30 Ottawa sand

$\sigma_d = 0.1$ psi			
1000	0.25	0.34	0.28
5000	0.28	0.38	0.26
10000	0.33	0.33	0.28
$\sigma_d = 1.0$ psi			
1000	0.25	0.34	0.28
5000	0.28	0.37	0.25
10000	0.32	0.36	0.35
$\sigma_d = 5.0$ psi			
1000	0.28	0.30	0.27
5000	0.29	0.38	0.25
10000	0.27	0.34	0.24

Manchester silt

$\sigma_d = 0.1$ psi			
1000	0.25	0.27	0.25
5000	0.27	0.26	0.22
10000	0.30	0.29	0.26
$\sigma_d = 1.0$ psi			
1000	0.25	0.28	0.25
5000	0.29	0.27	0.24
10000	0.30	0.29	0.22
$\sigma_d = 5.0$ psi			
1000	0.26	0.29	0.24
5000	0.30	0.31	0.23
10000	0.30	0.29	0.21

Goodrich clay

$\sigma_d = 0.1$ psi			
1000	0.72	0.35	0.51
5000	0.54	0.38	0.36
10000	0.52	0.40	0.32
$\sigma_d = 1.0$ psi			
1000	0.59	0.37	0.47
5000	0.52	0.40	0.34
10000	0.47	0.41	0.32
$\sigma_d = 5.0$ psi			
1000	0.58	0.40	0.46
5000	0.47	0.42	0.32
10000	0.42	0.43	0.32

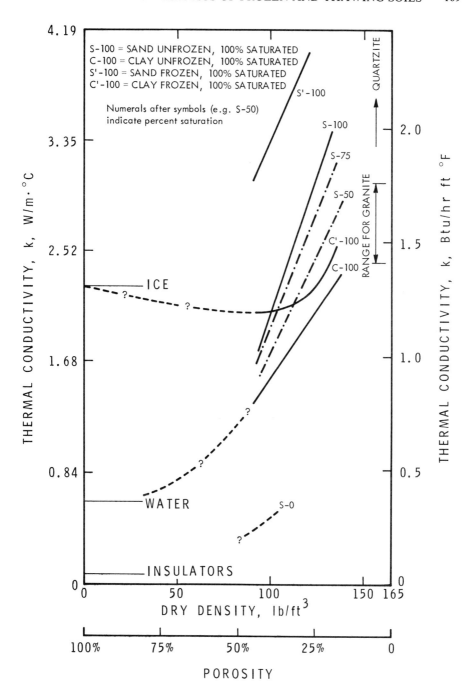

FIG. 3.17   Relationship between thermal conductivity and porosity for frozen and unfrozen sand and clay at various degrees of saturation (After Terzaghi 1952).

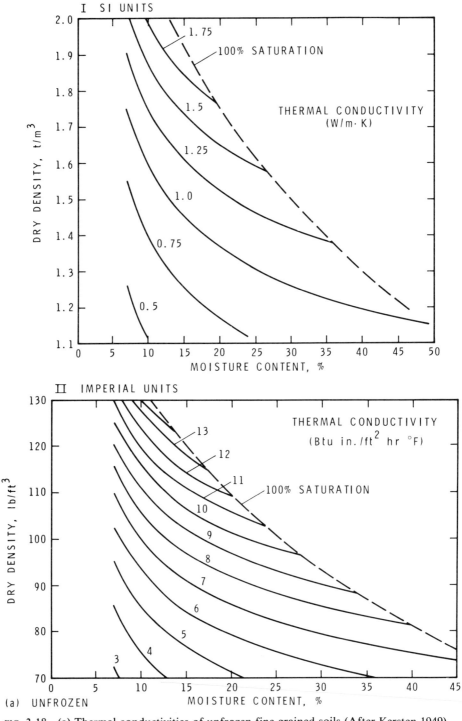

FIG. 3.18   (a) Thermal conductivities of unfrozen fine-grained soils (After Kersten 1949).

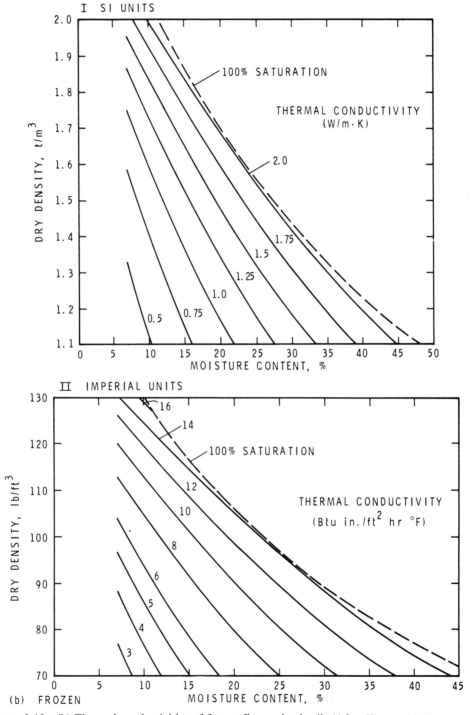

FIG. 3.18   (b) Thermal conductivities of frozen fine-grained soils (After Kersten 1949).

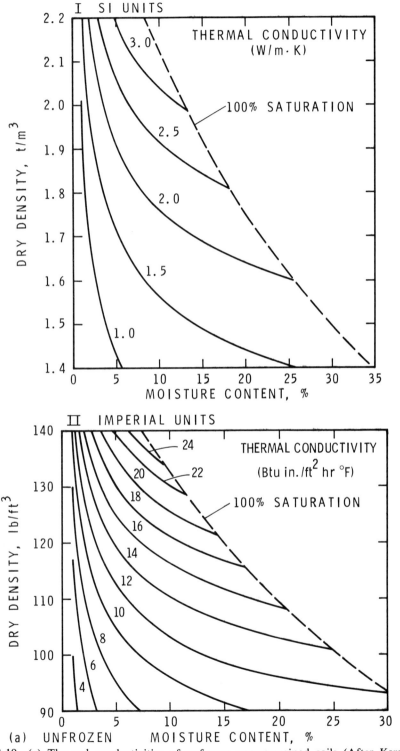

FIG. 3.19 (a) Thermal conductivities of unfrozen coarse-grained soils (After Kersten 1949).

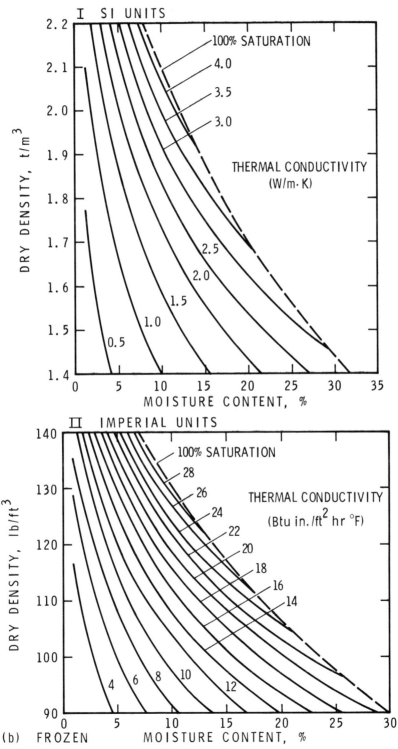

FIG. 3.19   (b) Thermal conductivities of frozen coarse-grained soils (After Kersten 1949).

deformation and Poisson's ratio for various types of dry, water saturated and frozen (ice saturated) rocks are reported by Voronkov et al. (1979).

3.5 Thermal Properties

The position of the interface between thawed and frozen soil with respect to the ground surface for a given surface-temperature regime depends on the thermal properties of the strata located above and immediately below the interface. These thermal properties are important parameters in the determination of frost and thaw penetration and are indeed fundamental to all ground heat transfer problems. The basic soil thermal properties are thermal conductivity, heat capacity and latent heat. These vary with phase composition and hence temperature, soil type, water content, porosity, degree of saturation, density and organic content. Their application in ground thermal analyses is discussed in Chapter 4. The thermal properties of typical building and insulating materials to be used in design are given by ASHRAE (1977).

3.5.1 Thermal Conductivity

Thermal conductivity k is a measure of the quantity of heat that will flow through a unit area of a substance of unit thickness in unit time under a unit temperature gradient. Its units commonly are Btu/hr. ft. °F (W/m·K). The essential relationships between the thermal conductivity of a soil, its porosity n and degree of saturation S, based mainly on experimental data reported by Kersten (1949), are presented in Fig. 3.17. Since the thermal conductivity of ice is much higher than that of water, the thermal conductivity of frozen soil is usually greater than that of unfrozen soil. A major exception is a sandy soil with a moisture content less than about 7%. In this case the k value in the unfrozen state is greater than that of the same soil when frozen.

As the porosity approaches 100%, the value of k for an unfrozen saturated porous substance approaches that of water, which is about 0.35 Btu/hr. ft. °F (0.61 W/m·K). For a frozen saturated porous substance, k approaches that of ice, which is approximately 1.30 Btu/hr. ft. °F (2.2 W/m·K). The k value of a very porous saturated frozen soil usually will not be less than that of ice, and k for a very porous soil with air-filled voids will not be less than that of some common thermal insulators, which ranges between 0.01 to 0.02 Btu/hr. ft. °F (0.02 to 0.03 W/m·K). On the other hand, as the porosity of a soil approaches zero, its k value must approach the average k value of its mineral constituents. These relationships determine the position of the horizontal tangents or asymptotes of the curves shown in Fig. 3.17. Coarse-grained soils are commonly dominated by quartz, which has a relatively large k value, and the finest soils by micaceous minerals, including the clay minerals, which generally have a substantially lower k value. This may be one of the reasons why the curve representing the relation between n and k for saturated sand is located well above the corresponding curve for clay soils.

Kersten (1949) conducted extensive tests on both frozen and unfrozen mineral soils. The thermal conductivities of fine- and coarse-grained soils calculated from Kersten's equations are summarized in Figs. 3.18 and 3.19 and will give, according to Kersten, conductivity values not more than 25% in error. It should also be noted that Kersten's values apply to soil moisture contents greater than 1% and 7% (by weight of dry soil) for coarse- and fine-grained soils respectively. Values for Leda clay and for several Mackenzie Valley soils are reported by Penner (1970a), Judge (1973c), Penner et al. (1975) and Slusarchuk and Watson (1975).

Kersten (1949) also determined values of k for frozen and unfrozen peat, but for one organic type only. De Vries (1952) applied Euken's theoretical formula to peat and found values that were in reasonable agreement with Kersten. Values obtained for a range of moisture contents and densities of frozen and unfrozen peat using this formula are given in MacFarlane (1969). Kersten's results for peat also lie within a range of values obtained for a variety of peat materials by Pavlova (1970). Data for organic soils are also given in Konovalov and Roman (1973).

Typical values of thermal conductivity for a variety of materials are given in Table 3.8. Thermal conductivities of some common rock types, generally water saturated and measured at room temperature, are included in the table. Depending on the rock type, values at 32°F (0°C) or below will be from 2 to 7% higher. In general, when rock pores contain ice rather than water, k will be about 14% higher for rock at 10% porosity and 30% higher at 20% porosity. Although the mineralogy of rocks can vary widely, values given in the table can be interpolated to obtain the approximate thermal conductivity of a formation, such as a shaly limestone. Bia and Combarnous (1970) give values for pure natural quartz, a common constituent of coarse-grained soils, for temperatures between -75 and $+70°F$ (-60 and $+20°C$). Values, determined at a temperature of about 100°F (40°C), for several well-defined carbonate rocks including a highly porous chalk, limestones, dolomite and magnesite are reported by Thomas et al. (1973).

3.5.2 Heat Capacity

Heat capacity c is the amount of heat required to raise the temperature of a unit mass of a substance by one degree. Its units are Btu/lb. °F (kJ/kg·K). Volumetric heat capacity C is the amount of heat required to change the temperature of a unit volume of a substance by one degree. Its units are Btu/ft.^{3} °F (kJ/m^3·K).

Since the heat capacity of a mixture is equal to the sum of the heat capacities of its components, the heat capacity of a soil can be found by adding the heat capacities of the different constituents in a unit mass of soil. Thus, if m_s, m_w, m_i, m_a denote the weight fractions of solid material, water, ice (if frozen) and air, respectively, contained in a total volume V of soil with a total weight m, the heat capacity of the soil is

$$cm = c_s m_s + c_w m_w + c_i m_i + c_a m_a \qquad (3.32)$$

TABLE 3.8

Typical Values of Thermal Conductivity For Various Materials

Material	γ lb./cu. ft.	Conductivity, k Btu/hr. ft. °F	W/m·K
Air, dry, still	0	0.014	0.024
Water	62.4	0.35	0.605
Ice (at 32°F)	57	1.29	2.23
Snow, loose, new	—	0.05	0.086
on ground	—	0.07	0.121
dense, compacted	—	0.20	0.340
Shale	—	0.9	1.5
Evaporites	—	3.1	5.4
Limestone	168	0.75-2.9	1.3-5.0
Dolomite	178	2.9	5.0
Sandstone	—	1.1-2.4	1.8-4.2
Schist	—	0.90	1.6
Gneiss	—	1.4	2.5
Greenstone	—	1.9	3.3
Slate	—	2.2	3.8
Argillite	—	1.9	3.3
Quartzite	—	2.6-4.1	4.5-7.1
Granite	—	1.0-2.3	1.7-4.0
Diabase	—	1.2	2.1
Gabbro	—	1.4	2.5
Grandiorite	—	1.5	2.6
Steel	490	20-30	35-52
Cast iron	—	29	50
Aluminum	—	90-110	156-190
Copper	—	223	386
Building brick	—	0.40	0.69
Concrete—			
—with sand and gravel aggregate	140	0.75-1.0	1.3-1.7
—with lightweight aggregate	120	0.43	0.74
(including expanded shale, clay or	80	0.21	0.36
slate, expanded slags, cinders,	40	0.10	0.17
pumice, perlite, vermiculite and	20	0.06	0.10
cellular concretes)			
—with polystyrene beads	40	0.18-0.21	0.31-0.36
Concrete, asphalt	131-138	0.61-0.88	1.05-1.52
Wood—			
—fir, pine, similar softwoods, dry	32	0.066	0.12
—maple, oak, similar hardwoods, dry	45	0.094	0.16

TABLE 3.8 (Cont'd.)

Typical Values of Thermal Conductivity For Various Materials

Material	γ lb./cu. ft.	Conductivity, k Btu/hr. ft. °F	Conductivity, k W/m·K
Building boards—			
Asbestos-cement board	120	0.33	0.57
Plywood	34	0.067	0.12
Wood fibreboard, laminated or			
homogeneous	26/33	0.035/0.046	0.061/0.080
Wood fibre—hardboard type	65	0.12	0.21
Insulating materials—			
Blanket and batt—			
Asbestos fibres	9-12	0.04	0.07
Mineral wool, fibrous form,			
processed from rock, slag or			
glass	1.5-4.0	0.022	0.038
Wood fibre	3.2-3.6	0.021	0.036
Board and slabs—			
Cellular glass	7.0-9.5	0.032	0.055
Corkboard (without added binder)	6-9	0.022	0.038
Glass fibre	9.5-11.0	0.021	0.036
Wood or cane fibre-interior			
finish (plank, tile or lath)	15	0.029	0.050
Mineral wool with resin binder	15	0.023	0.04
Mineral wool with asphalt binder	15	0.026	0.045
Polyurethane foam	2.0	0.009-0.022 (new) (aged)	0.016-0.038
Polystyrene, extruded or moulded,			
expanded	1.5-3.0	0.019/0.022	0.033/0.038
Straw, compressed	23	0.05	0.09
Sulphur foam	4-30	0.02-0.04	0.03-0.07
Loose fill—			
Asbestos fibres (bulk)	20-50	0.05-0.13	0.09-0.22
Cork (granules)	5-12	0.02-0.03	0.035-0.052
Expanded clay (powder)	37-41	0.07	0.12
Expanded perlite (powder)	3-4	0.025	0.043
Glass fibres	2-12	0.02	0.035
Glass, cellular (pellets)	6	0.03	0.05
Mineral wool (glass, slag or rock)	2.0-5.0	0.025	0.043
Sawdust or shavings	8.0-15.0	0.037	0.064
Slag, foamed (granules)	38-45	0.07	0.12
Straw fibres	7-8	0.025	0.043
Vermiculite (expanded)	7.0-8.2	0.040	0.069
Wood fibre: redwood, hemlock or fir	2.0-3.5	0.025	0.043

Note: Values of k for dry building materials are at a mean temperature of 75°F. Wet conditions will adversely affect values of many of these materials.

and, dividing by V and neglecting the very small term for air, the volumetric heat capacity of a frozen soil is

$$C = c\gamma_f = \gamma_{d_f}(c_s + c_w w_u + c_i w_i) \tag{3.33}$$

where γ_f and γ_{d_f} denote the bulk and dry densities of frozen soil respectively, and w_u and w_i are the unfrozen water and ice contents respectively.

The specific heat of a material is defined as the ratio of its heat capacity to that of water at 32°F (0°C). Typical values for mineral soil constituents, organic material and ice for temperatures near freezing are 0.17, 0.40 and 0.50 respectively. Volumetric heat capacities can therefore be calculated as follows

For mineral soil, unfrozen ($w_u = w$, $w_i = 0$)

$$C = a\gamma_d \; [0.17 + w]$$

For mineral soil, frozen ($w_i = w - w_u$)

$$C = a\gamma_{d_f} \; [0.17 + w_u + 0.5 (w - w_u)]$$

For organic soil (peat) unfrozen

$$C = a\gamma_d \; [0.40 + w]$$

For organic soil (peat) frozen

$$C = a\gamma_{d_f} \; [0.40 + w_u + 0.5 (w - w_u)]$$

where a = 1.0 Btu/lb. °F in British units,
   or a = 4.2 kJ/kg· °C in SI units.

The corresponding values of heat capacities c of soil can be obtained from the above C values using the relationship

$$c = C/\gamma = C/\gamma_d(1 + w) \tag{3.34}$$

Heat capacities c and C for various materials are given in Table 3.9.

TABLE 3.9

Heat Capacities of Various Materials

Material	Heat capacity, c		Volumetric heat capacity, C	
	Btu/lb. °F	kJ/kg·K	Btu/ft.³ °F	MJ/m³·K
Air	0.24	1.000	0.0187	0.00125
Water	1.00	4.187	62.4	4.187
Ice	0.50	2.094	28.1	1.88
Soil minerals	0.17	0.710	28.0	1.875
Organic soil	0.40	1.674	37.5	2.52
Extruded polystyrene insulation	0.24	1.000	0.65	0.0435
Concrete	0.21	0.895	30.0	2.01
Asphalt	0.4	1.674	37.5	2.52

3.5.3 Thermal Diffusivity

Thermal diffusivity α is an index of the facility with which a material will undergo temperature change. It is defined by the ratio

$$\alpha = k/C = k/c\gamma \qquad (3.35)$$

and its units are: ft.^{2}/hr. (mm^2/s).

Very few measurements of the thermal diffusivity of soils or rock have been made in the field. Estimates of α for common, non-porous rocks can be made, however, knowing their density and thermal conductivity; the specific heats are fairly constant between 0.17 and 0.23. It is of interest that whereas the k for typical rocks varies by a factor of perhaps five, α varies by a factor of less than three.

The diffusivities of frozen soils can be calculated in a similar manner using the relationships given above. At temperatures between about 26 and 32°F (-3 and 0°C), however, the amounts of ice and water contained in fine-grained soils, in particular, may vary considerably and are very temperature-dependent. At the same time, large amounts of latent heat are released, resulting in an apparent heat capacity for freezing soils that is much greater than the true heat capacity. Thus the thermal diffusivity is significantly reduced at these temperatures.

The diffusivity of ice is very much higher than that of water and consequently the diffusivity of hard frozen soil is considerably higher than that of the same soil in a thawed condition. If the pores of a frozen rock are filled with ice, the overall α is similar to that of solid rock. The diffusivity will be significantly reduced, however, if water is present in the pores. Values of α for mineral soils, based on Kersten's thermal conductivity data, are shown in Figs. 3.20 and 3.21. Values of thermal diffusivity for several other materials are given in Table 3.10.

TABLE 3.10

Thermal Diffusivities of Various Materials

Material	Thermal diffusivity, α	
	ft.^{2}/hr. $\times 10^{-3}$	m^2/s $\times 10^{-7}$
Water	5.61	1.45
Fresh snow	12.8	3.3
Ice	46.2	11.9
Granite	58	15
Limestone	27	7
Dolomite	78	20
Sandstone	39	10
Shale	31	8
Quartzite	174	45
Iron	670	173
Copper	4400	1133

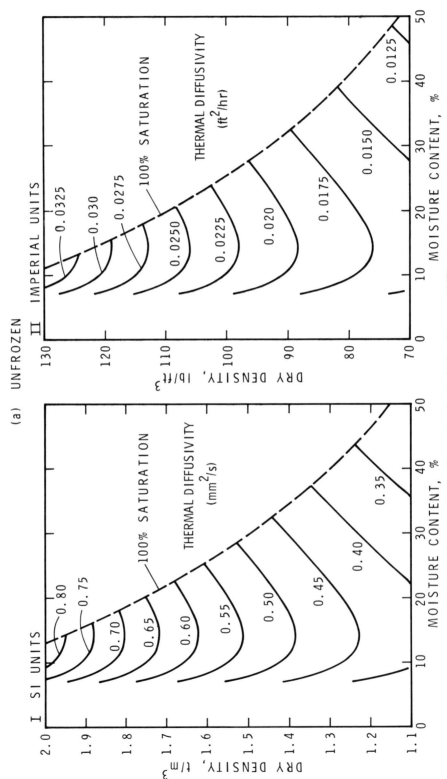

FIG. 3.20   (a) Thermal diffusivities of unfrozen fine-grained soils (After Kersten 1949).

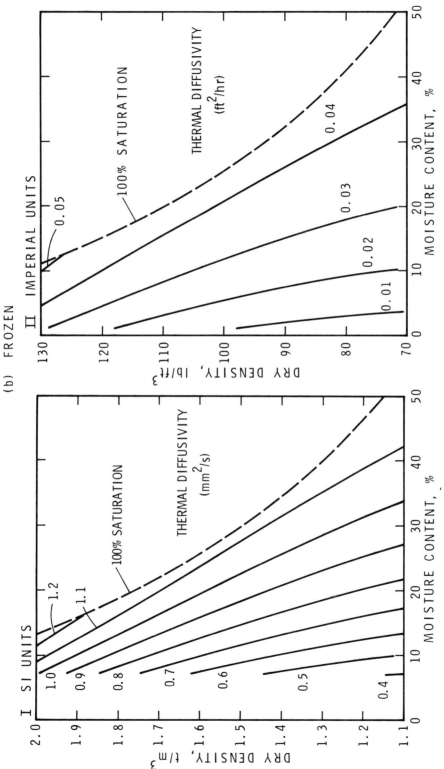

FIG. 3.20 (b) Thermal diffusivities of frozen fine-grained soils (After Kersten 1949).

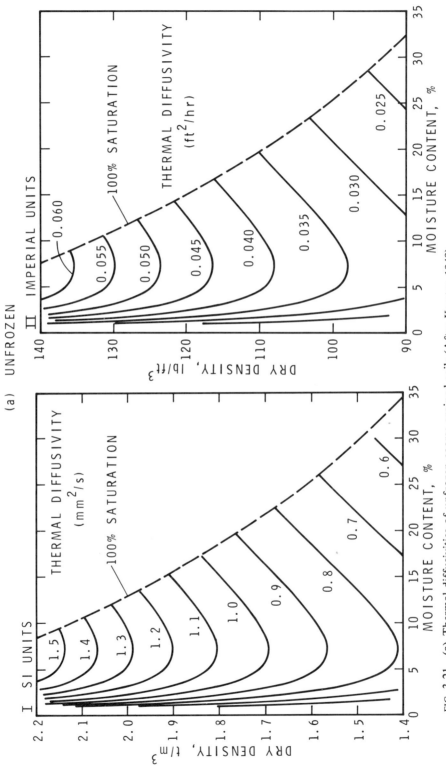

FIG. 3.21 (a) Thermal diffusivities of unfrozen coarse-grained soils (After Kersten 1949).

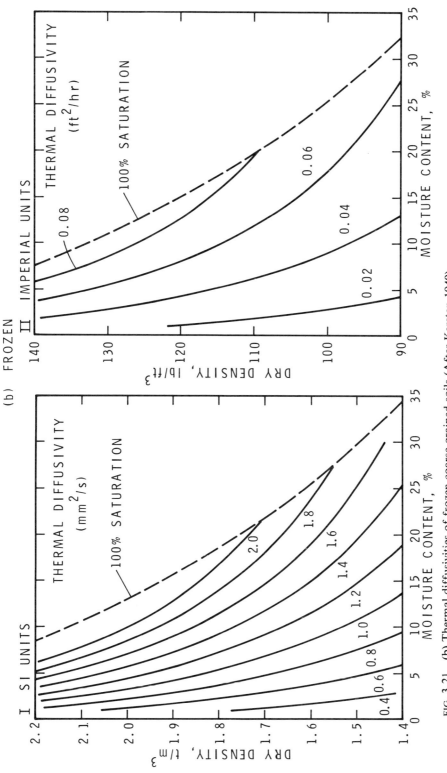

FIG. 3.21   (b) Thermal diffusivities of frozen coarse-grained soils (After Kersten 1949).

3.5.4 **Latent Heat of Fusion**

The volumetric latent heat of fusion L is the amount of heat required to melt the
ice (or freeze the water) in a unit volume of soil without a change in temperature.
The units of L are Btu/ft.^{3} (J/m^3). Latent heat depends only on the amount of
water in a unit volume of soil. Since the amount of heat given off by a unit mass
of water as it freezes, or absorbed when it thaws, is 143.4 Btu/lb. (334 kJ/kg),
then

$$L = 143.4 \, w\gamma_d \, \text{Btu/ft.}^3 \tag{3.36}$$

$$\text{or} \quad = 334 \, w\gamma_d \, \text{kJ/m}^3$$

Alternatively, because

$$w\gamma_d = Sn\gamma_w \tag{3.37}$$

where S is the degree of saturation, n the porosity and γ_w is the density of
water = 62.4 lb./ft.^{3} (1000 kg/m^3), then

$$L = 8950 \, Sn \, \text{Btu/ft.}^3 \tag{3.38}$$

$$\text{or} \quad = 334 \times 10^3 \, Sn \, \text{kJ/m}^3$$

Because not all the water is frozen in fine-grained soils, the above equations
yield maximum values for the latent heat. In many practical cases such values will
be acceptable for estimating purposes. For more accurate calculations, however,
it may be necessary to consider the moisture content-temperature relationship
and take into account the effect of the unfrozen water content.

3.6 **Electrical Properties**

Electromagnetic geophysical techniques for mapping permafrost and the electrical grounding of various types of machines and electrical equipment, power
transmission systems and radio transmitting antennas in permafrost areas require
a knowledge of frozen ground electrical properties, such as the dielectric constant
(or permittivity) and electrical conductance and resistivity.

The dielectric constant D of a soil is a measure of the ability of a dielectric to
store electrical energy in the presence of an electrostatic field and, in general, is a
basic property reflecting its molecular configuration, composition, texture and
porosity. The dielectric constant of a soil is the dimensionless ratio of its permit-
tivity ϵ to the permittivity ϵ_o of free space, or D = ϵ/ϵ_o. For a vacuum D = 1.0
and for air D $\cong$ 1. The electrical conductance λ in mhos (G in siemens in SI
units; 1 mho = 1S) of a material is the inverse of its resistance R in ohms to current flow or λ = 1/R in mhos. Both these parameters are sensitive to
temperature, porosity, water content and electrical frequency.

Current flow under an electrical gradient in a frozen soil occurs almost entirely through the unfrozen water films. Electrical conduction is related to the thickness of these water films, which decrease with decreasing temperature and increase with increasing pressure. It is dependent also on whether the films are interconnected. Conduction is due to the presence of charge carriers in the films. Soil particles usually carry a negative charge and, to remain electro-neutral, this charge is balanced by an excess of positive ions in the water layers close to their surfaces. Ionic mobility, and therefore electrical conductance, diminishes with decreasing temperature and increases with increasing pressure at constant temperature (Anderson and Morgenstern 1973).

Little information is available on the conductance of frozen soils. The electrical properties of some soils in the frozen and unfrozen states are reported by Cook (1960), Hoekstra (1965), Hoekstra and O'Brien (1969), Hoekstra and Delaney (1974), Jumikis and Slusarchuk (1974) and Olhoeft (1977). The conductance of a frozen silt as a function of temperature is shown in Fig. 3.22. It decreases rapidly between 32° and 26°F (0° and −3°C) and continues to decrease, but at a much slower rate, at temperatures below 26°F (−3°C). In general, frozen soil cannot be regarded as a good conductor. Ice and mineral particles are relatively poor conductors and the transition layer between them causes frozen soil to have a conductance factor 5 to 10 times less than the same soil in an unfrozen state.

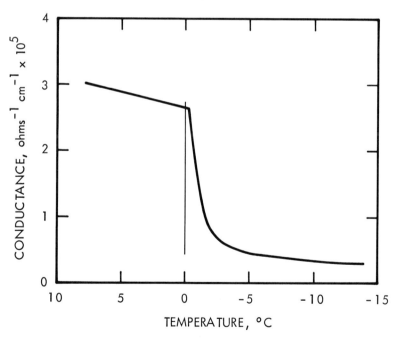

FIG. 3.22   Electrical conductance of a frozen silt as a function of temperature (After Hoekstra 1969).

In some frozen soils, movement of water can take place under electro-osmotic action, which requires an excess of charge in the liquid layers adjacent to a charged surface. Experiments by Verschinin et al. (1960) and Hoekstra and Chamberlain (1964) show that water is transported through frozen clay and silt toward the cathode under an electrical gradient, with ice being removed from around the anode and large bodies of ice being formed in the vicinity of the cathode. When the water film is depleted at a certain location, some ice will melt to replenish the film and, similarly, water will freeze where the amount of liquid water exceeds the equilibrium value.

The electrical resistivity ρ of a soil stratum is influenced mainly by soil type, water content, temperature and ice content. A number of less important factors, such as pressure and pore water salt content, also affect the resistivity. The soil type factor is independent of time over long periods, but water and ice contents and temperature will fluctuate daily and seasonally. All parameters often vary with depth as well as laterally.

The resistivity of unfrozen soils increases slightly with decrease in temperature. A significant increase in resistivity occurs with decrease in temperature when the soils are frozen, however, and the changes are directly related to the unfrozen water content of frozen ground. For both frozen and unfrozen soils, clay soils have the lowest resistivity, followed by silt, sand and gravel soils. The resistivity of frozen soils at 23°F (-5°C) is about a factor of 5 greater than the resistivity of the same soil when unfrozen. At 30°F (-1°C), the resistivity of a frozen clay soil varies by no more than a factor of 1.5 from its resistivity when thawed. Changes in water content can cause resistivity changes of from about 100 $\Omega \cdot$m to 1000 $\Omega \cdot$m in silts and, depending on the ice content, the resistivity of frozen silt can vary from about 1000 $\Omega \cdot$m to about 100,000 $\Omega \cdot$m. It is generally more difficult to classify rock resistivities because of the dependence on degree of fracturing and

TABLE 3.11

Approximate Electrical DC Resistivities For Several Earth Materials
(Barnes 1966, Ogilvy 1967, Foster-Miller Associates 1973a, b, Garg 1973)

Material	Resistivities, k$\Omega \cdot$m Frozen	Unfrozen	Approx. temp. °C
Pure ice	2.5-25	—	
Water	—	0.025-0.25	
Silt and organic matter	2-8	0.04-1.9	-1
Sand and fine gravel	6.3-24	0.22-0.71	-1
Gravel	7.8-41	1.0-1.85	-1
Conglomerate	12-16	0.22-0.70	-1
Iron ore (unsaturated)	23.6-26.4	0.55-1.53	-1
Gneiss	73-137	—	-11
Schist	1.3-1.5	0.1-0.2	?
Sandstone	3-5	0.2-0.4	?
Granite	2-6	~ 1	?

weathering, grain size and mineralogical composition, as well as temperature and water content.

Values for the direct current electrical resistivity of various materials determined by field measurements are given in Table 3.11, and the variation of resistivity with temperature for three soils, peat and one rock type, determined in the laboratory, is shown in Fig. 3.23. Resistivity values measured in the field and in the laboratory for some Antarctic soils and rock and in the field for some Mackenzie Delta soils are given by Hatherton (1960), McGinnis and Jensen (1971) and MacKay (1970). Extensive tables on rock resistivities, in general, are given by Parkhomenko (1967), Heiland (1940) and Keller et al. (1970).

Available data show that the resistivities of frozen soils and rocks may be from 10 to more than 100 times larger than those for the same materials when unfrozen. Differentiating between frozen and unfrozen ground solely on the basis of resistivity is not always possible, however, since the resistivity of frozen clay can be less than that of unfrozen silt, sand or rock. For mapping permafrost, therefore, resistivity surveys alone cannot always be depended upon; other geological information must be collected.

Collett (1974) concluded that:

— there is a pronounced increase in resistivity with decreasing temperature below 32°F (0°C),

— the resistivity at a given temperature below 32°F (0°C) depends on (unfrozen) water content, the chemical composition of the electrolyte and the composition and grain size of the mineral component,

— the resistivity of fine-grained rocks and soils, such as shales and clays, increases with freezing temperature decrease less abruptly than that of coarse-grained materials such as granite, sand and gravel, and

— increasing salinity of the pore water is associated with a corresponding reduction in resistivity.

3.7 Thaw Settlement and Consolidation

When permafrost thaws the amount of water resulting from ice melting may exceed the absorption capacity of the soil skeleton. Volume changes will result from both the phase change and the flow of excess water out of the soil. The suitability of thawed permafrost as a foundation material is directly related to the amount of deformation that occurs as a result of these volume changes and the strength of the soil during thaw. Thus, procedures to evaluate these soil characteristics are necessary.

Some examples of situations that require consideration of thaw settlement and consolidation are the design of building foundations and embankments where thaw is permitted, design of buried pipelines, design of oil, gas and water supply wells, design of water retaining structures and evaluation of engineering implications of terrain disturbance. When a soil is fully thawed and deformations associated with thawing have ended, conventional soil mechanics principles apply.

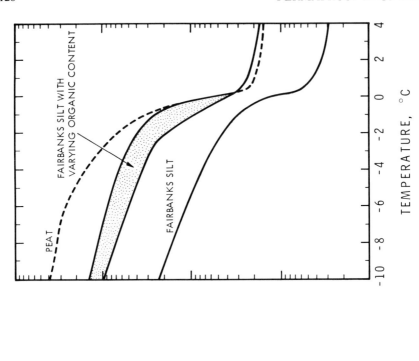

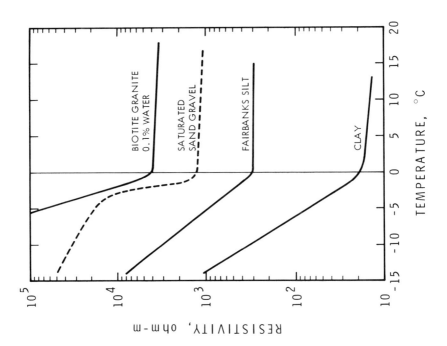

FIG. 3.23   Electrical resistivities of several soils and one rock type as a function of temperature (After Hoekstra et al. 1974).

The following section is concerned with the special features of soil deformation during thaw.

3.7.1 Thaw Settlement

If a saturated soil is at equilibrium with some applied effective stress so that no volume changes are occurring and if it is frozen under closed drainage conditions with no change in moisture content, the soil will expand in volume an amount equal to that due to phase change alone. That is,

$$\Delta V/V = 0.09n \tag{3.39}$$

where $\Delta V/V$ is the volumetric strain and n is the porosity.

If thawing is now permitted under undrained conditions, the soil will return to its original volume. If drainage is permitted, however, extra volume changes will occur that depend upon the degree of internal consolidation and structural change that occurred during the previous freezing cycle. In general, freezing occurs sufficiently slowly to permit ice segregation locally, even under closed drainage conditions. The local consolidation of the soil skeleton that accommodates this segregation is not a reversible process, so that upon thaw more water is generated than can now be absorbed by the soil skeleton. When drainage is permitted this results in more settlement.

Hence the settlement that occurs due to thaw depends upon the distribution of ice in the frozen soil and the swelling characteristics of the skeleton of the thawed soil. The amount and distribution of ice and the stress-deformation behaviour of the thawed soil depend upon a variety of factors, such as the stress, thermal and moisture change histories of the material. The thaw settlement characteristics of permafrost are best determined, therefore, by tests on representative samples under representative conditions.

The simplest procedure is to place about 1 cu. ft. (0.03 m³) of frozen soil in a bucket and allow it to thaw in an uncontrolled manner. The larger the amount of free water collected in excess of that absorbed by the soil, the larger will be the thaw settlement. Frost-susceptible soils such as silts and clayey silts are generally ice-rich, particularly near the active layer, and can give rise to large thaw settlements. Ice-rich permafrost is common in glacio-lacustrine basins, alluvial plains, and some till deposits. Some frozen sands and gravelly sands possess little ice but may be loose enough on thaw to give rise to significant settlements.

Identifying visible ice contents may be a guide to the possibility of large thaw settlements but the lack of visible ice does not preclude settlement problems. In fact, in some soils visible ice will be absorbed by the soil skeleton upon thaw and an estimate of settlement based upon the amount of free ice visible in a sample may result in significant errors. Representative testing is the most reliable procedure for evaluating the many variables that are of concern in practice.

Thaw settlement tests may be performed either isotropically in a triaxial pressure cell or, more commonly, one-dimensionally in a conventional consolidation device. Figure 3.24 illustrates a typical thaw settlement test result (Tsytovich

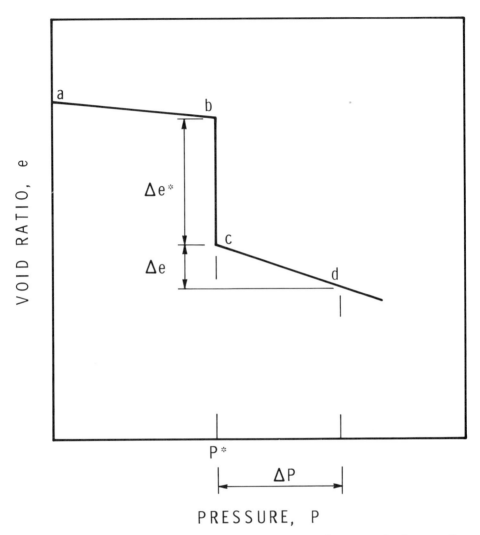

FIG. 3.24   Relation between change of void ratio and external pressures for frozen soils
subjected to thawing.

1960). Load is increased on a specimen of soil and the void ratio in equilibrium
with each load is recorded. While the sample is still frozen (a to b) a decrease in
void ratio occurs for an increase in load. This volume change is small with respect
to the volume change that will occur when the soil specimen thaws and may be
neglected. The sample is allowed to thaw under pressure p* and a substantial
change in void ratio Δe^* occurs, due in part to the phase change and in part to the
drainage of excess water. The thaw-strain parameter A is defined by

$$A (\%) = \Delta e^*/1 + e_o \qquad\qquad (3.40)$$

where e_o denotes the initial void ratio.

If the effective stress is increased from p* by an amount Δp it is convenient to regard the relationship between void ratio and stress for the thawed soil as linear, at least for small changes in pressure. Therefore, the vertical strain $\Delta H/H$ of an element thawed under p* and loaded to p* + Δp is

$$\Delta H/H = A + m_v \cdot \Delta p \tag{3.41}$$

where m_v denotes the coefficient of volume compressibility, and H the height of the element or layer.

The settlement of a layer H becomes

$$\Delta H = A \cdot H + m_v \cdot \Delta p \cdot H \tag{3.42}$$

If there are n layers, each with their own properties, the total thaw settlement may be estimated by summation so that

$$\Delta H = \sum_1^n A_i H_i + \sum_1^n m_{v_i} \cdot \Delta p_i \cdot H_i \tag{3.43}$$

where i has values from 1 to n.

When there is no subsequent loading after thaw or when the settlement during thaw dominates, as is often the case, the thaw settlement is simply given by

$$\Delta H = A \cdot H \quad \text{or} \quad \sum_1^n A_i H_i \tag{3.44}$$

It should be noted that A is to be determined under conditions of loading comparable to those acting in the field at the time of thaw.

Crory (1973a) developed an alternate relationship for predicting thaw settlement. It is entirely equivalent to the expression given above, but is expressed in terms of dry densities:

$$\Delta H = [(\gamma_{d_f} - \gamma_{d_t})/\gamma_{d_t}] H \tag{3.45}$$

where γ_{d_f} and γ_{d_t} are the frozen and thawed dry densities of the soil respectively.

It is of interest to correlate the thaw strain parameter A, which is obtained directly from a thaw settlement test, with the frozen bulk density γ_f of the soil because the latter is readily determined under field conditions. Speer et al. (1973) present a general correlation for several sites in the Mackenzie Valley as shown in Fig. 3.25. Most of the samples were thawed under a load equivalent to the total overburden pressure at sample depth. A least squares fit to the data gives

$$A = 73.60 - 101.8 \ln \gamma_f \tag{3.46}$$

The variation around the fit is substantial, however, and relations of this kind must be used with caution. For example, Keil et al. (1973) describe similar thaw settlement tests on permafrost samples from northern Manitoba that indicate

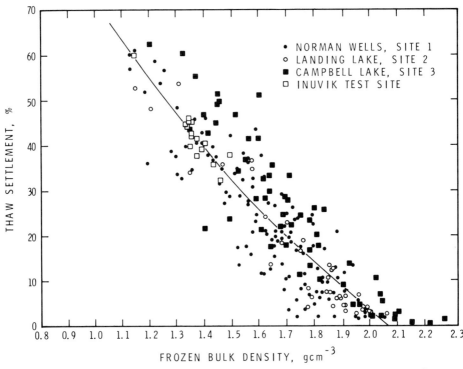

FIG. 3.25   Thaw settlement vs frozen bulk density relationships of some Mackenzie
Valley soils (After Speer et al. 1973).

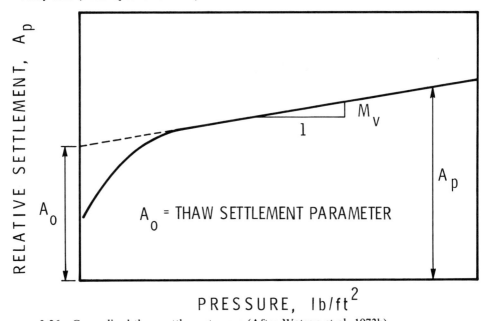

FIG. 3.26   Generalized thaw settlement curve (After Watson et al. 1973b).

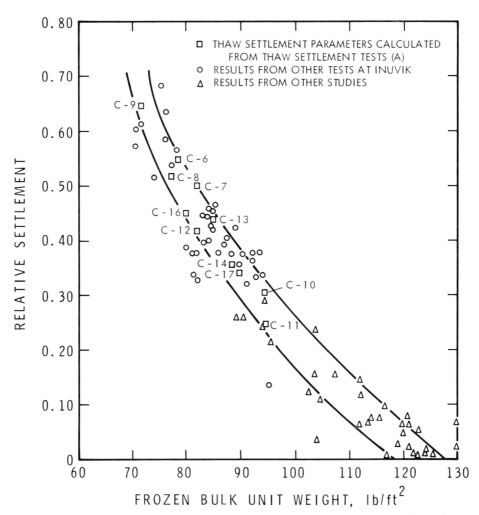

FIG. 3.27   Relationship between thaw settlement parameter and frozen bulk unit weight (After Watson et al. 1973b).

higher thaw settlements at a given γ_f than the data reported by Speer et al. (1973) and Rowley et al. (1973a). This appears to be related to differences in the nature of the frozen soil types tested.

Watson et al. (1973b) carried out a series of thaw settlement tests from zero applied pressure and suggest an approximation for finding A by extrapolation as shown in Fig. 3.26. This is reasonable for comparison with A values determined under low to moderate pressures and, as Fig. 3.27 confirms, thaw settlement parameters found in this way correspond reasonably well with those found in the more conventional manner. An extensive series of tests on Alaskan soils were conducted by Luscher and Afifi (1973). They present correlations between A, applied stress and frozen dry density for different types of soils. Problems of sample disturbance in the testing of frozen sands and gravels have been pointed out by them and also by Smith, W. S. et al. (1973).

In some cases soil will swell upon thaw (Crory 1973a) or, if not actually swell, the settlement may be less than that associated with phase change alone. This is accounted for by the residual stress, which is the effective stress in a soil thawed under undrained conditions (Nixon and Morgenstern 1973a). In some cases the residual stress will be greater than the effective stress due to loading on the sample and the soil skeleton will swell in order to come to equilibrium with the applied load. Methods for measuring the residual stress have been described. It is conservative to neglect it.

Several records exist to illustrate thaw settlement under field conditions. The best of these are papers on the settlements beneath dykes on the Nelson River (Brown, W. G. and Johnston 1970, Macpherson et al. 1970) and the pipeline test loop at Inuvik (Watson et al. 1973a). The settlements observed in the field are in reasonable agreement with predictions based upon the methods described here. While the calculation of thaw settlement on the basis of test data is a relatively simple matter, the implications of ground ice variability should always be considered. The study undertaken by Speer et al. (1973) is particularly instructive in this regard. By drilling an array of holes in a specific location, they show that high differential settlements can arise in some instances due to local variation in ground ice content.

3.7.2 Thaw Consolidation

If a thawing front is advancing in a soil according to some function $X(t)$ and if the flow of water from the thawed soil is unimpeded, then the variation of settlement with time is controlled solely by the position of the thaw plane. In a homogeneous soil the variation of settlement with time $S(t)$ is given by

$$S(t) = A \cdot X(t) \tag{3.47}$$

If the thawed soil is not sufficiently coarse-grained and flow is impeded, however, the development of settlement with time is also controlled by the compressibility and permeability of the thawed soil. Thaw consolidation must therefore be considered to understand this behaviour.

When a load is suddenly applied to a saturated fine-grained unfrozen soil, an increase in water pressure equal to the applied load is generated. Initially there is no decrease in void ratio and no change in shear strength. With time, water is squeezed out of the soil and settlements occur as the applied stress is gradually transferred from the pore water to the soil skeleton; that is, as the effective stress in the soil skeleton increases. Since the shear strength of soils is essentially frictional, the strength increases as the pore water pressures decrease. This decrease of pore water pressure with time and the associated processes are described by the theory of consolidation, which has been well explored in conventional soil mechanics (e.g., Lambe and Whitman 1969).

In the case of thawing soils, if the rate of thaw is sufficiently fast, water is released at a rate exceeding that at which it can flow from the soil, and pore pressures in excess of hydrostatic will be generated. If sustained, these excess pore pressures will cause severe problems. Slopes may become unstable, dam foundations may fail, and differential settlements of various types of structures may occur. Moreover, an estimate of the rate of development of shear strength in thawing ground can only be made with an understanding of pore pressure dissipation during thaw. It is therefore useful to apply a theory of thaw consolidation in order to investigate the factors controlling pore pressures generated in a thawing soil.

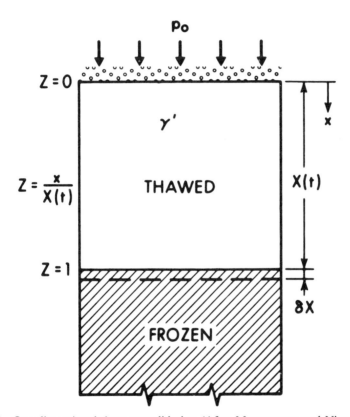

FIG. 3.28   One-dimensional thaw consolidation (After Morgenstern and Nixon 1971).

A simple linear theory of thaw consolidation has been developed by Morgenstern and Nixon (1971). As illustrated in Fig. 3.28, a one-dimensional configuration is considered where a step increase in temperature is imposed at the surface of a semi-infinite homogeneous mass of frozen soil. For these conditions, the movement of the thaw plane is given by

$$X(t) = a\sqrt{t} \qquad (3.48)$$

where X is the distance to the thaw plane from the soil surface, t denotes time and a is a constant determined in the solution of the heat conduction problem (Nixon and McRoberts 1973, see Section 4.3.3). Thermal conditions other than those specified above could be adopted. The example selected is not only simple but is also useful in practice.

The thawed soil possesses an effective or submerged bulk density γ', permeability k and coefficient of volume compressibility m_v. Hence, the dissipation of pore pressure in the thawed soil is governed by the Terzaghi theory of consolidation (Lambe and Whitman 1969) and solutions to the governing equation may be obtained once the boundary conditions have been specified. The new boundary condition is the one at the thaw line. Water is liberated at the thaw line and flows upward if excess pore pressures have been generated. For a saturated soil, the physical requirement here is that any flow from the thaw line is accom-

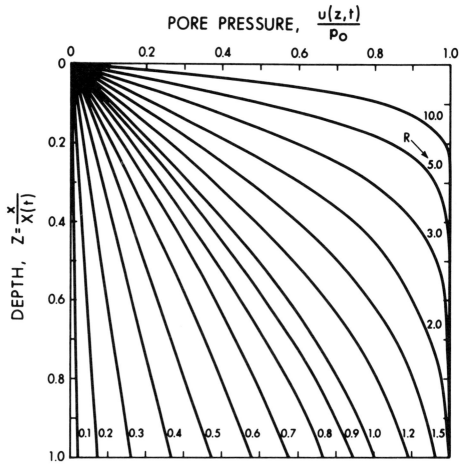

FIG. 3.29   Excess pore pressures, $W_r = 0$, weightless material (After Morgenstern and Nixon 1971).

modated by a change in volume of the soil. Analytically this can be stated in the general form

$$u\,(z,t) = f\,(R, z, W_r) \tag{3.49}$$

where u is the excess pore pressure, z denotes normalized depth $x/X(t)$ (see Fig. 3.28), W_r is a dimensionless load ratio $\gamma'X(t)/P_o$ (see Fig. 3.28), and R is the thaw consolidation ratio $a/2\sqrt{c_v}$ where $c_v = k/m_v\gamma_w$. Comparable solutions can also be obtained for the settlement that occurs during thaw and after thaw is completed.

The excess pore pressure distributions for two cases are of special interest. Figure 3.29 shows the variation of excess pore pressures with depth when the externally applied load is large with respect to the weight of the soil involved. Figure 3.30 gives the solution when the pore pressures are generated by the weight of soil alone. Excess pore pressures for intermediate values of W_r may be calculated from the solution given by Morgenstern and Nixon (1971) or by addition of the solutions given in the two figures.

Excess pore pressures and the degree of consolidation in thawing soils depend principally on the thaw consolidation ratio R. This parameter is a measure of the relative rates of generation and expulsion of excess pore fluids. A value of R greater than unity would predict the danger of sustained substantial pore pressures at the thaw line and hence the possibility of instability. If consolidation occurs during thaw, the soil shear strength will increase and the viscous fluid behaviour suggested by some will not materialize (e.g., Lachenbruch 1970). If the residual stress is large (Nixon and Morgenstern 1973a) the thaw consolidation process will become subdued since less pore pressure will be generated upon thaw.

The theory described above has been extended in a number of ways. The rate of thaw may be expressed as an arbitrary power law, or non-linear stress-strain relations for the soil may be assumed in order to simulate ice-rich materials (Nixon and Morgenstern 1973b). The movement of the heat source may be taken as finite (Nixon 1973a), and solutions for layered systems can be obtained (Nixon 1973b). This last extension is of particular interest because it shows that if the depth of burial and thaw rate of an ice layer lie within certain reasonable limits, ice layers at depth may be thawed without a significant increase in pore pressure. On the other hand, thaw of ice layers near the surface can readily lead to the development of critical stability conditions.

Experimental confirmation of the theory of thaw consolidation has been sought. Morgenstern and Smith (1973) constructed a special oedometer that could impose the necessary thermal and stress boundary conditions for one-dimensional consolidation. Controlled tests were carried out on three types of remoulded clays. The resulting data show that the excess pore pressures and the degree of consolidation in a thawing soil depend primarily on the thaw consolidation ratio R and that the theory adequately represents the soil behaviour. Experimental confirmation was sought for undisturbed permafrost by Nixon and Morgenstern (1974). Their tests also show that the observed pore pressures and settlements are consistent with predicted behaviour. Field records supporting the

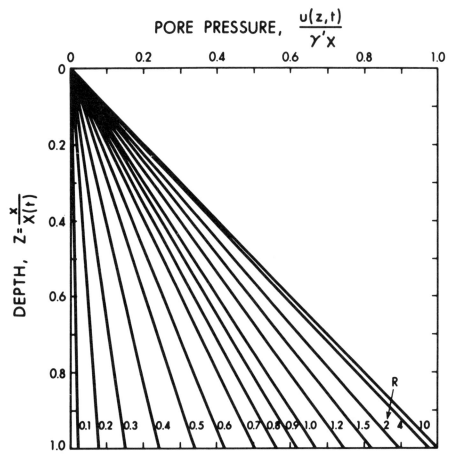

FIG. 3.30 Excess pore pressures, $W_r = \infty$, no applied load (After Morgenstern and Nixon 1971).

theory are presented by Morgenstern and Nixon (1975) in their analysis of the In-uvik test pipeline (Watson et al. 1973a).

Thaw consolidation theory can be applied to a variety of practical problems. The stability of dam foundations on thawing ground, for example, is discussed by Nixon (1973a), the settlement and stability of the thaw bulb around a buried pipeline by Nixon (1973a) and Morgenstern and Nixon (1975), the stability of slopes in thawing ground by McRoberts (1973), McRoberts and Morgenstern (1974a) and McRoberts and Nixon (1977) and the problems associated with dif-ferential settlement close to oil wells through permafrost by Palmer (1978).

3.8 Frost Action

Frost action in soils is a term used to describe the detrimental process of frost heaving resulting mainly from the accumulation of moisture in the form of ice lenses at the freezing plane in the soil during the freezing period and also thaw-weakening or decrease in bearing strength when the seasonally frozen soil thaws. Significant damage and costly maintenance result from frost heaving and thaw-weakening of soils and therefore the effects of frost action are a major considera-tion in the design and construction of various structures and facilities.

Differential or non-uniform frost heaving is one of the main detrimental aspects of the frost action process and arises because of the heterogeneous nature of most soils or variations in heat removal rate and water supply over short distances. It results in the distortion of structures due to heave of foundations and also seriously affects the riding quality and use of traffic surfaces. There may be a cumulative effect over several years, in addition, such that a foundation sub-jected to seasonal heaving may be permanently displaced upward. Long-term heaving will also be of concern to structures founded on either unfrozen or frozen soils in the permafrost region that are subjected to continuous freezing temperatures over a period of years rather than seasonal freezing. Refrigerated foundations and buried chilled gas pipelines are pertinent examples. Similar problems are experienced by structures such as cold storage plants and ice arenas that are operated year-round in non-permafrost areas.

Serious effects also occur during the thaw period to structures founded on the ground surface or in the active layer. Thaw-weakening is of particular concern to highways, railways and airports. Thawing of the ice lenses at a rate faster than the released moisture can escape, accompanied by loading of the soil, causes a large decrease in bearing capacity. Differential thaw, of course, will result in irregular settlement of the previously heaved foundation or traffic surface and further complicate internal drainage. The stability of both natural and man-made slopes may also be affected by frost action with sloughing and erosion occurring during the thaw period. The detrimental effects of frost action on foundations and earth structures and methods of controlling them are discussed in Sections 7.3 and 8.1.

3.8.1 The Frost Action Process

The frost action process is extremely complex and many studies of it and related problems have been carried out (Johnson 1952, Jessberger 1970). The three basic conditions that must exist for frost action to occur are a frost-susceptible soil, a water supply and sufficiently low soil temperatures to cause some of the soil water to freeze. The physics of the interaction of these factors is generally re-ferred to as the mechanism of frost heaving.

The frost heave that occurs in a frost-susceptible soil as the freezing plane penetrates is caused by the volume change resulting from freezing of the in situ pore water and to the ice segregation process when water flows to the freezing plane from outside sources. Freezing of pore water in soils will cause a volume ex-pansion or heave of 9%. The largest part of the total heave that occurs when a frost-susceptible soil freezes, however, and which is of major concern to the engineer, is due mainly to the growth of ice lenses at the freezing front caused by the ice segregation process. The lenses form normal to the direction of heat flow and are therefore usually parallel to the ground surface.

Frost heaving of the ground surface amounting to 1 or 2 in. (20 to 50 mm) in one season is common and movements of 6 to 8 in. (150 to 200 mm) are not unusual. The amount of frost heave in non-compressible soils is equal to the accumulated thickness of the ice lenses. The supply of moisture for ice lens growth is normally derived from water within the soil (active layer), either from the groundwater table or by a reduction in the water content of the soil near the zone of freezing. In soils that are partially compressible, removal of water from the unfrozen soil results in some shrinkage and hence the total heave is somewhat less than the accumulated thickness of the ice lenses. The 9% volume expansion that occurs when water changes to ice may be responsible for much of the heaving in marginally frost-susceptible soils.

It is well known, as shown by various investigators, that the heaving rate is sharply reduced and, in some cases, water is expelled when a load is applied to a freezing soil (Beskow 1935, Linell and Kaplar 1959, Penner 1959). More recent studies (Arvidson and Morgenstern 1974, McRoberts and Morgenstern 1975) confirm that the movement of water to the freezing plane decreases with load increase. It has also been shown, however, that although water may be expelled during the initial freezing stage when freezing rates were fairly rapid, the flow reverses and water again moves to the freezing plane after a period of time when the rate of frost penetration had decreased and when there is a positive total heave rate (Penner and Ueda 1977). Only when the total heave rate is zero will the expulsion of water not be followed by intake of water. This growth of ice lenses and heaving will continue. Even though the application of a load can reduce the rate of heave significantly, it appears that the rate of heave is always a finite quantity and relatively high confining stresses are required to stop heaving even in rather coarse materials.

It is also possible that additional and perhaps significant heaving and heaving pressures can be generated in already frozen soil due to migration, accumulation and freezing of the unfrozen water within the frozen soil, particularly when freezing conditions persist over long periods of time. It would be greatly dependent on the permeability of the frozen soil and the presence of suitable gradients of potential (Hoekstra 1966, Miller 1970, Miller et al. 1975, Williams 1977).

The migration of water in both unfrozen and frozen soils is complex and basic to frost action and heaving. It is dependent on a number of factors including soil type, permeability, stress history, rate of freezing and time and is the subject of on-going studies directed to a better understanding of the frost action process. The thaw-weakening process also is complex and may occur in soils, particularly clays, whether or not ice lenses have formed during the freezing period. The number of freeze-thaw cycles, closed system vs open system freezing, swelling and shrinkage of unsaturated soils and moisture movement are some factors that appear to influence the thaw-weakening process.

The mechanism of frost heaving and the frost action problems in the active layer in permafrost areas are, in general, similar to those found in seasonal frost areas. Differences to be noted are:

(a) the supply of water for ice segregation is normally contained in the active layer and, therefore, usually moves in what is in effect a closed system. In seasonal frost areas the unfrozen soil below the freezing plane is capable of continually supplying water for ice lensing and hence, the process occurs in an open system,

(b) freezing of the soil always occurs downward from the ground surface in both permafrost and seasonal frost areas, but freezing of the active layer can also take place upward from the permafrost table. Thus water can be extracted from the unfrozen portion of the active layer in two directions. Downward freezing is however usually dominant in the active layer,

(c) some of the water released upon thawing is retained within the active layer because of the underlying impermeable permafrost. Although the water may drain laterally, poor internal drainage may often cause a loss of strength in some active layer soils. After thawing is complete in seasonal frost areas, the moisture becomes a part of the groundwater system, although during the thaw period frozen layers may temporarily hinder internal drainage, and

(d) in permafrost areas, the thaw period lasts through the entire summer whereas in seasonal frost areas the thaw period may last for a month or so.

3.8.2 Frost Susceptibility of Soils

At present there is no generally accepted criterion that characterizes a non-frost-susceptible earth material. Johnson et al. (1974) review the various criteria for identifying a frost-susceptible soil. The most commonly used criteria are based on grain size. The amount of fines is usually specified although the smallest size and the amount of fines vary considerably. There is also a limitation on gradation. Linell and Kaplar (1959) note that the Casagrande (1932) frost criteria affords the most expedient rule-of-thumb for identifying soil in which damaging frost action may occur. Casagrande states, "under natural freezing conditions and with a sufficient water supply one should expect considerable ice segregation in non-uniform soils containing more than 3% of grains smaller than 0.02 mm and in very uniform soils containing more than 10% smaller than 0.02 mm. No ice segregation was observed in soils containing less than 1% of grains smaller than 0.02 mm even if the groundwater level was as high as the frost line."

A frost design soil classification system (Table 3.12), developed by the U.S. Corps of Engineers and based on the Casagrande grain size criterion, is widely used to evaluate the frost susceptibility of soils. The soil types are listed approximately in order of increasing susceptibility to frost heaving and/or weakening as a result of thawing. The F1 materials may be expected to have a higher bearing capacity during thaw than the F2 soils, even though both may have experienced equal ice segregation. The order of listing subgroups under F3 and F4 does not necessarily indicate increased susceptibility to frost heaving. F4 soils are highly

TABLE 3.12

U.S. Corps of Engineers
Frost Design Soil Classification

Frost group	Soil type	Percentage finer than 0.02 mm, by weight	Typical soil types under Unified Soil Classification System
F1	Gravelly soils	3 to 10	GW, GP, GW-GM, GP-GM
F2	(a) Gravelly soils	10 to 20	GM, GW-GM, GP-GM
	(b) Sands	3 to 15	SW, SP, SM, SW-SM, SP-SM
F3	(a) Gravelly soils	>20	GM, GC
	(b) Sands, except very fine silty sands	>15	SM, SC
	(c) Clays, PI >12	—	CL, CH
F4	(a) All silts	—	ML, MH
	(b) Very fine silty sands	>15	SM
	(c) Clays, PI < 12	—	CL, CL-ML
	(d) Varved clays and other fine-grained, banded sediments	—	CL and ML; CL, ML, and SM; CL, CH, and ML; CL, CH, ML, and SM

frost-susceptible and the F3 and F4 soils, grouped together for reduced strength design, show the greatest weakening during thaw.

It is recognized, however, that the "3% finer by weight than 0.02 mm" criterion is not a sharp dividing line. For example, laboratory studies have shown that some gravelly soils, which have about 1% of their particles finer than 0.02 mm, heave significantly and that some sandy materials having up to 20% finer than 0.02 mm do not exhibit undesirable frost heave characteristics.

When frost heaving is an exceptionally critical factor in the design of structures, the frost susceptibility of a soil may be established by laboratory "heaving rate" tests. A laboratory test and frost heaving classification (Table 3.13) have proved useful to the U.S. Corps of Engineers for evaluating soils of borderline or questionable frost action characteristics (Linell and Kaplar 1959, Kaplar 1974a). The rates of frost penetration used in these laboratory tests are between 0.2 and 0.5 in./day (6 and 13mm/day). Kaplar (1971b) indicated that useful frost heaving data can be obtained in 2 or 3 days (rather than 2 weeks or more in the above tests) by a more rapid freezing technique when freezing rates ranged from 3 to 8 in./day (76 to 200 mm/day).

These tests provide a relative measure of potential frost behaviour. Various studies have shown, however, that a number of factors influence such behaviour. It is known, for example, that when laboratory freezing tests are used to establish the frost susceptibility of soils, special attention should be given to the freezing rate, because rate of heaving and rate of frost penetration are interdependent

TABLE 3.13

U.S. Corps of Engineers
Classification of Frost Susceptibility
(Based on Laboratory Heaving Tests)

Average rate of heave (mm/day)	Frost susceptibility classification
0.0-0.5	Negligible
0.5-1.0	Very low
1.0-2.0	Low
2.0-4.0	Medium
4.0-8.0	High
>8.0	Very high

(Penner 1960). This relationship, expressed by Arakawa (1966) in terms of an ice segregation efficiency ratio E, is a useful index of the frost susceptibility of a soil:

$$E = \sigma L / [k_f(\partial T_f/\partial x) - k_t(\partial T_t/\partial x)] \qquad (3.50)$$

where σ = ice segregation rate, i.e. the mass of ice formed per unit area and time at the frost line, kg/m^2 per unit time

    L   = latent heat of fusion, J/kg

    k_f = thermal conductivity of the frozen layer, W/m·°C

    k_t = thermal conductivity of the unfrozen layer, W/m·°C

    $\partial T_f/\partial x$ = thermal gradient in the frozen layer, °C/m

    $\partial T_t/\partial x$ = thermal gradient in the unfrozen layer, °C/m

The ice lens growth rate in the soil is given by σL and the denominator is the net heat flow from the sample. When E = 1 the efficiency or condition for ice growth is at a maximum. When $0 < E < 1$ there is a strong dependence on rate of heat removal and this includes soils normally considered borderline with respect to frost susceptibility. No ice segregation will occur when E = 0. The efficiency ratio for soils showing widely different heaving characteristics is plotted in Fig. 3.31 (Penner 1972).

It appears, therefore, that laboratory heaving tests should be carried out at freezing rates that simulate the actual field conditions that will be experienced by the soils under consideration. These rates can be quite variable and different to those used in the tests noted previously.

Both theory and laboratory results emphasize two important features of the frost heaving process: (1) there is no sharp dividing line between frost-susceptible and non-frost-susceptible materials, and (2) the smaller particles in a material appear to have a dominating influence in establishing the maximum heaving pressures that are developed in a particular material.

3.8.3 Frost Heaving Pressures

Laboratory studies to determine frost heaving forces developed in a wide variety of materials suggest that the use of particle size is a valid criterion of frost susceptibility (Penner 1973). In the now generally accepted theory of frost heaving and

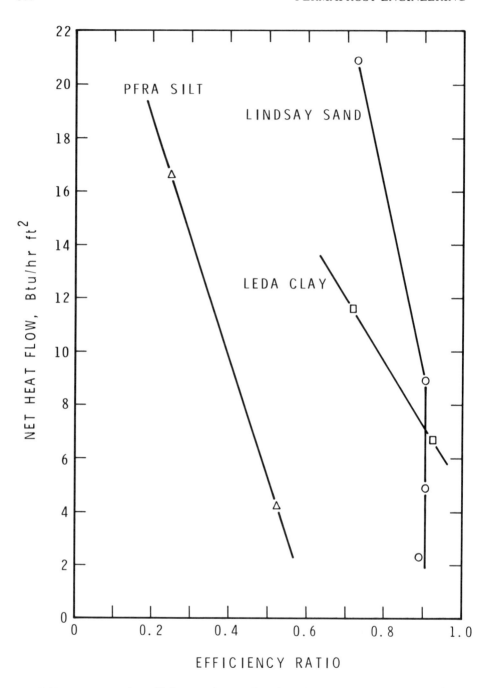

FIG. 3.31   Ice segregation efficiency ratio as a function of net heat flow (heat out minus heat in) (After Penner 1972).

ice lens growth, Everett (1961) predicts that ice growth in a saturated particulate material could be stopped by applying a suction to the water phase, by applying a pressure on the ice phase or by the simultaneous application of both. That is

$$\Delta p_i + \Delta p_w = \frac{2\sigma_{iw}}{r_1} \qquad (3.51)$$

where Δp_i = pressure on the ice, N/m^2
Δp_w = suction pressure in the water, N/m^2
σ_{iw} = ice-water interfacial energy, J/m^2, and
r_1 = pore radius, μm.

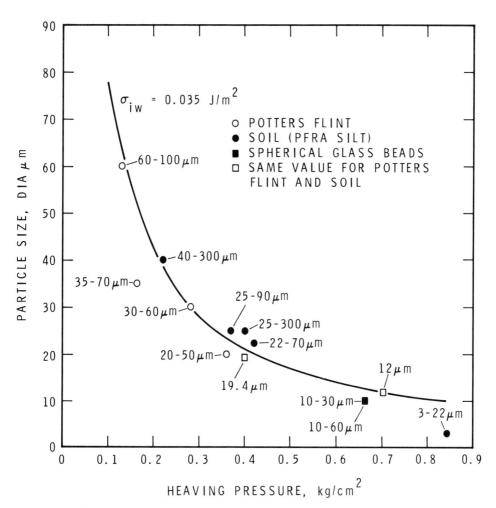

FIG. 3.32   Relation between experimental heaving pressures and smallest particle in sample (After Penner 1973).

(a)

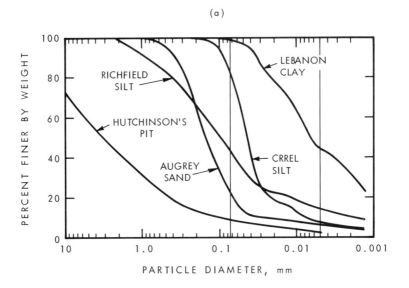

(b)

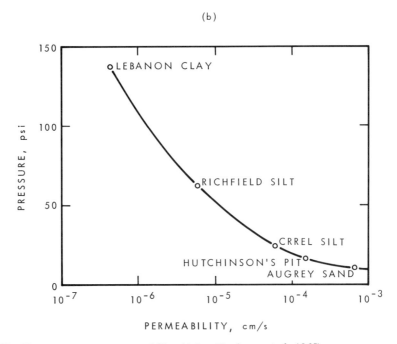

FIG. 3.33   Heave pressure vs permeability (After Hoekstra et al. 1965).

Subsequently, Everett and Haynes (1965) worked out theoretical heaving pressures for some model pore systems based on spherical particles. An equation of particular interest, which applies to closely packed spherical particles, is

$$\Delta p_i = \frac{2\sigma_{iw} \cos \theta \, (1 + B')}{r} \qquad (3.52)$$

where B' = $r/r_1 \cos \theta$, and
 r = particle radius

In Fig. 3.32 the solid line gives the Everett and Haynes relationship between Δp_i, the pressure on the ice or the heaving pressure, and particle diameter. The open squares are the maximum ice pressures determined on compacts of glass beads of uniform size. The other plotted points were determined with fragmented materials, such as potters flint and soil. The points plotted in this case are for the minimum particle diameter in the particular batch of material.

Pore size distribution, which is related to grain size, is an indicator of the permeability of a soil and therefore determines the heaving pressures that can be developed. The results of laboratory experiments by Hoekstra et al. (1965) under conditions of essentially complete restraint are given in Fig. 3.33 and indicate the magnitude of the heave forces involved. It should be noted that, although both the Richfield silt and the Augrey sand are silty sands, the well-graded Richfield silt has smaller pores than the poorly graded Augrey sand and, therefore, there is a large difference in heaving pressure.

Not only have various studies pointed out that rate of heave is a function of confining pressure, as noted previously, but also that heaving pressure is related to the confining pressure. It has been observed in both laboratory and field experiments that generated heaving pressures increase with increasing degree of constraint (Kinosita 1967, Penner 1970b, Yong and Osler 1971, Radd and Oertle 1973). The complex conditions encountered in practical field situations, including variations in temperature, soil type, impurities in pore water, groundwater locations, surcharge loading and surface cover, make the rational prediction of frost heaving pressures extremely difficult and indicate the need for further detailed studies on the frost action process and related problems.

CHAPTER 4

Ground Thermal Analysis

(Contributors–L. E. Goodrich and L. W. Gold)

The behaviour of soils in cold regions is strongly influenced by temperature and, therefore, an appreciation of the ground thermal regime and the changes that occur in it is of utmost importance to permafrost engineering. Ground temperatures and heat flow rates can be predicted in principle if the boundary conditions and thermal properties of the ground are known. Ground, however, is not a simple conducting solid. It is usually layered and has thermal properties that depend on soil type, density and moisture content, and whether the moisture is in a frozen or unfrozen state. The general effects of climate and terrain factors on the ground thermal regime and the distribution of permafrost are outlined in Chapter 2 and the thermal properties of earth materials are discussed in Section 3.5. The major techniques used for treating ground thermal problems, with emphasis on heat transfer by conduction with and without latent heat, are reviewed briefly in this chapter.

4.1 Heat Transfer in the Ground

Conduction is the dominant ground heat transfer process. Heat flow by conduction is described by the equation

$$C\frac{\partial T}{\partial t} = -\frac{\partial}{\partial x}F_x - \frac{\partial}{\partial y}F_y - \frac{\partial}{\partial z}F_z \qquad (4.1)$$

where $F_x = -k\frac{\partial T}{\partial x}$, $F_y = -k\frac{\partial T}{\partial y}$ and $F_z = -k\frac{\partial T}{\partial z}$ are the components of heat flux in the x, y and z directions, C is the volumetric heat capacity, k the thermal conductivity, T the temperature and t is the time. If the material is homogeneous, Eq. 4.1 reduces to

$$\frac{\partial T}{\partial t} = \alpha\left[\frac{\partial^2 T}{\partial x^2} + \frac{\partial^2 T}{\partial y^2} + \frac{\partial^2 T}{\partial z^2}\right] \qquad (4.2)$$

where $\alpha = k/C$ is the thermal diffusivity. Freezing and thawing of soil greatly modifies the ground thermal regime in permafrost areas, however, and the conductive heat flow equation must be accompanied by an equation to account for the liberation or absorption of latent heat.

If, as is the case for coarse-grained soils, essentially all the water changes phase at the freezing point T_f, the appropriate boundary condition at the moving interface separating the frozen and thawed phases is

$$L\frac{dX}{dt} = F_- - F_+ \tag{4.3}$$

where L is the latent heat released per unit volume of soil during freezing, X is the position of the moving interface and F_- and F_+ are heat fluxes in the frozen and thawed phases evaluated at the interface. For thawing problems, latent heat is absorbed and L in Eq. 4.3 is replaced by $-L$. When fine-grained soils are involved, latent heat is released (absorbed) over a range of temperatures $T \leq T_f$, and acts as a distributed heat source in the partially frozen soil zone. As a result, the partially frozen soil behaves as if it had a greatly increased heat capacity. This "apparent" heat capacity is defined by

$$C' = C + \frac{\partial L}{\partial T} \tag{4.4}$$

Equations 4.1 to 4.4 provide the basis for a description of ground thermal behaviour that is adequate for the majority of permafrost engineering applications. The more complex cases in which moisture movement and frost heaving or thaw settlement must also be considered are discussed briefly in Section 4.5.

4.2 Boundary Conditions for Ground Thermal Problems

In nature, the driving force that determines the ground surface thermal regime is the net flux of heat arising from absorbed solar and thermal radiation and from sensible and latent heat transfer between the ground and the overlying air. This net flux is given by the surface heat balance equation

$$Q_g = -\left.\frac{k\partial T}{\partial n}\right]_o = Q_{SW} + Q_{LW} + Q_H + Q_E \tag{4.5}$$

where Q_g is the ground heat flux at the surface and $\left.\frac{\partial T}{\partial n}\right]_o$ is the ground temperature gradient normal to and evaluated at the surface. Q_{SW} is the net flux of solar radiation whose value depends on surface reflectivity (albedo) and orientation, atmospheric and cloud conditions, latitude, season and time of day. Q_{LW} is the net thermal (long wave) radiation. Its value depends on surface and air temperatures, cloud conditions and temperature and humidity gradients in the atmosphere. Q_H is the sensible heat flux associated with air flow over the surface; its value depends on air and surface temperature, wind speed, surface roughness and whether the air flow regime is stable or unstable. Q_E is the latent heat flux associated with evaporation of moisture from the surface. Its value is determined by the factors that control sensible heat transfer and, in addition, depends on the availability of moisture at the surface and whether the ground is frozen or thawed. For vegetated surfaces, the plants themselves contribute to the latent heat flux through the process of evapotranspiration. Detailed discussions of these processes can be found in Sutton (1953), Scott (1964), Geiger (1965), Munn (1966) and Stringer (1972).

The individual heat flux components are much larger than the ground heat flux Q_g. Because they cannot be measured or estimated with great precision, and since the error is cumulative, large errors in the determination of Q_g are possible. For this reason and because the information required to calculate the components is generally not available, Eq. 4.5 is rarely used as a boundary condition for ground thermal design calculations.

Instead, ground temperature calculations are usually based on assumed surface temperatures. The net effect of the various heat balance processes results in a surface temperature that roughly follows seasonal variations in air temperature. The variation in air temperature over a year is approximately sinusoidal and, at least in the simplest cases, surface temperatures can be assumed to behave similarly. The nature of seasonal ground temperature variations that would occur in homogeneous frozen soil if the surface temperature varied sinusoidally is illustrated in Fig. 4.1. The seasonal progression of isotherms is shown in Fig. 4.1(a) and the changes in ground temperature in and below the active layer are seen in Fig. 4.1(b). The insert shows the envelope of annual maximum and minimum temperatures.

For seasonal freezing and thawing problems, surface temperature variations are usually not considered in detail and average values for the entire freezing or thawing period are used instead. In practice, the average seasonal temperature is replaced by the freezing or thawing index. The air thawing (I_{at}) and freezing (I_{af}) indices are determined by computing the sum, over the thawing or freezing season, of the deviations of mean daily air temperatures from the freezing point. Computations can be made with adequate accuracy from monthly mean temperatures, however, and Boyd (1976) presents charts of air thawing and freezing indices for Canada (Figs. 1.4 and 1.5) based on data compiled from nearly 900 stations for the period 1931-60 (Boyd 1973).

For design purposes, it is recommended that the design freezing (or thawing) index be taken as the average air freezing (or thawing) index of the three coldest winters (or warmest summers) in the most recent 30 years of record. If 30 years of record are not available, then the air freezing (or thawing) index for the coldest winter (or warmest summer) in the latest 10-year period should be used. If the record period is less than 10 years, then the relatively linear relationship between the recorded maximum and mean freezing and thawing indices, as shown in Fig. 4.2, may be used in conjunction with the distribution of mean freezing and thawing indices in the general area to determine design index values.

For time scales in the order of months, the ground surface temperature can be correlated reasonably well with air temperature. For design purposes, surface temperatures are commonly estimated using an empirically determined coefficient called the "n-factor" to relate them to air temperature. The n-factor is defined as the ratio of the surface freezing or thawing index, I_{sf} or I_{st}, to the air

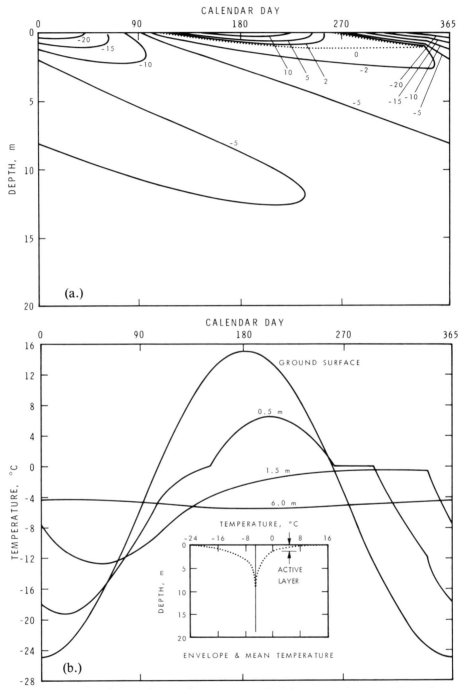

FIG. 4.1   Annual variation of ground temperatures (°C) in a permafrost area for soil containing moisture.

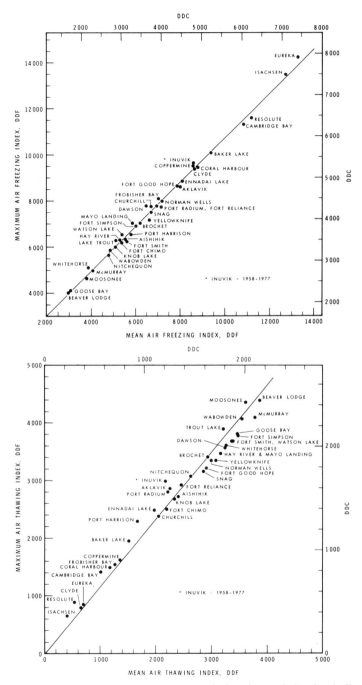

FIG. 4.2   Relation between maximum and mean air freezing and thawing indices (in degree days Fahrenheit—DDF and degree days Celsius—DDC) for northern Canada during the period 1949-1959 (After Thompson 1966).

freezing or thawing index:

$$n_f = I_{sf}/I_{af} \qquad\qquad\qquad\qquad (4.6a)$$

$$n_t = I_{st}/I_{at} \qquad\qquad\qquad\qquad (4.6b)$$

The application of these concepts for seasonal frost and thaw depth calculations is discussed in Section 4.3.3.

The magnitude of freezing and thawing n-factors depends on climatic conditions as well as on the type of surface. Approximate values of the n-factor for several different surfaces are given in Table 4.1 based on data compiled from a large number of sources. The extreme range of values given for gravel and pavement surfaces may reflect the range of geographical locations from which the data was compiled. Commonly accepted values for northern conditions are indicated in brackets. Information on the relation of thawing n-factors to average windspeed for pavement surfaces is given in U.S. Army/Air Force (1966c). Lunardini (1978) also presents a theoretical analysis for estimating n-factors for dry surfaces.

TABLE 4.1

Values of n-factors for Different Surfaces
(After Lunardini 1978)

Surface Type	Freezing-n_f	Thawing-n_t
Spruce trees, brush, moss over peat—soil surface	0.29 (under snow)	0.37
As above with trees cleared— soil surface	0.25 (under snow)	0.73
Turf	0.5 (under snow)	1.0
Snow	1.0	—
Gravel (probable range for northern conditions)	0.6 – 1.0 (0.9 – 0.95)	1.3 – 2
Asphalt pavement (probable range for northern conditions)	0.29 – 1.0 or greater (0.9 – 0.95)	1.4 – 2.3
Concrete pavement (probable range for northern conditions)	0.25 – 0.95 (0.7 – 0.9)	1.3 – 2.1

In summer, vegetation-covered but treeless surfaces that remain wet will have an average surface temperature that is about the same as the corresponding average air temperature. The n-factor for such surfaces during this period will be close to one. Dry or well-drained surfaces, such as gravel pads and paved roads, however, have surface temperatures that vary over a wider range than that of the air, due to their greater sensitivity to variations in solar and long wave radiation. Care must be taken in choosing an appropriate n-factor for such surfaces because of the greater possible range in its value. Under northern conditions, the average snow surface temperature tends to equal that of the air temperature over periods of a week or more, and the n-factor can normally be assumed to have a value of one.

The effects of snow cover have to be considered in certain thermal regime calculations. Snow is an excellent insulator and its presence causes the mean annual ground temperature to be several degrees warmer than it would be without snow cover. The amount of warming is very dependent on the seasonal air temperature amplitude, as well as on snow thickness, density and other factors that affect the thermal resistance of the snow pack. Soil thermal properties, including latent heat associated with freezing and thawing, are also important. The results of some theoretical computations of the effects of snow cover on mean annual ground temperatures are shown in Fig. 4.3. The dotted curve indicates the behaviour if the snow cover were absent. The rapid change in mean annual and maximum temperatures within the active layer is a consequence of the temperature dependence of the thermal properties of the ground.

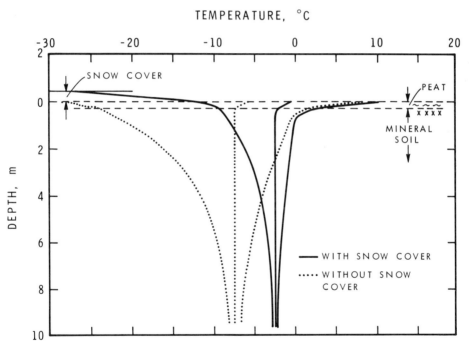

FIG. 4.3   Effect of snow cover on ground temperatures in a permafrost area.

As seen in Figs. 4.1 and 4.3, the amplitude of annual ground temperature fluctuations decreases with depth, and at sufficient depth the temperature remains practically constant, except for long-term drift associated with changes in mean annual temperature at the surface. Most engineering calculations are concerned with maximum depths of about 50 ft. (15 m) or less. In nature, the heat flux at these depths is typically two to three orders of magnitude smaller than that near the surface, and often can be assumed equal to zero. Mean annual temperatures in permafrost generally decrease with depth in the first few tens of metres, increasing thereafter to geothermal equilibrium values only at much greater depth.

4.3 Analytical and Graphical Methods for Solving Ground Thermal Problems

Analytical techniques can be used to provide practical solutions to the heat equation for a limited range of problems. With a few important exceptions, these problems involve homogeneous materials, regular geometries, no phase change and linear boundary conditions. Nevertheless, the solutions provide a useful basis for engineering design estimates.

4.3.1 Steady State Problems

Techniques used for steady state problems include direct integration and conformal mapping, which yield simple closed form solutions for regular one- and two-dimensional geometries. Fourier series expansions are useful for two- and three-dimensional problems. For linear cases, it is possible to rephrase the problem in such a way that the solution becomes the sum of the solutions of a number of simpler problems (superposition principle). In some cases, solutions for two- and three-dimensional problems can be obtained by multiplying together solutions for one-dimensional problems. These topics are covered in detail in basic references such as Ingersoll et al. (1954), Schneider (1955), Carslaw and Jaeger (1959) and Myers (1971).

The concept of a thermal resistance associated with a thermal circuit is invaluable for heat flow calculations. The thermal resistance R is defined as the difference in temperature between two surfaces divided by the rate of heat flow between them.

From Eq. 4.1, the steady temperature distribution in a slab (Fig. 4.4(a)) is given by

$$T(x) = T_1 + \frac{(T_2 - T_1)x}{\Delta x} \tag{4.7}$$

For a slab of area A and conductivity k, the heat flow rate is $-kA \cdot \partial T / \partial x$ and the corresponding thermal resistance is

$$R = \frac{\Delta x}{kA} \tag{4.8}$$

For N layers in series

$$R = R_1 + R_2 + - - - R_N = \frac{1}{A} \sum_{i=1}^{N} \left(\frac{\Delta x}{k} \right)_i \tag{4.9}$$

and for parallel connection

$$1/R = \Delta x \sum_{i=1}^{N} \frac{1}{(kA)_i} \tag{4.10}$$

These formulae can be used for estimating heat flow through layered materials such as the walls and floors of buildings. Several examples of their application are given in U.S. Army/Air Force (1966c).

For steady radial heat flow through a cylindrical region, Eq. 4.1 becomes

$$\frac{d}{dr}(r\frac{dT}{dr}) = 0 \tag{4.11}$$

and, by integration, the temperature distribution within the walls of a cylinder (Fig. 4.4(b)) is given by

$$T(r) = \frac{T_1 \ln(r_2/r) + T_2 \ln(r_1/r)}{\ln(r_2/r_1)} \tag{4.12}$$

The radial heat flow rate for a cylinder of length ΔZ is given by

$$-Ak\frac{\partial T}{\partial r}\Delta Z = -2\pi rk\frac{\partial T}{\partial r}\Delta Z = \frac{2\pi k(T_1 - T_2)\Delta Z}{\ln(r_2/r_1)} \tag{4.13}$$

and the corresponding thermal resistance is

$$R = \frac{\ln(r_2/r_1)}{2\pi k\Delta Z} \tag{4.14}$$

Results for a layered cylinder can be obtained by summing the resistances of each layer:

$$R = \sum_{i=1}^{N} R_i = \frac{1}{2\pi\Delta Z} \sum_{i=1}^{N} \frac{\ln(r_i + 1/r_i)}{k_i} \tag{4.15}$$

The application of these equations for the design of buried water and sewer lines and for utilidors is described in U.S. Army/Air Force (1966c), Alter (1969a, b) and Fryer (1970). Calculations for above-ground water pipes are given by Stephenson (1977a). Deviation from radial heat flow can be significant for pipes buried at shallow depths, particularly in the soil layer between the ground surface and the top of the pipe. More appropriate formulae which take these effects into account are given in Section 10.3.3.

Provided the material is homogeneous, the theory of conjugate functions can be used to obtain both temperature and heat flow fields for two-dimensional problems by applying coordinate transformations to existing solutions. This method is particularly effective if the material surfaces coincide with isotherms. In such cases, simple formulae for the thermal resistance can be developed. Carslaw and Jaeger (1959) discuss the mathematical details and provide results for a number of frequently occurring cases.

The thermal resistance per unit length R_1 between a cylinder and a plane (Fig. 4.4(c)) can be expressed as

$$R_1 = \frac{1}{2\pi k} \cosh^{-1}(d/a) \tag{4.16}$$

while that between the two cylinders of Fig. 4.4(d) is

$$R_1 = \frac{1}{2\pi k} \cosh^{-1}\left(\frac{d^2 - a_1^2 - a_2^2}{2a_1 a_2}\right) \tag{4.17}$$

and between the cylinders of Fig. 4.4(e) is

$$R_1 = \frac{1}{2\pi k} \cosh^{-1}\left(\frac{a_1^2 + a_2^2 - d^2}{2a_1 a_2}\right) \tag{4.18}$$

The temperature distribution beneath a flat surface whose temperature changes value at the origin (Fig. 4.4(f)) is given by

$$T(x,y) = T_1 + \frac{(T_2 - T_1)}{\pi} \tan^{-1}(x/y) \tag{4.19}$$

This equation describes approximately the steady temperature distribution beneath a lakeshore or under the edge of a large building (Brown 1963a). The equation for the temperature distribution beneath an infinitely long heated or cooled strip (Fig. 4.4(g)) can be found by superposition of solutions starting from Eq. 4.19. After a change of coordinates and rearranging terms the result is

$$T(x,y) = T_1 + \frac{(T_2 - T_1)}{\pi} \tan^{-1}\left(\frac{2ax}{x^2 + y^2 - a^2}\right) \tag{4.20}$$

Eq. 4.20 describes approximately the steady temperature under a roadway, river or similar long, narrow geographical feature. Using superposition and by taking advantage of symmetry, results can be written for more involved situations. Brown (1963a) discusses several cases that are applicable to ground temperature calculations.

Although the elementary solutions given here are convenient closed form expressions, the algebra rapidly becomes intractable with increasing problem complexity and solutions must be written as cumbersome infinite series. Lachenbruch (1957c) and Brown (1963b) describe graphical superposition, with application to the calculation of ground temperature distributions under building foundations as well as under heated or cooled, irregularily shaped areas at the ground surface. A purely graphical method, based on the orthogonality of heat flow and temperature fields, can be used for two- and three-dimensional regions of arbitrary shape (Schneider 1955). This method, however, has been largely superseded by numerical techniques.

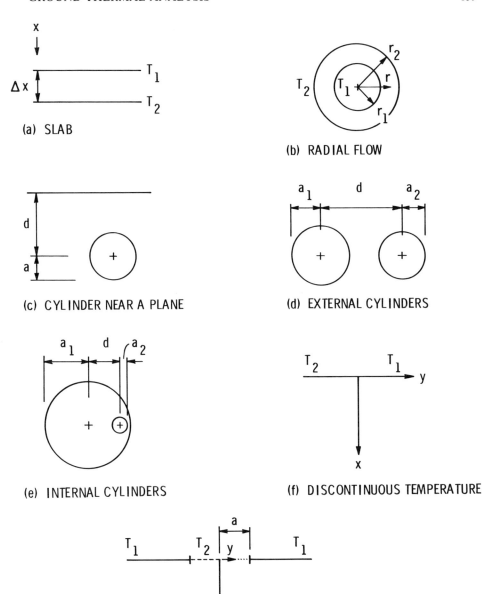

FIG. 4.4   Geometries considered for temperature and thermal resistance—Equations 4.7 to 4.20.

4.3.2 Analytical Solutions for Time-Dependent Problems Without Latent Heat

Ground temperatures fluctuate daily and seasonally in response to the weather. In addition, long-term transient changes may be induced by man. When a building, road or airstrip is constructed, for example, mean annual temperatures in the ground beneath will adjust to new equilibrium values as a result of the conditions imposed at the ground surface. Thermal design must therefore ensure that such changes will not lead to unacceptable foundation conditions and, in particular, that long-term thawing of ice-rich frozen ground will not occur.

Transient disturbances at depth are induced during freeze-back of foundation piles, during drilling operations and as a result of operating oil, gas and even water wells. Construction and operation of oil or gas pipelines causes long-term transient changes, due to thermal disturbance at and below the ground surface. For heated or chilled lines it may also be necessary to consider ground and pipe movements associated with thaw settlement or frost heaving in addition to calculating rates of advance of the thaw or frost bulb. Time-dependent behaviour is fundamental to all the above problems, and steady state formulae, if they can be applied at all, provide only a very general description. As with steady state problems, simple closed form solutions can be given for only the simplest cases. Nevertheless, these formulae can provide general guidance for design purposes and indicate some of the main features of the ground thermal regime.

For undisturbed conditions, the surface thermal regime will be similar from one year to the next. If there is no freezing or thawing and thermal properties are constant, then ground temperatures can be described approximately by the periodic steady state solution for one-dimensional heat flow in a semi-infinite homogeneous medium:

$$T(x,t) = \bar{T} + A \exp\left(-x\sqrt{\frac{\omega}{2\alpha}}\right) \cos\left(\omega t - x\sqrt{\frac{\omega}{2\alpha}}\right) \quad (4.21)$$

where $\bar{T}$ is the mean annual temperature, A the temperature amplitude at the surface, ω the angular frequency (equal to $2\pi/$period) and α the thermal diffusivity. The nature of annual ground temperature variations calculated using this equation is shown in Fig. 4.5. These curves are for a material containing no moisture and can be compared with those shown in Fig. 4.1, which take freezing and thawing and the effect of latent heat into account. In Eq. 4.21 the periodic surface temperature is assumed to be

$$T(o,t) = \bar{T} + A \cos(\omega t) \quad (4.22)$$

This may not be appropriate when, for example, the surface is snow covered. In such cases an arbitrary surface temperature variation represented by

$$T(o,t) = \bar{T} + \sum_{n=1}^{\infty} A_n \cos(n\omega t) \quad (4.23)$$

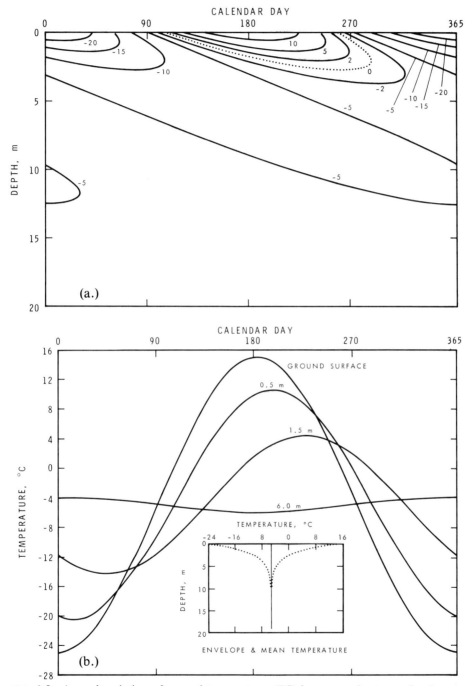

FIG. 4.5   Annual variation of ground temperatures (°C) in a permafrost area for dry soil.

can be used, and the corresponding temperature behaviour at depth is

$$T(x,t) = \bar{T} + \sum_{n=1}^{\infty} A_n \exp\left(-x\sqrt{\frac{n\omega}{2\alpha}}\right) \cos\left(n\omega t - x\sqrt{\frac{n\omega}{2\alpha}}\right) \quad (4.24)$$

Eq. 4.24 is frequently used as a basis for estimating the thermal diffusivity of the ground (for example, Gold 1964). Extension of the method to include cases where the thermal diffusivity is depth-dependent is given, with examples, by Lettau (1954).

The transient response of a one-dimensional semi-infinite homogeneous medium, initially at temperature T_o throughout, and whose surface temperature is suddenly changed to a new value T_1 is given by

$$T(x,t) = T_o + T_1 \, \text{erfc}\left(\frac{x}{2\sqrt{\alpha t}}\right) \quad (4.25)$$

where erfc is the complementary error function. Carslaw and Jaeger (1959) include tables for this and many other functions needed for heat flow analysis. Eq. 4.25 describes approximately the long-term transient response of the ground when surface temperatures are changed; for example, by the construction of roads or buildings or by flooding of land areas. The formula is applicable at distances far enough removed from boundaries so that vertical heat flow is predominant.

The temperature distribution around a line heat source of constant power P per unit length, embedded in an infinite homogeneous medium initially at uniform temperature T_o throughout is given by

$$T(r,t) = T_o + \frac{P}{4\pi k} \int_{r^2/4\alpha t}^{\infty} \frac{e^{-u}}{u} \, du \quad (4.26)$$

which, for $r^2/4\alpha t \ll 1$, can be approximated by

$$T(r,t) = T_o + \frac{P}{4\pi k}\left(\ln t + \ln \frac{4\alpha}{r^2} - \gamma + \text{-------}\right) \quad (4.27)$$

where γ is Euler's constant ≈ 0.5772. Eq. 4.27 forms the basis of the transient probe method for measuring the thermal conductivity of materials (Section 5.5.4). Wechsler (1966) discusses the use of these devices and provides a comprehensive literature review. Lachenbruch and Brewer (1959) apply Eq. 4.27 to estimate the rate of dissipation of the thermal disturbance caused by drilling in permafrost and describe the conditions under which the formula is suitable.

For problems only slightly more complex than those just discussed, analytical methods lead to solutions that cannot be expressed in a simple closed form based on elementary functions. Instead, solutions will be in the form of infinite series involving special functions. Evaluation of the series requires finding the roots of an additional auxiliary equation. For most cases, this is best done numerically with the results presented as a nomograph in terms of dimensionless parameters. Many such solutions are given by Carslaw and Jaeger (1959).

By superposition of solutions similar to Eq. 4.21, with additional terms to account for initial transient behaviour, Lachenbruch (1957c) presented expressions for a "heated building problem." The solution gives the three-dimensional time-dependent temperature distribution in the ground beneath an arbitrarily shaped ground surface region whose temperature differs from that of the surrounding surface. The ground is assumed to be homogeneous and phase change is ignored. Although a solution can be obtained by graphical superposition in steady state cases, the effort required for time-dependent problems is prohibitive and Brown (1962) developed a computer program for numerical evaluation. Using it, Brown et al. (1964) compare calculated with observed temperatures under and adjacent to a lake in the Mackenzie Delta.

Practical solutions can be given for only a few cases when time-dependent problems involve layers of different materials. Lachenbruch (1959) presents results for the periodic steady state regime in a semi-infinite material with thermal constants k_1, C_1 overlain by a second material with thermal constants k_2, C_2. Expressions are also derived for a similar problem involving three separate layers.

For the two-layer problem the maximum and minimum values of the interface temperature are given by

$$T(d) = \bar{T} \pm A \left(\frac{1 + M}{\sqrt{S}}\right) \qquad (4.28)$$

where $\bar{T}$ is the mean annual temperature, A is the sinusoidal surface temperature amplitude, $M = (\sqrt{k_1 C_1} - \sqrt{k_2 C_2})/(\sqrt{k_1 C_1} + \sqrt{k_2 C_2})$ and $S = e^{2W} + 2M \cos 2W + M^2 e^{-2W}$, where $W = d\sqrt{\frac{\omega}{2\alpha_1}}$, d is the thickness of layer 1, ω is the angular frequency and $\alpha_1 = k_1/C_1$. Eq. 4.28 can be used to estimate the thickness of fill required to prevent thaw penetration into a frozen subgrade. A nomograph for solution evaluation is given by Lachenbruch (1959). Since phase change in the fill material is ignored, the solution will tend to overestimate the thickness required. Using a trial and error technique to correct for the effect of latent heat, Lachenbruch calculated corrections in the order of 20% for a typical (dry) gravel fill (w = 2%) in conditions appropriate to interior Alaska. The magnitude of the correction increases with increasing moisture content and for the usual range of moisture contents the calculation methods discussed in the next section are more appropriate.

Stephenson (1977b) derives a formula to determine the interface temperature when the surface temperature changes linearly with time and presents approximate results for the two-layer transient problem. The expression is used to estimate the amount of insulation (dry straw) required to keep the ground from freezing.

4.3.3 Freezing and Thawing Problems

One of the ground thermal problems most frequently encountered in design is that of estimating the depth of frost X_f or thaw X_t penetration in embankments or under engineering structures. A good first approximation to one-dimensional freezing is provided by the Stefan formula, which assumes a material initially isothermal at the freezing point T_f, whose surface temperature is suddenly lowered to a freezing value $T_s < T_f$. Ignoring heat flow from the underlying thawed material, which is assumed to remain at the freezing point, the boundary condition at the freezing front (Eq. 4.3) becomes

$$L\frac{dX_f}{dt} = F_- = -k_f \frac{\delta T}{\delta x}\bigg]_{x = X_f} \tag{4.29}$$

If the temperature profile in the frozen zone is assumed to be linear (quasi-steady state assumption), Eq. 4.29 becomes

$$L\frac{dX_f}{dx} = \frac{k_f(T_s - T_f)}{X_f} \tag{4.30}$$

Integrating, Eq. 4.30 becomes

$$X_f = \sqrt{\frac{2k_f}{L}(T_f - T_s)t} \tag{4.31}$$

where X_f is the frost depth at time t, k_f the thermal conductivity of the frozen material and L the volumetric latent heat. In the Stefan formula, both the heat capacity of the frozen layer and heat flow from the underlying thawed zone are neglected. Since both quantities act to retard penetration of the freezing or thawing plane, the Stefan equation will overestimate frost or thaw penetration depths.

The Neumann formula provides an exact solution for determining the depth of freeze or thaw. The problem described is similar to that of Stefan, except that the material is assumed to be initially isothermal at some temperature $T_o > T_f$. All the moisture is assumed to freeze entirely at temperature T_f and the thermal properties to change abruptly from thawed to frozen values at the freezing plane. The Neumann formulation leads to

$$X_f = a\sqrt{t} \tag{4.32}$$

where the parameter a is determined from the equation

$$\frac{\sqrt{\pi L}}{2}a = \frac{\sqrt{k_f C_f}\,(T_f - T_s)e^{-a^2/4\alpha f}}{\mathrm{erf}\left(\dfrac{a}{2\sqrt{\alpha_f}}\right)} \\ - \frac{\sqrt{k_t C_t}(T_o - T_f)e^{-a^2/4\alpha t}}{1 - \mathrm{erf}\left(\dfrac{a}{2\sqrt{\alpha_t}}\right)} \tag{4.33}$$

To apply these solutions to practical field cases where the surface temperature varies, the average surface temperature for the freezing period is used for T_s and

T_o is taken as the mean annual air or ground temperature $\bar{T}$. With these assumptions, Eq. 4.33 is referred to as the Berggren equation. The average surface temperature is estimated from the air temperature freezing index using an n-factor correction as discussed in Section 4.2. Using formulae from Kersten (1949) to determine soil thermal properties and empirical data to relate freezing index to mean annual temperature, Brown, W. G. (1964) evaluated Eq. 4.33 and concluded that, for a given value of soil surface freezing index, frost penetration in mineral soils will vary by not more than a factor of 2 for the range of soil moisture and densities normally encountered in the field.

Using the average of frozen and thawed values for the thermal properties and defining three dimensionless parameters, the "thermal ratio," β, the "fusion parameter," μ, and the coefficient "λ", as follows:

$$\beta = \frac{\bar{T}-T_f}{T_f-T_s} = \frac{(\bar{T}-T_f)t}{I_{sf}} \tag{4.34}$$

$$\mu = \frac{C(T_f-T_s)}{L} = \frac{CI_{sf}}{Lt} \tag{4.35}$$

$$\lambda = a\sqrt{\frac{L}{k(T_f-T_s)}} \tag{4.36}$$

where t is the duration of the freezing season, Eq. 4.33 can be rewritten in the dimensionless form:

$$\sqrt{\pi}\,\frac{\sqrt{\mu}}{2}\,\lambda = \mu\left[\frac{1}{\mathrm{erf}\left(\frac{\sqrt{\mu}}{2}\lambda\right)} - \frac{\beta}{1-\mathrm{erf}\left(\frac{\sqrt{\mu}}{2}\lambda\right)}\right]e^{-\frac{\mu\lambda^2}{4}} \tag{4.37}$$

and Eq. 4.32 becomes

$$X_f = \lambda\sqrt{\frac{2k}{L}\cdot I_{sf}} \tag{4.38}$$

which is the equation recommended by Aldrich and Paynter (Aldrich 1956) and referred to as the "modified Berggren" equation. This and other modified versions of the Neumann formula are compared and various empirical formulae are given, together with an extensive bibliography, in a detailed review by Moulton (1969).

The modified Berggren equation is, except for the multiplying parameter λ, the same as the Stefan equation (Eq. 4.31). The relationship between the coefficient λ and the parameters β and μ of Eq. 4.37 is shown in Fig. 4.6. The coefficient λ is seen to be always less than unity and becomes smaller for increasing values of the fusion parameter or thermal ratio. For the climatic conditions of southern Canada (Ottawa), β based on air temperatures is about 0.7 or less while μ ranges from about 0.08 for a typical fine-grained soil (w = 30%, density 1.4 t/m³) to

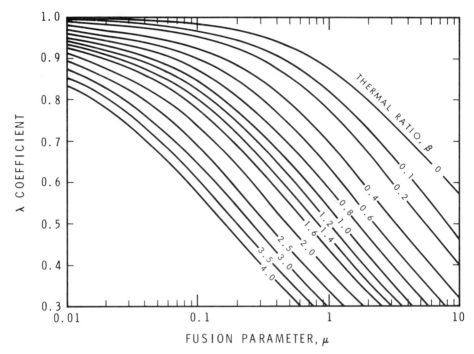

FUSION PARAMETER, μ

FIG. 4.6 λ coefficient for the modified Berggren equation (After U.S. Army/Air Force 1966c).

0.18 for coarse-grained soil (w = 5%, density 1.8 t/m³). Using Fig. 4.6 this implies that $\lambda \geq 0.88$.

For seasonal thawing problems, Eqs. 4.34 and 4.35 must be suitably redefined in terms of the thawing index:

$$\beta = \frac{(T_f - \bar{T})t}{I_{st}} \tag{4.39}$$

$$\mu = \frac{C\,I_{st}}{Lt} \tag{4.40}$$

where t is now the duration of the thawing season. For typical northern conditions (Mackenzie Delta area) the thermal ratio β based on air temperatures is about 1.0 while the fusion parameter μ ranges from 0.1 for fine-grained soils to 0.23 for coarse-grained soils. This corresponds to $\lambda \geq 0.78$. Frost or thaw penetration depths calculated using the simpler Stefan formula (Eq. 4.31) in the above examples would be, even in the worst case, about 20% greater than those obtained from the modified Berggren.

Surface freezing and thawing indices cannot generally be estimated with great accuracy owing to uncertainty in the n-factor. This alone will contribute to an uncertainty in the frost or thaw penetration depth of about 25 to 30%. When either the Neumann or the modified Berggren formula is used, the ground is assumed to be initially at the same temperature throughout, whereas under field conditions, ground temperatures at the beginning of the freezing or thawing season may be far from isothermal, particularly at shallow depths. In practice the initial temperature T_o is usually equated to the mean annual air temperature but the mean annual ground temperature may be several degrees warmer. In nature, surface temperatures vary periodically and the use of seasonal average freezing or thawing indices leads to some error. If the periodic boundary condition is fully accounted for, the T_f isotherm will be found to retreat slightly during the latter part of the freeze or thaw season, as shown in Fig. 4.1(a). Although freezing and thawing with periodic boundary conditions can be treated analytically (Lock et al. 1969), the additional calculation required is not justified for design purposes.

All three analytic formulae, the Stefan, the Neumann and the modified Berggren, assume that the phase change occurs at a single temperature, whereas in fact latent heat is released over a temperature range which may amount to several degrees in the case of fine-grained soils. If the freezing range is accounted for, then frost penetration will be increased while thaw penetration will be decreased. Nixon and McRoberts (1973) present calculations for the thawing case. Both freezing and thawing are examined by Kudryavtsev (1977) who suggests differences of as much as 25% for typical cases when comparisons are made with and without a freezing range. These estimates may be exaggerated since the competing effect of temperature-dependent thermal conductivity in the partially frozen soil was not taken into account. None of the formulae account for the effects of moisture changes nor ground movements due to frost heaving or thaw settlement and this restricts their validity when applied to real soils.

When all these difficulties are considered, it appears that more elaborate calculations do not necessarily lead to more reliable results. The simple Stefan formula is adequate except for the driest soil conditions and where the seasonal average surface temperature is close to the freezing point while temperatures at depth are quite different from it. The Stefan formula may even be preferred for design purposes since it overestimates frost or thaw penetration depth and is therefore conservative.

Problems involving layered systems arise frequently, for example, in the design of embankments for roads and airstrips. An approximate solution for these cases requires following the progress of the freezing (thawing) plane through successive layers, adjusting the thermal resistance between the surface and the freezing (thawing) front as additional layers change phase, and at the same time using the soil latent heat appropriate to the layer currently being frozen or thawed.

The following example of thawing in a two-layer system will illustrate the method. Assume material properties k_1, L_1 in the upper layer of thickness x_1, and k_2, L_2 in the lower layer. Using the Stefan assumptions, when the thaw plane penetrates into layer 2 the boundary condition described by Eq. 4.3 becomes

$$L_2 \frac{dx_2}{dt} = F = \text{heat flux in from the surface} \qquad (4.41)$$

where x_2 is the distance of the thaw plane below the material interface with layer 1. Since the thermal resistances of the layers are in series, the heat flux in from the surface is given approximately by

$$F = -k_2 \frac{\partial T}{\partial x_2} \approx \frac{T_s - T_f}{(x_2/k_2) + (x_1/k_1)} \qquad (4.42)$$

Combining Eqs. 4.41 and 4.42 gives

$$\left(\frac{x_2}{k_2} + \frac{x_1}{k_1} \right) dx_2 = \left(\frac{T_s - T_f}{L_2} \right) dt \qquad (4.43)$$

which, upon integration, gives

$$\frac{x_2^2}{2k_2} + \frac{x_1 x_2}{k_1} = \left(\frac{T_s - T_f}{L_2} \right) t_2 \qquad (4.44)$$

where t_2 is the time elapsed since the thaw plane entered layer 2. Solving Eq. 4.44 gives

$$x_2 = k_2 \left[\frac{x_1}{k_1} \pm \sqrt{\left(\frac{x_1}{k_1} \right)^2 + \frac{2(T_s - T_f)t_2}{k_2 L_2}} \right] \qquad (4.45)$$

This equation can be extended to an arbitrary number of layers by simply replacing the term x_1/k_1 by the total resistance of all layers above the current one. Also, by introducing a partial thawing index $I_i = (T_s - T_f)t_i$ for the ith layer, then when the thawing plane is within the layer n

$$x_n = k_n \left(R_{n-1} \pm \sqrt{R_{n-1}^2 + \frac{2 I_n}{k_n L_n}} \right) \qquad (4.46)$$

where R_{n-1} is $\sum_{i=1}^{n-1} \frac{x_i}{k_i}$. The unexpended number of degree-days available for thawing layer n is computed as the difference between the total thawing index for the season I_{st} and the sum of the partial indices required to thaw completely all the layers above layer n

$$I_n = I_{st} - \sum_{i=1}^{n-1} I_i \qquad (4.47)$$

where

$$I_i = L_i \left(\frac{x_i}{2k_i} + R_{i-1} \right) \qquad (4.48)$$

The applications of these formulae to road and airstrip pavement design are given in U.S. Army/Air Force (1966c).

The effects of heat capacity can be accounted for approximately by introducing a coefficient λ as in the modified Berggren equation (Sanger 1966, Jumikis 1977). The thermal ratio β is assumed constant while the fusion parameter μ is evaluated for each additional thawed layer using average values of heat capacity and latent heat weighted for layer thickness, and assuming that the appropriate temperature is represented by the surface temperature.

For embankment problems involving a dry layer, both the Stefan and modified Berggren equations imply that this layer will freeze or thaw instantaneously. This approximation is appropriate for a concrete or asphalt surface layer, but is not acceptable for problems involving a layer of insulation placed below the surface. In such a case, thaw or frost penetration within or below the insulating layer is significantly retarded by heat flow to or from the underlying soil. These problems are readily treated by numerical methods.

Two- or three-dimensional freezing or thawing problems arise in the thermal design of pipelines, building foundations, dams on permafrost, pile foundations, well drilling and production operations and in many other situations. Exact analytical solutions cannot be given but approximate solutions are possible for those cases where the geometry is sufficiently simple. The quasi-steady assumption (neglecting heat capacity) is usually made and the material is assumed to be homogeneous. A computer is frequently required for final evaluation. Dyer and Sunderland (1971), Rathjen and Jiji (1971), Budhia and Kreith (1973), Habib (1973) and Pedroso and Domoto (1973) illustrate some of the techniques used.

These methods all lead to formulae that give the position of the freezing or thawing interface throughout the entire problem space. Often the engineer is only concerned with knowing whether the frost or thaw interface will penetrate certain subregions and useful results can be calculated from more restricted but simpler formulae. Porkhaev (1966) gives approximate results for thawing under the centreline of a long, narrow, heated strip, under the centre of a heated rectangular area and beneath a heated tube such as a pipeline. Using somewhat different approximations, Thornton (1976) developed a formula for estimating the thaw bulb radius around a heated pipeline. A similar problem is considered by Lunardini (1977). Thornton's method is applicable to both bare and insulated pipes. Hwang (1977a) compares Porkhaev's and Thornton's formulae with results from finite element and finite difference calculations and suggests a correction to improve the accuracy of estimates made with Porkhaev's formulae. Other approximate formulae by Thornton are given in Section 10.3.3. Fryer (1970) applied a simplified quasi-steady analysis to estimate the time of freeze-up of buried water and sewer lines and gives several formulae and graphs that are useful for design purposes.

4.4 Numerical Methods for Conductive Heat Flow

Although analytical methods may be effective in providing rapid answers in simple cases, frequently it is necessary to consider problems involving a great deal more physical detail than that which can be readily treated analytically. The usual range of geotechnical problems involves layered systems with latent heat, temperature-dependent thermal properties and time-dependent boundary conditions. In many cases it is essential to consider two- and occasionally three-dimensional heat flow. Numerical methods are capable of handling most of these complexities with relative ease. In addition these methods are very flexible and, once established, the same program can be used to treat a range of problems without the need to devise a new solution for each case.

The most widely used numerical techniques are the finite difference and the finite element methods. Myers (1971) describes both techniques in detail as they apply to heat transfer problems and gives much practical information as well as extensive references. A brief review of numerical methods applied to ground temperature problems is given by Goodrich (1973).

4.4.1 Applications of Numerical Methods for Conductive Heat Flow to Ground Thermal Analysis

Dempsey and Thompson (1970) present a one-dimensional heat transfer model and compare predicted values with field measurements made under the centreline of a paved, multilayered road embankment. The model uses a heat balance to establish the surface boundary condition. Latent heat is treated as an apparent heat capacity. The time-stepping scheme used makes the model relatively expensive to operate. Goodrich (1976) describes an efficient one-dimensional model to simulate the natural ground thermal regime and discusses the reliability of heat balance methods for estimating surface boundary conditions. A snow cover simulation model is developed and the combined snow/soil model is used to study the long-term influence of snow cover on the ground thermal regime. A summary of results of this work is given by Goodrich (1978). Ho et al. (1970) present a one-dimensional model for road embankment simulations. The model is similar to that of Dempsey and Thompson (1970), but uses prescribed temperatures rather than surface heat balance to establish the surface boundary conditions.

Nakano and Brown (1972) compare field measurements in natural tundra terrain with computer simulations made using a one-dimensional numerical model described in Nakano and Brown (1971). The model results are compared with temperature observations made during the summer at depths within and just below the active layer in soil with a thin organic cover at Barrow, Alaska. Agreement was satisfactory for daily values but the model was less successful in simulating diurnal variations in the first few centimetres. A natural thermal regime model using heat balance formulae to represent the surface boundary condition is described by Outcalt (1972). Its application to the simulation of snow melt and the soil thermal regime at Barrow, Alaska is described by Outcalt et al. (1975). Smith (1975b) compared predictions made using this model with field data from Eureka, N.W.T. Additional model comparisons with field data are given by Smith (1977). Smith and Tvede (1977) propose application of a similar model to simulate frost penetration in highway embankments.

Calculations of the thawing around a hot oil pipeline buried at shallow depths in permafrost are described by Lachenbruch (1970) and Gold et al. (1972). These analyses were done using the simplified two-dimensional finite difference scheme of Doherty (1970). The calculations ignore the effects of settlement of the pipe during thawing. Hwang et al. (1972) and Wheeler (1973) present results for the same problem based on a more elaborate finite element scheme. Mohan (1973) uses a finite element analysis for pipeline problems that is essentially identical to that of Hwang et al. (1972).

Thawing of permafrost around gas and oil wells caused by drilling and production operations has been studied using two-dimensional finite difference models by Couch et al. (1970) and Kazemi and Perkins (1971). In this case, useful approximate results may be obtained with one-dimensional models, since the heat flow is predominantly radial (Eikmeier et al. 1970). Lin and Wheeler (1978) apply a two-dimensional finite element model (Wheeler 1973) to simulate thawing of permafrost around oil wells at Prudhoe Bay, Alaska. The analysis simulates conditions during drilling, production and freeze-back for different well geometries and completion schemes. Computed results are shown to compare satisfactorily with field measurements of well temperatures and thawing radius in the surrounding permafrost. Results of a similar study for drilling conditions in the Mackenzie Delta are given by Pui and Kljucec (1977). The range of problems that can be treated with conductive heat transfer numerical models is very broad and the above examples represent only a few of the applications of interest to permafrost engineering.

4.5 Application of Numerical Methods to More Complex Problems

An analysis based on pure conductive heat flow, including the latent heat of freezing and thawing, is adequate for the majority of engineering ground thermal calculations. In the design of embankments and foundations, changes in geometry caused by ground movements resulting from frost heaving and thaw settlement are usually not taken into account in the thermal calculations. This is acceptable since the main purpose of the calculations is to achieve a design which will avoid, or at least reduce, potential heaving or thaw settlement to tolerable amounts.

In the case of a hot oil pipeline buried in frozen ground, however, thawing and subsequent settlement of ice-rich materials is usually unavoidable. Not only does settlement of the pipe modify the thermal picture but, in addition, estimating the amount of settlement becomes in itself a major design problem. Hwang (1976) describes a two-dimensional model that allows for thaw settlement and uses heat balance boundary conditions. Satisfactory agreement was found when model predictions were compared with field data from a test hot pipeline at Norman Wells, N.W.T. The model assumes that thaw settlement can be determined from excess ice contents alone but does not account for the effects of thaw consolidation. Its use is limited to cases where the pipeline causes moderate thermal disturbance. This assumption is appropriate for a warm gas pipeline but for a hot oil pipeline thaw rates are much more rapid and the process of consolidation must be taken into account.

Thaw consolidation is examined numerically in a one-dimensional theoretical model by Charlwood and Svec (1972). A two-dimensional finite element model for the filtration consolidation of thawing permafrost, described by Sykes et al. (1974a), is used to calculate temperature, pore pressure and settlement changes as a function of time for a hot oil pipeline buried in permafrost (Sykes et al. 1974b). A more complex model that accounts for nonlinear stress-strain relations is described by Sykes and Lennox (1976). Approximate analytical methods for estimating thaw settlements have also been developed and are discussed in Section 3.7.

Frost heaving becomes a major consideration for chilled gas pipelines passing through frozen and unfrozen areas in the discontinuous permafrost zone. Simplified frost heaving models have been tentatively proposed and compared with laboratory measurements. Harlan (1973) describes a finite difference model based on an analogy between the mechanisms of water transport in partially frozen soils and those in unsaturated soils. This analogy leads to a relatively simple formulation requiring the simultaneous solution of both heat and mass transport equations. A similar model using the finite element method is described by Guymon and Luthin (1974). Additional details including model improvements are given by Guymon and Berg (1976) and Berg et al. (1977). Refinements of Harlan's model are described by Taylor and Luthin (1976). Other similar models are described by Outcalt and Carlson (1975), Outcalt (1976, 1977), Kay et al. (1977) and Sheppard et al. (1978).

All the models just mentioned are essentially phenomenological. Bresler and Miller (1975) and Miller (1978), however, present a model that attempts to describe more fully the basic physics of the ice lensing process. At present, however, all these models are primarily research tools whose purpose is to improve understanding of frost heaving. No model has yet been developed that allows practical prediction of frost heave in field situations. It may be that estimates of the maximum and minimum heaving expected will prove adequate for design purposes. Simplified analytical calculations leading to maximum and minimum values for heaving around a chilled gas pipeline are given by Hwang (1977b).

CHAPTER 5

Site and Route Studies

(Contributors–J. M. Hunter, G. H. Johnston, J. D. Mollard,
N. R. Morgenstern and W. J. Scott)

The importance of proper selection and investigation of sites and routes in permafrost areas cannot be overemphasized. Reconnaissance and detailed site and route studies must be made, and environmental considerations and the availability of construction materials must be taken into account. Increased costs of construction, operation and maintenance, as well as unsatisfactory performance of engineering structures, inevitably result when there is a lack of information on permafrost conditions and other terrain factors (Brown 1970a).

5.1 Project Planning

Adequate information must be gathered during carefully planned office and field studies so that the best available site or route is selected, the most suitable foundation designs and construction methods used, and a practical work schedule established (Johnston 1966a). In addition to the vagaries of the distribution of permafrost and particularly of ground ice, severe problems are imposed by cold climate, remoteness and difficult access. Moreover, it has been mandatory in the last few years, when making major project assessments, to evaluate environmental and social concerns in addition to the more obvious terrain and geotechnical aspects. For a route study all of these considerations may be indicated on a map depicting a wide corridor. This is often done before commencing selection and detailed study of a route along a much narrower corridor.

The scope of office and field investigations depends on the type of project, its geographical location and the amount of information that is already available. The investigations required to locate a road or railway hundreds of miles long over highly variable terrain, with few or no reliable data, are far different from those required for the siting of a building in a subarctic town or an arctic village. Although considerable latitude may exist in the location requirements for some projects (such as highways and railways), for others (such as mines, communication towers and pipeline pumping stations) the location may be either predetermined or fixed within narrow limits regardless of terrain conditions. In addition, different types of structures may require different types of foundations, as well as different sizes and shapes of construction areas.

Another important consideration is the effect that a proposed new structure will have on an existing adjacent one; for instance where a heated building is placed next to an unheated building, or a hot oil pipeline is built next to a highway or railway. The environmental impact of alternative methods of construction must also be critically compared and evaluated before making the final selection of a site or route in permafrost regions.

Factors that should be considered during the planning stage of engineering projects are set out in Table 5.1. A great deal of information is now available from government agencies and universities that have conducted intensive scientific and

TABLE 5.1

Project Planning Considerations

A. *Type of Project*
   (1) *Linear*
       Highway
       Railway
       Pipeline
       Power line

   (2) *Areal*
       Townsite
       Airport
       Dam, dyke
       Tank farm
       Borrow pit

   (3) *Individual Structures*
       Building
       Tower
       Bridge, wharf
       Stockpile

B. *Project Information Required*
   Size and location
   Natural physical conditions
   Magnitude and type of loading
   Design life (temporary or permanent)
   Tolerance of movement (total and differential)
   Ancillary works or structures
   Cost and time limitations

C. *Site or Route Information Required*
   (1) *Terrain*
       (a) *Relief*
           Topography
           Slope (degree and
             orientation)
           Features
           Vegetation cover
       (b) *Hydrology*
           Drainage (surface
             and subsurface)
           Water bodies
           Groundwater
           Stream flow
           Flooding
           Ice jams
           Icing
       (c) *Geology and Soils*
           Surface and subsurface
             geology
           Ground ice
           Thermal regime
             (temperature profiles)
           Engineering properties
             (soil and rock)
           Construction materials

   (2) *Climate*
       Temperature
       Precipitation
       Wind
       Snow drifting

   (3) *Environmental—Social Impact*
       Land, water, air, noise
       Wildlife (animals, fish, birds)
       Local people

   (4) *Logistics*
       Project scheduling
       Transportation
         facilities
       Access to and on
         site/route
       Summer and winter
         roads
       Local labour,
         materials and equipment
         available
       Equipment and
         transport costs

   (5) *Economics*
       Time and money available

technical studies in the North. Many private organizations have published results of detailed investigations of northern conditions carried out for various development programs. All potential sources of assistance, including local experience, should be checked for possible usable information on climate, topography, hydrology, geology (surficial as well as bedrock), geomorphology, vegetation, wildlife habitats, land use and population (social aspects), permafrost, construction effects and performance of existing man-made structures.

Careful scheduling and coordination of field and office studies are essential. Usually the appraisal of information available from existing maps and reports, and an evaluation of topography, terrain and hydrology interpreted from airphotos and other remotely sensed images, is followed by aerial and ground reconnaissance surveys. Such surveys are made to check the accuracy of previously collected information and to obtain the additional facts needed to compare sites or routes and select the best one. Reconnaissance data are also used to plan further site exploration programs.

Preliminary study of a site includes observation of as many as possible of the factors listed in Table 5.1 and steps to collect information on the other factors as required for the particular project. For this purpose, weather observations and hydrological measurements may be initiated. General geotechnical data and samples of soil, rock and ground ice are obtained, ground temperature measuring devices and other instrumentation installed and various types of field tests conducted. Decisions on design and construction are made after all information from office, field and laboratory studies has been assembled and assessed. A general sequence of carrying out these studies is given in Fig. 5.1.

The scheduling of field operations is highly important. Some field work is best carried out during the winter, when access is better and less environmental damage will be done when the ground is frozen. Snow cover may, however, prevent accurate identification of surface features and, together with low temperatures, hinder the selection of sites for future detailed field work and the acquisition of critical subsurface information. Visual observations and assessments of terrain conditions are usually best made during the spring, summer and fall. To evaluate the many significant factors that should be considered, field studies should preferably be conducted during all seasons of the year.

To make the necessary terrain analyses and to obtain surface and subsurface data required for engineering design and decisions regarding construction, several investigational tools and techniques are used. They fall conveniently into two categories: indirect, including the evaluation of published information and the interpretation of airphotos and geophysical records; and direct, including drilling, sampling and laboratory testing.

5.2 Terrain Evaluation Considerations

Many factors must be kept in mind when making a preliminary evaluation of terrain for an engineering project dealing with a route or site in permafrost terrain.

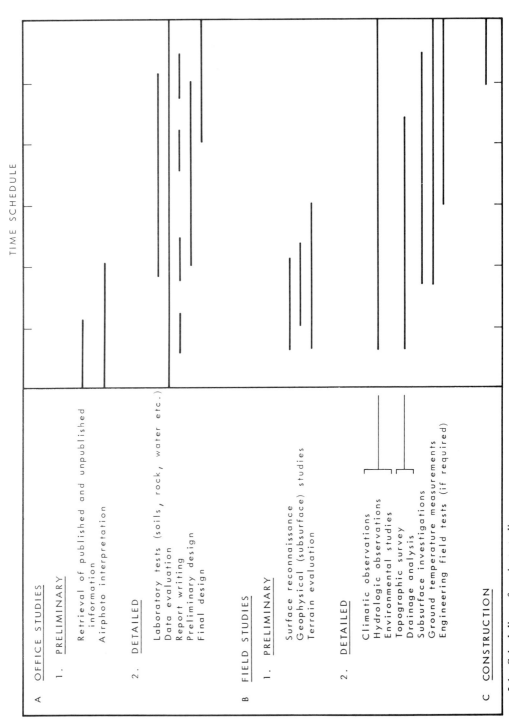

FIG. 5.1   Scheduling of project studies.

No site or route studies in permafrost areas should be undertaken without a thorough appreciation of the surficial geology, geomorphology and hydrology of the area to be investigated and an understanding of the engineering and terrain problems that are unique to permafrost (Mollard 1960, 1968, 1972, Mollard and Pihlainen 1966, Harwood 1966, U.S. Army 1966, Johnston 1969, Brown 1970a, Fuller 1971, Kachadoorian and Ferrians 1973, Linell and Johnston 1973).

Many engineering, construction and environmental-social considerations can be inferred from observations on the terrain along a proposed route right-of-way. Each consideration can be classified, usually in relative terms, and shown along with the terrain records on preliminary plans. Such qualitative assessments or ratings may include evaluations of stream crossing width and water depth, evidence of flooding, indications of active shifting or downcutting of a channel, signs of bank instability and erosion, bed load and suspended sediment, the locations of ice jams and icings, surface and subsurface run-off parallel and perpendicular to the route alignment, spring run-off and its effects, intermittent versus continuous water flows, groundwater drainage in the active layer and drainage and erosion control measures. The distribution and depth of snow cover, snowpatch erosion, snow drifting patterns and places where snow will probably accumulate to great depth should be noted. Sites where frost heave, thaw settlement and thermal erosion problems may arise and the stability of old and recently failed slopes, as well as potentially unstable slopes, can also be evaluated.

The type and availability of construction materials (suitable and accessible timber, sand and gravel aggregates and bedrock materials), the location of material stockpiles and borrow pits and excavation characteristics of borrow materials (by scraper, ripping, blasting) can be noted. Right-of-way trafficability by different types of vehicles, the amount and type of clearing and grubbing required, preferred construction season (if any) and possible construction procedures can be assessed. Also of importance are terrain sensitivity to a given kind and level of man-made disturbance and environmental and social concerns that may arise from disturbance of mammal, bird and fish habitats and disturbance of traditional hunting and trapping areas.

Ground relief is important and varies with the type of project. A transmission line may be built over highly irregular topography that is unsuitable for a road or a pipeline, but a route that is satisfactory for a road or a pipeline may be unsuitable for a railway, which requires low gradients. Topography is generally more important in permafrost terrain than in areas free of permafrost, due to sloughing of thaw-unstable cut and fill slopes in the warm season, problems associated with the excavation of frozen ground and the generally high cost of earthwork. Route selection in permafrost areas is usually based on a search for the shortest distance that combines smooth, gentle longitudinal slopes with minimum sidehill location, the absence of steep-sided valleys and scarps and a minimum number of river crossings. More stable ground conditions are generally associated with dry and low-angle longitudinal and sidehill slopes.

All landforms containing stratified fine-grained sediments, with or without thermokarst depressions, should be avoided where possible. The more desirable locations for roads, pipelines, railways, airfields and new townsites will generally be found in landscapes underlain at shallow depth by smooth bedrock and in landforms composed of sand and gravel containing little or no excess ice (raised beach ridges, alluvial terraces, valley trains and outwash plains, eskers and crevasse fillings, and large kames, kame terraces and flat-topped kame deltas). Raised beach ridges, valley trains and end moraine ridges containing a high proportion of granular material may sometimes be followed in route location for distances ranging from 50 to 150 miles (80 to 240 km), except for short gaps which usually occur at drainage crossings.

Much of northern Canada is underlain by till, which occurs in a variety of landforms, and often cannot be avoided when new routes and sites are to be selected. Engineers prefer to locate routes and sites on certain types of these till landforms but not on others. Distinguishing and mapping them on airphotos can therefore be important. Lodgment (basal) till in fluted and drumlinized till plains and in undulating ground moraine may be only slightly less desirable for a route than certain glaciofluvial landforms. Below a thin (3 to 12 ft.; 1 to 4 m) weathered surficial layer, most lodgment tills generally have relatively little ice and high bulk densities. Generally, lodgment till contains substantially lower amounts of ground ice than ablation till in hummocky moraines where complex hydrologic, textural and topographic variations commonly produce equally complex and unpredictable patterns of ground ice.

Variations in the amount of ground ice that may be encountered in the different tills are closely associated with the mode of accumulation of materials laid down by glacier ice. Lodgment till was deposited beneath the ice while it was still actively flowing and is therefore more compact and less variable than the material in hummocky moraines. The latter is commonly composed of two types of ablation till: flow till, which consists of material that accumulated on the glacier surface and was subject to flow and deformation as a fluid mass, and underlying melt-out till, which consists of material in the ice that was deposited as stagnant ice slowly melted. Even in areas of fluted till plains and undulating ground moraines the route location engineer tries to avoid hollows that are poorly drained. The ice-rich peat, slopewash and ponded fine-grained organic sediments found in them commonly overlie 3 ft. (1 m) or so of weathered till having a high ice content, which in turn overlies unweathered till having a low ice content.

In summary, the terrain analyst working in permafrost regions should try to avoid:
   — thick, stratified, fine-grained deposits regardless of their mode of deposition, particularly in the continuous permafrost zone,
   — hummocky moraine possessing moderate to high relief,
   — poorly drained depressions in till plains,
   — frozen (as well as thawed) peatlands, including peat plateaus and palsas in the discontinuous zone, polygonal peat plateaus and palsas in the discontinuous zone and polygonal peat plateaus and peaty low centre polygons in the continuous zone,

TABLE 5.2

Favoured and Undesirable Landforms in Permafrost Regions
(Note: Favoured sites and routes depend on other factors besides landforms.)

Usually good (favoured) landforms

1) Smooth, low relief bedrock controlled terrain with or without a thin colluvial, residual or drift veneer

2) Long, wide, sandy and gravelly raised beach ridges

3) Well-drained, granular alluvial terraces

4) Smooth, low-relief sand and gravel landforms (outwash plains, valley trains, glacial deltas, elongated kame deltas and kame terraces)

5) Glacier-streamlined forms composed of compact till, such as drumlins and dumlinoid features

6) Well-drained end moraine ridges, which contain appreciable granular material and may run for long distances with only short gaps

7) Large eskers and crevasse fillings (sinuous, sub-linear and linear ridges)

8) Well-drained fluted till plains and low relief ground moraine containing unweathered lodgment till at relatively shallow (1 to 3 m) depths

9) Well-drained erosional terraces, where not dissected by ravines and small tributary valleys

10) Well-treed, higher, gravelly and sandy floodplains, which are rarely subject to flooding

11) Narrow, well-drained, densely wooded strips bordering the tops of creek and river banks and valley walls

12) Hard (*e.g.* Precambrian) bedrock for small building sites, even if the topography is somewhat irregular and requires blasting to level it

13) Large sand dunes (mostly transverse and longitudinal dunes, but including parabolic dunes in some areas)

Usually poor (undesirable) landforms

1) Glaciolacustrine and postglacial pond basins composed mostly of stratified silt, clay and fine sand; with or without a peat cover

2) Glaciomarine and postglacial marine plains composed mostly of stratified silt, clay and fine sand; with or without a peat cover

3) Hummocky moraines generally containing ice-rich permafrost in the continuous permafrost zone

4) Smoothly rounded, sloping colluvial and wind-laid landforms containing silt, pebbly silt and organic silt

5) Fluvial-lacustrine (deltaic) plains composed of stratified silt, clay and fine sand; often with a peat cover and widespread thermokarst features

6) Very rough rocky (bedrock, frost-shattered rubble) terrain, which requires expensive blasting or construction of thick fills to provide a level surface

7) All types of peatland (muskeg); includes bogs (peat plateaus, palsas, peat polygons), fens and transitional peatland types

8) Areas characterized by thermokarst depressions

9) All finely lined slopes having subparallel (feather, horsetail) drainage patterns, commonly on silty slopewash deposits in the continuous and widespread discontinuous permafrost zones

10) All slope failures (falls, flows, slides and creep), including talus and rock glaciers

11) Overbank (vertical accretion) floodplains, including backswamps and oxbows, in which a thick top stratum composed of organic silt and silty fine sand commonly overlies a coarser (granular) stratum at depth

12) Ice-cored, hummocky terrain in the Arctic Coastal Lowland, which may be pre-Classical Wisconsin in age

13) Fell fields (felsenmeer, block fields and rock streams), mostly at high altitudes in mountains or in the High Arctic

14) Permafrost and frost-action generated mounds; *e.g.* mudboils (non-sorted circles), cemetery mounds and pingos

15) Poorly drained ice wedge polygons, especially low centre polygons

— thermokarst terrain,

— pingos and cemetery mounds,

— highly irregular bedrock surfaces where excessive and costly rock blasting is required and

— frost-shattered bedrock, generally indicative of intensive frost action and possible large ice masses.

A more detailed list of unfavourable terrain features is given in Table 5.2. An attempt is always made to locate a route or site close to places where adequate quantities of gravel are available for use as fill, if this can be done without sacrificing other desirable aspects.

5.3 Terrain Analysis

Terrain analysis refers to the identification and interpretation of features on the earth's surface, taking into consideration the relationships among these features, the processes that created them and the materials of which they are composed (Mollard 1975). The main objectives of terrain analysis for engineering projects include the delineation of landforms and the recognition of surface materials, which in large measure determine the best locations for a new site or route, the identification of places where detailed field investigations are required, and a preliminary appraisal of the types of problems that are likely to be encountered. Terrain analysis may be carried out with and without airphoto study, but the use of airphotos is almost universal. Among the elements of a landscape studied in airphotos for terrain analysis are landform, drainage, erosion, tonal patterns of different soil and rock materials, vegetation and land use.

Airphoto analysis of terrain deals with the recognition of landforms and surface materials and conditions, whereas airphoto interpretation presupposes an understanding of their significance and implications for a particular engineering or construction project. The interpreter must therefore be able to recognize terrain features and know what to look for before he can intelligently appraise areas for sites or routes and plan further investigations.

Airphoto interpretation is only one of several tools used in the location and assessment of routes and sites in permafrost terrain, even though it is most important and helpful. Information contained in reports and maps that describe topography, engineering and agricultural soils, surficial or bedrock geology, hydrography, vegetation and land use will contribute to and improve the quality of an investigation. Information extracted from such maps and reports complements and supplements airphoto interpretation. Field investigations usually follow preliminary airphoto interpretation, permitting the airphotos to be reinterpreted following receipt of pertinent field and laboratory information on soil and rock materials.

5.3.1 Air Photographs and Other Remotely Sensed Images

The relative usefulness of air photographic and other images is indicated in Table 5.3. The application of various types of remote sensors to environmental studies

TABLE 5.3

Comparison of Imagery

Type of imagery and common scales	Applicability and relative usefulness for site and route studies in permafrost areas
High altitude black and white panchromatic photography. Common scales: 1:60,000 to 1:80,000	Very useful. Essential for almost all important site and route investigations in northern Canada. Many permafrost terrain features are recognizable or can be inferred reliably. Permits wide stereoscopic view.
Medium level to low level panchromatic photography. Common scales: 1:10,000 to 1:40,000	Very useful. Usefulness usually increased by prior stereoscopic study of high-level airphotos. Microrelief features identifiable. Provides a cross correlation of many features of the landscape.
Black and white infrared photography. Common scales: 1:30,000 to 1:60,000	Greatest assistance over the southern fringe of permafrost in mixed wood (coniferous and deciduous) forests. Shows much detail in drainage and high water table; commonly reveals the relationship of vegetation to local drainage conditions. This film is best for identification of tree species (coniferous vs deciduous) and is relatively inexpensive.
Colour infrared photography. Common scales: 1:30,000 to 1:60,000	Applicable mainly to detecting healthy or stressed vegetation, one of several stresses being a thin active layer. This layer often increases in thickness after fires, slides, or clearing; and this may be revealed on colour infrared photos. Also shows thicker active layer (pinkish) around water bodies, where thawing is taking place or has taken place.
Radar. Scales: variable	Limited. Provides overall visualization of broad physiographic features (mountains, plains, lakes, etc.). Many terrain details are obscure and fuzzy. Almost all-weather capability. Can be taken day or night, but is of limited use.
Thermal infrared imagery. Scales: variable	Limited. Mainly, with some exceptions, confirms terrain relationships already suspected and better observed on suitably scaled panchromatic photographs. Requires a knowledge of the many factors that influence dark and light grey tones on imagery, some of which cannot be evaluated if details are not known at time of image-taking. Two-dimensional image analysis restricts use. Also, the change in surface temperature in response to vegetational-climatic effects (e.g. evapotranspiration) and recent rainfall may cause tonal anomalies and give erroneous or misleading results.
Satellite imagery (ERTS now LANDSAT) at 1:1,000,000 contact scale; enlargements to 1:250,000 scale	Limited. Reveals general hydrographic and vegetation patterns and effects of fire. Shows major geomorphic features. Most terrain details are obscure and fuzzy. Provides overview for initial appreciation of terrain along transportation routes.

in the Arctic is discussed by Rinker and Frost (1969) and McQuillan (1975a, b). Conventional black and white (panchromatic) aerial photography at several scales is still the most useful and reliable remote sensing tool for the investigation of northern sites and routes (Frost 1950, 1952, Frost and Mintzer 1950, Frost et al. 1966, Sager 1951, Mollard 1960, 1968, 1972, 1975, Ray 1960, Fletcher 1964).

Black and white infrared aerial photography provides additional, often helpful, information when mapping small creeks and ponds, seepages and areas having a high water table. It also aids in distinguishing deciduous and coniferous stands of trees. Colour infrared airphotos are used to interpret vegetation stressed by disease or other causes and the effects of forest and tundra fires. Pinkish and reddish colours of vegetation seen in these airphotos may indicate a deeper active layer or the absence of permafrost locally, such as along cleared trails, in areas surrounding bodies of water and in wet fenlands.

Radar imagery and thermal infrared (heat sensing) imagery have marginal and specialized applications in most northern site and route surveys. Side-looking air-borne radar (SLAR) imagery may be helpful where an initial wide view of high relief terrain is desirable, particularly in places where persistent clouds and haze prohibit the taking of conventional airphotos. Thermal infrared imagery is seldom helpful because it is difficult to interpret with confidence in the absence of a great deal of ground control. This is particularly true in the case of long route corridors because atmospheric and landscape factors influence the character of heat signatures at ground surface. Moreover, the resolution of most thermal imagery is poor and the images cannot be studied stereoscopically. Cihlar (1976) has compiled a bibliography on thermal infrared remote sensing.

Satellite imagery in four wavelength bands (green, red and two near-infrared bands) and two false colour composites is now available for most of Canada and Alaska through the LANDSAT (formerly ERTS) program. Colour composites of good quality show synoptic views of larger terrain features and conditions and allow a broad and general appreciation of regional landscapes.

TABLE 5.4

Recommended Scales of Examination of Imagery for Different Stages of Investigation

Stage of investigation	Type of imagery	Recommended scales*
Broad corridor or areal evaluation	Mosaics of LANDSAT imagery (two-dimensional viewing only)	1:1,000,000 to 1:125,000 (1:250,000)
Selection and evaluation of one or more alternate routes or sites	High altitude black and white panchromatic aerial photography (stereoscopic viewing)	1:80,000 to 1:40,000 (1:60,000)
Intermediate stage terrain examination and evaluation of selected route or site	Black and white panchromatic, black and white infrared and colour infrared (optional) aerial photography (stereoscopic viewing)	1:40,000 to 1:20,000 (1:30,000)
Detailed terrain classification and mapping followed by detailed centre line location for routes and structure layout for sites	Conventional black and white panchromatic and infrared aerial photography (stereoscopic viewing)	1:20,000 to 1:10,000 (1:15,000)

* The scale in brackets is commonly preferred for most site and route investigations.

The type and scale of imagery suggested for different stages of air investigation are given in Table 5.4. The interpretation of good quality, high altitude photography is an essential requirement in carrying out site and route investigations in permafrost regions. Preliminary terrain typing and mapping should first be carried out using airphotos at scales of approximately 1:60,000. Areas of bedrock outcrop and bedrock-controlled relief, muskeg and a variety of glacial landforms are commonly identifiable and mappable at this scale.

Air photographs at 1:60,000 scale commonly disclose a large amount of relevant information about the terrain in the discontinuous permafrost zone that cannot be easily seen at larger scales. Even so, airphotos of larger scale should be studied at a later stage. Other scales commonly used are 1:30,000 and 1:15,000. On major engineering projects, larger scale photography may be specially flown to obtain specific data. Such photography may be taken at a particular season of the year to highlight certain types of terrain important to the project.

All of Canada has been photographed from the air, and many areas have been photographed several times at different scales. Mosaics and contact prints of air-photos can be obtained from the National Air Photo Library in Ottawa, from air-photo libraries maintained by provincial government agencies and from private companies. Contour and orthophoto maps of high quality can be prepared from airphotos of similar high quality. During the initial stages of an investigation it is common practice to plot terrain information on mosaics and contact prints of air-photos.

5.3.2 Permafrost Terrain Indicators Identifiable on Airphotos

Each feature of the terrain reveals information about the local ground and climatic conditions that prevailed when the feature developed, existed or deteriorated. Many permafrost terrain features or indicators occur in both the continuous and discontinuous zones. Some indicators are usually more con-spicuous and common in one zone than in the other (Table 5.5).

In the continuous permafrost zone all land areas are underlain by frozen ground. Typical surface expressions of permafrost (Fig. 5.2) include different kinds of thermokarst features (oriented and non-oriented small lakes, ponds with either smooth or irregular cave-in margins, drained former lakes and ponds, partly and wholly peat filled basins, beaded or buttonhole drainage, cemetery mounds), block fields (felsenmeer) and block streams, a variety of solifluction forms (sorted and non-sorted stripes, steps, sheets, terraces, lobes, lobate ter-races), ice wedge polygons (low centre and high centre), patterned ground (sorted and non-sorted varieties that are best studied in low altitude airphotos), small mounds formed by alternate cycles of freezing-thawing and/or wetting-drying (tussocks, turf hummocks, earth hummocks, mud hummocks), open- and closed-system pingos and collapsed pingos, nivation hollows and benches and asym-metric valleys—all related to the presence or former presence of permafrost (Frost 1950, 1952, Sager 1951, Ray 1960, Hussey 1962, Hamelin and Cook 1967, Brown 1970a, 1973b, 1974, 1975, Johnson 1970, Washburn 1973, Mollard 1960, 1975).

Closed-system pingos are characteristic of the continuous zone but occur sporadically in the discontinuous zone. Conversely, open-system pingos occur principally in the discontinuous zone, although a few exist in the continuous

TABLE 5.5

Landscape Features Associated with Permafrost

(Smaller features best observed on 1:10,000 photographs)

Permafrost zone(s)	Surface feature*	Implications for site and route studies
Continuous and discontinuous	Thermokarst (ponds, drained lakes, peat-filled depressions)	Ice-rich permafrost in waterlaid sediments; an indication of high contents of ground ice in hummocky terrain; less common in other materials; potential for bi-modal flows, thaw settlement, and frost action; depth of thaw basins significant
Mainly continuous	Solifluction lobes, sheets, stripes, terraces, steps	Frost action and drainage are important; often indicates bedrock or compact till layer near ground surface; rate of solifluction creep is a function of slope; usually 1/2 to 5 cm/yr and rarely more than 20 cm/yr
Continuous and discontinuous	Vegetation: cotton-grass tussocks	Poor overland trafficability. Frost-susceptible (fine-grained) materials—thus frost heave
Continuous and discontinuous	Earth hummocks	Poor overland trafficability. Frost-susceptible (fine-grained) materials—thus frost heave
Continuous and discontinuous	Cemetery mounds	Differential thaw subsidence, and slope failures in the active layer
Continuous and discontinuous	Active and fossil ice wedge polygons	Low centre polygons suggest ice-rich permafrost and poor surface drainage. High centre polygons in granular deposits suggest better surface drainage. Ice wedge polygons generally underlie but are not commonly evident on long smooth slopes, being obscured by mass-wasting. Distinct active ice wedge polygons are limited at present to the continuous zone, whereas less conspicuous and commonly incomplete polygons with inactive ice wedges can sometimes be identified in the discontinuous zone, as well as fossil polygons in sand and gravel plains from which the ice wedges are melted out, with the sand and gravel unfrozen
Continuous and discontinuous	Beaded drainage	Stream erosion of wedge ice at intersections of polygon fissures

zone. Active ice wedges and active solifluction forms (Washburn 1973) are generally confined to the continuous permafrost zone. Essentially inactive ice wedges and fossil polygons also exist in the discontinuous zone. Cemetery mounds occur in both the continuous and discontinuous permafrost zones.

Most actively caving and relic cave-in lake banks surrounding thermokarst basins and drained lakebeds indicate that ice-rich, often silty, sediments underlie and adjoin them. Deep thermokarst depressions generally suggest the presence of large amounts of ground ice in surrounding areas. Low centre ice wedge polygons commonly represent poor drainage and ponding of rain water and snow melt in areas where evaporation is low. Many are associated with ice-rich silty waterlaid sediments in depressions and flatlands. Large ice wedge polygons with distinctive trough outlines and more or less regular sides are commonly associated with somewhat elevated and better drained granular materials in the continuous per-

TABLE 5.5 (Cont'd.)

Landscape Features Associated with Permafrost
(Smaller features best observed on 1:10,000 photographs)

Permafrost zone(s)	Surface feature*	Implications for site and route studies
Continuous (sporadic in discontinuous)	Pingos; breached and/or collapsed pingos	Closed-system pingos occur in fine-grained, frost-susceptible material in former lakebeds; open-system pingos form where groundwater moves through taliks beneath slopes
Continuous and adjoining discontinuous	Peat polygons	Indicator of southern margin of continuous permafrost; sometimes found on high plateaus well south of continuous permafrost zone
Discontinuous	Peat plateaus	Ice-rich Sphagnum peat over other peat types; elevated and dry at ground surface
Discontinuous	Palsas	Ice-rich peat and organic silt, commonly prominent in vicinity of 25°F (-4°C) mean annual air isotherm but extending to 30°F (-1°C); usually occur in very wet settings, as at the intersection of "strings" in patterned fens
Discontinuous	Collapse scars (thaw "windows") and wide flat-bottomed drainage ways	Wet, thawed peat; in near-circular wet sedge meadows and marshes (thawed "windows" in permafrost) and along drainageways
Continuous and discontinuous	Reticulated and ribbed fens (string "bogs")	Thought to be polygenetic features, common in southern fringe of the discontinuous zone but occur rarely in the continuous zone as well; usually very wet and follow broad, low-gradient drainageways
Continuous and discontinuous	Skin flows and bi-modal flows	Indication of local slope instability and a warning of a construction hazard
Continuous and discontinuous	Talus and rock glaciers	Indication of potentially unstable ground conditions
Continuous (mostly)	Subparallel (feather, horsetail) drainage	Often an indicator of massive ice bodies and icy sediments in the High Arctic

* Engineering problems associated with frost action in the active layer are commonly encountered in many of these features.

mafrost zone. Frost-generated microrelief features (patterned ground and solifluction features) are best studied in low altitude good quality airphotos at 1:10,000 scale or larger.

Experience, based on interpretation of permafrost indicators and ground investigation, has shown that ground ice contents are typically substantially higher in the top 3 to 7 ft. (1 to 2 m) weathered zone of shale and harder rocks, compact lodgment till and coarse granular deposits. Notable exceptions occur, however, even in apparently competent bedrock, whether outcropping or covered with drift, and especially in the thermokarst-studded Arctic Coasta Plain of North America. In both cases, large quantities of ice have been encountered at significant depths below the ground surface. In the latter case, massive ice bodies and icy sediments can be expected in materials that have accumulated, perhaps slowly and intermittently, over a long period of time in a periglacial environment. Ex-

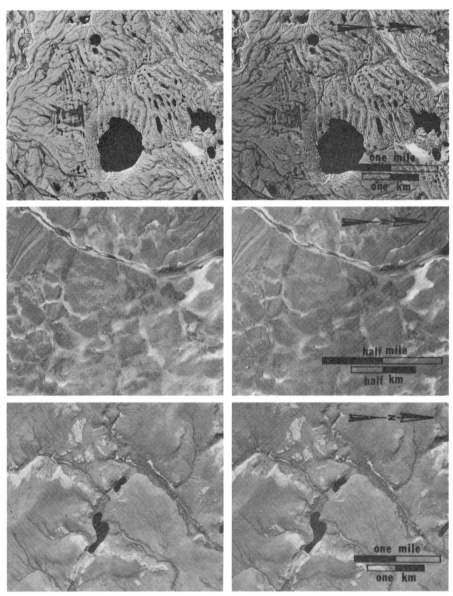

FIG. 5.2 Stereograms of some tundra landscapes in the continuous permafrost zone (J.D. Mollard photographs). *Top: Cave-in shore* around an actively thawing pond; nearby *slump* and *collapse features* resulting from melting of underground ice; *ice wedge polygons*; and *relict channel scars* on a sand and gravel outwash delta. Southwest of Deans Dundas Bay, Victoria Island, N.W.T. *Middle: Solifluction stripes* (upper left) and solifluction *terraces* and *lobes* on thinly drift-mantled bedrock (lower left and vicinity of north point). South of Deception Bay, northern Quebec. *Bottom:* Silty and pebbly *glacial* and *colluvial sediments* containing massive *icy beds* (medium gray tones, smooth slopes); small whitish-toned, tabular *outwash* bodies; *ice wedge polygons, meltwater channels* and whitish effects of *wind erosion.* Southern border of the Yukon Coastal Plain, south of Herschel Island, N.W.T.

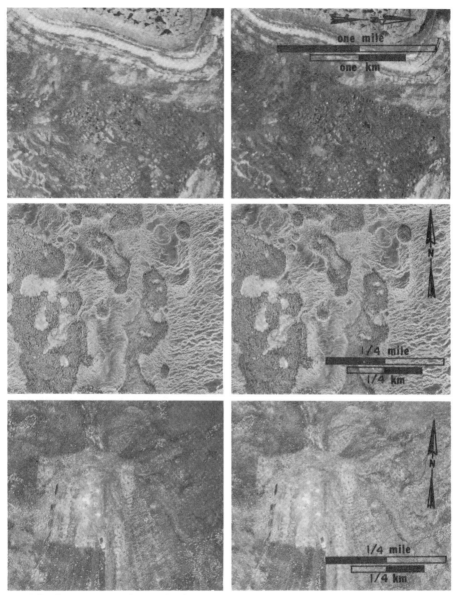

FIG. 5.3 Stereograms of some landscape features in the discontinuous permafrost zone (J.D. Mollard photographs). *Top: Cemetery mounds* developed in thick marine silt deposits. Note the polygonal dissection of predominantly silty sediments, with and without a peat cover, and the numerous small *thermokarst* ponds and *thaw slumps*. Near the mouth of Little Whale River, Quebec. *Middle:* Well-developed, thawed *ribbed fens* surrounding large ice-rich *peat plateaus* containing small subcircular (whitish) *collapse scars*, which are *through taliks* resulting from melting of ground ice in the peat and underlying mineral soil deposits. Typically, the ice-rich *peat plateaus* and smaller oval-shaped *palsas* (west of scale bar) rise 3 to 10 ft. (1 to 3 m) above the surrounding wet fen areas. Near Gillam, Manitoba. *Bottom:* This small deposit of gravelly sand composing the *raised beach ridges* offers better foundations for a tower site than the surrounding ground. The low *wave-cut escarpment* (top, centre) occurs at about 400 ft. (120 m) above sea level, and marks a major break between dominantly silty marine sediments to the east and lacustrine or till materials beneath peat to the west. Southwest of Bird, Manitoba.

amples are loess and transported loess, silty slopewash colluvium (regardless of the origin of the materials from which the silt was derived) and postglacial pond deposits. Interbedded clayey, silty, and fine sandy marine and glaciolacustrine deposits, which may be thin or thick, and which may or may not overlie sand and gravel, lodgment till or bedrock having a lower ice content, usually have a high ice content as well (Table 5.2).

Distinctive if less common terrain features may be seen on and at the base of mountain, valley and escarpment slopes in the continuous permafrost zone. These include active-layer detachment slides (skin flows) and retrogressive flow slides (bi-modal flows), talus creep and rock glacier forms and protalus lobes and ramparts (Mollard 1975). Skin flows and bi-modal flows also occur in the discontinuous zone. Rock glaciers occur in the continuous zone (Richardson Mountains, N.W.T.), in the discontinuous zone (The Norman Range, N.W.T., where they are spectacular) and in alpine permafrost areas at high elevation (Jasper National Park, Alberta).

The main surface features indicating the existence or former existence of permafrost and ground ice in the discontinuous permafrost zone are peatlands studded with thermokarst basins and patterns revealing the intermingling of frozen peat plateaus and palsas with unfrozen wet fens, the latter often occupying low-gradient drainageways and collapse scars (Fig. 5.3 and Tables 5.5 and 5.6). In North America, both peat plateaus and palsas (Zoltai 1972, 1973, Brown 1975, Zoltai and Tarnocai 1975, Mollard 1975) are commonly best developed in silty lacustrine and silty marine overlap sediments covered by thick (3 to 13 ft., 1 to 4 m) peat near the 25°F (-4°C) mean annual air isotherm. Wooded peatlands with collapse scars appear, however, in areas as far south as about the 30°F (-1°C) isotherm. Palsas usually occur in very wet terrain such as the intersection of peat ridges in reticulated fens (Zoltai and Tarnocai 1975).

Dark-toned peat plateaus covered by stunted trees and shrubs (mostly black spruce, with perhaps some birch and widespread Labrador tea) are discernible on

TABLE 5.6

Checklist of Features to Evaluate in the Discontinuous Permafrost Zone

Component of landscape	Features where permafrost is usually less common or absent, the permafrost table depressed or the surface material likely to have a lower content of ground ice	Features where permafrost is usually more widespread, the permafrost table nearer ground surface or the surface material likely to have a higher content of ground ice
Topography	South- and west-facing slopes.	North- and east-facing slopes. Summits of elevated plateaus, hills and mountains. Thaw slumps, skin flows and bi-modal flows on hill and valley slopes.
Drainage	Below lakes, rivers, most wet thermokarst depressions and wet sedge meadows (wet fens)—*i.e.* more water lies at or near the ground surface.	Imperfectly drained sites. Conifer covered river and creek flood plains in deep, shaded valleys. Subparallel rill drainage.

TABLE 5.6 (Cont'd.)

Checklist of Features to Evaluate in the Discontinuous Permafrost Zone

Component of landscape	Features where permafrost is usually less common or absent, the permafrost table depressed or the surface material likely to have a lower content of ground ice	Features where permafrost is usually more widespread, the permafrost table nearer ground surface or the surface material likely to have a higher content of ground ice
Vegetation	Wet sedge meadows. String (reticulated, ribbed) fens. Willow belts bordering creek and river banks and thermokarst features. Cleared lines in areas south of the 25°F mean annual air isotherm. Below tall, dense, mature stands of aspen, white spruce, lodgepole and jack pine on well-drained ground. Recent "deep" burns (fire history is an important factor that must be considered in the discontinuous zone).	Beneath open stunted black spruce-lichen woodlands. Beneath dense black spruce and white birch "islands" in south (shaded). Below dry lichen/Sphagnum/Labrador tea ground cover in southern fringe. Beneath elevated dry, wooded peat plateaus and palsas. Trees by themselves are not always a reliable permafrost indicator; and lichen and Sphagnum may also occur on non-permafrost areas. "Drunken" forests are usually an indication of near-surface ice-rich silt and clay and frost-susceptible materials.
Materials	Bedrock; weathered shales may be ice-rich locally but the ice content is typically less in sandstones, carbonate rocks and crystalline metamorphic and igneous rocks. Coarse-grained granular deposits (braided channels and floodplains, river terraces, glaciofluvial deposits, beach ridges). May contain "dry" permafrost. Permafrost sporadic if present in southern fringe. Windlaid sand (in dunes) usually contains no permafrost or "dry" permafrost. Compact lodgment till, especially in glacier-streamlined forms. Little or no ice below cleared trails and south-facing slopes south of 25°F mean annual air isotherm. Typically lower ice contents below upper weathered layer (about 7 ft.; 2 m). Peatland that is wet (areas of shallow standing or slow-moving water).	Silty slopewash and postglacial pond deposits. Some scree (talus) with fines. Solifluction deposits. Rock and talus glaciers. Windlaid silt (loess). Ice-rich permafrost in more northern areas, especially in thick sheetwash (water) re-transported loessial sediments. Fine-grained waterlaid sediments (lacustrine, glaciolacustrine, deltaic, vertical accretion floodplain, marine, glaciomarine). Mostly ice-rich permafrost in northern portion; ice content decreases with depth and increases with latitude. Pre-Wisconsinan sediments usually have high excess ice contents. Hummocky terrain associated with dead-ice moraine and some parts of end moraines. Closely spaced earth hummocks, mud hummocks, mudboils and nonsorted circles are indicators of frost-sensitive materials. Dry peatland sites. Peat plateaus, palsas and peat polygons. The high ice content in peaty palsas may extend into the underlying silty mineral soils. Whether the ground ice in peat plateaus extends into the underlying mineral soils depends partly on latitude (climate) and fire history. Peat plateaus and palsas may indicate former, now nonexistent, permafrost, but this is uncommon in widespread discontinuous permafrost.

airphotos. Their irregular oblong and pancake shapes, including coalesced varieties, are perhaps the most characteristic indicator of present and past permafrost in the peatlands of subarctic Canada (Brown 1968, 1975, Crampton and Rutter 1973, Mollard 1975). Palsas up to 13 ft. (4 m) or more in height are also a common feature of wet peaty lowlands and are especially well expressed in coastal regions (Zoltai 1973). Along the southern fringe of the discontinuous zone, distinctively patterned peatlands represent relic patches of permafrost formed under a previous climatic regime as well as, less frequently, contemporary permafrost formed and maintained under the present climatic regime (Brown 1975).

Patches of permafrost may occur beneath north-facing slopes in colluvium and till and on and near the tops of elevated plateaus and mountain summits where polygonal features are often evident. They may also be found in areas that have a thin organic cover but are well shaded by spruce. They may also occur under strips of ground, insulated by moss and shaded by spruce, that form the drier margins of drainageways incised into stratified fine-grained (clayey) soils. Here, the occurrence of permafrost may be revealed locally by thaw slumps. The use of certain tree species as indicators of permafrost requires a great deal of local experience because of the variations that exist from one region to another. In certain regions tree types by themselves cannot be used as reliable permafrost indicators (Brown 1975).

In the southern fringe of the discontinuous zone, it is difficult to predict the occurrence of permafrost in soil deposits, such as compact lodgment till, that are dense and have a low moisture content. Although isolated patches or islands of permafrost are found south of the 30°F (-1°C) mean annual air isotherm, these occurrences are confined mainly to special terrain and climatic conditions, such as areas of thin snow cover, a thick dry peat cover, a dense cover of black spruce, shaded topographic aspects and silty soil deposits.

5.3.3 Terrain Classification

Most terrain classifications are based on landforms and the materials composing them (Frost 1950, Belcher et al. 1951, Hughes 1972, Hughes et al. 1970-75, Monroe 1972-74, Mollard 1972, Boydell et al. 1974, Netterville et al. 1976). Landforms vary from large-scale features (mountains, plains), to features having a moderate areal extent and relief (sand dunes, deltas, eskers, moraines) and to microrelief features (patterned ground). The correct recognition of a landform allows the interpreter to predict, within certain limits, the origin and composition of soil and rock materials in that landform. Within different climatic and vegetational zones the interpreter can, in addition, usually relate plant associations, weathering, erosion and other mass-wasting processes to the landform.

Almost all of the mainland of northern Canada has been glaciated, hence most surface features and materials are products of the last glaciation. In the central Arctic Archipelago, however, many landforms and surface materials are the result of long-continued weathering and colluvial processes acting on bedrock terrain. In the continuous permafrost zone many terrain features have been modified significantly in form and appearance by periglacial processes that have been operative throughout postglacial time.

Terrain classification based on landforms in permafrost regions must consider regional geomorphic, vegetational and climatic controls because these factors not only influence the occurrence of permafrost, but they also affect variations in the content of ground ice. The occurrence of permafrost and the ground thermal regime on the one hand and climatic-vegetational zonation on the other are closely related. A map showing regional climatic-vegetational zones provides a helpful indication of some of the terrain characteristics and a guide to more detailed classification and mapping (Tarnocai 1973, Zoltai and Tarnocai 1974, Zoltai and Pettapiece 1973).

Many environmental factors must be considered in evaluating terrain for engineering works. Some are less important than others and depend on the type of project being investigated. Among the more important ones are:
—climate and microclimate,
—snow cover,
—significant geomorphic features and their evolutionary history,
—relief and microrelief,
—kind and distribution of surface and near-surface soil and rock materials,
—the occurrence of permafrost and the amount and distribution of ice in
    frozen soil and rock,
—the occurrence and movement of surface and groundwater,
—erosion by wind and water,
—vegetation including fire history and
—ecology and present land use (Brown 1970b, 1972).

The terrain analyst often prepares checklists when studying airphotos and carrying out subsequent aerial or ground surveys. Some checklists deal with project considerations (Table 5.1), and others with favoured and undesirable landforms and other terrain elements that need to be identified, classified and mapped in the search for proposed sites and routes. A typical listing of landforms in permafrost areas is given in Table 5.2. Because the amount of information to be collected varies with the kind of site or route, terrain factors should be rated in terms of their relative significance so that the less desirable conditions can be avoided when choosing among two or more potential sites or routes.

The process of selecting a route or site is generally a complex one and requires considerable experience in airphoto interpretation and field checking. Basic knowledge of the significance of climatic factors, vegetation, the origin, history and composition of geomorphic features, a good appreciation of the particular requirements of the project being investigated and a sound understanding of northern construction problems and techniques are desirable if not essential.

Based on information from available maps, airphotos and preliminary field surveys, most areas under study, whether large or small, can be divided into different terrain units. For project purposes these different classes or types of terrain are nearly always marked on contact airphotos and airphoto mosaics. They are marked on topographic maps less frequently. Descriptions of the various terrain units permit engineers working on the location of sites and routes to infer qualitative information about surface and near-surface soil and rock conditions, topography, and drainage, and thus avoid difficult engineering and construction problems.

5.3.4 Legends for Terrain Maps

A great deal of information can be presented on a terrain map or photo, particularly on a 1:60,000 to 1:100,000 aerial mosaic covering a large area. A suitable legend must be developed so that the information presented on the map or photo is clear and helpful to the user.

TABLE 5.7(a)

Terrain Typing Legend

The legend comprises four main components arranged as follows:

1 MATERIAL		2 LANDFORM
3 TOPOGRAPHY		4 DRAINAGE

1 MATERIAL

Bedrock material

ca	carbonate rocks (limestones/dolomites)
x	crystalline rocks (igneous/metamorphic rocks)
ss	sandstones/conglomerates
sh	shales/siltstones

Overburden material

b	boulders	(dense concentration of boulders at ground surface and/or deposits containing many boulders)
c	clay	(laminated; admixed with some silt and fine sand)
d	diamicton	(mixed, unsorted to crudely sorted, fine and coarse debris of non-glacial origin, such as slopewash or soliflucted material)
g	gravel	(layered; admixed with sand and cobbles)
m	silt	(laminated; admixed with fine sand and some clay, mostly between 0.002 and 0.2 mm in diameter)
o	organic material	(as a substantial component, i.e. 20 to 50 per cent, in mineral soils)
p	peat	(forest peat type: Sphagnum moss, or bog, type; and sedge-reed, or fen, type)
r	rubble	(loose, angular frost-shattered bedrock; largest size in Canadian Shield areas)
s	sand	(layered; poorly and well graded sand; interbedded fine to coarse sand, mostly between 0.2 and 4.8 mm in diameter)
t	till	(commonly very bouldery in Canadian Shield areas)

2 LANDFORM

A	*ALLUVIAL*	**M**	*MORAINE*	**C**	*COLLUVIAL*
c	channel	d	drumlinized moraine	f	**flow**
d	delta	g	ground moraine	m	slopewash/
f	fan	h	hummocky moraine		solifluction sheet
p	floodplain	r	ridged moraine/end	s	slide/slump
t	terrace		moraine	t	talus/fall
		w	washboard/ribbed		
			moraine		

O	*ORGANIC*	**R**	*BEDROCK*	**G**	*GLACIOFLUVIAL*
b	bog, patterned (peat plateau/palsa/collapse scar)	**d**	dipping beds	**c**	crevasse filling
		f	foliated rocks	**d**	delta
		h	horizontal beds	**e**	esker
f	fen, patterned/ribbed	**j**	jointed/fractured rocks	**k**	kame
u	unpatterned and un-differentiated peatland	**m**	massive rocks	**o**	outwash plain
				v	valley train

E	*EOLIAN*	**L**	*LACUSTRINE*	**W**	*MARINE*
l	loess blanket	**b**	beach ridge, abandoned	**b**	beach ridge, abandoned
d	dunes	**d**	deltaic plain	**d**	deltaic plain
		n	near shore/offshore plain	**n**	near shore/offshore plain

MODIFICATIONS TO LANDFORMS

a	terraced	**g**	glacier-streamlined	**s**	smoothed/striped by mass-wasting
b	braided/channelled	**k**	kettled/pitted	**t**	modified by thermo-karst activity
d	dissected	**p**	patterned ground		
e	wind-eroded	**r**	stream-eroded	**w**	wave-eroded

3 TOPOGRAPHY

Forms

H	HILLY
K	KNOBBY
L	LEVEL
M	ROLLING
R	RIDGED
S	SLOPING
U	UNDULATING

Varieties

d	depressed
e	elevated
g	gently
h	hummocky microrelief
j	jagged
m	moderately
r	rounded/smoothed
s	steeply/strongly
v	very little/slightly

4 DRAINAGE

Forms

D	DRYLAND (seasonal)
W	WETLAND (seasonal)
M	MIXED DRY AND WET LAND (seasonal)

Varieties

b	beaded drainage
g	gullies and ravines
n	nival (snowpatch) forms
r	rills
t	thermokarst forms

TABLE 5.7(b)
Examples Of Legend Use

1. *Combined symbols:*

MATERIAL

m, c	Stratified silt and clay, with silt dominant
s, g	Stratified sand and gravel, with sand dominant
b, t	Very bouldery surface layer over till

LANDFORM

Go-d	Glaciofluvial outwash-delta
Ge-k	Glaciofluvial esker-kame
Af-d	Alluvial fan-delta
Mg, s	Ground moraine modified by slopewash and/or solifluction
Gv, a	Glaciofluvial valley train, terraced
Ac, b	Alluvial channel, braided

TABLE 5.7(b) (Cont'd.)
Examples Of Legend Use

TOPOGRAPHY

Mr   Rolling terrain, with slopes
         rounded/smoothed
Rj   Ridged terrain, with a
         jagged/irregular surface

DRAINAGE

Wt   Wetland (seasonal), with
         thermokarst forms
Dr   Dryland (seasonal), with
         numerous rills

2. *Single landform:*

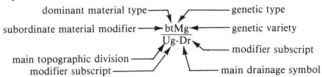

3. *Veneer (less than 1.5 m thick) on material of different origin:*

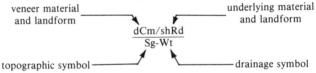

4. *Intermingled landforms:*

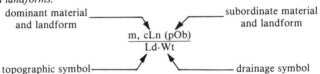

TABLE 5.7(c)
Additional Terrain Components and Information[a]

I VEGETATION

PD   polar desert (mosaic of extensive bare areas and local patches of lichens, mosses, sedges and grasses)

ST   stony tundra (stony sedge-moss-lichen tundra)

HT   heath tundra (dwarf shrub-sedge-moss-lichen tundra)

WT   wet tundra (moist-loving sedges and coarse grasses in poorly drained areas)

TS   tundra-forest transition (sparse, open, slow-growing northern portion of black spruce forest)

BF   boreal forest (mostly black and white spruce with tamarack along margins of water bodies. Some balsam fir, white birch, trembling aspen, and jack pine. Dense, closed, faster-growing southern portion of coniferous forest)

TM   treed muskeg ("weed" trees (black spruce, tamarack) growing in peatlands in boreal forest; includes peat plateau/palsa/wet fen complexes)

OM   open muskeg (non-treed peatlands in boreal forest)

MW   mixed-wood forest (mixed coniferous and deciduous trees)

DF   deciduous forest

II PERMAFROST[b]

1. *permafrost zone*
   (a) continuous
   (b) widespread permafrost in the discontinuous zone
   (c) southern fringe of permafrost in the discontinuous zone

2. *microfeatures resulting from permafrost or frost action*
   (p) peat plateaus and palsas
   (c) cemetery mounds
   (k) thermokarst depressions
   (i) large ice wedge polygons
   (s) solifluction forms including sheets, terraces, lobes and stripes
   (m) sorted and nonsorted patterned ground features

3. *thickness of active layer*
   (a) less than 1 ft. (<0.3 m)
   (b) 1 to 3 ft. (0.3 to 1 m)
   (c) 3 to 7 ft. (1 to 2 m)
   (d) over 7 ft. (>2 m)

4. *excess ice (content in percent of volume)*
   (h) high, 50% to 500%
   (m) medium, 15% to 50%
   (l) low, 0 to 15%
   (n) none, little or no excess ice
   (v) variable, includes more than one of the above categories

(a) can be added to legend and map (or air photo) if desired.

(b) selection of the applicable symbol depends upon prior correlations between airphoto interpretation and borehole drilling and sample testing. It may not be possible to show items 3 and 4 unless a great deal of field borehole exploration and laboratory testing of frozen samples has been carried out prior to airphoto interpretation. Where two or more symbols follow a numeral, the first mentioned is considered to be dominant.

III *FIELD EXPLORATION OF SITES**

Purpose of exploration	Status of site	
	Suggested	Confirmed

1 Determination of thickness (probed)
   a) peat
   b) active layer		

2 Borehole location		
3 Borrow site		
4 Field observation site		

* Located from and marked on airphotos

IV *CARTOGRAPHIC SYMBOLS*

Glacial striae (ice direction known, not known)

Drumlin, drumlinoid, fluting (ice direction indicated, not indicated)

Crag-and-tail (ice movement in direction of arrow)

Moraine ridge

Esker (direction of flow assumed, uncertain)

Meltwater channel (large, small)

Abandoned beach ridge

Escarpment

Retrogressive thaw-flow slide

Ice wedge polygons (areas known to contain ice wedges)

Terrain legends cannot be completely standardized, as they reflect personal preferences of the mapmaker, the scale of airphotos used in mapping, the final map scale and particularly the type and requirements of the project involved. The sample legend detailed in Table 5.7 has been used extensively in terrain mapping in northern Canada (Mollard 1972) and a number of modifications of it are in existence. It was designed for the mapping of a long, narrow corridor traversing permafrost areas in Subarctic and Arctic Canada, but it can also be applied to wider corridors and areas. It is based on a classification of landforms, materials, topography, surface drainage, vegetation, permafrost and a key to show the field exploration of sites. The landforms are those which the interpreter can commonly identify in different scales of airphotos if he has experience in the region to be mapped and access to a certain amount of back-up ground data. Such airphoto interpretation done in the office should be checked against and correlated with further field data collected at selected sites.

Most legends of terrain maps follow arrangements much like that in Table 5.7. It is basically similar to that used by the Geological Survey of Canada in mapping terrain in northern Manitoba, the Mackenzie River Valley, the Keewatin District and the Arctic Archipelago (Hughes 1972, Hughes et al. 1970-75, Klassen and Netterville 1973-74, Hodgson 1975, Boydell et al. 1974, Barnett et al. 1975, Netterville et al. 1976). Comparison of the terrain legends now in use reveals many variations (Hora and Stepanek 1977).

The sample legend shown in Table 5.7 uses a system of upper and lower case letters to describe materials, landforms, topography and drainage over the extent of a route or site. Symbols for selected characteristics of vegetation and permafrost can also be shown where they correlate closely with the main legend components within a particular climatic-vegetational region. Whether or not the inferred thickness of the active layer and excess ice content of the soils or rock are shown on the terrain map depends on the amount of field and laboratory data available to the mapmaker.

When a legend such as that in Table 5.7 is used in a project report, it should be accompanied by a written interpretation. This should explain differences in the origin, size and appearance of certain physical features that may not otherwise be obvious, such as dissected or stream-eroded rills, gullies and ravines, and to indicate where duplication of lower case letters may cause confusion, such as when thermokarst features (t) are shown under both topography and drainage. Cross sections should be used to illustrate intermingled landforms and materials or stratified materials and veneers.

Qualified predictions of certain geotechnical properties, the implications of the types of materials available for construction and such environmental considerations as the sensitivity of terrain to a given type of disturbance may be displayed in the margin of a terrain map. Separate breakdowns can be set up for each component of the master legend. If too many components are shown on photo mosaics, however, the number of delineations required may become too great and overly cumbersome. This need not be the case in mapping the right-of-way for a route, where each component of a legend can be shown directly on or below the mosaic showing the route. Selected geotechnical information, such as natural water content, plasticity limits, density and frozen and thawed thermal conductivities for individual terrain components, may be added on the plans after field drilling and laboratory testing is done. For northern transportation route studies, information relating to engineering and construction performance may be shown with the terrain evaluation. This information may be used to prepare preliminary cost estimates of design, construction and maintenance.

5.4 Geophysical Surveys

Conventional geophysical techniques can be used effectively in permafrost-mapping applications. Technical requirements for their use in detailed studies have not yet been met, although considerable development work is underway and offers reasonable promise of future success. Effective application of geophysical techniques requires an understanding of the dependence of the physical parameters on temperature and consequently on depth of the strata below the ground surface. The most commonly measured parameters are the seismic compressional wave velocity and the electrical resistivity. The temperature dependence of velocity and resistivity for various materials is discussed in Sections 3.4.2 and 3.6.

For most unconsolidated materials, velocity and log resistivity behave in approximately the same manner with temperature. Qualitative temperature-depth functions for thick and thin permafrost and the corresponding depth function for either velocity or log resistivity are shown in Fig. 5.4. For purposes of geophysical interpretation, models can be constructed using layers in which velocity and log resistivity are either constant or linearly dependent on depth.

Application of geophysics to permafrost problems can be divided into three main groups. The first is the detection and delineation of permafrost in the discontinuous zone and of taliks in the continuous zone. The second is the detection of ice-rich ground or massive ice. The third is the identification of subsurface materials within permafrost. Solutions for these problems can be sought by the use of either airborne or ground-based geophysical methods, depending on the scale and detail required.

5.4.1 Ground and Airborne Geophysical Techniques

Several conventional ground-based techniques are applicable to the mapping of discontinuous permafrost (Ferrians and Hobson 1973, Roethlisberger 1972, Scott and Hunter 1977). The most commonly used are shallow seismic refraction and direct current (DC) resistivity. The variation of observed velocities or resistivities is correlated with temperature distribution in the ground. A good estimate of the thickness of the active layer can be obtained using the refraction method, because it can delineate the boundary between the relatively low-velocity unfrozen ground overlying the high-velocity permafrost. Refraction methods cannot be used to

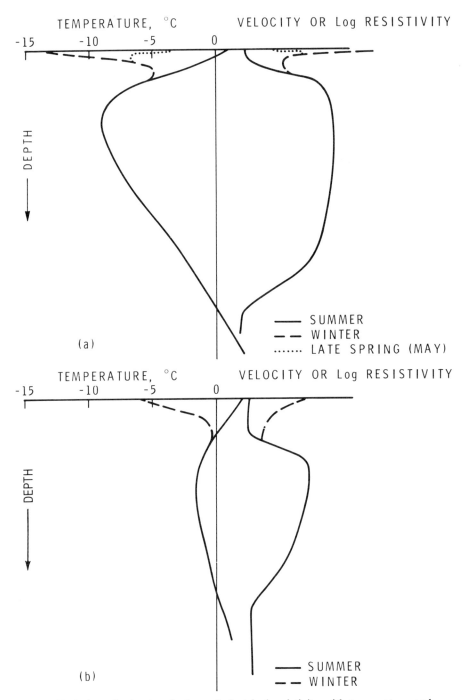

FIG. 5.4 Variation of seismic velocity and electrical resistivity with temperature and depth for (a) thick permafrost, (b) thin permafrost.

estimate the thickness of permafrost, however, since the permafrost base
represents a velocity inversion with depth.

The thickness of the active layer and of permafrost can be determined by DC
resistivity soundings, although the technique is most useful where thick permafrost occurs in the continuous zone (Scott and Mackay 1977). The areal
distribution of permafrost can be inferred from an evaluation of the lateral variation in velocity or resistivity. Increasing use is being made of very low frequency
(VLF) resistivity determinations for the mapping of discontinuous permafrost.

The most effective mapping procedure is a combination of the three techniques. The result of such an approach applied in the discontinuous zone is illustrated in Fig. 5.5. In this survey, comparison of the various measurements
facilitated the identification of permafrost, near-surface bedrock and thawed
zones in overburden. Determination of the thickness of permafrost is important
in the drilling of petroleum exploration and production wells. Hnatiuk and Randall (1977) describe several geophysical methods that are used with varying
degrees of success.

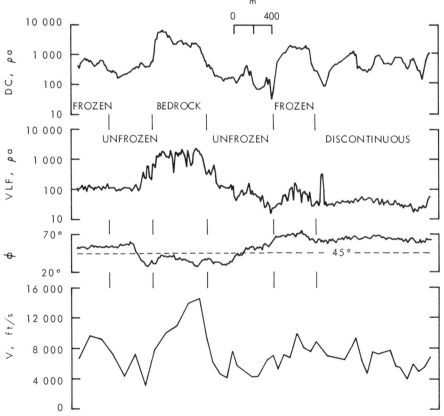

FIG. 5.5   Comparison of DC resistivity, VLF resistivity and seismic velocity results in
an area of discontinuous permafrost.

Detection of massive ice or ice-rich ground is a more difficult problem. Gravity techniques have been used with considerable success in some areas to outline large bodies of massive ground ice (Rampton and Walcott 1974). No routine methods exist, however, for detailed studies of local variation in ice content, although seismic refraction has given indications of the thickness of large bodies of massive ice (Hunter 1973). Most of the common geophysical techniques give average measurement over considerable volumes and thus lack the necessary fine-scale definition. Some techniques presently under development that show promise in dealing with the problem of ground ice are discussed in Section 5.4.2. Identification of subsurface materials other than massive ice is at best a difficult problem that has not yet been handled successfully by geophysical techniques.

Airborne geophysical techniques are preferred for regional reconnaissance. The only airborne method presently in use is the Barringer E-Phase radiowave system. It has been used successfully to outline taliks in thick continuous permafrost and with varying degrees of success to map discontinuous permafrost (Sellman et al. 1974). Experiments using electromagnetic systems mounted on helicopters to map the distribution of thin discontinuous permafrost in the Mackenzie Valley have not given encouraging results (Fraser and Hoekstra 1976).

5.4.2 Techniques under Development

A number of techniques at present under investigation offer promise in the study of permafrost problems. Analysis of the dispersive properties of Rayleigh and horizontal polarized shear waves is a promising method for detailed mapping of velocity distribution in geologically complicated situations. Up-hole seismic techniques under development will permit the mapping of irregular boundaries within permafrost circumjacent to boreholes (Kurfurst et al. 1974). High frequency reflection techniques are being used in studies sponsored by the Geological Survey of Canada to investigate the variation of compressional-wave attenuation and dispersion with moisture content in permafrost.

Ground-based radar experiments show promise in the delineation of near-surface massive ice (Scott et al. 1974, Annan et al. 1976a, b). These techniques have been successful in measuring the thickness of glacier ice (Davis 1973) and sea ice (Campbell and Orange 1974). Further equipment refinement is expected to add to the usefulness of this technique for permafrost applications, although its utility will be seriously limited in areas with fine-grained, near-surface soils or thick peat cover.

Variable-frequency electromagnetic (EM) sounding techniques are being applied to the measurement of thick permafrost using large-scale systems with considerable separations between transmitter and receiver. The utility of small-separation, high-resolution EM equipment for detailed mapping of near-surface permafrost has been demonstrated by Henderson and Hoekstra (1977).

Some experiments have been carried out in the use of borehole logging systems to identify permafrost boundaries and to determine ice content (Wyder et al.

1972, Scott and Hunter 1977). Velocity measurements in boreholes have been made using "crystal cables" to determine permafrost distribution with depth (Smith and Rempel 1974).

5.5 Subsurface Exploration

Although subsurface conditions can be fairly reliably predicted by interpretation of air photographs and other remote sensing data, it is essential that subsurface exploration be carried out to confirm these predictions and to obtain the detailed information required for engineering design and construction (Johnston 1966a, Linell and Johnston 1973). This is particularly important in the case of large, critical structures such as powerhouses, industrial complexes (e.g. mine, oil and gas plants), bridges, dams, dykes, major airfields and associated facilities. Sites located near water bodies and in the discontinuous permafrost zone, especially in marginal permafrost areas where the distribution of permafrost and ice in the ground is quite irregular and difficult to predict, merit special consideration. Special attention must be given to areas on land and below the sea bottom where saline frozen soils are anticipated. Very little is known about the distribution of permafrost, ice content and properties and behaviour of saline soils in such areas.

5.5.1 Extent and Scope of Exploration Program

Field investigations must not only determine the existence and distribution of seasonally and perennially frozen areas but also, and most important, the type and distribution of ice in the ground (see Section 2.4). The types and properties of soils and rock, groundwater conditions, thickness of the active layer, depth of seasonal frost penetration in unfrozen soils in the discontinuous permafrost zone, presence of unfrozen layers and ground temperatures must also be determined. All can be quite variable, not only areally but also with depth, and will significantly influence the location of structures or facilities, the design of foundations and construction methods to be used.

Conditions at depth may be completely different from those at or near the surface. For example, dry (ice-free) granular materials quite often overlie ice-rich fine-grained soils and buried massive ice in the form of ice wedges or large tabular sheets. Old stream channels and peat deposits containing excess ice may also exist some distance below the ground surface. Rock that outcrops at the ground surface or is covered by shallow overburden is often badly frost shattered in the top 10 to 20 ft. (3 to 7 m). Cracks in this zone and in joints, seams, fissures, bedding planes and cavities in the underlying rock mass frequently contain substantial masses of ice, which would result in unacceptable settlements when loads are applied and if thawing occurs.

The location and depth of exploration depends a great deal on the type of structure or facility being considered. For example, an initial boring is normally located in each different type of terrain when a route or large area is under study.

For a single structure, such as a large building or wharf, a minimum of three borings should be considered unless the subsurface conditions are known to be very uniform. They should be located so that a reasonably accurate estimate of the extent and character of the intervening soil, rock mass and permafrost conditions can be obtained. When non-uniform conditions are suspected or encountered, the explorations should be spaced as close as is necessary to determine the extent and nature of these erratic subsurface conditions under and adjacent to the structure.

As a general rule, exploration is carried out to a minimum depth equal to the width of the structure unless sound bedrock or a suitable bearing stratum is positively identified at a shallower depth. The fact that sound rock, and not a boulder, has been encountered should be verified by boring at least 10 ft. (3 m) below the rock surface or weathered zone of the rock. It is important to investigate all the foundation materials within the zone that might be subjected to thawing during the service life of the facility. Subsurface exploration for roads, runways, railways and pipelines should extend to at least 10 ft. (3 m) below final subgrade elevation in cut areas and to about the same depth below the existing ground surface in fill areas. For building foundations designed according to either the passive or active methods (Chapter 7) exploration should be conducted to a depth of at least 10 ft. (3 m) below the estimated depth of thaw and, in all cases, to a depth about 10 ft. (3 m) below the base of foundation support. Exploration is often carried out to a depth of at least 20 ft. (7 m) for many structures and in some cases to more than 100 ft. (30 m). Exploration to the greater depths will be required to determine the character of the lower strata because of the type of structure or foundation.

The scope of the subsurface investigation, including methods and equipment used and the kind and detail of information required, will depend on a number of factors. Access to the site (water, helicopter, overland), geographical location (marginal or continuous permafrost, offshore), type of structure and information already available are important considerations. The time of year when the work is best carried out will similarly vary.

For small or temporary structures only limited information obtained by relatively simple methods (such as hand borings) at a few locations may be required. On the other hand, for special structures and facilities and where permafrost and ground conditions are particularly complex much more detailed information must be gathered, sometimes at relatively closely spaced locations. The routes for linear structures such as roads, railways, pipelines and power transmission lines that cross highly variable terrain usually require extensive subsurface investigations. Detailed investigations are also required in offshore areas where subsea permafrost will greatly influence offshore operations (Sangrey 1974, U.S.A. National Academy of Sciences 1976).

A comprehensive program is frequently conducted, therefore, to obtain undisturbed frozen soil and rock samples not only for identification and classification of the materials and distribution of ice, but also for determination of frost susceptibility characteristics, deformation and strength behaviour and physical and thermal properties of the materials in the frozen, thawing and thawed states. Special instrumentation or equipment may also be installed or used to determine, for example, the annual variation in ground temperatures, groundwater conditions, thermal properties and in situ strength and deformation behaviour of the materials. Evaluation of frost heave, thaw settlement and slope creep and solifluction movements may also be required. Furthermore, full-scale field experiments, such as pile load tests and test fills, may be conducted in advance of construction to provide information for evaluation of the interaction between the atmosphere, the structure and the ground, performance of proposed foundation designs and selection of construction methods.

5.5.2 Subsurface Exploration Techniques

Conventional techniques are used for sampling unfrozen materials (ASTM 1975) and are not discussed here. Although such work is best carried out during the summer months, it may have to be conducted during the winter because of difficult access conditions or environmental restrictions. In this case undisturbed samples of unfrozen materials will have to be protected against freezing.

Techniques used for sampling seasonally or perennially frozen ground are similar to those used for unfrozen materials but procedures and equipment may have to be modified in some cases. Particular attention must be given to avoid or minimize thermal disturbance and chemical contamination of samples. At present there are no set standards or guidelines for sampling frozen materials. The selection of appropriate methods and equipment will depend to a large extent on the experience and judgment of the field engineer and on the needs of the project. Procedures that have proved successful for procuring, handling and transporting samples are described later.

One or more of the following methods (Cass 1959, Johnston, G. H. 1964) may be used to obtain soil and rock samples and information on subsurface conditions: sampling of natural exposures, hand borings, test pits and drilling. The first two methods are used for shallow depths and general information while the last two will give detailed information to greater depths. Various features of each method pertaining to its use in permafrost are summarized in Table 5.8 as a general guide.

Much information can be gathered with little effort by examining natural exposures along stream, lake or sea shores, gullies and landslide scarps. Colluvial or thawed material can be removed by hand to expose the frozen face or a series of test pits dug at intervals down the slope. Thawed and frozen core or block samples can be taken but judgment should be exercised in making extrapolations as the frozen materials may be disturbed and modified due to their proximity to the face of the slope. If frozen soil is not encountered in the excavations, then its location should be established by hand probing.

Hand borings are not practicable in frozen stony materials but may be used in warm temperature, frozen fine-grained soils to obtain samples for identification

TABLE 5.8

Application of Sampling Methods

Method	Investigation Preliminary	Investigation Detailed	Approximate[a] maximum depth ft. (m)	Material Fine grained	Material Coarse grained	Material Rock	Sample Condition Unfrozen	Sample Condition Frozen	Sample Condition Disturbed[b]	Sample Condition Undisturbed	Tests Water content	Tests Unit weight	Tests Special[c]	Tests Ground temperature[d]
(1) Natural exposures	X	—	—	X	X	—	X	?	X	?	?	—	X	—
(2) Hand borings	X	—	5–20 (1.5–6)	X	—	—	X	?	X	—	?	—	—	X
(3) Test pits or trenches														
Natural thawing	X	—	5 (1.5)	X	X	—	X	—	X	—	—	—	—	—
Hand excavation	X	X	10 (3)	X	X	—	X	X	X	?	X	?	—	?
Power hand tools	X	X	25 (7.5)	X	X	?	X	X	X	?	X	X	X	X
Heavy equipment														
Dozer/Ripper	X	X	20 (6)	X	?	?	X	X	X	?	X	X	X	—
Backhoe/Shovel	X	X	20 (6)	X	—	—	X	X	X	?	X	X	X	X
Large auger	X	X	40+ (12+)	X	—	—	X	X	X	—	X	—	—	X
Explosives														
Single shot	X	—	10 (3)	X	?	—	X	X	X	?	X	X	?	—
Shaft	—	X	No Limit	X	X	X	X	X	X	?	X	X	X	X
(4) Drilling														
Churn	X	—	No Limit	X	X	X	X	?	X	—	?	?	?	—
Overburden drill	X	—	50+ (15+)	X	X	X	X	X	X	—	X	?	?	X
Hammer drill	—	X	20+ (6+)	X	X	X	X	X	X	?	X	X	?	X
Core drill—Warm fluid	—	X	No Limit	X	X	X	X	X	X	?	X	X	X	X
—Cool fluid	X	X	No Limit	X	X	X	X	X	X	X	X	X	X	X
Drive sampling[e]	X	X	20+ (6+)	X	—	—	X	X	X	?	X	X	?	X

Notes (a) Average values given—influenced by many factors. No Limit indicates depth of at least 100 ft. (30 m) is possible.

(b) Undisturbed refers to good quality—sample is frozen but may have been subjected to some relatively minor thermal, mechanical or other effects.

(c) Special tests (e.g. thaw consolidation, creep, thermal properties, etc.)—may be block sample from test pits or cores from boreholes; whether sample is suitable or not will depend on possible disturbance during sampling operation.

(d) Ground temperature refers to suitability of properly backfilled hole or pit for installation of temperature sensors for immediate (several days) or long term measurements.

(e) Drive and core drill samples can be obtained below bottom of hole (cased or uncased) or pit, but quality and size of sample will depend on type and temperature of material and size of hole or casing.

and classification purposes. Holes have been hand drilled to depths of 25 ft. (7 m) using post-hole type augers to remove soil and ice fragments produced by a chopping bit or ice chisel. Heavy walled steel pipes or Shelby tubes can be driven with a sledge hammer or a drop hammer and tripod to obtain relatively undisturbed cores to a depth of about 5 ft. (2 m) or below the bottom of a hole advanced by a chopping bit and hand auger. A much better indication of the ice segregation in the soil can be obtained from pipe or tube samples than by a visual examination of cuttings.

Test pits or trenches permit detailed examination of materials in situ and may be the only way to get reliable information in frozen granular soils. Not only can the soil types and ice distribution be logged for the complete profile, but disturbed and excellent undisturbed block or core samples can be taken from the pit or trench walls. Test pits can be excavated to depths of from 5 to 40 ft. (6 to 13 m) by several methods: natural or artificial thawing (using solar heat, fires, steam or water jets), pick and shovel, power hand tools (air, electric or self-contained gas engine-powered jackhammers), heavy equipment (bulldozers, rippers, backhoes, power shovels and large auger drills) and explosives.

FIG. 5.6   Excavating test pit in frozen gravel with compressed air jackhammer, Inuvik, N.W.T.

Thawing and hand-excavation methods are generally very slow and excavation depths may not exceed 5 to 10 ft. (1.5 to 3 m). Pits have been dug to about 30 ft. (9 m) with jackhammers in two or three days (Fig. 5.6). Trenches have been excavated by bulldozer, backhoe or power shovel to about 30 ft. (9 m) in a few hours (Fig. 5.7), but progress is highly variable depending on the type of material,

FIG. 5.7   Test pit excavated by backhoe in ice-rich, fine-grained soil, northern Manitoba.

ice content and ground temperature. Best results are obtained in warm temperature, frozen fine-grained soils compared to hard frozen or granular materials. Large diameter (2 to 3 ft.; 0.7 to 1 m) holes, down which a man can be lowered, have been drilled to depths of about 40 ft. (13 m), again in warm temperature, fine-grained soils. Limited success has been obtained when explosives are used for test pitting because of uncontrollable "break" of the frozen ground. A regular shaft-sinking type of operation is usually more successful although much more costly.

Rotary power drilling is by far the most widely used method for exploration to depths ranging from 10 ft. (3 m) to more than 100 ft. (30 m). Churn drills have been used but rotary drills using non-coring drag or roller bits, or single or continuous flight augers with hard metal or tungsten carbide teeth, are commonly used to drill holes of from 3 to 12 in. (75 to 300 mm) diameter or larger. Cuttings are collected for classification of the materials and auger samples may be suitable for water content tests. An indication of the type and location of ice deposits may be obtained from evaluation of drill performance and examination of the cuttings. A combination of rotary drilling and drive sampling with heavy-walled tubes gives reasonable results in fine-grained frozen soils whose temperature is 25°F (−4°C) or warmer (Kitze 1956, Davis and Kitze 1967). Standard, hollow-stem flight augers or specially modified auger core barrels on the end of drill rods have also been used (Veillette 1975a). Drive or auger sampling is not effective, however, in hard frozen soils at very low temperatures or in stony frozen soils. Methods and equipment used for offshore subsea permafrost exploration are described by Osterkamp and Harrison (1976b) and Sellman et al. (1976).

Excellent samples of all types of frozen soil and rock can be recovered from any depth using special core drilling equipment and techniques (Hvorslev and Goode 1966, Lange 1966, 1973, Lange and Smith 1972, Roggensack 1979, Sellman and Brown 1965). Diesel fuel, brine solutions, water, antifreeze (alcohol and glycols), special muds and compressed air have been used as circulating mediums; diesel fuel, water, muds and air are the most satisfactory. The surface of cores may be partially contaminated or disturbed by thawing by the fluid or sublimation, but if they have a diameter greater than 2 or 3 in. (50 or 75 mm), the thin disturbed layer can be removed to give good undisturbed samples. The drilling fluids can be cooled to ground temperature relatively easily during the winter but special refrigeration equipment may be required for summer operations.

Various types of drills, core bits and barrels and auxiliary equipment can be used depending on the nature of the investigation, type of frozen material, ice content, depth and size of hole and type of power equipment. Drills range in size from helicopter-transportable rigs (Pihlainen and Johnston 1954, Veillette 1975a, b) to large truck- or track-mounted machines (Figs. 5.8 and 5.9). Special rigs, such as "overburden drills" (Atlas Copco 1964) and "hammer drills" have been used with good results on some jobs. Limited field trials have indicated that good cores of large diameter can be obtained very rapidly but at high cost by advancing and retracting steel pipe using a vibratory (sonic) pile driver (Bendz 1977).

FIG. 5.8 Lightweight, helicopter-transportable drill rig used for taking core samples to depths of 75 ft. (25 m) (After Brown 1970a).

FIG. 5.9 Track mounted drill for core sampling to depths greater than 100 ft. (30 m).

5.5.3 **Sampling**

The soil profile, and particularly the ice inclusions, should be logged at the site as accurately and in as much detail as possible according to the unified frozen soil description and classification system (Pihlainen and Johnston 1963, Linell and Kaplar 1966). A typical exploration log and record of soil test results are given in Figs. 5.10 and 5.11 respectively. It is recommended that photographs of test pit walls and all frozen cores and samples be taken for a permanent record (Fig. 5.12).

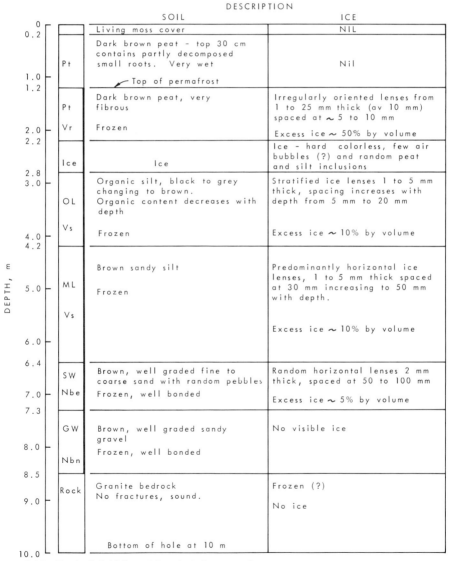

FIG. 5.10   Typical field log of borehole in permafrost.

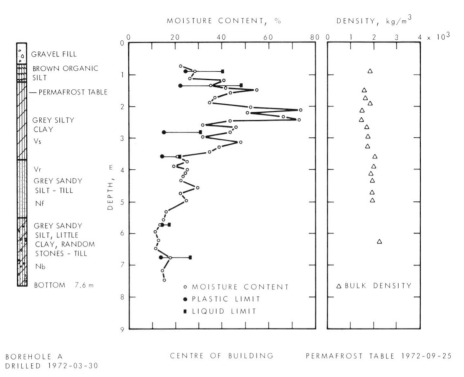

FIG. 5.11   Soil test results from permafrost borehole.

The types of samples required for determining properties of the materials depend both on the nature of the subsurface conditions and on design requirements for the proposed structure or facility. Information derived from auger holes and cuttings may be adequate for temporary structures or those than can tolerate some movement, or for evaluation of construction materials in borrow areas. If ice contents are large, partially disturbed drive samples may be adequate as a basis for design decisions. For low ice contents, however, and when structures have heavy foundation loadings or are sensitive to small movements, undisturbed samples will be required for consolidation and creep tests.

As a standard procedure, samples should be taken for determination of water and organic contents, bulk- and dry-unit weights, grain size analysis and other classification tests. Some of these tests may be done on site; in other cases samples may have to be shipped to a laboratory. If undisturbed block or core samples must be transported for special tests, such as for strength, creep and thermal properties, then precautions must be taken to prevent thermal and mechanical disturbance or sublimation of the specimens (Baker 1976). The soil structure, ice distribution and unfrozen water contents may be radically changed, thus altering the properties and behaviour of the material. The effects of sample disturbance on test results for frozen cores obtained from great depths (>1000 ft.; 300 m) are described by Smith, W. S. et al. (1973).

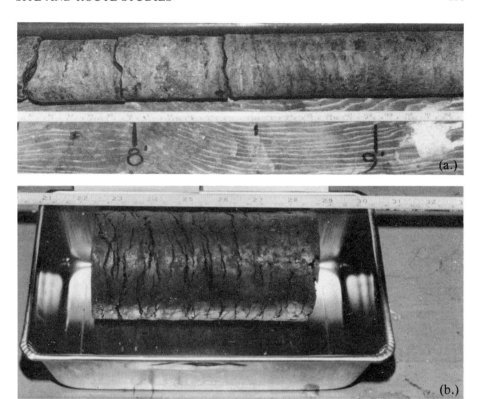

FIG. 5.12   Photograph of permafrost core, taken from a depth of 7.5 to 9.5 ft. (2.3 to 2.9 m) below the ground surface, is shown in (a) immediately after extrusion from the core barrel. A sample taken from this core is shown in (b) after it was partially thawed in the field laboratory. Note the ice lenses.

Samples are commonly placed in de-aired and tightly sealed plastic bags and transported in well-insulated boxes. Snow or crushed ice and additional insulation is packed around the samples in the boxes to reduce or prevent sublimation and maintain, as closely as possible, the original sample temperature. Dry ice (carbon dioxide) has been used in some cases but care must be taken to ensure that it is not in direct contact with the samples to prevent thermal shock or "burning." Samples have also been shipped in portable freezers; temperature control is very good but the cost is greatly increased.

5.5.4 Ground Thermal Regime

Information on the ground thermal regime is usually required and gathered during a site or route investigation. In some cases, only the position of the 32°F (0°C) isotherm, which can be obtained by relatively simple methods, may be required. For most projects, however, detailed information on ground temperatures and their annual variation at different depths will be required, not only for thermal design, the determination of depths of freeze and thaw and the existence of unfrozen zones within the permafrost, but also to assist in specifying temperature conditions for the testing of samples in the laboratory. The selection of appropriate methods and equipment to obtain information on the ground thermal regime will depend on a number of factors including the location (remote area compared to a site with easy access), the depths at which temperatures are required, measurement accuracy, frequency of observations and cost of equipment, installations and making observations.

Hand probing with steel rods about 0.5 in. (15 mm) in diameter until refusal is reached is often used to determine the rate and depth of thaw in the active layer. Care must be taken, however, in relatively ice-free soils or in cohesive soils having a high unfrozen moisture content, for probes can be pushed with ease as much as 1 ft. (30 cm) or more below the frost table. On the other hand, stones may prevent penetration of the probe and cause the thaw depth to be underestimated. Mackay (1977b) discusses methods of probing. More reliable results are obtained using hand coring tools that take a sample from 0.5 to 2 in. (15 to 50 mm) in diameter and 6 to 12 in. (150 to 300 mm) long (Day et al. 1961, Hughes and Terasmae 1963). Frozen peat and fine-grained soils have been sampled to depths of about 12 ft. (4 m) with these tools.

Determination of the boundary between the frozen active layer and the permafrost table from examination of frozen cores taken during the winter is difficult at best. In some cases, a distinct difference in the type or amount of ice segregation may be an indicator. In general, however, the depth of the active layer is best determined in the fall at the end of the thaw season.

The depth and rate of freezing and thawing in the active layer and seasonal frost zone are commonly measured using a "frost tube" (Gandahl 1963, Rickard and Brown 1972, Mackay 1973c). One type is shown in Fig. 5.13. This instrument, which is inexpensive, easy to fabricate and read, and is accurate to at least ± 2 in. (50 mm), is installed in a drill hole carefully backfilled to ensure good contact between the casing and the wall of the hole. The degradation of permafrost occurring over several years beneath engineering structures has been observed using this device (Johnston 1969). Multi-sensor electrical resistance probes have also been used successfully to measure depths of freezing and thawing (Atkins 1979, Banner and van Everdingen 1979).

The probes and frost tubes indicate the position of the 32°F (0°C) isotherm but no information on the soil temperature profile is obtained. Mackay (1974b), however, obtained good results with a self-positioning thermistor probe, which fitted inside a frost tube and was designed to measure freeze-back of the active layer from the permafrost table. It can also be used to monitor the aggradation of permafrost under thick fills or the degradation of permafrost in disturbed areas.

Various types of temperature sensors are available but thermocouples or thermistors are the ones commonly used to measure ground temperatures (Hansen 1966, Johnston 1963, 1973, Judge 1973d, Mackay 1974d, Veillette 1975c). An accuracy of ± 0.4F° (± 0.2C°) is desirable for most engineering purposes and can be obtained with either thermocouples or thermistors. Multiconductor cables

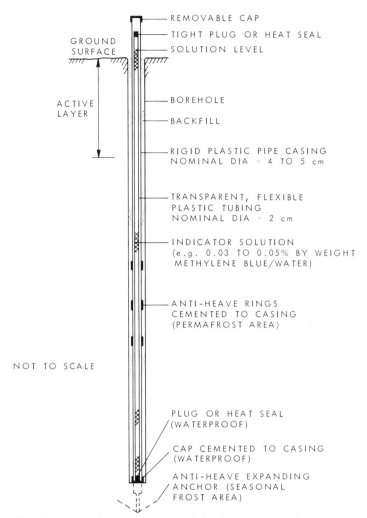

FIG. 5.13   Frost tube for measurement of depth and rate of thaw or seasonal frost penetration.

with sensors placed at selected positions can be fabricated and installed in carefully backfilled boreholes. Individual sensors may alternatively be inserted into small holes drilled into the side of test pits, which are then carefully backfilled. Depending on the amount of disturbance caused by the drilling or excavation operation, it may take several hours, days or weeks before thermal equilibrium is reestablished. However, Mackay (1974d) and Veillette (1975c) found that temperatures, measured in air-filled drill holes 20 to 100 ft. (6 to 30 m) deep but plugged at the surface, stabilized within one day.

Many types of read-out equipment, ranging from simple manually-operated potentiometers or resistance bridges to sophisticated automatic, power-operated data acquisition systems that record data on charts or tapes at pre-selected times, are available for the measurement of ground temperatures. The type selected will depend largely on project requirements. The measurement of ground temperatures is also discussed in Section 11.2.

The thermal conductivity of frozen and thawed materials can be measured in the field and laboratory using special cylindrical probes (Lachenbruch 1957b, Wechsler 1966, Penner 1970a, Penner et al. 1975, Slusarchuk and Foulger 1973, Slusarchuk and Watson 1975) or the divided-bar apparatus discussed by Judge (1973c).

5.6 Field and Laboratory Testing of Frozen and Thawing Soils

When frozen ground is thawed and at equilibrium with the stress and drainage conditions imposed on the material, conventional techniques of testing soil are generally applicable (ASTM 1964, 1970). Attention need only be given here, therefore, to the testing of frozen and thawing soils. Neither field nor laboratory testing of such soils has been used extensively in North American practice to date, mainly because the greatest emphasis in foundation design has been on either preserving frozen conditions or completely thawing the ground and proceeding in a conventional way. When frozen conditions have been preserved, the frozen ground has generally been sufficiently strong and stiff to perform well under the light foundation loads used so far in northern Canada.

Although there is substantial laboratory testing of frozen ground at the research level, its application in practice is not yet clear. For this reason and because of the costs involved, testing programs should be carefully planned and reviewed to ensure that the results will provide valid and needed information. This requirement is not as critical with regard to tests on thawing characteristics of soils where results from laboratory and field testing are used to explain performance (Keil et al. 1973, Morgenstern and Nixon 1975). A Soviet manual describing methods and equipment for determining the physical, thermal and mechanical properties of frozen and thawing soils has been published (USSR 1973b). It deals mainly with laboratory procedures but also includes some field methods.

5.6.1 In situ testing of frozen ground

In the case of unfrozen soil and rock mechanics, parameters representative of behaviour under prototype conditions are frequently obtained from in situ tests and problems of mechanical disturbance and size effect are minimized. The same advantages would be anticipated in the case of frozen soils, provided that care is taken to minimize thermal disturbance.

Ladanyi and Johnston (1973) have investigated the use of the pressuremeter to evaluate in situ creep properties of warm temperature, frozen, fine-grained soil. The apparatus is illustrated in Fig. 5.14. They conclude that creep parameters can be determined and indicate how to extrapolate from these tests of relatively short duration to longer term behaviour. Rowley et al. (1975) performed pressuremeter creep tests to evaluate test pile performance at Inuvik. More experience is needed in order to establish the reliability of this technique in practice.

Plate bearing tests can also be used to study strength and deformation properties. Zaretskii (1972) discusses the settlement of a test plate on plastic frozen soils. The performance of actual loaded structures to deduce in situ parameters provides one of the most reliable means for determining frozen ground characteristics.

Penetration tests may be used as soundings in frozen ground and to establish correlations. Bakakin and Zelenin (1966), for example, describe the use of a

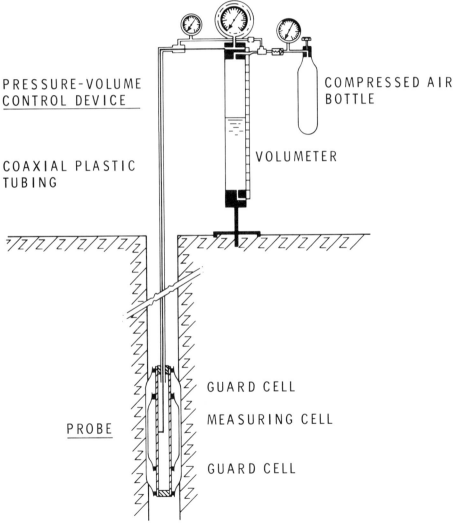

FIG. 5.14   Ménard pressuremeter type G, test setup (After Ladanyi and Johnston 1973).

penetration test to evaluate the properties of frozen ground for purposes of excavation. A preliminary field study of stress- and penetration rate-controlled tests using an electric penetrometer in frozen soils was carried out by Ladanyi (1976). The results indicated that valuable information on the time-dependent strength of frozen soils can be obtained provided the penetration rate was very accurately controlled or the test was conducted by applying constant loads in stages. A static cone penetrometer has been used offshore in the Beaufort Sea to determine engineering properties and distribution of material types, including ice-bonded sediments (Blouin et al. 1979). Nuclear probes appear promising for the in situ determination of densities and ice contents in boreholes (McKay and O'Connell 1975).

5.6.2 Laboratory Testing of Frozen Ground

Density and water contents of frozen ground are important index properties in estimating thermal properties and thaw settlement characteristics. No special problems arise in their determination in the laboratory, although particular consideration should be given to questions of structure and scale; that is, are the samples large enough to be representative of the actual field situation? Litvinov (1966) discusses problems of obtaining representative water contents where segregated ground ice is present and suggests a logical system for ice or water content evaluation. Thermal properties can also be determined in the laboratory either directly (Williams 1964, Penner 1970a, Penner et al. 1975) or by correlating with mass properties and index tests (Dillon and Andersland 1966, Anderson et al. 1973, Nixon and McRoberts 1973).

The strength and deformation properties of frozen ground depend upon temperature, time and ice or soil structure. The properties are also probably dependent on sample size, although no relevant systematic investigations have been performed on naturally frozen soils. Anderson and Morgenstern (1973) note that in the western hemisphere the study of frozen soils is still in the stage where most work is done on reconstituted frozen soils with well-controlled temperature environments. This permits a systematic exploration of the influence of the dominant variables on the mechanical properties. However, the actual strength and deformations of frozen ground, which develop in situ under the loading and thermal boundary conditions that might arise in practice, are not readily estimated with accuracy.

When it is decided that naturally frozen samples warrant testing and representative samples have been obtained, strength and deformation tests can be performed using equipment and techniques common to soil and rock testing. Even for relatively routine testing, particularly of fine-grained soils, there should be provision for accurate control of the test temperature and allowance should be made for the long time needed to investigate rate-dependent properties.

Among the tests that can be performed conveniently on frozen ground are unconfined compression, triaxial compression and direct shear. If these tests are performed at a constant strain rate, strength and deformation characteristics that will be a function of the strain rate are obtained. Tests can also be carried out at different constant stress levels to investigate creep characteristics and limiting strengths (Sayles 1968, Akili 1971, Alkire and Andersland 1973). Shuster (1971) describes some laboratory techniques in detail. Fig. 5.15 illustrates the triaxial cell system that he used.

Long-term uniaxial tests are widely used in the Soviet Union for creep and strength testing. Details of techniques are given by Vyalov et al. (1966b). The results of these simple tests must be used with reservation, however, since there is increasing evidence that many frozen soils are frictional in behaviour and that extrapolating from unconfined tests seriously underestimates the ultimate strength of the material (Sayles 1973). On the other hand, a study comparing creep deformations observed in situ with those predicted from uniaxial creep tests on undisturbed samples showed that an ice-rich silt deformed 3.3 times faster in the field than in the laboratory (Thompson and Sayles 1972). The testing of frozen soils to determine their response to dynamic loads such as high stress earthquake shocks and low stress vibratory loads has only recently been explored (Kaplar 1969, Stevens 1975).

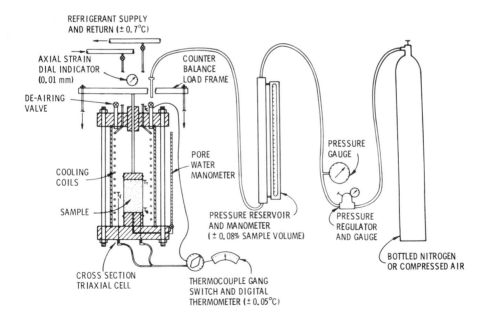

FIG. 5.15   Refrigerated triaxial cell system (After Shuster 1971).

5.6.3 Testing of Thawing Soils

Fully thawed soils can be studied both in the laboratory and in situ using well-established soil mechanics techniques. In situ studies of thawing soils are not normally carried out because it is difficult to control the thermal regime and because of the large cost involved. It should be noted, however, that data of great value can be obtained by monitoring actual structures (Watson et al. 1973a, Morgenstern and Nixon 1975).

The settlement and strength characteristics of thawing soils can be studied conveniently in the laboratory. A number of investigations to study the one-dimensional settlement of thawing ground have been performed but no standard procedure has been established. Depending on the equipment used, tests may be conducted under conditions ranging from completely uncontrolled to fully controlled thaw rates. In the former case, no use can be made of the data giving the rate of settlement (Crory 1973a). Watson et al. (1973b) describe simple equipment for thaw settlement tests, consisting of a sample holder made from an acrylic cylinder 3.5 in. (90 mm) inside diameter and 4 in. (100 mm) high. The bottom of the cell consists of a porous stone sitting on an acrylic plate containing holes to permit drainage. The sample is loaded by a lever system through a loading cap and a porous stone. If tests studying pore pressure effects are needed, equipment similar to that used by Morgenstern and Smith (1973) must be adopted. The strength of thawing soils is influenced by the consolidation and drainage conditions during the test. These can be controlled using conventional soil mechanics triaxial compression equipment. Broms and Yao (1964) give results of the behaviour of thawed soil subjected to triaxial compression.

CHAPTER 6

Cold Regions Earthwork

(Contributors–T. H. W. Baker and G. H. Johnston)

6.1 General Considerations

Excavation and placement of frozen as well as unfrozen materials are carried on throughout the year on many engineering projects in the North. Suitable fill must be obtained from borrow pits and placed for roads, airfields, dams, dykes and building pads. Trenches and pits for buried services, including pipelines and electrical cables, and building foundations must be excavated and backfilled. Ore from underground and open pit mines must be removed and transported. Effective and economic excavation and handling of frozen and thawed ground the year round is therefore an important and basic requirement for construction operations in permafrost regions. Difficult excavation and handling problems can be experienced, however, depending on the type of materials, whether they are frozen or unfrozen, their temperature and water content, the type of facility being constructed (e.g. a haul road vs the impervious core for an earth dam) and the time of year when the work is carried out. The feasibility of conducting cold weather earthwork operations must be carefully evaluated (Yoakum 1966, Lovell and Osborne 1968, Havers and Morgan 1972, Roberts 1976).

Dry granular materials and quarried rock are frequently used to construct embankments because they are more stable and are usually more easily excavated during the winter when much of the fill is placed. Glacial till and clay shales with low ice content have been used extensively when gravel is in short supply. The shales may disintegrate rapidly, however, and need to be capped with a granular wearing course to carry heavy traffic. Difficulties with handling, placement and compaction, unacceptable settlements and possible instability are some of the problems encountered when attempts are made to use high-moisture-content frozen and unfrozen cohesive soils (Fig. 6.1). Only in extreme or special cases will they merit consideration as construction materials.

Some operations are best conducted during the summer, when air temperatures are above freezing, the active layer is thawing and ground temperatures are warmer. Poor drainage conditions in borrow pits and at construction sites, soft haul roads, and the handling and compaction of thawed or thawing high water content materials may, however, severely complicate the work.

On the other hand, it may be advantageous to carry out some operations when air temperatures are below freezing: drainage and de-watering problems are

FIG. 6.1   Frozen high ice content fine-grained soil used for road fill flowed when
thawed. Attempts to backfill with granular material were not successful in stabilizing
embankment until fill material had completely thawed and drained.

reduced or eliminated, haul roads, if graded prior to freeze-up, require little
maintenance other than snow removal and well-drained materials stockpiled during the summer can be readily loaded and hauled. Problems do arise in winter
work: excavation of seasonally and perennially frozen soils and rock is more difficult when hard frozen (ice is relatively easy to excavate by comparison) and
proper compaction of frozen materials is not possible in most cases. Frozen
materials containing appreciable moisture freeze to the surfaces of handling and
hauling equipment, such as loaders, conveyors, truck boxes and railroad cars,
and operation and performance of equipment is more difficult and uncertain at
very low temperatures. There are fewer hours of daylight and the efficiency of
workers is greatly reduced during the winter.

Careful preplanning of earthwork operations in permafrost areas is essential,
not only for small jobs such as foundation excavations, but also and in particular
for large-scale operations. Selection of methods, suitable equipment, time of year
and scheduling of the work are most important. Some of the problems encountered and methods used in the excavation, handling and placement of frozen
and thawed earth materials in cold regions are discussed in this chapter.

6.2 Excavation

Frozen soil particles are usually well cemented by ice, forming a dense, hard mass, similar to well-cured concrete or rock, that is difficult to penetrate and loosen. If allowed to thaw, however, a soil with a significant ice content can turn into a slurry and flow like a viscous liquid. Frozen, moisture-free soils present no real excavation difficulties and normal procedures can be followed.

The strength properties and behaviour of frozen soils are discussed in Chapter 3. These characteristics can indicate the degree of technical difficulty in excavation and can aid in selecting the most advantageous method. Not only the physical and mechanical properties of the frozen material influence the method of excavation; the size and shape of the excavation, the quantity of material to be removed and the construction schedule and season must also be considered.

Various methods of excavating or breaking frozen soil, including some novel processes, have been investigated (Bakakin and Zelenin 1966, Foster-Miller Associates 1973a, b). The principal methods used in practice are thawing, mechanical fracturing and drilling and blasting; combinations of these are widely used on many construction or mining projects. Of the conventional techniques, ripping, shearing, shear or drag bit cutting and controlled explosive loading offer the best prospects for work in frozen ground and soft rock. Of the novel concepts, Mellor (1972a) concluded that high pressure water jets offer the most promise.

In general, no special problems are experienced in the excavation of competent hard rock and standard methods and equipment are used. Freezing of explosives, drillhole stemming material and drilling fluids may be troublesome but can be overcome by taking suitable precautions.

6.2.1 Thaw Excavation

Thawing of frozen materials can be accomplished in several ways, including solar thawing and the use of fires, cold water, steam or fuel-fired jets and electric "needles." All of these methods are slow and labour-intensive, and hence costly. Cold water and steam jet thawing of frozen materials were widely used in the placer gold fields in the Yukon and Alaska but are seldom used now as work in these areas has virtually ceased (Beistline 1966). Flooding of large areas to thaw the frozen soils overlying the gold-bearing gravels (and to float the dredges—Fig. 6.2) and removal of frozen and unfrozen material by sluicing with large hydraulic monitors and by bulldozers are the principal methods used today in placer mining.

Steam jets are used occasionally to thaw small areas for the placement of foundation footings and piles in permafrost (Fig. 6.3), but steaming must be carefully controlled to avoid excessive thawing (Johnston 1966b). In addition, condensate water may saturate the ground or pond on the ground surface creating drainage, frost action and icing problems. Electric probes (needles) for thawing frozen

FIG. 6.2 Dredge removing overburden thawed by ponded water in placer gold mining operation in eastern Siberia, Soviet Union.

FIG. 6.3 Steam jetting holes to 20 ft. (6 m) for pile foundation.

ground have been investigated and used in the Soviet Union, but high power consumption does not make this method practical for most construction jobs, especially in remote areas.

The "thaw-scrape" operation is commonly used in summer to obtain borrow materials, make cuts and prepare relatively large surfaces for foundation construction. Trees and moss cover are removed (by bulldozer or hand cutting) and burned. The frozen ground thaws, usually by exposure to solar radiation. Occasionally fires or steam and water jets are used to accelerate thawing. Thawed material is removed as soon as it has thawed to a depth of 3 to 6 in. (70 to 150 mm), so that a frozen surface is always exposed to the sun. Thawed material is usually stockpiled to drain or, if not suitable for construction purposes, is disposed of in carefully selected locations. Thawing of frozen ground prior to excavation, although successful, can only be applied where time or cost is not a major consideration and where relatively large areas, such as borrow pits, can be worked by bulldozer.

6.2.2 Mechanical Excavation

Mechanical excavation includes all methods by which a frozen soil is mechanically fractured or broken by stressing the material to failure. Zelenin (1964) studied the force and energy requirements for various methods of producing failure in frozen soils and compared them on the basis of relative resistance to failure as follows:

Unconfined tension	1.0
Unconfined compression	3.0
Cutting, cutter width 3 cm	
depth of cut 1 cm	11.5
Static penetration	21.0

It can be seen that methods causing tensile failure will also minimize energy consumption (see also Haynes et al. 1975). This is an important consideration when adapting soft-ground excavating equipment for use in frozen ground as, for example, when modifications are made to the geometry and material composition of the cutting edges used (Zelenin 1964, Mellor 1972b, c, 1975a, b, 1976a, b, 1977). Excessive wear of cutting edges is one of the major problems with mechanical excavation equipment in frozen ground.

Various types of equipment (such as rippers, cutters, saws, vibratory or impact breakers, percussion and rotary drills and bucket excavators) used for excavating, drilling or tunneling in unfrozen ground and soft rock have been used in frozen ground excavation with varying degrees of success. Table 6.1, adapted from Foster-Miller Associates (1973a), compares the rate of removal and energy effectiveness of several mechanical methods of excavating frozen ground.

For small excavations such as foundation footings, compressed-air jackhammers are often used to loosen frozen material for removal by hand or power shovels (Harding 1962). Layers up to 1 ft. (0.3 m) thick can be broken or

TABLE 6.1

Comparison of Various Methods of Excavating Frozen Ground

Method	Details	Material	Rate of Removal		Effectiveness $\times 10^{-9}$ m³/J	Remarks	Ref
			m³/min.	m/min.			
D-8 Bulldozer, No. 8 ripper	–single tooth ripper –trench 0.2m² in cross sectional area	Frozen clean beach gravel, moisture content above saturation, air temp. –1°C	13.7	—	1295 (short term)	Effectiveness based on rated power of bulldozer. Borrow pit at Barrow, Alaska	1
D-9 Bulldozer, No. 9 ripper	–single tooth ripper	Silty gravel (18% silt), moisture content = 6%, air temp. –2°C	—	—	283 (short term)	Borrow pit, Denali Highway	1
D-8 Bulldozer, Two-toothed ripper	—	Frozen clay	1.3	—	119 (day long)	Stripping, Usibelli Mine, Healy, Alaska	1
Tractor-pulled ripper	–tractor weight = 40,500 kg. –developed 28,350 kg pull at the ripper	1.5 m thick layer sandy clay with cobbles, air temp. –21°C	1.1	—	83 (day long)	Area cut into 1 to 1.5 m square grid. Cut pieces easily handled by shovel or bucket excavators	1
Disc saw, tractor mounted	–saw diameters varied from 0.8 m to 2.5 m with peripheral speed up to 15m/s	Very dense clay, air temp. –13°C	—	—	62 (highest)	Pebbles caused breakage of saw. Stability of large disc saw was low	1
Chain saw	–2.5 m deep trench made in one pass	2 m layer of frozen material	—	—	—	High wear—expensive materials for parts	1
Combination disc cutter and shovel excavator	–narrow slits 60-80 cm apart, 0.8 m deep –2.5 m diameter cutter –peripheral velocity 3.5-20 m/sec	—	—	—	—	High power consumption for the disc cutting process. High cutting speed causes rapid wear of cutting edges	1
Trench excavator	–scoops on excavator chain –cuts trenches 1.8 m deep by 0.85 m wide	1.3 m layer of frozen material	0.1	0.1	52	Trench excavation made by cutting two narrow trenches and chopping in between	1

Method	Specifications	Soil conditions				Remarks	
"Arctic Ditcher" Model 7-10 Banister Pipelines Ltd. "Polar Bear" Henuset Bros. Ltd. "Ditcher" Barber-Greene Co.	—rotary wheeled trenchers with buckets —conical carbide teeth —trenches 3.5 m deep	Sandy gravel, till, Churchill, Manitoba	—	—	—	Extensive teeth wear. Additional weight necessary in the bucket wheel. Greatly assisted by blasting	3
Rotary excavator (FP-7A, FP-2M, FP-4) with special teeth	—trench cut 1.7 m deep by 1.2 m wide	2 m layer of frozen material	0.2	0.2	—	More efficient than chain sawing	1
Rotary excavator	—trench cut 1.1 m wide by 1.7 m deep —cutting speed 1 m/s	Frost line 50 cm deep	2.5	1.2	—	Cutting speed of 1 m/s too high, causing rapid wear of surface	1
		Frost line 120 cm deep	1.7	0.8	—		1
Rotary excavator	—same size trench as above —cutting speed = 0.5 m/s	Frost line 100 cm deep	1.7	0.8	391	Modifications made to bucket teeth design	1
Wedge-shaped hammer	—50 cm wide wedge splits 30-40 cm wide pieces of frozen soil	—	0.3	—	—	—	1
Wedge impact	—wedge width = 18 cm	Frost line 1-1.2 m deep	0.2	—	18	Based on an average value of 100 m/day of 1-1.2 m deep frozen ground requiring 10 impacts/min. of 8000 kg-m impact energy	1
Vibrating hammer attached to tractor	—hammer weight = 990 kg, width = 50 cm, frequency = 7-12 Hz, impact energy per cm of cutting edge = 30 J	Clay soil	—	—	—	Motor (22 kw) Cost 50% of drilling and blasting	1
Vibrating hammer on excavator bucket	—	—	1.43	—	—	—	1
Alkirk cycle miner	—	Frozen Fairbanks silt, air temp. −2°C	—	—	801 (short term) 79 (day long)	Digging Fox tunnel	1

TABLE 6.1 (cont'd.)
Comparison of Various Methods of Excavating Frozen Ground

Method	Details	Material	Rate of Removal m³/min. m/min.		Effectiveness ×10⁻⁹ m³/J	Remarks	Ref
Thermal drill (Browning)	—uses diesel fuel and compressed air	Frozen Fairbanks silt air temp. −1°C	—	—	1	Slots cut at rates ranging from 3 m²/hr. in silt to 6.5 m²/hr. in gravel	1
		Frozen gravel <5 cm, air temp. 1°C	—	—	2		
Explosives	—ammonium nitrate in diesel fuel	Frozen sand or gravel	—	—	1006	Explosive energy only. Does not include shot hole drilling	1
Explosives	—cratering, single charge	Frozen till, Churchill, Manitoba	—	—	81	—	1
Steam thawed—hand shovelled	—volume = 765 m³	Silt and gravel	0.24 × 10³	—	—	Power plant excavation, Alaska	2
Blasting—hand shovelled	—volume = 418 m³	Gravel and bedrock (Mica Schist)	0.13 × 10⁻³	—	—	Diversion dam and gates, Alaska	2
Jackhammer—hand shovel	—volume = 31 m³	Heavy gravel (partly frozen)	0.15 × 10⁻³	—	—	Water tower foundation, Alaska	2
Jackhammer—hand shovel	—volume = 176 m³	Heavy gravel with sand and silt partly frozen	0.14 × 10⁻³	—	—	Warehouse, Alaska	2
Steam thawing—jack hammer	—volume = 505 m³	Silty sand with gravel (frozen)	0.10 × 10⁻³	—	—	Steam lines, Alaska	2
Hand shovel	—volume = 689 m³	Silt, sand and gravel (not frozen)	0.24 × 10⁻³	—	—	Sewer mains and laterals, Alaska	2
Hand shovel	—volume = 230 m³	Sand (not frozen)	0.44 × 10⁻³	—	—	Garage and repair shop, Alaska	2

References—1. Foster-Miller Associates 1973a (Tables V and VI)
2. U.S. Navy 1955 (Table 3A3-1)
3. Joy 1973

FIG. 6.4 Excavating frozen silt using compressed air jackhammers for building foundation at Ft. McPherson, N.W.T.

loosened, but this lightweight equipment is not very productive (Fig. 6.4). Most frozen soils are too resilient to be easily shattered by pneumatic equipment. Heavy power shovels have been used to make large excavations in warm temperature (30°F; −1°C) permafrost but production is relatively low (Fig. 6.5).

Single- or double-toothed rippers employ the principle of shear or drag bit cutting and are the most economical means of loosening or fracturing large areas of frozen material. A combination of ripping and drilling and blasting can be used effectively to break frozen ground (Haley 1959). Rippers mounted on or pulled by tractors, and equipped with replaceable shanks and teeth, are widely used and are most effective when working areas are not less than 10,000 ft.^{2} (1000 m^2) (Roads and Streets 1972). Best results are obtained by cross-ripping on a grid pattern with passes spaced about 5 ft. (1.5 m) apart both ways. Only slight penetration is usually achieved on the first pass because of poor traction on the frozen ground surface. Deeper penetration of the ripper is obtained on subsequent passes as traction improves. When working on slopes, ripping is best done perpendicular to the slope to give maximum grouser penetration. To control melting and drainage, small sections should be ripped and the material excavated to grade before the cut is enlarged.

FIG. 6.5   Power shovel excavating warm temperature (30°F, −1°C) permafrost, northern Manitoba.

Slots and trenches in frozen ground have been excavated using saws (Levitin 1957, Sergeev 1961, Nalezny 1971, Mellor 1975a), chain or bucket excavators (Gal'perin et al. 1955, Sergeev 1961, Joy 1973, Bridges 1978), drop hammers (Sergeev 1961, McCullough 1958), air blasting (McAnerney et al. 1969) and water jets (Mellor 1972a). Narrow slots may be cut in frozen ground for burial of cables or to aid in excavation of large blocks; trenches are excavated primarily for burial of pipelines (Fig. 6.6). Hironaka (1974a) and Mellor (1978) describe methods that can be used in the Arctic for trenching and burial of cables and pipelines on shore and in the ocean floor.

Rapid tooth wear and breakage make disc sawing of frozen soil impractical, particularly in frozen gravels, although modifications developed by the U.S. Army (CRREL) produced a dramatic improvement in cutter durability (Mellor 1975a). Tooth and chain wear account for poor performance of chain excavators in most frozen materials (Mellor 1976b). Drop hammers have very low efficiency due to high power consumption, rapid deterioration of the striker point and low speed of operation.

Trials using a combined auger-airblast tube for trenching and tunneling in frozen materials have been successful. Efficiency is greatly dependent on the

(a.)

(b.)

FIG. 6.6   Large bucket wheel machine (a) used to excavate 7 ft. (2.1 m) wide by 10 ft.
(3 m) deep trench (b) in dense, stony frozen glacial till at test site, Churchill, Manitoba.

speed at which the auger penetrates the ground prior to air discharge (McAnerney et al. 1969). Difficulties were encountered when air blasting was used to aid ripping operations because of insufficient confinement of the air blast. Mellor (1972a) investigated the use of high velocity water jets for making slots in frozen ground. Major problems are caused when large stones or gravel deflect the jet and divert much of the imparted energy toward widening instead of deepening the cavity. The technique works well in fine-grained frozen material.

An Alkirk continuous mining machine equipped with drag bit cutters was used to successfully excavate a tunnel in frozen silt (mean annual ground temperature about 30°F (-1°C)) near Fairbanks, Alaska (Swinzow 1970). To compare excavation techniques, trials were carried out in the same tunnel using several other methods, including drilling and blasting and conventional coal cutting machinery, but no definite conclusions could be drawn (McAnerney 1967, McAnerney et al. 1969).

More research and development work on equipment to excavate frozen material is required to reduce the high power consumption and overcome the effects of machine inefficiencies. Particular attention must be given to cutter and ripper teeth design geometry and material for improved efficiency and durability.

6.2.3 Drilling and Blasting

Explosives are widely used by the Canadian mining industry to excavate frozen overburden and ore in open pit and underground mines. At present, drilling and blasting is the most economical method for dealing with the large quantities of frozen material involved in a mining operation. An experimental tunnel was excavated in 12°F (-11°C) glacial till at Thule, Greenland by conventional drill and blast techniques following the usual sequence of drilling, blasting, ventilating and mucking, similar to that of conventional tunneling operations (Swinzow 1964, 1966).

Attention has been given to the drilling of small and large diameter holes in frozen ground by different methods. Foster-Miller Associates (1973a, b) and Mellor and Sellman (1975) discuss the design of drill systems. The drilling operation can have a great effect on the proper placement of explosives in boreholes. If improperly done, it often allows or causes the sides of the borehole to melt and slump. The resulting reduction in hole depth and diameter, or plugging of the hole, may not permit placement of the explosive charge at the correct depth. It is important that holes be kept as dry as possible, otherwise it may be difficult to place and detonate the explosive before the water freezes (Horsley 1965). The most common problem in drilling is the formation of an ice collar around the top of the hole, caused by meltwater freezing. The ice collar and sloughing prevent proper stemming of the hole. Stemming is important and is usually achieved by filling the hole with clean dry sand or fine rock chips. For the excavation of the permafrost tunnel in Greenland a mixture of silt and clay was tamped in the hole and allowed to freeze to provide stemming during drilling and blasting (Swinzow 1964, 1966). This mixture sealed the entire hole and gave excellent results.

Explosive consumption in frozen material is quite high (Bauer et al. 1965), ranging from 0.6 lb./ton (0.3 kg/t) to as much as 1.2 lb./ton (0.5 kg/t) depending on the ice content. When the ice content of a frozen material exceeds 10% by dry weight the ice absorbs a large proportion of the energy generated by a blast (Ives 1962). This greatly reduces the efficiency of the blasting operation and has prompted a great deal of research by the mining industry.

Depending on their degree of saturation with water, freezing soils have a number of important characteristics that affect blasting efficiency. These are primarily related to the increase in shear strength developed by the cementing properties of the ice, and the effective removal of water as a pore fluid thereby nullifying the build-up of pore pressures. The efficiency of the blasting operation is also dependent upon the type of explosive used, the amount and shape of the charge, the shot hole configuration, the placement depth of the charge, the "coupling" or contact of the charge with the hole wall and the delay period and firing sequence. For any particular frozen material it is the usual practice to conduct drilling and blasting trials at each site to determine optimum values for the type and amount of explosive and the depth and spacing of holes. An optimization procedure that can be used to analyze the results of such trials is given by Livingston (1956). It involves varying the depth of placement and weight of a particular explosive to blast the maximum crater volume.

Of particular interest in crater trials is the relationship between the volume of frozen soil removed per pound of explosive and the ratio Δ of the depth at which the charge is placed to the "critical depth." The critical depth N is the minimum depth, for a particular weight of charge, at which all the energy of the blast is contained without breaking the surface or to just cause failure at the surface. In frozen materials:

$$N = EW^{1/3} \tag{6.1}$$

where N is the critical depth in feet (metres), W is the weight of the charge in pounds (kilograms) and E is a proportionality constant. Livingston (1956) defined the proportionality constant as the strain energy factor. As the material becomes more brittle, E increases and the optimum crater volume occurs at lower values of depth ratio Δ. For softer, more plastic materials, E decreases and the optimum crater volume occurs at higher values of depth ratio. It should be noted that the softer the material, the less the drilling cost.

Bauer et al. (1965) reported on blasting trials in frozen ground based on cube root "scaling." The scaling of the blast pattern, as already noted, refers to the placement of the charge at a depth that is proportional to the ratio of the depth in feet (metres) and the cube root of the charge weight in pounds (kilograms). The optimum charge burial depth is found from cratering tests. This is similar to the "lambda" scaling method discussed by McCoy (1965). The optimum scaled charge burial depths for several frozen materials are shown in Fig. 6.7.

Crater trials were carried out by several investigators in different frozen materials. Livingston (1956, 1960) and Livingston and Murphy (1959) conducted trials in frozen silt and glacial till at Churchill, Manitoba. McCoy (1965) per-

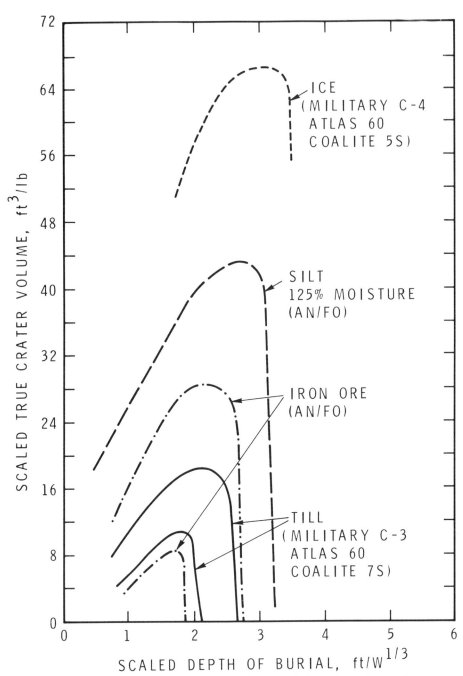

FIG. 6.7 Optimum scaled charge burial depths for several frozen materials and explosives (After Bauer et al. 1973).

formed blasting tests in ice and frozen silt in Alaska. Bauer et al. (1965) and Lang (1966) report on trials in frozen iron ore and glacial till at Schefferville, Quebec. Mellor and Sellman (1970) presented data on crater tests in frozen silt and gravel in Alaska and Riddoch (1979) conducted tests in a frozen gravelly silt at Inuvik, N.W.T.

From a study of all available data, Morgenstern et al. (1978) concluded that it is possible to predict cratering in frozen ground with about the same accuracy as in unfrozen ground. Whether a soil is frozen or not appeared to make little difference to the relationships between charge weight and optimum crater dimensions. Optimum scaled burial depths for frozen soils varied from about 1.5 to 2.0 with no apparent correlation with respect to, for example, detonation velocity, soil type and ice content. Ice behaves quite differently, however, having a value of about 1.0 for the optimum scaled burial depth. Crater dimensions were affected more by variation in soil type than by variation in the type of explosive, which had little effect. In general, low detonation velocities tend to create larger craters and larger craters are produced in frozen fine-grained soils for a given charge weight. It was not possible, from the data available, to quantify the effect of factors such as stemming practice, packing of charge and shape of charge on the resulting craters in frozen ground.

Bauer et al. (1965) performed blasting tests in seasonally frozen ground, where holes were drilled on a staggered alignment grid. Best results are obtained when the shot holes are drilled to about 1 ft. (0.3 m) above the bottom of the frozen layer. It was found that explosives placed below or too near the bottom of the frozen layer in fine-grained soil expend a large part of their energy in forming a cavity in the soft, unfrozen material beneath. On the other hand, thin layers (2 to 3 ft.; 0.6 to 0.9 m) of frozen material are broken most economically using heavier charges placed below the frozen layer and on a larger grid spacing. The results of these trials are presented in Table 6.2.

TABLE 6.2

Placement of Explosive Charges in Seasonally Frozen Ground
(After Bauer et al. 1965)

Material type	Single hole scaled optimum depth of burial	Row breaking conditions	
		Depth of row charge	Spacing of charges in units of row charge burial depth
Mechanical excavation and frozen layer fragmentation			
Frozen hard iron formation	1.8	1.8	1.3 to 1.5
Frozen till	2.1	2.1	1.6 to 1.8
Frozen silt	2.1	2.1	1.6 to 1.9
Frozen iron ores	2.3	2.3	1.6 to 1.9
Estimated conditions for explosives excavation, ditching			
Frozen rock and till	1.3	1.3	1.4 to 1.6

In deep excavations and open pit mining in frozen ground, improper blasting of the face can initiate an undesirable cycle of events due to unsatisfactory breakage and extensive backbreak as illustrated in Fig. 6.8 (Ives 1962, Lang 1966, 1976). Successive blasts increase the backbreak, the pit floor becomes higher and finally the removal of shattered material by power shovels or loaders becomes impossible. Reblasting of the material from the unsuccessful primary blast or blasting the toe and pit floor are necessary. Large blocks resulting from insufficient fragmentation must be broken by secondary drilling and blasting or by mechanical percussion (e.g., drop ball) so they can be handled by a shovel (Fig. 6.9). Sometimes the large blocks are left to thaw naturally. Extensive backbreak makes further drilling difficult. In such cases, preshearing in multiple row or controlled perimeter blasting is used to reduce backbreak (Ives 1962, Mellor 1975c). By staggering the firing sequence and using lighter charges at the limit of the excavation, backbreak and the need for secondary fragmentation can be reduced.

Mellor and Sellman (1970) found distinct advantages in the use of liquid or slurry explosives placed in slots for excavating frozen materials. Shot hole drilling is less expensive since only small holes are required. Coupling characteristics of liquid explosives are superior to those of solid explosives. Some sensitive explosives may be unsafe in cold climates, but slurries have not presented any unusual safety problems. A special slurry explosive that is still pliable at $-30°F$ ($-35°C$) was developed for use under the low ambient temperatures experienced at an open pit mine at Asbestos Hill, Quebec. Good results were obtained when it was used to blast perennially frozen asbestos ore having a mean temperature of $19°F$ ($-7°C$) (Lang 1976). A manual on drilling and blasting for loosening frozen ground has been published in the U.S.S.R. (1972).

6.2.4 Borrow Pits and Stockpiles

The choice and development of borrow pits requires considerable study and care to yield an economic construction operation with minimum effects on the environment. The quantity of suitable material available and the amount of stripping required must be established by drilling and sampling investigations carried out in advance of construction. Where the volume of material to be stripped and wasted is great, the development of large, deep borrow pits, will generally be economical and have less impact on the environment. All wasted material is normally stockpiled well away from streams; much of it may be used for restoration of the pits.

The advance preparation of borrow pits and materials intended for winter excavation and placement is essential to an efficient construction operation. Podkopaev (1973) reports on the technique used in connection with the construction of dams and dykes in the Soviet North. In the fall, the borrow pits are protected against freezing by cross-ripping the moss cover and underlying peat and mixing them with harrows. The area is then covered with an additional 2 ft. (0.6 m) of topsoil. During the winter the borrow material is excavated in narrow

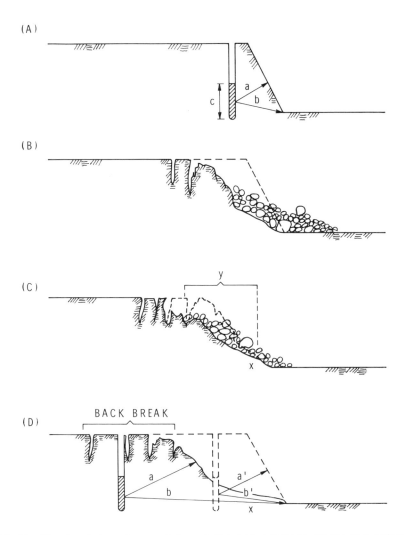

(A) Idealized mining face - (a) and (b) are critical distances between
    centre of the "charge" (c) and the mining face.   (a) is termed the
    "burden", and (b) the "toe distance".

(B) Moderately successful blast on initial idealized face.

(C) Successive blast leaving extended "toe" at (x).   Shattered ore in
    sector (y) difficult to remove because electric shovel unable to
    approach over (x).

(D) Actual mining face compared with idealized face showing situation
    which would result in serious production hold-up. Compare critical
    distances (a) and (b) with (a') and (b').   Extensive secondary drilling
    and blasting of the extended toe (x) would be required here.

FIG. 6.8   Blasting problems in a deep excavation (After Ives 1962).

FIG. 6.9 Large blocks of frozen ground in foreground at toe of blasted pit face will require secondary blasting or will be left to thaw. Note man amongst blocks for scale (After Brown 1970a).

sections not more than 60 ft. (20 m) wide. The optimum number of scrapers and trucks is used so that the soil can be delivered continuously to the construction area. When sufficient material has been delivered to one site, dumping is started on the next while the first is leveled and compacted. Salt solutions are added to the soil to prevent freezing during transport. At an air temperature of $-4°F$ ($-20°C$) 0.5 to 1 gal. (2 to 4 L) of salt solution (27% salt to water by weight) per 35 ft.^{3} (1 m^3) of soil was used.

Before excavation is started in a borrow pit the organic material overlying the borrow material should be stripped and pushed to one side. When the excavation is complete, this material can be spread on the pit slopes to insulate and reduce degradation of the permafrost and provide a seed bed for revegetation. When feasible, frozen or wet borrow material to be used as fill should be stockpiled as early as possible in the spring so that it will thaw and drain before it is placed. Soviet experience with this procedure is described by Biyanov (1970a) and Zhilenas et al. (1973). The organic layer is removed from the borrow pits in the spring and during the summer the thawed material is scraped into piles or wind-rows. The soils are blended to a fairly uniform composition and placed in stockpiles. The moisture in fine-grained soils then has time to distribute itself uniformly throughout the pile before the soil is used; any excess moisture can drain off. Heat accumulated through solar radiation is retained within the pile and with the onset of cold weather will retard freezing to a certain extent. Salt can be mixed into the top 6 to 10 ft. (2 to 3 m) of the material if required to limit the depth of freezing.

Pit-run, screened or crushed material stockpiled for use in future years will usually freeze completely and may be difficult and costly to recover. Snow melt water and summer precipitation, in addition to the moisture in the material when it was stockpiled, will freeze and solidly bond the mass. Consideration should thus be given in advance to methods that can be used to protect the pile or reclaim the material when needed. The materials can be covered with tarpaulins, placed within sheds, or closed-end pipes may be installed as the pile is built so that heat can be introduced to thaw the material. In some cases, rippers or drilling and blasting may be required. The approach taken will depend on the type and quantity of material stockpiled, the time of year it will be required (summer or winter) and the cost of reclamation. Consideration should also be given to the geometry of the stockpile, e.g. conical vs trapezoidal, high vs low.

6.2.5 Drainage

Drainage problems can be troublesome and should be anticipated and taken into account when planning an excavation operation in any part of the permafrost region. Water can greatly complicate excavation work during winter or summer, whether it be for a highway cut, borrow pit or foundation. Water may enter the excavation from the surface or percolate through the active layer. It may result from melting of ice deposits in frozen materials, or it may be found in taliks or springs in the permafrost. Large-scale sloughing of pit walls, wetting of otherwise dry construction materials, uncontrolled thawing of the bottom of an excavation and serious icing conditions in the pit are some of the problems encountered.

To ensure proper drainage, ditches, culverts and pumps should be provided and the excavation worked so that water will always drain to a sump or drainage outlet at a low spot (Fig. 6.10). The walls of the excavation may have to be protected to retard thawing, sloughing and inflow of water. South-facing walls will thaw more quickly than others. Excavated materials stockpiled to dry or for future use should be stored in carefully selected areas on higher ground. Similarly, waste piles of unsuitable material, such as ice-rich fine-grained soils and organic materials, should be located so that when thawing they will not flow into the excavation or nearby streams, nor interfere with the local natural drainage.

All abandoned borrow pits that have no natural drainage outlet will fill with water. In some cases a permanent ice layer will be formed in the bottom. Special consideration must be given to those that are deep and will not be used again, to ensure that they are left in a safe and environmentally acceptable condition. Waste material can be used to backfill them, or a protective fence may have to be erected if they are near communities or readily accessible to the public.

FIG. 6.10   (a) Borrow pit is worked so that melt water from thawing ground ice in
granular deposit drains to low spot. (b) Abandoned highway borrow pit in
discontinuous permafrost zone. Note neatly trimmed waste piles and pit slopes, minimal
disturbance to surrounding forest cover and angled access road and tree barrier so that
pit cannot be seen from the road.

6.3 Transport

Dry frozen materials can be handled readily throughout the year and hard frozen materials during the winter, using standard earth moving equipment including loaders, dozers, trucks, scrapers, belt conveyors and railroad cars. Dust may prove troublesome, however, even during the winter when it will adhere to heated windshields, plug radiators, cause problems with bearings, rollers and sprockets and drastically reduce visibility on haul roads during the long dark periods. On the other hand, wet thawed or thawing materials are usually difficult to handle, mainly because they will freeze to virtually every surface with which they come in contact, except during the relatively short summer period when temperatures are above freezing.

Depending on the type and ultimate use of the material (e.g., road fill, dam core, mine ore), if it is wet it is usually necessary to reduce its moisture content to improve handling efficiency and prepare it for its intended use. This can be accomplished by mixing it with dry material, storing it in heated sheds or placing it in windrows where it can be turned over and mixed to dry. Alternatively, salts can be added to prevent freezing, or the surfaces with which the material comes in contact can be heated. The problem of freezing to surfaces appears to be most acute at air temperatures between 14° and 32°F (-10°C and 0°C). The moisture content of ore concentrates at a mine on Baffin Island is maintained between 4 and 6% to facilitate handling and transport, prevent freezing and control dust (Northern Miner 1974).

Heavy duty trucks of various sizes and self-powered scrapers are used to haul materials from borrow pits and open pit mines over long distances (>0.5 mile; 1 km). Floating dredges have been used occasionally to remove overburden in mining operations, such as the placer gold fields in the Yukon and open pit nickel mines at Thompson, Manitoba, and to build oil and gas drilling platforms in shallow water at the mouth of the Mackenzie River. Various types of conveyors, trucks, bulldozers, loaders and shuttle cars are used to transport frozen materials over short distances. For example, they are used to move materials at rock quarries, aggregates at crushing and concrete and asphalt batching plants, and to transport mine ores underground and within mineral processing plant areas.

Aitken (1970) discusses the transport of frozen soils and Foster-Miller Associates (1965) investigated several concepts, including mechanical, hydraulic and pneumatic systems. The mechanical systems included belt conveyors, screw conveyors, vibratory conveyors and shuttle cars. Belt conveyors have been used on mine operations in northern Canada (Dubnie 1972) with the entire system enclosed and either heated or kept cold. If a cold system is selected the materials must be dry to avoid icing and freezing problems. Belts of synthetic rubber become stiff and brittle at cold temperatures so natural rubber must be used. By careful selection of materials and procedures, there is little difficulty in operating conveyors at temperatures down to -40°F (-40°C) but some increase in operating power is to be expected. Shuttle cars are used underground, but the buildup of frozen fine particles in the cars is a serious problem. Sprinkling salt on the empty cars prevents freezing to some extent. The only way to avoid this problem completely is to keep the soil as dry as possible and periodically clean the equipment.

Hydraulic systems investigated involved mixing the frozen material with a hot liquid in a large tank. The resulting slurry is then pumped to a settling pond or tank and the liquid recirculated. This system is highly impractical for transporting frozen soils. Pneumatic systems studied ranged from pressure and vacuum systems to a jet stream conveyor, but were extremely sensitive to particle size and impractical due to high costs.

6.4 Placement

Placement of soils in cold regions has been carried out with varied success. Cold weather problems and the handling of materials are described in several case histories (MacDonald et al. 1960, Bernell 1965, Low and Lyell 1967, Nikiforov 1968, Biyanov 1970a, Tsytovich and Kronik 1970, Batenchuk et al. 1968, Heiner 1972, Myznikov et al. 1973, Podkopaev 1973, Zhilenas et al. 1973, Kane 1974, Pepler and MacKenzie 1976).

In most cases, the placement of frozen material is prohibited unless it can be satisfactorily compacted and maintained in a frozen condition for the life of the particular structure. Sometimes, frozen low-ice-content soils can be placed in berms and side slopes of an embankment, provided that on thawing they will not detrimentally affect the main structure (Fig. 6.11). The main concerns with the use of frozen soils in an embankment are those of excessive settlement and loss of stability upon thawing, due to the difficulty of obtaining proper compaction and the resulting low densities.

In backfilling foundation excavations and completing placement of materials behind walls and abutments, the use of dry, cohesionless, non-frost-susceptible materials is most important. Backfilling an excavation should begin as soon as possible to preserve the surrounding permafrost. This is particularly important when ice-rich fine-grained soils are present.

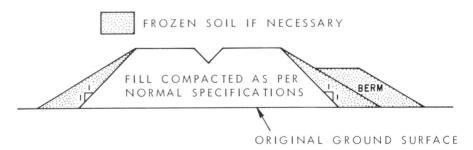

FIG. 6.11   Locations where relatively low ice content frozen soil can be placed without significant detrimental effects to the structure or the environment.

COLD REGIONS EARTHWORK   241

6.4.1 Compaction

Frozen soils cannot be compacted satisfactorily and those with high ice contents, upon thawing, may contain large voids, exhibit loss of strength, and flow or slump. Proper compaction of unfrozen soils placed at freezing temperatures is difficult, depending on their moisture content. Most agencies limit or prohibit the placement of unfrozen soils in embankments and fills during freezing weather due to the difficulty of obtaining specified densities and the implied problems of frost heave, settlement and inadequate strength upon thawing of frozen material. Highter et al. (1970) recognized that low temperature compaction is equivalent to a reduced compactive effort and results in a decrease in density, degree of saturation, and undrained strength. Cold but unfrozen soil may be successfully compacted by increasing the compactive effort.

The moisture content of sands and gravels must be low if they are to be compacted satisfactorily at low temperatures. Bernell (1965) determined that the moisture content must be less than 1% if the required density is to equal the maximum value that can be obtained for the same material in an unfrozen condition. Good drainage of the borrow area is generally required to achieve lower moisture contents. Lowering the ground water table before excavation may be expedient, depending upon the grain size distribution and permeability of the material. Frozen sand and gravel having a low moisture content can be properly compacted at subzero temperatures using heavy tractors, trucks and rollers.

Heiner (1972) conducted laboratory studies of the compaction properties of several soils at freezing temperatures. Two test procedures were used: (1) water was mixed uniformly with the soil, which was then spread loosely in a thin layer, allowed to freeze and then compacted and (2) the soil was compacted and frozen, crushed to a maximum lump size of 5/8 in. (16 mm) in diameter and then compacted again. It was found that the energy used to compact frozen soils has a large effect on the relative compaction, and the effect increases with increasing water content. The compaction curves obtained for a granular material compacted at subzero temperatures are shown in Fig. 6.12. To achieve a relative compaction of 90% of the maximum modified AASHO value, the test results obtained for two typical soils showed that the water content of these soils should not exceed the following values:

Soil Type	-5°C		-10°C	
	Case 1	Case 2	Case 1	Case 2
Husby sand	6%	10%	3.5%	3.5%
Silty sandy moraine	5%	6%	3.5%	3.5%

The results of an experimental program conducted to determine the effect of low temperatures on the compaction characteristics of a silty sand, including increased compactive effort and the use of chemical additives to improve the densities of soils, are reported by Haas et al. (1978).

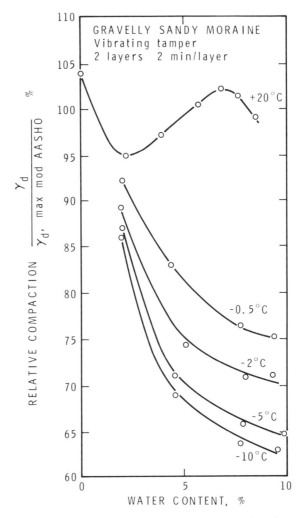

FIG. 6.12 Compaction curves for a granular material placed at freezing temperatures (After Heiner 1972).

Placement of impervious core material for dams and dykes, where it is essential that compaction and void ratio be closely controlled, is normally carried out during the summer. Fill can be placed in cold weather, however, if the effect on stability and settlement is considered both in design and during construction. Materials should be dried and then placed and compacted in layers about 1 ft. (300 mm) or less in thickness. Every effort should be made to ensure uniform compaction. Over-compaction of some layers due to the passage of heavy equipment can cause shear failures within the fill.

When the air temperature is below freezing, placement and compaction of unfrozen soil should be carried out as soon as possible after the soil has been excavated to prevent the material from freezing. The temperature of soil that is un-frozen when excavated decreases relatively slowly since a large amount of heat (heat of fusion) must be dissipated during freezing. If the soil is already frozen, then its temperature will decrease rapidly after excavation. Nikiforov (1968) found that placement of sand and clay was severely affected by air temperature and wind and the size of the working area had to be restricted.

When compaction is being carried out at low air temperatures, density tests should be made much more frequently (compared to normal warm weather prac-tice) to ensure adequate control. If the tests indicate that the required compaction is not being achieved, adjustments can be made to the type or water content of fill being placed, the compactive effort increased or further placement stopped until conditions become more favourable.

The temperature of the soil on delivery greatly affects placement and compac-tion operations. During construction of the Portage Mountain Dam in British Columbia (Low and Lyell 1967), placement of the impervious core material was successfully completed to the optimum density at an air temperature of 25°F (-4°C), provided the delivery temperature of the core material was between 35° and 40°F (2° and 5°C) and it was spread and compacted without delay. Similarly, granular material was successfully placed when the air temperature was about 16°F (-9°C) and the delivery temperature of the materials was about 34°F (1°C). A careful check was made on delivery temperatures and on surface and in-terior temperatures of the fill. The fill was placed in relatively small areas and the frequency of density testing was increased over normal practice. When the dens-ity tests indicated that the required compaction (within 10% of optimum) was not being achieved, further placement of fill was stopped.

During construction of the impervious core of the main dam at the Kelsey Generating Station in northern Manitoba (MacDonald et al. 1960) it was impossi-ble to drain and dry the clay borrow material. Clay with a moisture content up to 130% of Proctor optimum was used and densities as low as 90% of the Proctor maximum were accepted. To compensate for the low densities the upstream slope of the dam was flattened and a berm added. When freezing temperatures were ex-perienced in September and October, calcium chloride was added to the fill in amounts of 5 lb./yd.[3] (3 kg/m³) of clay as it was loaded in trucks at the borrow pit. In November when air temperatures were between 0° and 15°F (-18° and -9°C) the fill was placed and compacted within a movable heated enclosure con-sisting of a timber frame covered with polyethylene tarpaulins. The temperature within the enclosure was maintained between 25 and 35°F (-4 and 2°C). The calcium chloride content was increased to 10 to 15 lb./yd.[3] (6 to 9 kg/m³) and the trucks were covered by tarpaulins during transit. Clay was not placed when the outside temperature fell below 0°F (-18°C).

If freezing of the soil in place is a problem, then additives such as calcium chloride mixed with the soil prior to placement will lower the freezing point and maintain a relatively plastic condition (Alkire et al. 1975). Lifts can be placed on a slope to reduce the area exposed to freezing (Fig. 6.13). Straw can be spread

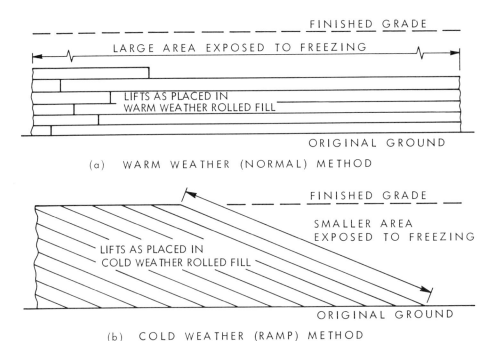

FIG. 6.13   Embankment profiles comparing placement of soil in warm weather vs cold weather lifts for compacted fills (After Lovell and Osborne 1968).

over the exposed surface or tarpaulins can be laid down and hot air forced underneath to retard freezing. Various materials, including gravel blankets, artificial snow and straw, have been used to insulate and reduce or prevent frost penetration into and deterioration of the impervious cores of dams during the winter (Engineering News-Record 1967, Engineering and Contract Record 1975, Low and Lyell 1967, McKeown and Matheson 1977). Frozen material in the body of dams and dykes should be removed before successive lifts are placed.

Displacement or movement of frozen lumps when frozen soil is being compacted is an important problem. To obtain a high relative density, the lumps must be crushed. High relative compaction is usually obtained with sheepsfoot rollers; rubber-tired or smooth wheel rollers are generally not effective. This difference can partly be explained by the high contact pressures from the sheepsfoot and the resultant crushing of the frozen lumps.

A laboratory study of the compaction of frozen lumps of silty sand at a temperature of $20°F$ ($-7°C$) was undertaken by Alkire et al. (1975). The curve of dry density vs water content is bilinear (Fig. 6.14) with the intercept at a water content of about 3% where all the soil particles are found to be coated with ice. The addition of calcium chloride to the soil water before freezing caused an increase in dry density as shown in Fig. 6.14. The calcium chloride lowered the freezing temperature of the soil water and thus reduced the shear strength of the frozen lumps.

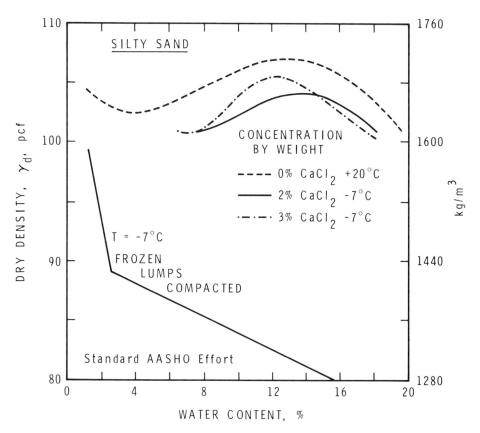

FIG. 6.14   Low temperature compaction of a silty sand (After Alkire et al. 1975).

6.4.2 Placement in Water

In the Soviet Union, the placement of cohesive soils in fills and embankments is usually not permitted when the air temperature is below 14°F (−10°C). When local materials and construction schedules require, however, Soviet engineers have successfully placed frozen cohesive soils, such as loess and clay, in water during summer and winter construction of several earth dams (Batenchuk et al. 1968). An exceptional example was the placement of cohesive soils in water heated electrically to 60°F (15°C) when the air temperature was as low as −12°F (−25°C), carried out during construction of the dam at the Irkutskaya Generating Station. Salt and an air bubbler system were used to prevent the formation of an ice cover on the water within the cofferdams.

Winter placement of frozen soils in artificial ponds to enable construction operations to proceed involves a number of successive operations, including the construction of containing dykes in the dry prior to the winter (Evdokimov 1970). The size of the settling pond created can be critical. Depending on the surface area and depth of the pond, heat may be required to keep the water from freez-ing. It is desirable that surface area of the pond be limited but this means that the volume of soil placed in the dry for the perimeter dykes can be a large portion of the total fill required. If an ice cover forms on the pond, holes or trenches have to be cut in the ice and kept open so that the soil can be placed.

Placement of frozen soils in natural ponds, lakes or rivers can be done if re-quired, subject to environmental restrictions. Such an operation can be useful in building cofferdams, temporary dykes, causeways for light traffic and other structures where some settlement and distortion can be tolerated or corrected. Materials with an ice content greatly in excess of optimum moisture content should not be used. A small-scale test is advisable at the start of the operation to determine the characteristics of the thawed submerged soil. It should include a sufficient proportion of gravel and stone sizes to resist erosion by water currents after it thaws.

The material should be dumped on the end of the fill and bulldozed into the water so that it slides into place and displaces rather then entraps water (Adams and Bazett 1963). If an ice cover is present it must be broken by a backhoe or dragline bucket ahead of the fill placement area. In cold weather rapid accumula-tion of ice can be a problem, limiting the extent to which the fill can economically be placed. Excavation of the accumulated ice may be necessary.

More than fifteen temporary artificial islands have been constructed for drill-ing platforms by various petroleum companies in water up to 40 ft. (12 m) deep in the Beaufort Sea since 1972 (Hayley and Sangster 1974, Riley 1976, Brown 1976, Oilweek 1976). Many were built using granular material from borrow pits on shore, hauled by trucks over the ice or by tug and barge in the summer. Material has also been salvaged from abandoned islands and dredged from the sea bed. As much as 2.5 million cu. yd. (1.9 Mm^3) of fill has been placed for some of these structures. Design and construction aspects are discussed in Section 7.13.3.

CHAPTER 7

Foundations

(Contributors–D. M. Davison, M. C. Harris, D. W. Hayley,
G. H. Johnston, B. Ladanyi, G. McCormick,
J. F. Nixon and E. Penner)

PART I—DESIGN CONSIDERATIONS

7.1 General Considerations

The design and construction of foundations in the North are affected by a number of factors that are different either in kind or degree or will have a greater influence than they would in non-permafrost areas. They must be given thorough consideration, both individually and in combination, if economical, safe and sound foundations are to be constructed. The existence of permafrost (a thermally sensitive soil state) presents special engineering problems. The severe climate, short construction season, lack of local building materials, remote location of many sites and environmental concerns affect logistics and construction methods and scheduling, as discussed in Chapter 1.

Other important considerations include the type and use of the structure to be supported, site conditions, the results of analyses of the ground thermal regime and the strength and deformation characteristics of foundation soils, frost action and drainage. Site conditions will frequently dictate the location of the structure and the type of foundation and design approach to be used. Detailed site investigations are mandatory; many failures can be attributed to lack of subsurface information or to incorrect interpretation of site information and test results. Careful office evaluation of all factors is not always enough; much will also depend on the designer's previous northern experience and sound engineering judgment in the design and construction of foundations to ensure they will perform satisfactorily.

To ensure the satisfactory performance of structures in permafrost areas, foundations must be selected and designed so that neither failure of the foundation soil nor unacceptable deformations will occur during the service life of the structure. The usual design procedure for unfrozen soils is to determine the foundation design loads, determine representative soil strength and deformation characteristics, select a foundation type and assess the allowable settlement and factor of safety against soil failure. The latter are usually carried out using acceptable theoretical solutions or empirical formulae (Canadian Geotechnical Society 1978).

Although this design procedure is essentially valid for both unfrozen and frozen materials, it is clear that, whereas unfrozen soils are normally considered to be "temperature-stable," the mechanical properties and deformation (creep) behaviour of frozen soils are greatly affected by changes in temperature and are frequently "temperature-unstable" due mainly to their high ice and unfrozen water contents, as discussed in Chapter 3. Within the usual range of permafrost temperatures the strength of frozen soils decreases rapidly and settlements increase significantly with increase in temperature but the most radical changes occur at temperatures near 32°F (0°C), when much or all of the ice is transformed into water. The decrease in strength near or at thawing is much less for dense granular materials containing only pore ice than for fine-grained soils with segregated ice. On thawing, significant settlements of fine-grained and loose, coarse-grained soils can be expected to occur under their own weight and the imposed foundation loads. Little is known about the strength and deformation behaviour of frozen saline soils. Since they may be encountered not only in coastal areas but also at some inland locations, special attention must be given to determining their distribution, properties and behaviour under load.

The anticipated service life of a particular type of structure and the degree of maintenance that can be tolerated will influence foundation design. Important structural and thermal characteristics of the structure include dead and live loads, dynamic loads due to machinery or earthquakes, structural flexibility or rigidity, tolerable total and differential movements (both settlement and heave), floor elevation relative to surrounding grades, temperatures to be maintained in the structure, the location and influence of heat generating equipment within the structure and special functional requirements.

The correct choice of construction method can be made only when all engineering and economic factors have been evaluated. A simple comparison of estimated construction costs is not always the deciding factor. Planning and scheduling of foundation construction will also greatly influence final decisions and costs.

Regardless of the construction method used, building sites should be carefully selected and prepared to prevent detrimental disturbance of the ground surface and thermal regime due to construction activity and to ensure proper drainage of surface and subsurface water (including waste water and snow melt water) away from the structure(s) and the site as a whole. The site should preferably be located on high ground. Fill is normally placed on the ground surface and graded to ensure good drainage and provide access and a working surface for construction equipment. Poor drainage and ponding of water can seriously affect the ground thermal regime and cause damage to structures due to permafrost degradation and frost action.

The surface of a fill must be graded so that water will not pond under or adjacent to a structure and measures taken to minimize percolation of water through the fill pad and prevent erosion of its surface and side slopes and the surrounding ground surface. Subsidence and sloughing of the slopes may occur due to degradation of permafrost at the toe and under the slopes of a compacted fill pad. The fill should extend at least 6 to 10 ft. (2 to 3 m) beyond the perimeter of a structure to ensure that the integrity of the foundation is not endangered. Ditches should be avoided wherever possible, for they may cause serious soil erosion and permafrost degradation problems, particularly in ice-rich ground. If ditches are essential, they should be wide and shallow with low gradients.

Both shallow and deep foundations are frequently subjected to large uplift forces caused by frost action in the active layer. Heaving may result from vertical forces acting on the base of a foundation or on a grade beam or pile cap, and from adfreeze forces, sometimes called "frost grip," on the sides of foundation units including footings, posts, piers and piles. The heave forces can be significant and must be taken into account as discussed in Section 7.3.

The ground thermal situation should be evaluated once the design criteria and site conditions are known. Due to the particular sensitivity of frozen soils to temperature change, foundation design in permafrost areas must include an accurate assessment of the ground thermal regime not only prior to and at the time of construction but also during the entire life of the structure. The settlement of a foundation on frozen ground at any point in time is a function of the previous history of soil temperature variation up to that time, while its safety against failure depends upon the most unfavourable temperature conditions that may occur during the life of the structure. On the other hand, the rate of settlement and safety of a foundation placed on thawing soil depends on the rate of thaw and its relationship to the rate at which consolidation of the thawed soil takes place. Changes that will occur in the location of the permafrost table and in the ground thermal regime under and around a structure can be estimated using methods described in Chapter 4 to provide a basis for bearing capacity and settlement analyses. Thermal calculations can be made with greater confidence when soil and air temperature records (or previous experience) are available than when estimates have to be made without the benefit of site information.

After the ground thermal situation for the design life of the structure is evaluated, the time- and temperature-dependent engineering properties of the soil, such as thaw-consolidation, thawed and frozen strength and deformation characteristics, including frozen creep behaviour, must be determined (Chapter 3 and Section 5.6). Analyses of settlement, bearing capacity and stability of the foundation soil and dynamic analyses, when required, related to the specific structure and type of foundation can then be carried out.

7.1.1 Foundation Design Approach

If the foundation materials consist of sound, ice-free rock or dense glacial till or clean, non-frost-susceptible, well-drained sand or gravel deposits that are stable when thawing or thawed, then the frozen condition can be neglected in most cases and conventional foundation designs used. If the materials are thaw unstable, however, then two principal methods or approaches to foundation design in permafrost areas are usually considered. The "Passive Method" is the most

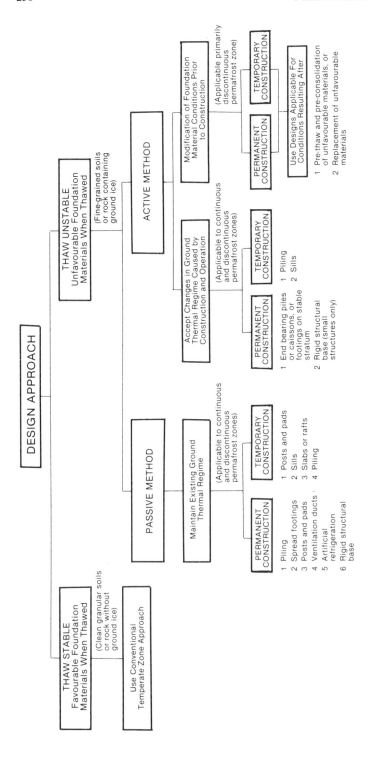

FIG. 7.1 Foundation schemes for permafrost areas.

desirable approach and the one commonly used for permanent structures. In the passive method the foundation materials are maintained in a frozen state for the entire service life of the structure. When permafrost degradation cannot be prevented, the "Active Method" must be considered. In this case, two main approaches are possible. Unfavourable foundation materials are thawed and compacted or removed and replaced with more suitable materials prior to construction or, alternatively, the foundations and structure are designed to accommodate the settlements that will occur as thawing progresses while the structure is in use. These methods are outlined in Fig. 7.1 together with the types of foundations that can be used for buildings and similar structures.

7.1.1.1 *Passive Method*

The passive method is used when the foundation soils are hard frozen in their natural state and contain little or no unfrozen water. When plastic-frozen soils that have a relatively high unfrozen water content and will deform significantly under load are encountered, measures must be taken to reduce and maintain the temperature of the soil below that of its original natural state. Special attention must be given to foundation soils that contain excess ice, particularly when large, massive ice deposits are present, because of the significant creep deformations that will occur with time at any frozen ground temperature.

It is usually economically feasible to maintain foundation soils in a frozen condition in the continuous permafrost zone, but more difficult, if not impossible, to do so in the southern part of the discontinuous permafrost zone. Between these two areas, careful investigation and consideration of the particular site conditions and structure requirements are necessary to establish whether or not the permafrost condition can be preserved economically. As a rough guide, the situation should be critically evaluated when the mean ground temperature is warmer than about $27°F$ ($-3°C$), if the ground is to be maintained in a frozen condition following construction.

The thermal interaction between a heated structure and the underlying frozen ground is complex. A heated structure placed directly on grade will ultimately cause the underlying frozen material to thaw and result in settlement of the structure. Heat flow from a structure to the underlying frozen ground is a fundamental consideration but degradation of permafrost may occur not only from structure heat loss but also from other heat sources resulting from disturbance to the surrounding ground surface, solar radiation, surface drainage, underground utilities and groundwater flow. Ventilation and insulation techniques are the principal methods used in the passive approach to maintain the frozen ground within a specified design temperature range.

Ventilation is accomplished either by raising the structure above the ground surface on piles or posts so that there is a clear space between the bottom of the structure and the ground surface or by placing ducts in the floor system or a fill pad under the structure. Movement of cold air through the airspace or ducts during the winter dissipates heat from the structure above and refreezes and chills the

FIG. 7.2   Duct-ventilated foundation pad for small heated oil tank.

foundation soils, controlling the thickness of the active layer and the temperature of the frozen ground. Air movement by wind or natural convection will occur in the clear space under a structure and, because the ground surface is shaded and cool in summer and relatively snow free and cold in winter, a net cooling of the ground generally will occur in time (Lobacz and Quinn 1966). A clear airspace of at least 2 ft. (0.6 m) should be provided under most structures; it may have to be increased for large structures. In many cases, if a well-ventilated airspace is provided and maintained, it may be safe to assume that the original ground temperature conditions will not change during the life of the structure and the existing warmest soil temperature profile can be used for design purposes.

Duct-ventilated fill pads are used to support various types of structures, such as aircraft hangars, oil tanks and maintenance garages, that are heated and must be placed on grade for easy access and to distribute heavy loads (Williams 1959, Sanger 1969). For small structures the system may simply consist of a series of parallel, open-ended pipes through which air moves by natural convection (Fig. 7.2). For large structures, and particularly those operated at relatively warm temperatures the year round, air must usually be moved through the ducts by fans to ensure adequate air circulation and removal of heat from the structure and the ground below. In this case, the pad ducts are connected to buried manifolds or header pipes, having vertical inlet and outlet stacks (Fig. 7.3). Fans are mounted in the stacks and move cold air through the system at a predetermined rate during

FIG. 7.3 Duct-ventilated foundation for small powerhouse. During winter air is forced through buried manifolds and duct system by fan mounted in inlet duct on left and exhausted through outlet duct on right. Inlet and outlet ducts are closed during summer.

the winter only. All types of duct systems must be closed when air temperatures are above about 27°F (-3°C) to prevent circulation of warm air and undesirable changes in the ground thermal regime. This will depend primarily upon the length of the warm season and maximum air temperatures experienced during it, the type of duct system and structure operating conditions (heat losses), as well as the effect on the foundation soil temperatures.

Several factors must be considered in the design of a ventilated foundation. These include, in addition to the type of structure and its operating characteristics, the amount of heat that must be removed to control the depth of thaw in the summer and to ensure freezeback of the foundation soils in winter, local wind direction and velocities, particularly in the winter (so that the structure and ducts can be located and oriented properly), air temperatures, air movement in a clear space beneath a structure, friction losses and resistance to air flow in a duct system, provision of temperature instrumentation to monitor performance of a ventilated foundation (and, in some cases, to control operation of fans in a forced air system) and the reliability of the mechanical components in a forced air system. The design of several types of duct-ventilated systems are described by U.S. Army/Air Force (1966c), Sanger (1969), Auld et al. (1978) and Nixon (1978a).

Structures supported on duct-ventilated foundations where circulation of air is by natural convection utilizing the "chimney" or "stack" effect have experienced operating and foundation settlement problems (Tobiasson 1973). Ducts must be watertight and stack inlets and outlets should be equipped with louvres to prevent snow entering the system and to allow them to be closed in the summer. Consideration should be given to providing ready access to ducts so that obstructions such as snow, ice, water or sediment can be removed. Problems have also been experienced by structures raised above the ground surface when water has been allowed to flow or pond under the building or movement of air during the winter has been obstructed by snowdrifts, storage of materials or the installation of skirting around the perimeter of the structure. It is vital that circulation of cold air be unimpeded in an airspace or duct system during the winter. To reduce the effect of solar radiation in summer, light coloured panels can be installed around the perimeter of a structure (Fig. 7.4). These reflective panels must be louvred or have sufficiently large openings in or under them, so that they do not inhibit free movement of air in the space under the structure during the winter and yet will provide shade around the perimeter during the summer.

FIG. 7.4 Light-coloured reflector panels mounted on south side of building on piles to reduce solar heat gain and thawing.

It is common practice to place a granular fill pad on the ground surface for most types of foundations. In many cases the pad, which should extend at least 10 ft. (3 m) beyond the edge of the structure, not only helps to level a site and provide a working surface during construction, but may also offer resistance to heat flow into the ground if it is sufficiently thick. Where permafrost degradation will occur a layer of insulation, such as peat or a synthetic material, may be placed in the pad, on the original ground surface or beneath footings or piers embedded in frozen ground. This will help to reduce or control the depth of thaw and the wide fluctuations in ground temperature that normally occur at shallow depths below the original ground surface and to maintain the foundation soil in a frozen state. It must be recognized that, in most situations, no reasonable thickness of fill and insulation will prevent ultimate thawing of the permafrost under a heated building placed on ground. In such cases, ventilated foundations must be used, together with insulation.

The "in-ground" insulations used are usually synthetic rigid board or foamed-in-place types that have a high compressive strength and will not absorb moisture while they are in service. The type selected will depend on site conditions, thermal design requirements, the loads to be carried during construction and subsequent operation of the structure and method of installing the insulation. Significant cracking or displacement of the insulation during installation or under load, or absorption of moisture will rapidly destroy its effectiveness as a thermal barrier. Conventional types of building insulations are used in floor systems to reduce heat losses from structures.

The frozen ground condition can also be maintained by a mechanical refrigeration system, but, because of high cost, it is normally employed only when warranted by special structures and foundation conditions or for remedial purposes (Essoglou 1957, Henderson 1959, Fife 1960 and Crory 1973b). Refrigerated foundations may be justified for structures, such as radar towers, that have stringent foundation rigidity and movement requirements, and for facilities requiring deep excavations in frozen ground. A refrigeration system can also be used to accelerate freezeback of slurried piles or backfilled footings or piers, particularly in warm permafrost, and to stabilize existing structures that are in distress due to serious differential settlement caused by unanticipated local thawing or inadequate design. The use of other devices or systems for cooling the ground are discussed in Section 7.7.1. Convection cells have been installed to reduce ground temperatures and stabilize the ground thermal regime under buildings supported by shallow foundations but their efficiency and reliability have not been established (Cronin 1977, Rayner 1976).

7.1.1.2 *Active Method*

The active method is used only if the foundations can bear on a stable stratum (such as competent bedrock or a dense, thaw-stable soil stratum at shallow depth), or when total or differential settlement of the foundation soils within the estimated thaw zone will not exceed tolerable limits and if the thawing soil will maintain adequate shear strength. It may also be used, regardless of the soil compressibility, when very permeable frozen soils can be thawed or when it is not economically feasible to keep such soils frozen. The choice of whether gradual thawing of foundation soils may be allowed while the structure is in operation or whether preliminary thawing is required prior to construction should be based on estimates of probably settlement during and following thawing of the frozen foundation materials using procedures described in Section 3.7. If allowable settlements will be exceeded, then preconstruction thawing using steam points, electrical or gas heaters or some other means of applying heat should be carried out and the troublesome material compacted. Alternatively, the undesirable material can be excavated using explosives, rippers or other means and replaced by well-drained, compacted, non-frost-susceptible granular material. The excavation and backfilling operations should be carried out as rapidly as possible to avoid undue disturbance to the surrounding frozen ground. Adequate drainage must be provided to ensure that water will not enter or be trapped in the backfilled excavation surrounded by frozen ground and cause problems in the future.

It may also be possible to design a strong and rigid structure that will withstand settlement deformations and not suffer structural distress. Structures with foundation systems that can be adjusted as settlement occurs are another alternative. Differential ground settlements due to thawing are inevitable not only because the frozen materials are rarely homogeneous, but also because the rates of thaw will vary under a building. Thaw rates and settlements will usually be greater under

(a.)

(b.)

(c.)

FIG. 7.5 Examples of thaw settlement due to permafrost degradation under heated buildings: (a) warehouse and office building superstructure was removed after failure caused by settlement of concrete slab on gravel fill (no ducts or insulation), Norman Wells, N.W.T. (b) differential settlement of maintenance garage—concrete slab on thin gravel fill, Norman Wells, N.W.T. (c) failure of house with basement underlain by permafrost, Thompson, Manitoba.

the centre than at the edge of a building placed on grade and may be quite variable under a building whose various parts are maintained at different temperatures, unless measures are taken to compensate for the varying thermal loads. Settlement problems are particularly difficult when patches of frozen ground underlie a building site (Fig. 7.5). Construction of below-grade basements is not permitted in most areas because thawing cannot be prevented and large differential settlements and drainage problems will inevitably be experienced. Basements will perform satisfactorily only when founded on ice-free, dense frozen soils that are stable when thawed or when supported on piles.

It is usually difficult and very costly to design and construct foundations that will perform satisfactorily using the techniques just described. Normally, the design of foundations anticipating degradation of permafrost during the operating life of the structure or facility is only considered when foundation materials are thaw-stable or temporary construction is involved. A study by Paige and O'Brien (1972) indicated that the differential settlement experienced by the floor of a hangar at Barrow, Alaska could be controlled successfully by post-construction thawing using cold water.

Frequently, site conditions are such that either the passive or active method can be applied, but the choice must include consideration of both current and future uses of the site. Care must be taken to ensure that the foundation design of one structure will not have any detrimental thermal effects on the foundations of adjacent structures. This does not necessarily infer that thawing will occur. Even a small increase in the frozen ground temperature surrounding a new building may alter the strength and deformation characteristics of the soils under an adjacent building sufficiently to cause distress for the existing building. This is particularly critical, for example, if thawing is permitted under a building constructed next to a structure founded on piles that depend on frozen ground for their support. Foundation designs of adjacent structures must be thermally compatible; the thermal regime for which a foundation was designed must be maintained at a particular site if the existing structure is modified or added to or if new structures are erected nearby.

It is good practice to install temperature, movement and other instrumentation during construction to monitor the performance of foundations. Information collected will allow the validity of design assumptions to be checked and warn of any developments requiring attention.

7.2 Bearing Capacity of Foundations in Frozen Ground

Allowable foundation loads for unfrozen soils are based primarily upon soil deformation and shear strength considerations. For frozen soils, however, the effects of temperature on soil strength and deformation add a new dimension to the design and may become a primary factor in selecting allowable foundation pressures. Various aspects of the mechanical behaviour of frozen soils have been discussed in Chapter 3.

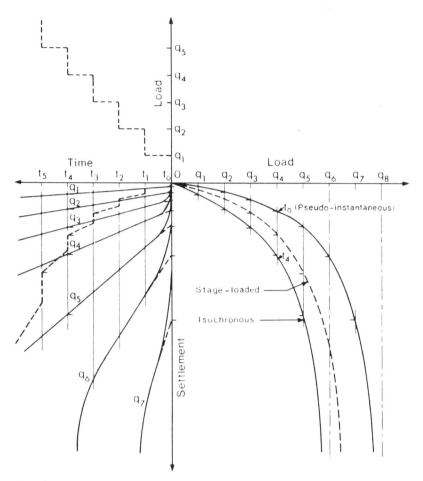

FIG. 7.6   Schematic presentation of load-settlement-time relationships in loading tests
(After Ladanyi and Johnston 1974).

The deformation-time (rheological) characteristics of frozen soils are responsible for the appearance of creep and decrease of strength with time, and must be
considered in the design of foundations bearing on frozen ground. The
phenomenon of creep involves deformations which increase with time under constant load as shown schematically in the lower left quadrant of Fig. 7.6. If the soil
is ice-poor, so that there is some particle to particle contact, and if the load is not
excessive the deformation will gradually stop. Ice-rich soils will probably creep at
a steady or secondary rate under low or intermediate loads (Fig. 7.6—curves q_1 to
q_5). Heavier loads may produce non-attenuating deformation, however, and
cause failure after some period of time (Fig. 7.6—curve q_6).

   The isochronous load-settlement curves in the lower right quadrant of Fig. 7.6
illustrate how the settlement of a loaded plate develops with time and how its

ultimate (asymptotic) bearing capacity decreases. Similar curves obtained by Vyalov (1959) for small circular plates subjected to constant loads for long periods of time are shown on Figure 7.7. These clearly confirm that the settlement rate increases significantly with increased load. The relationship between the load and the time to failure has been investigated by Vyalov (1962), Ladanyi (1972) and others. Evaluation of the time-dependent strength using Vyalov's method is based on the observation that the reciprocal of stress, $1/\sigma$, is related linearly to the logarithm of the time to failure. The strength at any time beyond the range of test duration may be obtained by extrapolating the data, as explained in Section 7.6.

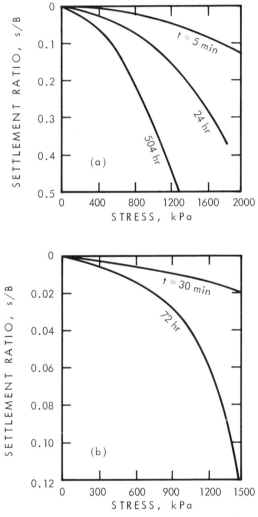

FIG. 7.7   Isochronous load-settlement curves from tests on circular plate—plate diameter (B) = 5 cm (After Vyalov 1959).

Small changes in ground temperature when the soil temperature is near 32°F (0°C) can cause a significant difference in soil behaviour. An increase in ground temperature from 30.0 to 30.6°F (−1.1 to −0.8°C) beneath a piled structure in Fairbanks, Alaska caused a considerable increase in settlement rate and required expensive remedial measures (Womick and LeGoullon 1975). On the other hand, a reduction in ground temperature of a few tenths of a degree, due to a well maintained airspace or the use of thermal piles, can induce a beneficial increase in strength and reduction in creep rate. Quantitative aspects of bearing capacity are discussed in Sections 7.6 and 7.10.

7.3 Frost Action and Foundations

Frost action in the active layer and seasonally frozen ground (discontinuous zone) in the permafrost region can subject foundations and structures to large uplift forces and destructive movements. It is an important consideration in the design of foundations for unheated buildings, bridges, power transmission and communication towers and structures supported by ventilated foundations such as piles and duct-ventilated pads. The frost action process and associated mechanisms are discussed in Section 3.8.

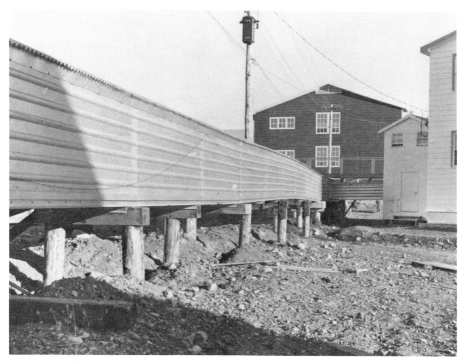

FIG. 7.8 Utilidor piles have heaved more than 30 cm due to frost action. Piles embedded about 3 m in permafrost but poor drainage caused increase in active layer depth with subsequent increase in frost heave forces.

Differential frost heave is a particularly serious problem and can result in severe distortion of structures (Fig. 7.8). In addition, heaved foundations may not return to their original position at the end of the thaw season because the underlying voids have been filled with soil or ice. After several seasons of frost heaving, the cumulative effect may be a permanent upward and uneven displacement of the foundations and structure (Péwé and Paige 1963).

Equally serious effects may occur during the thaw period if thawing occurs below foundations placed on the ground surface or in the active layer. A large decrease in bearing capacity and stability problems may result if ice lenses, resulting from the ice segregation process during the freezing period, thaw at a rate faster than the released moisture can escape. Differential thaw will result in irregular settlement of the previously heaved foundation and further complicate internal drainage.

When the required conditions exist, that is when frost-susceptible soils are present, free water is available and cooling conditions cause the soil and water to freeze, and when there is no physical restraint, theoretically there is no limit to the amount of heaving that a surface exposed to cooling will undergo due to the growth of ice lenses in the soil. Ground surface movements of 2 to 6 in. (5 to 15 cm) are common and movements of as much as 12 in. (30 cm) have been observed during a freezing season.

The maximum depth and rate of freeze and thaw penetration at a site may be determined with reasonable accuracy using methods outlined in Chapter 4. All estimates, particularly for layered systems, should be confirmed where possible by field observations.

7.3.1 Frost Heave and Adfreezing Forces

Heaving forces developed in frost-susceptible materials are transmitted to foundations in two ways: by "basal" or vertical forces acting on the underside of a foundation or grade beam or by adfreezing of the soil to the sides of a foundation unit. Because of the many variables involved, it is difficult to predict the magnitude of heave forces mobilized when the growth of ice lenses in a frost-susceptible soil is influenced by overburden pressure, foundation loads or other factors. These variables include soil type and heterogeneity variation of soil temperature with depth and time, rate of freezing, availability of water, type of foundation surface (smooth or rough, coated or uncoated wood, steel, concrete or other material), method used to place the foundation and rate and duration of loading. For critical structures where heaving problems are anticipated and cannot be avoided, it may be necessary to conduct field studies and laboratory experiments to determine design values for frost heave forces or heave rates. Relatively few studies of uplift forces on foundations have been reported. Except for those by Crory and Reed (1965), Trow (1955), Kinoshita and Ono (1963), Penner and Irwin (1969), Penner and Gold (1971) and Penner (1970b, 1974), most of the available information is in the Soviet literature (Vyalov 1959,

Tsytovich 1959, 1973, Kiselev 1974, Orlov 1974). An indication of the potential forces involved can be obtained from Figs. 3.32 and 3.33.

Extremely large heave forces can be exerted on the bottom of a foundation if frost-susceptible soils freeze below it. These forces increase as the frost line penetrates and the frozen soil begins to act as a plate. When the basal frost heave forces exceed the load on the foundation it will be lifted. Heave force values of as much as 110 psi (760 kPa) have been estimated from the weight of buildings known to have been lifted by frost heaving soil. Penner (1970b) measured forces in excess of 260 psi (1800 kPa) on a 12 in. (30 cm) diameter anchored steel plate. The way in which the forces developed on the plate as the frost line penetrated at an average rate of about 0.5 in./day (1 cm/day) is shown in Fig. 7.9. It is evident that foundations should not be designed to resist such large uplift forces but should be placed well below the depth of seasonal frost penetration and degradation of permafrost prevented.

The adfreeze strength of frozen ground is defined as the resistance to the force that is required to separate the frozen ground from the object to which it is frozen. The tangential adfreeze strength is the resistance to the force that is required to shear off an object that is frozen to the ground and to overcome the friction along the plane of its contact with the ground. It varies with the moisture content, temperature, texture and porosity of the ground and the nature of the surface of the foundation. In most cases the maximum adfreeze strength occurs when the ground is completely saturated with ice.

Little information is available on the magnitude of the adfreezing bond strength when soil freezes to the perimeter of foundation units, but field experiments indicate average values of about 15 psi (100 kPa) for steel surfaces and about 10 psi (70 kPa) for wood and concrete. Peak bond strengths usually range from 20 to 35 psi (140 to 240 kPa) (Penner and Gold 1971, Penner 1974) but Crory and Reed (1965) report average adfreeze bond stresses greater than 40 psi (275 kPa) on uncoated steel piles. Adfreeze bond strengths ranging from about 6 to 30 psi (40 to 210 kPa) in various types of soil have been measured in the field by Soviet investigators (Kiselev 1974).

Various studies show that the tangential adfreeze bond strength is a function of the ground temperature and ice content (both of which vary with depth and time) in the seasonally frozen zone. As would be expected, peak and average adfreeze values vary during the freezing season and from winter to winter. It appears that peak adfreeze values frequently occur early in the season when heaving rates are high but maximum uplift forces often occur near the time of maximum frost penetration.

The total uplift force on a foundation is a function of the unit tangential adfreeze bond stress and the area of the foundation in contact with the frozen soil. Thus it can be expected to increase as the frost line penetrates and the perimeter contact area increases. It is not possible to make precise quantitative predictions of either the maximum or average adfreeze bond strengths, however, because of

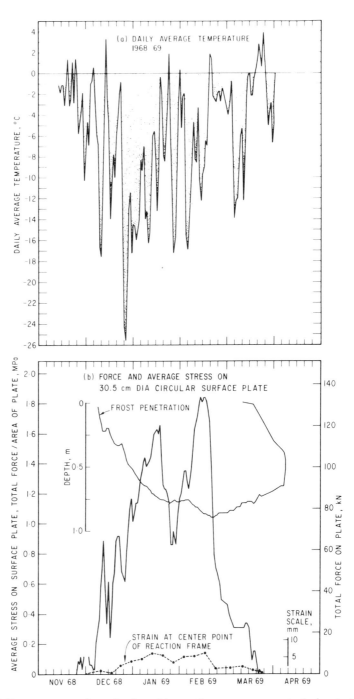

FIG. 7.9 Soil temperature, frost depth and heave force measurements during test on circular plate in Leda Clay, Ottawa (After Penner 1970b).

the influence of the many factors noted previously. An indication of the maximum adfreeze heaving forces acting on a pile or column can be obtained using Dalmatov's equation given by Tsytovich (1959) and confirmed by field experiments in the Soviet Union:

$$F = Lh_a (c - 0.5 bT_m) \tag{7.1}$$

where F is the total upward force due to frost heaving (kg), L the perimeter of the foundation in contact with frozen soil (cm), h_a the thickness of the frozen zone (cm), T_m the minimum soil temperature (°C) in the frozen zone and b and c are parameters determined experimentally. Average values of 6-10 psi (40-70 kPa) for c and 1.5-2.8 psi (10-19 kPa) for b are suggested by Soviet workers (Tsytovich 1973) for icy silty clayey soils (loams and sandy loams).

Penner and Irwin (1969) found that Dalmatov's equation, said to hold for ground temperatures down to about 10°F (−12°C), gave values that agreed closely with data obtained in their field experiments. Although this approach might serve as a guide for design purposes, a good deal of judgment must be exercised in evaluating local conditions and selecting appropriate values for tangential adfreeze bond stress and total heave forces that must be resisted. It is important to note that the adfreezing heave force is significantly decreased by relaxation of stress due to soil creep or a small displacement of the foundation unit. Maximum forces are transmitted when the foundation is rigidly anchored. Soviet experience and design methods are described by Tsytovich (1973) and in a design handbook (USSR 1969).

7.3.2 Control of Frost Heave

Several methods can be used to prevent or reduce the effects of frost heave on structure foundations. Elimination of one or more of the basic conditions causing the growth of ice lenses and frost heaving is the general approach taken.

Frost-susceptible soils in the layer subjected to seasonal freezing can be excavated and replaced with granular material during installation of shallow foundations such as footings, posts and piers. Good drainage is essential for eliminating a water supply for ice lens growth. Control of or reduction in the depth of the active layer should be attempted. Layers of insulation placed on or just below the ground surface around the foundation can be effective in preventing or reducing the depth of frost penetration or thawing (Robinsky and Bespflug 1973). Surcharge loading of the ground surface (for example with a gravel pad), together with improved drainage, can reduce but may not eliminate seasonal heaving (Section 8.1.1). Impermeable membranes have been used to prevent moisture movement in the soil and chemicals have been added to soils to modify their frost susceptibility (Lambe and Kaplar 1971) but these methods are generally not practicable, are expensive and may afford only temporary relief.

In most cases, it is not practicable to resist the very large basal heave forces and therefore it is standard practice to place the foundation below the depth of frost penetration in seasonal frost areas and below the permafrost table in permafrost areas to prevent basal heaving. This technique may not completely eliminate heaving, however, because the uplift effects of adfreeze bond or "frost grip" on the lateral surfaces of a foundation unit in contact with the freezing soil in the active layer must be considered.

The effects of adfreeze uplift forces can be overcome by anchoring the foundation pile or footing and by isolating the portion of the foundation in the frost zone from the frost-susceptible soil. Anchorage is usually achieved by providing sufficient embedment in permafrost when the foundation design ensures that permafrost degradation will not occur. Experience indicates that to resist frost heave adfreeze forces, the minimum embedment below the permafrost table should be at least twice the maximum thickness of the active layer. This is a guideline only and should always be checked by calculating the resistance to uplift mobilized by adfreezing along the lower portion of the foundation and comparing it with the heave forces generated in the active layer. Care should be taken to ensure that foundation members of concrete and wood have sufficient tensile capacity to resist the induced forces. Attempts have been made to increase pullout resistance by roughening the surface of a pile, post, footing or pier, adding plates to the base of a pile, notching or placing wood piles butt end down, and welding angle iron to steel piles, or using special tips (Muschell 1970), but these are usually only partially and temporarily effective.

The use of casing around foundation units to isolate them from frost heaving soils has been successful and may be the only practical method that can be considered, particularly when foundations carry small dead and live loads and in warm permafrost areas where extremely long piles may otherwise be required to resist the uplift forces. The pile or foundation member is cased, wholly or partly, through the frost zone and the annular space between the member and the casing is usually filled with an oil-wax mixture or heavy grease to prevent entry of soil, water or other material. A plate or flange can be attached to the bottom of the casing to prevent it from being "frost-jacked" out of the ground (Fig. 7.10). It should be noted that the resistance of a pile or post to lateral loads may be greatly decreased when it is cased through the active layer.

Various other methods of preventing or reducing adfreeze bond and heave have been tried but are not always reliable or effective and are usually considered as temporary measures only. These include coating the surface of a pile or post in the active layer with a low friction material, adding chemicals or oil-wax mixtures to the soil backfill in the active layer and using tar paper, plastic or similar collars. Placing insulation in the ground around the foundation is a possible method of reducing frost penetration and therefore the total heave force in areas of deep seasonal frost. The type and thickness of insulation required, the area to be covered and its location with respect to the ground surface should be determined by a special investigation. In some cases, thermal piles have been installed with posts or piles. Radial freezing outward is induced early in the freezing season by the heat removal device and can freeze the active layer around the post relatively quickly and thus reduce seasonal frost jacking (Waters 1974). The device will also

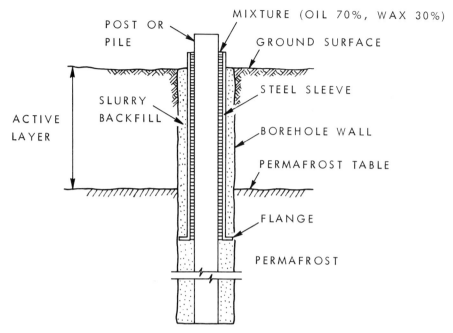

FIG. 7.10   Sketch of casing installation to prevent frost heaving of pile.

lower the ground temperature around that part of a foundation embedded in permafrost and thereby provide increased anchorage against uplift. Thermal piles are discussed in more detail in Section 7.7.1.

7.4 Seismic and Vibration Loads

Foundations may be subject to vibrations from a number of natural and artificial sources. Earthquakes, wind on tall narrow structures, high-velocity water currents on bridge piers and wave action on marine structures produce both transient and continuous vibrations under some conditions. Machinery is the most frequent cause of vibration. Internal combustion engines, compressors, pumps and other relatively slow-moving, reciprocating and oscillating machinery are important sources of continuous, low-frequency vibrations and usually cause the most serious problems. Rotating machinery such as electric motors, rotary pumps, and turbines can produce continuous high-frequency vibrations. Shock and transient vibrations often are caused by stamping machines, forges, pile drivers, moving vehicles, blasting and earthquakes.

   Vibrations consist of complex repeating motions and can include both rotation and translation in all three directions. Continuous vibrations usually have a constant frequency determined by the source and complicated by harmonics generated by its supports while transient vibrations from shocks may have a variable frequency, depending on both the source and the foundation system.

If an impulse of short duration is applied to a body, it will vibrate at its natural frequency, which depends on its mass and elastic properties. For a perfectly elastic body whose mass is M (weight W = M · g) and whose resistance to deflection in force per unit of deflection (in pounds/ft.; kN/m) is K, the natural frequency, f_n, assuming little or no damping, is given by (Richart et al. 1970, Sowers and Sowers, 1961):

$$f_n = (1/2\pi) \sqrt{K/M} = (1/2\pi) \sqrt{K \cdot g/W} \tag{7.2}$$

This means that the natural frequency increases with the square root of the rigidity and decreases with the square root of the mass or weight of the body. When energy is lost in the process the vibration is said to be damped and the natural frequency is somewhat less.

When the vibration applied to a structural member or the soil is different from its natural frequency, the amplitude of the vibration is limited by the energy received. If the vibration should occur at the natural frequency, the vibration amplitude in that body increases tremendously. This is called resonance and is the most serious condition because of the magnified severity of the vibration.

The natural frequency of a structural column or beam can be estimated from its weight and rigidity using a modification of Eq. 7.2 or tables given in handbooks such as by Harris and Crede (1961, 1976). The natural frequency of a foundation-soil system, however, is much more complex. The resistance per unit of deflection K can be estimated from the distortion settlement ρ. This depends on both the modulus of elasticity of the soil and the size of the foundation. The weight of the vibrating body W can be considered to be the sum of the weight of the foundation and the weight of a portion of the soil mass below the foundation which is vibrating. The natural frequency of the soil is, therefore, not only a property of the soil alone, but also depends on the weight and size of the foundation and the load it carries (Richart et al. 1970).

The intensity of the vibration is also a factor because the modulus of elasticity of some soils changes with confining pressure and with the strain. Tests conducted on unfrozen soil masses with vibrators having masses of from 1 to 3 tons (0.9 to 2.8 tonnes) and with square bases from 2 to 3 ft. (0.6 to 1 m) wide indicate natural frequencies of from 10 Hz for peat to 30 Hz for very dense sand. For heavier and wider foundations the natural frequency would be less. These natural frequencies, unfortunately, are similar to the vibrations or multiples of the vibrations generated by many reciprocating machines such as pumps and compressors but they are much lower than the frequencies generated by turbines and high-speed motors.

Soil vibrations have a number of important effects. First, the vibrations can be transmitted to other foundations and to other structures at some distance from the vibration source. These transmitted vibrations can be annoying and even damaging. Severe damage can result when a foundation-soil system is in resonance. Second, the vibrations can cause a reduction in the void ratio of unfrozen cohesionless soils and result in significant settlement. Ordinarily the settlement will be small if the relative density is greater than 70 per cent, but if the vibrations are severe, as in the case of resonance, settlements can occur until the relative density is nearly 100 per cent. Third, vibrations in loose, saturated cohesionless soils can bring about a quick condition, liquefaction loss of strength, and failure. On the other hand, cohesive soils are frequently resistant to vibration settlement and are not affected appreciably.

It appears, based on limited investigations, that unless ice is present, the dynamic engineering properties of frozen ground will not be significantly different from those of the same soils in the unfrozen state (Finn and Yong 1978). In general, therefore, design procedures used for unfrozen foundation soils can be applied to ice-poor frozen soils. Design criteria, test techniques and methods of analysis are not yet firmly established, however, and problems related to the dynamic loading of foundations in frozen ground should be the subject of a special investigation. In permafrost areas, the natural frequency of a vibrating foundation in frozen ground will usually be higher (100 Hz or more) because of the higher dynamic shear modulus (G_D = 21 to 73 × 10^6 psf; 1.0 to 3.5 × 10^6 kPa) of the frozen soil. This may prove to be a problem when high speed equipment (such as gas turbines) is involved. In frozen soils, and especially in plastic frozen materials containing relatively large amounts of unfrozen water, vibratory loading will generally increase the unfrozen water content in addition to all the effects of compaction observed in unfrozen soils. This is due principally to two effects: (1) grain-boundary pressure-melting of the pore ice, and (2) increase of soil temperature due to the instantaneous transformation of the kinetic energy into thermal energy. As a result, when a plastic frozen soil is subjected to vibratory loading over a long time period, an effect similar to an increase in soil temperature will occur.

The effects of dynamic loading on adfreeze strength and long-term creep settlements have not yet been investigated. These may have serious consequences due to loss of soil strength and increased settlement (Aamot 1966). On the other hand, the same phenomenon may be useful in excavating (cutting) frozen soil and driving piles in permafrost (Kovacs and Michitti 1970, Bendz 1977). A field investigation carried out by Vyalov et al. (1966), showed that excellent results can be obtained when vibratory hammers are used to drive piles in plastic frozen soils. When driving was completed it was observed that the temperature of the soil adjacent to the pile had increased to about 50°-60°F (10°-15°C) from its initial value of 30°F (−1°C).

A state-of-the-art review and several other papers dealing with some aspects of the behaviour of frozen soils subjected to vibration loads were presented at a specialty session of the ASCE (1977). The dynamic properties of frozen soils are discussed in Section 3.4.2. The liquefaction potential of thawed layers of saturated cohesionless soils sealed between the frozen active layer and permafrost was assessed by Finn et al. (1978). Great caution must be exercised in extrapolating experience with alluvial deposits of saturated cohesionless soils in temperate regions to similar deposits in permafrost areas. When subjected to dynamic loading, such as by earthquakes, it appears that, within limits yet to be established, the coarser the material the greater the risk of liquefaction at low relative densities.

PART II—SHALLOW FOUNDATIONS

7.5 Types of Shallow Foundations

Shallow foundation units or systems may be founded on or in a compacted gravel pad laid on the ground surface, in a pit excavated (and backfilled) in the active layer or residual thaw zone or they may be embedded in perennially frozen ground, usually to a depth not exceeding 6 ft. (2 m) below the permafrost table. Important factors to be considered in the selection, design and construction of shallow foundations are outlined in Part I. They are generally used when a competent bearing stratum is found at shallow depths and when superstructure loads and local site conditions do not require deep foundations.

Common types of shallow foundations used in permafrost areas include ground sills, posts and pads, spread footings, piers and mats or rafts on grade. All types may consist of wood, steel and/or concrete. It should be remembered that steel and concrete conduct heat much more readily than wood; this may be an important thermal design consideration. Similarly, when cast-in-place concrete members are to be used, the temperature of the concrete must be such that curing will occur within a reasonable time without freezing and the concrete must not cause thawing of the adjacent frozen soil. All wood members in contact with the ground, and particularly those in the active layer, must be treated with a preservative to prevent decay. Steel and concrete members may also require protection against corrosion or deterioration, depending on the local environment.

Timber ground sills and post and pad foundations, commonly referred to as surface foundations, are the simplest types of shallow foundations. They are normally used only to support relatively small, lightly loaded and temporary, heated or unheated structures that can tolerate some movement. The foundation is usually placed on or just below the surface of a compacted fill pad but, occasionally, may be placed on the original ground surface if used to support a light, temporary structure (Figs. 7.11, 7.12, 7.13, 7.14 and 7.15). A clear airspace must be provided between the floor of the structure and grade level. Differential movements resulting from frost heave and thaw settlement can be expected unless special precautions have been taken, and therefore provision should be made for jacking and shimming of posts and columns so that the structure can be levelled when required. Extra-long anchor bolts should be used to fasten the posts to the pads to allow adjustments to be made. Experience has shown that small light structures placed on surface foundations may be moved laterally by the strong, gusty winds, which frequently occur in the North. Consideration must therefore be given to providing adequate anchorage.

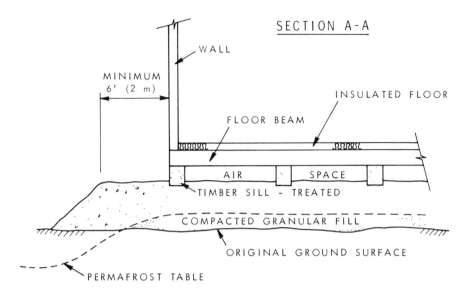

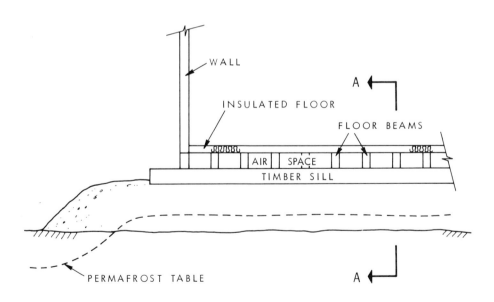

FIG. 7.11   Typical timber sill surface foundation.

FIG. 7.12   Timber sill foundations (a) on timber cribs on natural ground surface for small temporary building, and (b) on gravel pad for permanent house.

(a.)

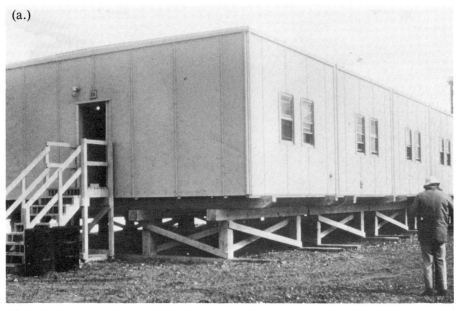

(b.)

FIG. 7.13   Post and pad surface foundations on thick gravel fills for (a) permanent communications building in Arctic Islands and (b) office and warehouse buildings in discontinuous permafrost zone. Note clear air space under buildings and crawl space delineated by siding in (b) for utilities under the main floor.

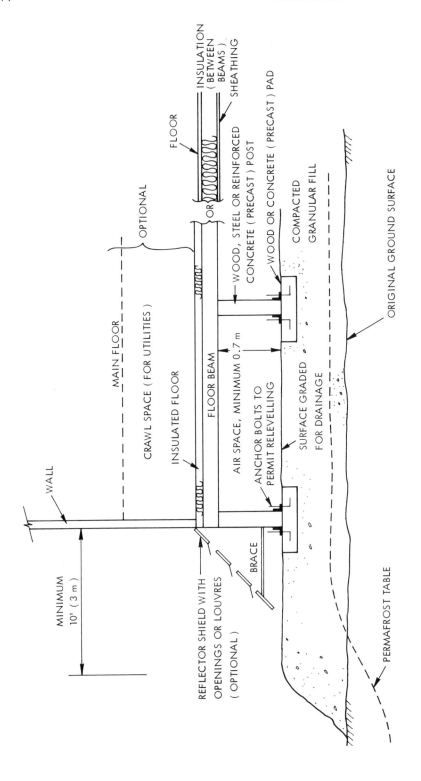

FIG. 7.14   Sketch showing some details of a typical post and pad surface foundation.

FIG. 7.15 Two-storey building founded on stub wall on perimeter strip footings on gravel pad. Note very small openings in wall for ventilation of air space under building floor and differential movements indicated by shimming. Concrete work done one summer and erection of superstructure begun following year.

Footings or piers may be used for structures that can tolerate little or no movement, provided the permafrost table will remain above the foundation or the foundation soil is thaw-stable. They may also be founded on unfrozen ground if a residual thaw zone exists between the base of the active layer and the permafrost table, and if thawing of the underlying permafrost will not occur and the allowable pressure on the unfrozen soil will not be exceeded. Several types of footings may be considered: individual footings carrying one column or post, combined footings carrying more than one column or post, or continuous or strip footings carrying a wall. Individual column footings are preferred to continuous footings in permafrost since there is less risk of structural damage to the foundation if movements are experienced. Piers are prismoidal or cylindrical units with large bases to distribute the loads to a suitable bearing stratum. Many variations and combinations of structural designs of foundation members are possible. Footings and columns may be combined in the form of pedestals, piers may be stepped, tapered, hollow and so on.

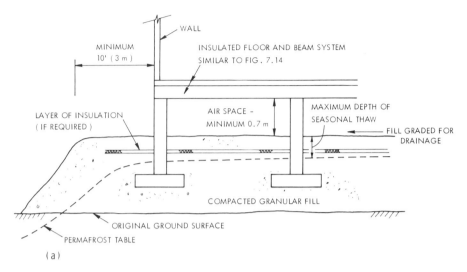

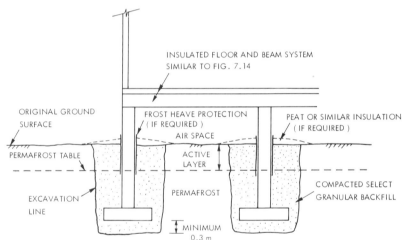

FIG. 7.16   Sketches of typical footings in permafrost in (a) thick, insulated gravel pad placed on the ground surface, and (b) backfilled pits excavated below original ground surface.

Footings and piers may be founded in perennially frozen ground below the original ground surface or in a fill pad into which the permafrost has risen (Fig. 7.16). If footings and piers are to perform satisfactorily, special attention must be given to the following design and construction aspects: (1) provision of a clear airspace below the structure and use of floor and in-ground insulation, if required, to dissipate heat losses from the structure and maintain frozen ground conditions and the permafrost table at the desired levels, (2) protection against frost action adfreeze uplift forces on piers and footing columns, (3) long-term bearing capacity and creep settlement of the frozen foundation soil, (4) minimum ground thermal disturbance during excavation and placement of backfill for the footings and piers and (5) provide sufficient time in the construction schedule to allow the ground to refreeze around the footings or piers, particularly if summer construction is planned. Design and construction experience with pier-supported buildings that have performed satisfactorily is described by Dickens and Gray (1960) and Harding (1962). Crory (1978) describes differential settlement of a building supported by footings at Kotzebue, Alaska, where extremely complex foundation soil and permafrost conditions, including erratic distribution of frozen ground, layered organic, silts, sands and gravels, saline soils and ground-water, were encountered.

A raft or mat foundation covers the entire area beneath a structure. It is normally placed on a fill pad and supports the walls and columns. This type of foundation is used mainly for structures, such as powerhouses, hangars, garages and warehouses, that have heavy floor loads and special access requirements. It acts as a unit and minimizes differential movements that could occur were individual footings to be used. A reinforced concrete slab placed on a gravel fill is the most common type but a mat of closely spaced timbers may be used for some temporary structures (Fig. 7.17). In some cases, separate foundations, such as footings or piles, may be used to support columns, walls or machinery; heavy floor loads are taken by a reinforced concrete slab (Fig. 7.18).

FIG. 7.17 Temporary timber mat foundation on gravel pad for heated oil tank.

FIG. 7.18   Natural convection, duct-ventilated gravel fill foundation for small powerhouse on permafrost. Superstructure will be supported by the concrete mat placed on a gravel pad. Generating units will be founded on steel pipe piles driven to bedrock and isolated from the concrete mat.

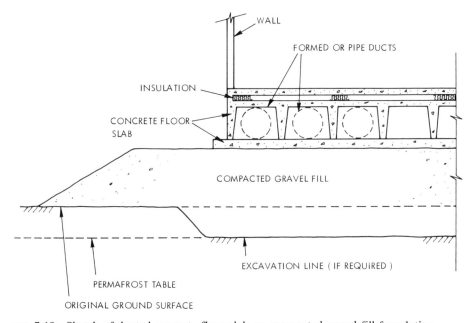

FIG. 7.19   Sketch of ducted concrete floor slab on compacted gravel fill foundation.

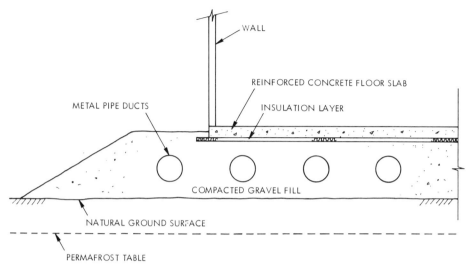

FIG. 7.20   Sketch of insulated concrete floor slab on duct-ventilated compacted fill
foundation.

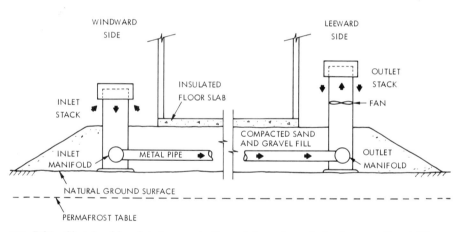

FIG. 7.21   Sketch of insulated concrete floor slab on forced air, duct-ventilated fill
foundation.

A mat foundation must be ventilated and insulated to control heat losses and
prevent thawing of the underlying frozen ground. A duct-ventilated fill pad is frequently used to support a mat foundation. The ducts, together with insulation,
may be incorporated as part of the concrete slab floor system (Fig. 7.19) or they
may be placed in the compacted fill below the slab (Figs. 7.3, 7.20 and 7.21).
Duct-ventilated and insulated fill pads with or without a concrete slab are also
used to support heated water or oil storage tanks (Figs. 7.2, 7.22, 7.23 and 10.3).
Occasionally, a mat or slab may be supported by piles to provide a clear airspace
between the base of the structure and the ground surface (Fig. 7.24).

FIG. 7.22   Large heated oil tank supported on duct-ventilated gravel fill.

It is apparent that a variety of shallow foundation types or combinations of them can be used to support structures in permafrost areas. It is impossible to provide guidance for all the situations and variations in foundation types that will be encountered or anticipated. The design and selection of an appropriate shallow foundation for a particular structure will depend on the factors and principles noted previously and in the following sections.

7.6 Design for Vertical Loads

As is the case for shallow foundations in unfrozen soil, the design of footings on frozen soils to resist vertical loads is primarily concerned with preventing shear failure in the frozen soil and limiting settlements to tolerable amounts. The design of footings involves: (a) selecting the desired footing depth so that it is greater than the depth of frost penetration or the maximum depth of thaw; (b) estimating the warmest temperatures that will occur under the footing to permit assessment of appropriate soil properties; (c) selecting a footing size using bearing capacity theory to give the required factor of safety; (d) conducting a settlement analysis using time-deformation relationships for the foundation soil and (e) changing the footing size to reduce bearing pressures if calculated settlements are not acceptable. Thus, both bearing capacity and settlements (total, differential and particularly those due to creep) must be evaluated for footings in frozen ground. Although either bearing capacity or settlement criteria may provide the limiting condition, settlement is frequently the governing factor.

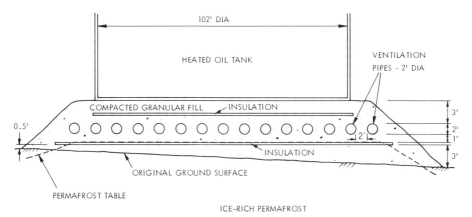

FIG. 7.23 Sketch of heated oil storage tank supported by duct-ventilated and insulated gravel fill.

FIG. 7.24 Large heated oil tank under construction supported by concrete slab on timber pile foundation. Pressure creosoted piles were placed in drilled and slurry backfilled holes to a depth of 10 m. Note clear air space under slab.

Spread footings are not widely used for heavily loaded structures because of the wide fluctuations in ground temperatures and extreme variations in soil type and ice content that can occur at shallow depths. Deep foundations, such as piles, are usually considered in such cases so that the loads can be distributed at depths where conditions are more uniform or stable.

7.6.1 Bearing Capacity

Allowable bearing pressures for footings, pads or sills placed on or in unfrozen, compacted, well-drained granular fill are based on the unfrozen strengths of these materials. The thickness of the granular mat between the footing and the underlying natural soil must be such that concentrated stresses on the natural soil will be reduced to an acceptable value and degradation of the underlying permafrost prevented or the depth of thaw controlled. On the other hand, the allowable bearing pressure for footings embedded in permafrost is controlled by the time- and temperature-dependent shear strength of the frozen soil. Their influence is discussed in Section 3.4.1 and the short- and long-term strengths of some typical frozen soils are compared in Table 3.3.

Assuming that suitable steps have been taken to maintain the ground in a frozen state, such as by the use of sufficient fill or insulation, the highest temperature in the ground under a footing will control the resistance to shear failure. Most footings are usually placed at shallow depth below the permafrost table. The maximum ground temperatures at footing depth will be just below $32°F$ ($0°C$) in the late summer and fall and therefore design values for soils at temperatures one or two degrees below freezing are normally applicable. Stresses in the weakest underlying frozen soil layer must be kept within tolerable limits. It may be necessary in critical situations to lower the ground temperature beneath the footing to increase the strength and reduce the deformations to acceptable values.

Mechanical properties of the frozen soils are determined from laboratory tests on undisturbed samples or from in situ tests. The long-term strength of frozen soils is usually only a small fraction of the short-term (instantaneous) strength determined by a conventional unconfined compression test; frequently it is in the order of 10 to 20 percent or less, depending on the ice content, soil type and temperature and stress conditions. Although there are, as yet, no standard procedures for strength testing of frozen soils, several test and calculation methods have been used to determine the long-term ultimate strength (Sections 3.4.1, 5.6.1 and 5.6.2, Sanger 1969, Ladanyi 1972, Sayles 1973, Sayles and Haines 1974). Most of them are essentially similar to, or modifications of, the method suggested by Vyalov (1959), which can be used, for most practical purposes and within certain limits, to obtain the long-term shear strength from short-term constant stress laboratory tests. The long-term strength at a design life of (say) 50 years can be estimated from a plot of $1/\sigma$ vs log (t_f), where σ and t_f are the compressive stress and the time to failure determined from laboratory tests.

The ultimate bearing capacity of a foundation on frozen soil may be determined by assuming that the material is purely cohesive or non-frictional. This approach is conservative since internal friction is neglected, that is, it is assumed equal to zero. Although the internal friction component will be significant in some materials, such as unsaturated or "ice-poor" frozen soils (Roggensack and Morgenstern 1978), determination of ϕ requires that triaxial creep or similar tests be performed. On the other hand, the cohesion factor can be determined by relatively simple unconfined compression creep tests on undisturbed samples at representative temperatures, as noted above. Values obtained can then be used in an appropriate bearing capacity equation (Canadian Geotechnical Society 1978). This approach is applicable for frozen silts and clays and can also be applied to frozen fine- to medium-grained sands.

There is very little published data on the long-term shear strength of soils at temperatures usually encountered in field situations (27 to 32°F; -3 to 0°C) and having excess ice contents. Most of the data has been obtained from tests on artificially-prepared frozen soils; few tests have been carried out on undisturbed materials. Data that are available for natural soils are presented in Fig. 7.25.

Since there is only limited information available, every effort should be made to carry out laboratory tests on the soils in question at representative temperatures. If test data are not available, values for preliminary design purposes can be estimated from Fig. 7.25. A tentative relationship giving the lower limit for the 50 year shear strength c_f (in kPa) is also shown, as derived from

$$c_f = 35 + 28T \qquad \text{(kPa)} \qquad (7.3)$$

where T is in °C below freezing (with positive sign). For heavily loaded footings, these values must be confirmed by laboratory compression tests conducted at accurately controlled temperatures representative of design conditions and with careful analysis of the test results.

The footing size can then be determined, based on the requirement that there be adequate safety against failure for the dead load plus maximum live loads. The allowable bearing capacity, q_{all}, may be calculated from

$$q_{all} = N_c \cdot c_f/F \qquad (7.4)$$

where F is a safety factor that takes into account all uncertainties involved in the design, and N_c is the usual bearing capacity factor for "cohesive" soils depending on footing shape. Selection of a suitable safety factor must be based on judgment of the particular design problem but it is suggested that a value of at least 3 be used. The effect of confining pressure on the shear strength of ice-rich soils is not significant and can be neglected. It may be taken into account when dealing with frozen soils containing little or no ice, however, if further testing or research shows it is justified.

Empirical relationships are generally used in the Soviet Union for solving bearing capacity problems (Vyalov 1959, Tsytovich 1973, U.S.S.R. 1969) involving both "frictionless" ($\phi = $ o) and "frictional" ($\phi > $ o) soils. Frozen soil time- and

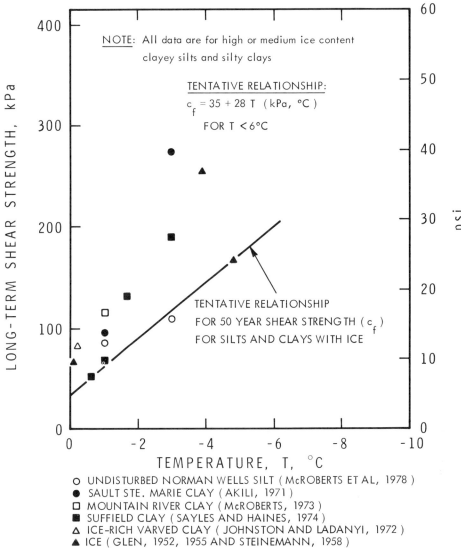

FIG. 7.25   Long-term shear strength of fine-grained frozen soils with ice.

temperature-dependent strength and deformation parameters are substituted in appropriate formulae borrowed from unfrozen soil bearing capacity theories. North American practice essentially follows this approach but cavity expansion theory has been presented by Ladanyi and Johnston (1974) and Ladanyi (1976) to predict creep settlements and the time-dependent bearing capacity of deep circular and strip foundations. Values for the bearing capacity factors for "frictional" and "frictionless" frozen soils are given and an empirical depth factor is derived which allows the solution to be used for estimating the bearing capacity of footings of any shape and at any depth of embedment.

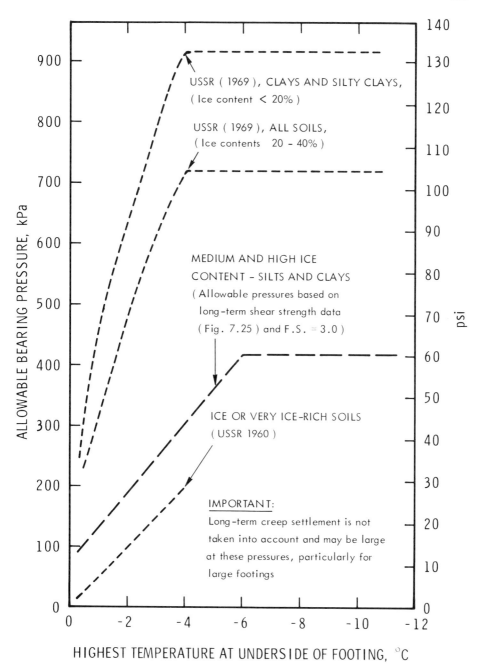

FIG. 7.26 Allowable bearing pressures for footings in frozen ground based on shear strength only. Note that this curve was obtained using a bearing capacity factor of 6 and a factor of safety of 3. The other 3 curves show values taken from the Soviet literature.

A typical relationship for allowable bearing pressure versus temperature for medium and high ice content silt and clay soils, using a bearing capacity factor of 6 and a factor of safety of 3, is shown in Fig. 7.26. Information on other North American soils is very limited. Some values from U.S.S.R. standards (1960, 1969) for ice and low and medium ice content soils are also included in Fig. 7.26. It must be emphasized that the values shown are for soils that are, in general, well cemented by ice and should not be used for calculations involving soils that contain significant amounts of segregated ice. Such soils must be the subject of a special investigation. Footings should never be placed on an ice layer but must be separated from it by a layer of compacted sand at least 1 ft. (0.3 m) thick.

Allowable pressures for short-term wind, seismic or live loadings would be considerably greater than those shown on Fig. 7.26. Some short-term (instantaneous) strength properties of frozen soils and the effect of loading rate are given by Kaplar (1971a). Approximate ranges of uniaxial compressive strength for ice and frozen soils that have water contents near saturation are shown in Fig. 7.27. In the absence of reliable data, it is suggested that the bearing pressures shown in Fig. 7.26 might be doubled for loads applied for less than one day.

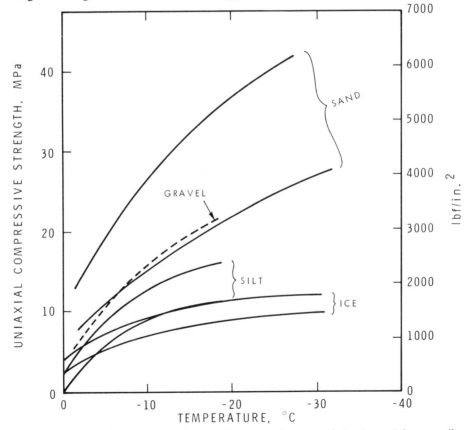

FIG. 7.27 Approximate ranges of uniaxial compressive strength for ice and frozen soils that have water contents near saturation (After Mellor 1972c).

It is most important to remember that the bearing capacities discussed in this section do not account for the creep settlements that may occur, particularly in plastic frozen and ice-rich frozen soils. Creep settlements are usually the governing design parameter and are discussed in the following section.

7.6.2 Settlement of Footings

Although instantaneous elastic settlements occur on loading of permafrost, and some consolidation has been noted in plastic frozen soils at temperatures near 0°C, most settlement in the long term arises from creep in the ice phase of the frozen soil. Soils with significant excess ice contents are common in the near-surface permafrost strata, and these generally have the lowest bearing capacities and highest creep rates. At ice contents greater than the normal range of water contents exhibited by the same soil in the unfrozen state, the frozen soil will tend to creep in a steady (secondary) mode for indefinite time periods. As shown by McRoberts et al. (1978) and discussed later with regard to pile foundations, the creep strain rate $\dot{\epsilon}$ can be expressed in terms of stress by the non-linear law

$$\dot{\epsilon} = B\sigma^n \qquad (7.5)$$

where σ is deviator stress and B and n are creep parameters. Values for B and n can be determined from a series of creep tests at different stresses, or can be estimated based on published data as shown by Nixon (1978b). A review by Nixon and McRoberts (1976) based on the creep behaviour of ice suggested that B and n are temperature-dependent but McRoberts et al. (1978) found that n for ice-rich soils appears to be independent of temperature but is certainly stress-dependent.

The settlement rate of a footing on frozen soil may be calculated by subdividing the ground beneath the footing into a number of layers having different temperatures (if required), calculating the deviator stress on each layer for a specified footing pressure, and then using the above creep law to calculate the strain rate in each layer. The settlement rate $\dot{s}$ of the footing is then the sum of the strain rates multiplied by the respective layer thicknesses. Thus for n layers

$$\dot{s} = \sum_{i=1}^{n} \dot{\epsilon}(z)\Delta z \qquad (7.6)$$

where Δz is the thickness of layer i and $\dot{\epsilon}$ is the strain rate in layer i. It should be noted that if the soil is in a plane strain condition, such as under a strip footing, then the resulting strain rate should be multiplied by $(\sqrt{3}/2)^{n+1}$.

If the soil is at a uniform temperature, then the settlement rate $\dot{s}$ based on Boussinesq stress distribution beneath a footing founded on a linear elastic material, can be written as (Nixon 1978b)

$$\dot{s} = IaB\,(\Delta p)^n \qquad (7.7)$$

where Δp is the footing pressure, a is the half-width of the footing, and I is an influence factor that depends only on the creep exponent n. Values of I for strip

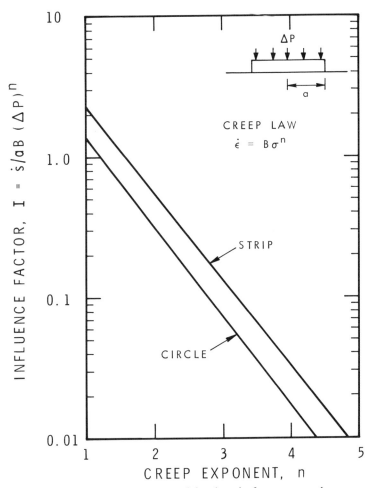

FIG. 7.28   Influence factors for creep rate of footings in frozen ground.

and circular footings are given in Fig. 7.28. The effect of a compacted gravel layer between the footing and the viscous frozen soil was also investigated by Nixon (1978b). Significant reductions in creep rate can be attained if the thickness of the gravel layer is of the same order as the footing width. This can be used to advantage in design. The influence factor I now depends on the ratio of the gravel layer thickness to footing width, as well as on n, as shown on Fig. 7.29.

It will often be found (as for unfrozen soils) that consideration of shear strength will govern for small footings whereas creep settlements become more important for larger footings. Settlement predictions for footings depend greatly on the soil creep parameters and considerable emphasis must be placed on correctly determining the creep law and parameter values for the undisturbed frozen soil at the applicable temperature range for the problem in question. Following construction, efforts should be made to monitor the settlement of selected

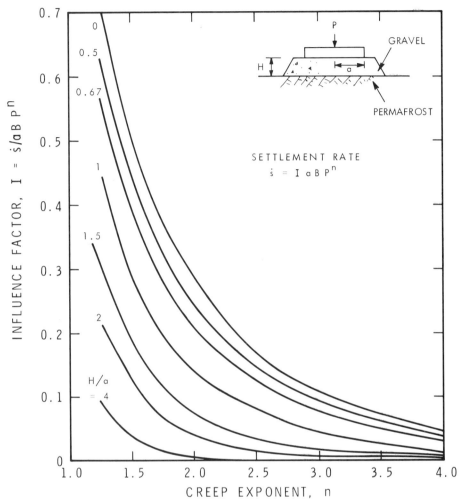

FIG. 7.29 Settlement rate for circular footing based on linear elastic stresses (After Nixon 1978b).

footings to evaluate long-term creep and thus design parameters. Settlement observations should be made once a month for at least the first two years.

PART III—PILE FOUNDATIONS

Pile foundations are widely used in permafrost areas to support structures ranging from large, heavy, heated buildings to single microwave communication towers erected at remote sites (Fig. 7.30, 7.31). They can provide reliable support even when extremely heavy loads are to be carried and very difficult permafrost conditions are encountered. The structure loads are transferred by the pile through weak and unstable materials to a suitable stratum some distance below the ground surface that will remain structurally and thermally stable for the service life of the structure. The loads are taken either by end bearing, when there is a strong, competent stratum at reasonable depth, or by adfreeze bond in frozen soils or friction in unfrozen ground. In some cases, resistance may be mobilized by a combination of adfreeze bond and end bearing. Pile foundations can be installed with minimum disturbance to the ground thermal regime, but must be designed and constructed so that the structure is not subjected to heave and settlement caused by seasonal frost action or permafrost degradation.

7.7 Pile Types

The type of pile, and the method of installation, used at any site will depend on several factors, including soil and permafrost conditions, ground temperature regime, loads to be carried, depth of embedment, available pile material, construction schedule, logistics and types of construction equipment required or available. Timber, steel H-section, steel pipe and precast reinforced concrete piles

FIG. 7.30   Large building on pile foundations. Each column is supported by a group of 3 or 4, 25 cm square, timber piles placed in 8 m deep, dry-augered holes backfilled with compacted saturated medium sand.

are the main types used in permafrost areas. Although seldom used, composite piles may also be considered. They can be designed to provide a larger surface area in permafrost and smaller surface area in the active layer and thus increase the bearing capacity and decrease the uplift forces due to frost heave respectively.

Wood piles are used extensively in northern Canada, particularly in areas

FIG. 7.31   Guyed communication tower, 50 m high, is supported by a single timber pile placed to a depth of 8 m in permafrost. Note tapered concrete cap on top of pile.

FIG. 7.32   Large building supported by 9 m long wood piles. Note size of crawl space for utilities, clear air space under false floor, protective gravel mat placed on ground surface and that piles extend through crawl space to main floor.

where suitable timber can be secured locally (Fig. 7.32). In the Mackenzie River Valley, for example, logs from 20 to 45 ft. (6 to 15 m) in length can be obtained as far north as Arctic Red River and in the Mackenzie Delta. Round and square timber piles are shipped from the south to northern locations where local timber is not long or strong enough or is not available.

Steel H piles are normally used where heavy vertical or lateral loads are to be carried (Fig. 7.33). They can often be successfully driven directly into warm plastic-frozen fine-grained soils with little damage or excessive deformation; frozen gravels are penetrated only with difficulty. Thermal disturbance is minimized when piles are driven and placement may be quite rapid. Davison et al. (1978) describe several case histories and discuss the various factors, including soil type, ice content and temperature, pile shape, hammer size, pile-energy transfer characteristics and "pilot hole" size (if used), that influence driving of piles into frozen ground. Transportation costs and the difficulties of securing suitable driving equipment are also important considerations.

Steel pipe piles are used extensively in permafrost areas (Fig. 7.34). If necessary they can be filled with concrete or sand to increase their load capacity. Pipe piles are superior to H-sections when placed in a slurry-backfilled hole as less backfill is required. They have a uniform section modulus in all directions when designing for lateral loads. They can also be readily modified to permit installation of cool-

FIG. 7.33   Steel H piles placed to depth of 8 m in permafrost to provide anchorage point for heating and service lines in utilidor.

ing devices inside them if remedial cooling of the ground is required at some later date.

Precast, reinforced concrete piles are expensive and seldom used in northern Canada (Fig. 10.13). Transportation of cement and precast piles from the south is costly. Local gravels, if available, usually require washing, screening and crushing to obtain suitable aggregates. On-site fabrication is only economical if large numbers of piles are required. They are used extensively in the Soviet Union where they are the preferred type on large construction projects. They may be cast in round, square, H or multi-sided shapes. Precast concrete piles must be handled with care to prevent damage during transport and installation and field design changes in length are difficult. High tensile stresses may be induced by frost heave, and will cause the concrete to crack if insufficient reinforcing steel is provided. Careful analysis is required to ensure that reinforcing steel is sufficient for the structural loading. Pretensioned precast concrete piles might be considered for some situations (Myska and How 1978).

Compacted, cast-in-place concrete piles should not be used in permafrost. In addition to the high cost of transporting cement and obtaining suitable aggregates locally, the main drawbacks are the effects of the heat of hydration, which may

FIG. 7.34 Settlement of steel pipe piles supporting large single-storey building in
northern part of discontinuous permafrost zone. Note ground surface cover totally
destroyed during construction, ground settlement of more than 0.7 m and ponding of
water under building. Permafrost table receded more than 3 m in about 6 years as a
result of gross disturbance to area.

thaw the frozen ground for some distance around the pile, thus increasing or impeding freezeback, and the low ground temperatures, which may inhibit proper curing and strength gain of the concrete. The very weak, powdery or scaly surface of the concrete pile, caused by freezing and improper curing, results in little or no adfreeze bond or friction being mobilized between the pile and the soil. They have been used occasionally with some success in marginal permafrost areas, when the lower part of the pile is in unfrozen ground below the bottom of the permafrost layer and the design has allowed for long-term thawing of the permafrost and the resulting additional loads imposed by downdrag (negative skin friction) as the thawing soil settles and consolidates. Downdrag loads can be very large.

Special types of piles, called thermal piles, may be used to promote freezeback after installation and to maintain or lower the ground temperature around the piles. These are described in Section 7.7.1.

All types of piles require protection against rot or corrosion in the active layer and above ground, particularly when they will be exposed to wetting and drying or a toxic or marine (salt water) environment. Protection within permafrost is not considered necessary. Studies in Canada and Alaska showed that the part of a timber or steel pile that was embedded in permafrost was unaffected by rot or corrosion (Sedziak et al. 1973, Romanoff 1969). Sufficient decay of untreated timber poles and piles can occur at the groundline and in the active layer, however, to warrant application of a protective coating. A "paint-on" preservative can be applied at the site to that part of a timber pile that will be above the permafrost table but proper procedures must be followed if the protection is to be effective using this diffusion process (Sedziak et al. 1973). Creosote-treated timber piles shipped to a site from the south are frequently used for major structures. Although little is known concerning the corrosive effect of saline frozen soils on steel and concrete piles embedded in them, some form of protection may be needed. Site conditions should always be evaluated to determine whether or not protection is required.

A coating of any kind, such as creosote on wood or paint on steel, will significantly reduce the tangential adfreeze shear stress below that developed for the untreated material in contact with the soil (Aamot 1966, Parameswaran 1978). The tangential adfreeze working stresses for the treated portion of a pile that is embedded in frozen ground must therefore be reduced accordingly. Unfortunately, there is little information available on the reduction of adfreeze strength but a decrease of at least 20% should be considered. On the other hand, the reduction in adfreeze bond or "frost-grip" of the soil to a coated pile in the active layer will assist in resisting frost heave.

7.7.1 Thermal Piles

Thermal piles are piles (usually wood or steel) on which natural convection or forced circulation cooling systems or devices have been installed to remove heat from the ground. They can be used to decrease the time for and ensure freezeback of a soil slurry, prevent or control long-term degradation of permafrost and to decrease the existing ground temperatures around piles, particularly in warm temperature permafrost areas. A reduction in freezeback time will assist construction scheduling and a lowering of the ground temperature will increase the adfreeze strength and thus the bearing capacity of the piles. Artificial methods for cooling the ground around piles have been employed when ground temperatures are just below freezing and natural refreezing will not occur or will take an unacceptably long time (Essoglou 1957, Crory 1965). They can ensure long-term thermal stability of foundations, particularly for structures such as communications and power transmission towers or above-ground pipelines supported by piles where the ground is not shaded from the effects of solar radiation and the accumulation of an insulating snow cover and may also be influenced by disturbances caused by construction activity (Miller 1971, Luscher et al. 1975). They can also be used to stabilize the ground thermal regime of a foundation suffering distress due to permafrost degradation (Womick and LeGoullon 1975). Seasonal frost heave may also be reduced, since radial rather than vertical extraction of heat (freezing) can be induced in the active layer. They are generally not necessary when the mean annual ground temperature is $25°F$ ($-4°C$) or colder.

Two basic types or concepts of thermal piles can be considered. Passive or natural convection systems utilize self-powered devices, commonly referred to as thermosyphons, thermotubes, convection cells or heat pipes, that have no moving parts, require no external power for operation and function only when air temperatures are lower than the ground temperature. Forced circulation refrigeration systems require external power and mechanical equipment to circulate refrigerants, such as antifreeze liquids or cool air, and may be operated throughout the year or only during the winter. Some types are illustrated schematically in Fig. 7.35.

Passive devices may be either single- or two-phase systems. Single-phase devices, which are usually liquid- or air-filled vertical pipes, have been investigated but to date have received limited use (Johnson 1971, Babb et al. 1971, Jahns et al. 1973, Reid et al. 1975). During the winter, heat from the soil surrounding the embedded portion of the pipe is absorbed by and thus warms the working fluid, which rises to the above-ground "radiator" section of the pipe exposed to the cooler air and loses its heat by conduction and natural convection. A two-phase device is a sealed tube containing a suitable working fluid—part liquid and part vapour. Propane, carbon dioxide and ammonia have been used. When the ambient temperature falls below the ground temperature, the vapour condenses in the radiator section of the tube. The pressure in the tube is reduced and the liquid in the lower section starts to boil. The resulting cycle of boiling, vapour flow up the tube, condensation and return of condensate by gravity flow is a very effective way of transferring heat up the tube. The use of the thermal rectifier property of this device was first suggested by Long (1966) and has been investigated by others for permafrost applications (Larkin 1971, Johnson 1971, Waters 1973, Jahns et al. 1973 and Larkin and Johnston 1974). The two-phase

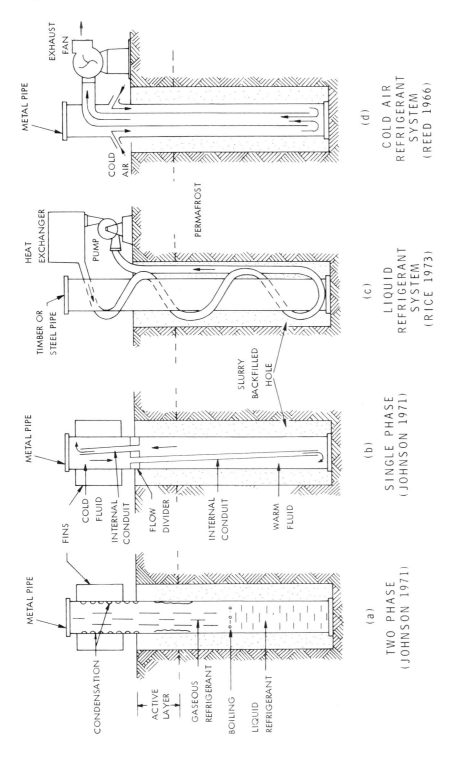

FIG. 7.35   Schematic representation of several thermal pile systems.

device shown in Fig. 7.36 was used extensively for piles supporting the above-ground section of the trans-Alaska oil pipeline (Waters 1974, Waters et al. 1975 Heuer 1979). Some results of studies conducted by Jahns et al. (1973) to predict ground temperatures around a pile are given in Fig. 7.37.

In most cases, the heat pipes serve as heat transfer devices only and not as a structural member. One or more small diameter heat pipes may be placed inside a steel pipe pile (Fig. 7.36), attached to the outside of a timber, steel pipe or H pile, inserted separately in the slurry with the pile or placed in holes drilled adjacent to a driven pile. Occasionally, a sealed steel pipe pile filled with a working fluid may serve as both a heat transfer device and a load bearing member. The passive devices operate only during the winter; during the summer when air temperatures are greater than the ground temperatures little or no heat is transferred by the heat pipes to the ground. Some heat will be conducted into the ground along the

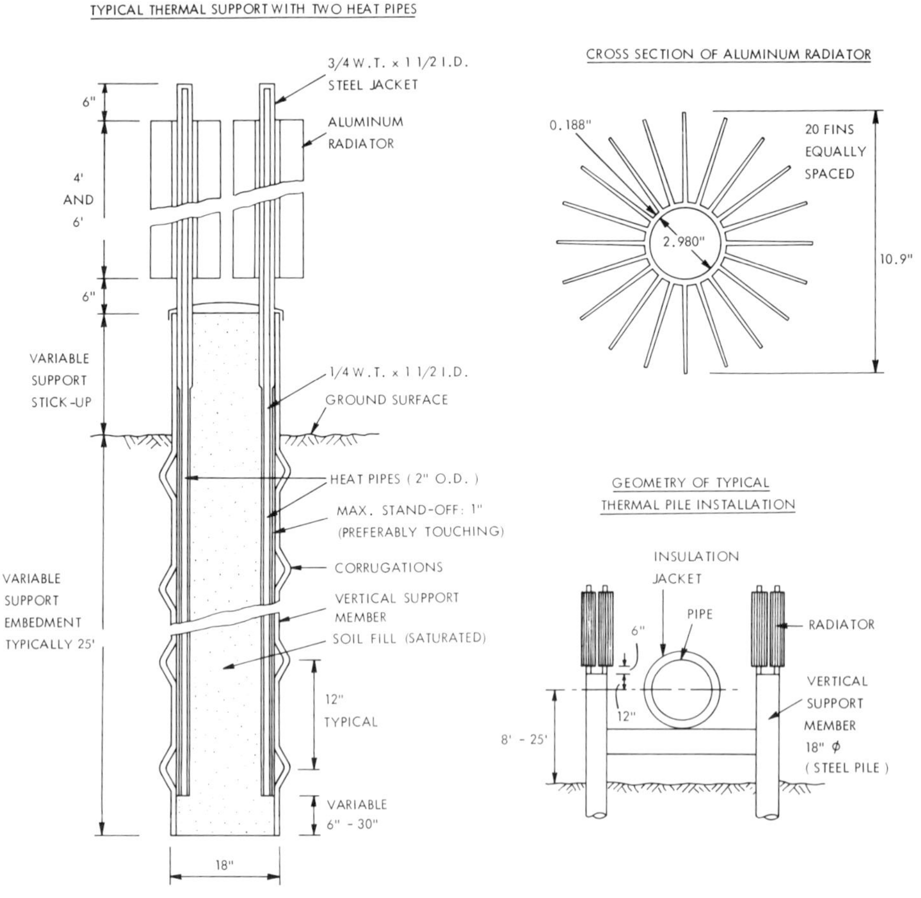

FIG. 7.36 Typical vertical support member (VSM) for Alyeska oil pipeline (After Alyeska Pipeline Service Company 1976).

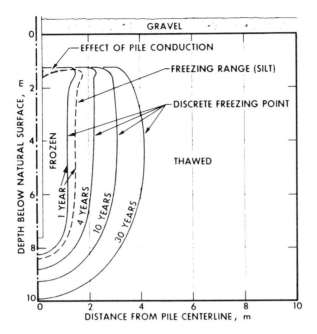

(a) Growth of freeze front around a thermal pile with heat transfer coefficient of 3.0 W/m² K, installed in thawed ground with 60 cm gravel pad.

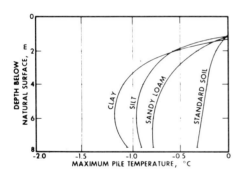

(b) Maximum pile temperature profiles after 3 years for -0.5°C permafrost with 60 cm gravel pad; h_p = 3.0 W/m²K, pile diameter: 46 cm, length: 7.6 m below natural surface.

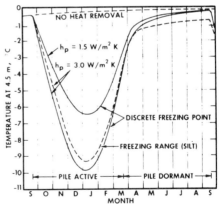

(c) Temperature at 4.50 m depth adjacent to thermal pile during first year after installation in -0.5°C permafrost with 60 cm gravel pad.

FIG. 7.37 Predicted ground temperature effects around thermal piles in unfrozen ground and warm temperature frozen ground—discontinuous permafrost zone (After Jahns et al. 1973).

steel piles, however, due to the effect of solar heating on the part of the pile above the ground surface and from heat gained from the surrounding warmer permafrost and active layer. Generally, it has been found that although large amounts of heat can be extracted and a significant lowering of ground temperatures can be expected during the winter, the ground temperature will be no lower than about $2F°$ ($1C°$), at best, of its normal temperature at the end of the thaw season (Fig. 7.37). Small net changes in ground temperatures can significantly increase adfreeze strengths and reduce annual creep settlements, however, particularly in warm temperature permafrost areas. The efficiency of passive type thermal piles can be improved if the above ground radiator section of the devices or pile is covered with a reflective paint or other coating and if a layer of insulation is placed in the active layer.

When antifreeze liquids are used in forced circulation systems on thermal piles they are pumped through freezing coils installed on the piles (Crory 1973b). Freezing coils are either straight pipes running parallel to the pile axis on a driven pile or, for a slurried pile, the tubing is wound in a spiral around the pile. An exchanger is used to remove the heat from the circulating liquid refrigerant. Specially designed compact propane plants of one ton refrigeration capacity, which do not require a secondary coolant and heat exchanger, are available. In some instances, refrigeration pipes have been installed on piles to permit cooling of the permafrost to increase pile capacity at a later date, should this become necessary. Pipe piles can usually be modified readily to take cooling devices.

Instead of liquid refrigerants, cold air can be circulated by intermittent or seasonal operation of a fan in a pipe pile as shown in Fig. 7.35. No heat exchanger is required to cool the circulating air. An air system is less expensive than a liquid system and may provide satisfactory cooling of the ground (Reed 1966, Jahns et al. 1973). Air systems are normally operated only when air temperatures are below freezing. More complex designs incorporating heat exchangers may be considered but power requirements may not be acceptable.

7.8 Pile Installation Methods

Heavy equipment is normally required to install piles and therefore access roads and gravel working pads are usually constructed on the site prior to pile placement to prevent undesirable disturbance of the natural ground cover and to allow easy movement of equipment and materials around the site. The work pad should cover the entire building site and be graded to ensure proper drainage and prevent ponding of water under and adjacent to the pile supported structure (Figs. 7.34, 7.38). If piles are to be placed during the summer and fill is not available, it will be necessary to provide a temporary working surface (such as metal mats, corduroy or timber pads) for the equipment. If pile installation is to be undertaken during the winter and fill is not available or required, a compacted snow work pad should be used to protect the ground surface.

FIG. 7.38   Differential movement of unheated warehouse supported by 7 m long timber piles. Movements are due to both thaw settlement and frost heave caused by gross disturbance to area and poor drainage.

Piles may be placed in steam-thawed holes, in augered or bored holes or by driving into predrilled "pilot" holes or directly into undisturbed frozen ground. Although many piles have been successfully installed in northern Canada by steam jetting frozen ground (Fig. 6.3), this method has seldom been used since about 1960 (Pihlainen 1959, Johnston 1966b). Large quantities of heat are introduced into the ground and holes are frequently made too large (oversteamed), particularly in ice-rich and stony soils. As a result, the time required for the sludge around the pile to refreeze is greatly prolonged, sometimes for several weeks or months, and construction schedules may be seriously affected. Maximum hole depths are generally limited to about 25 ft. (8 m). There is little control over the type of slurry in contact with the pile and hence the adfreeze bond that can be mobilized, unless the hole is bailed and a properly mixed slurry is placed. This method is limited to areas where ground temperatures are 27°F (-3°C) or lower but the risk of excessive thermal disturbance still exists even with careful control of the steaming operation.

Most piles are now placed in slurry-backfilled drilled holes or by driving (Kitze 1957, Crory 1966, 1968, 1973b, 1975, Rowley et al. 1973b, 1975, Tobiasson and Johnson 1978, Myska and How 1978). Modern drilling and driving techniques

permit piles to be placed to depths exceeding 50 ft. (15 m) with minimum disturbance of the ground thermal regime. Freezeback is generally quite rapid, a matter
of hours or a few days, although in warm temperature frozen soils, special
methods may be needed to assist refreezing of slurried piles (Section 7.7.1). Adfreeze strengths can usually be predicted with greater confidence since slurry or
soil properties are usually controlled or are better known.

Many piles are installed in dry-drilled (augered) and slurry-backfilled holes
(Fig. 7.39). Most frozen soils can be augered quite rapidly and easily, but hard
frozen materials with little ice and even warm temperature (31°F, −0.5°C) silts
and fine sands can be very abrasive and difficult to auger and can reduce penetration rates significantly and increase costs due to wear and tear on the equipment.
In some situations, such as when very stony frozen soils are encountered, rotary
or churn drills using air or water to remove cuttings may be required, but the
operation must be carefully controlled to prevent excessive thermal disturbance.
Holes may range from 12 to 48 in. (30 to 130 cm) in diameter depending on pile or
casing size but are usually from 12 to 24 in. (30 to 60 cm).

The usual procedure is first to auger or drill and clean the hole to the required
depth, the hole being from 4 to 8 in. (10 to 20 cm) greater in diameter than the
pile. The extra width provides some leeway for aligning the pile if the hole is not

FIG. 7.39   Truck-mounted auger drill boring holes for pile foundation.

truly vertical or off-line and permits a vibrator or rod to be used when the slurry is placed. If the hole is drilled too deep, that is the design depth is exceeded either in error or purposely because extensive ice deposits were encountered, it can be backfilled with tamped sand or fine gravel to the desired depth. The pile is then placed (or dropped) and aligned properly in the hole and pushed or driven to ensure it is well seated; rarely is it possible to remove all cuttings and, therefore, some loose material will always remain at the bottom of the hole. In some cases the bottom 10 ft. (3 m) or so of the hole may be backfilled with a dry sand and the pile driven into it to ensure good soil-pile contact and improved bearing capacity. The final step is to backfill the annular space around the pile with a properly mixed and placed soil slurry, which will freezeback quickly (Section 7.9).

Free-running dry sands, gravelly sands, silty sands and silt with low water contents (6 to 15%) are normally used for slurries. A gradation range for a suitable backfill material is shown in Fig. 7.40. Gravel, clay and water should not be used and organic material must be kept out of the mix as they will radically affect the adfreeze strength and freezeback time. When "select" slurry material is in short supply, frozen auger cuttings or sludge from churn-drilled holes may be used. The cuttings should be thawed and dried, particularly if they contain much ice, so that there is no excess water in the mix. On most jobs the slurry is prepared in a portable concrete mixer (Fig. 7.41). Frozen or thawed cuttings can be mixed with predetermined quantities of water and select material to give the desired slurry. Close control of the water content, in particular, and the batching operation, in general, is necessary to ensure that a slurry having a consistency like that of a 6 in. (15 cm) slump concrete is obtained. The temperature of the slurry should never exceed 40°F (4°C) when it is placed in the hole.

The slurry is usually placed in the hole from wheel-barrows on small jobs and with concrete buckets and cranes on large jobs. In a summer operation every precaution should be taken to prevent water from entering the hole. The hole may have to be cased through the active layer and the water removed by pumping or bailing. The water content of the slurry mix should be adjusted to take excess water into account. Not only will excess water inhibit or extend the refreezing time and affect adfreeze bond, but timber piles will tend to float when the hole is backfilled. In such cases, the pile must be anchored or weighted down until freezeback has occurred; the hole may be partially backfilled until the bottom has refrozen and excess water bailed from the upper part of the hole. The slurry must be vibrated or rodded as it is placed to ensure good soil-pile contact and eliminate bridging and voids.

Steel open-end pipe or H piles can often be driven into fine-grained, plastic-frozen soils where the ground temperature is as low as about 27°F (−3°C). Timber and precast concrete piles generally cannot be driven into frozen ground as they cannot withstand the heavy driving required (Fig. 7.42). Standard drop or single- and double-acting diesel hammers are frequently used but the equipment should be carefully chosen, because the energy required will be considerably greater than that needed for driving piles in most unfrozen soils. Vibratory hammers have also been employed for driving these "displacement" piles and some

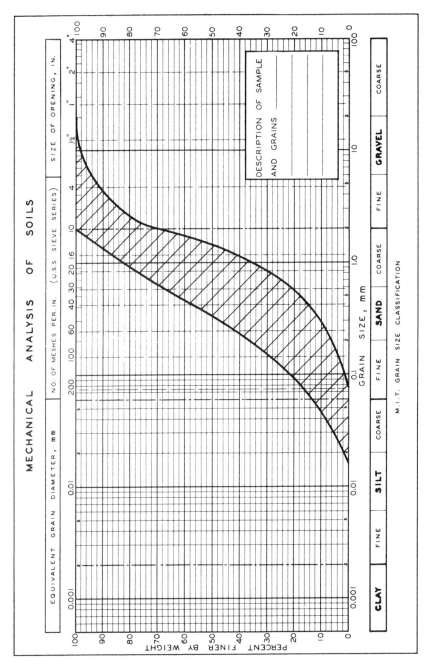

FIG. 7.40   Gradation range for typical slurry backfill.

FIG. 7.41   Preparing sand slurry backfill in portable mixer for placement around steel
H piles at bridge abutment.

success has been achieved using sonic (high frequency) driving equipment (Bendz
1977). Vibratory hammers may also be used to extract damaged or incorrectly
placed piles.

The main advantages of driving piles are that freezeback usually occurs within
a matter of minutes or hours and a soil slurry and a drill are not required. Some
warming and perhaps thawing of a thin layer of soil around the pile may occur
due to frictional resistance when standard driving equipment is used but the effect
on freezeback is usually negligible and can be neglected. Vibratory and sonic
drivers may have a somewhat greater influence on ground temperatures,
however, depending on the soil conditions, and this effect should be monitored
and taken into account. Once begun, driving of a pile should be carried on continuously since stops exceeding about 30 minutes may allow the soil to "set up"
due to friction and densification or freezeback, to the extent that further ad-
vancement of the pile is impossible or accomplished only after a long period of
heavy driving.

When dense, hard frozen, fine-grained soils are encountered and when piles are
closely spaced, it may be advantageous and necessary to drive piles into predrilled
"pilot" holes of slightly smaller diameter than the largest dimension of the pile.
The soil is more easily displaced and the driving energy required will be reduced.
Frozen gravels are penetrated only with great difficulty and, in most cases, pilot
holes must be drilled in these materials (Rooney et al. 1977). Pilot holes must be

carefully drilled to ensure the driven pile will be correctly positioned; slight deviations in the hole will cause the pile to wander out of alignment. Unfrozen coarse sand and gravel layers may often be encountered in the discontinuous permafrost zone or near water bodies. These can be penetrated relatively easily by heavy-wall steel pipe or H piles, although large boulders and very dense strata may cause problems. Both a drill and a pile driver are required when piles are driven into pilot holes, but for pipe piles, at least, a soil slurry does not have to be prepared and placed since the perimeter of the pile will be in good contact with the soil.

FIG. 7.42   Unsuccessful attempt to drive 8 m long wood piles in pilot holes. Note treated portion of piles to be placed in active layer and ground temperature cable attached to pile to monitor freezeback.

Steel H piles driven into pilot holes should be designed for end bearing only, unless it can be proved that the displaced soil completely and compactly fills the pilot hole void such that good adfreeze bond or friction can be mobilized; it will be extremely difficult, if not impossible, to place slurry in the void.

If special driving shoes that are larger than the pile diameter are used on piles driven into frozen ground, a void may remain between the pile shaft and the wall of the hole produced by the shoe, so that adfreeze bond or friction cannot be fully mobilized or relied upon. Such piles depend mainly on end bearing to support the loads and therefore must be driven to refusal on a known competent and thermally stable stratum unless previous experience in the area or local tests prove otherwise. Pile load tests (Section 7.12) should be carried out on representative piles no matter what installation method is used and especially for piles supporting critical structures. A steel template can be used to ensure that driven piles are accurately located. It may be left in place if required to provide lateral stability.

A number of factors must be given careful consideration in selecting the time of year to place pile foundations. These include mobilization and transportation of equipment and materials, construction schedules, effect of weather on the efficiency of workmen and equipment, ground thermal regime and drainage. Piles are frequently installed in the late winter or early spring. Ground temperatures are at or approaching their coldest values at that time and therefore refreezing will take place quickly, the active layer is still frozen so water will not interfere with drilling and pile placement operations, equipment can move readily around the site on the frozen ground surface, and, provided freezeback has occurred, erection of the structure on the piles can take place during the warm summer months. During the summer, fall and early winter, pile refreezing will take longer, and in marginal permafrost areas may have to be assisted using artificial ground cooling methods because of warmer ground temperatures. Drilled or augered holes will have to be cased through the active layer to avoid water problems and sloughing of the holes, and soft ground conditions may hinder equipment movement on the site, unless a gravel work pad has been placed.

Augering, drilling and slurry placement operations can usually be conducted with equal, if not greater, efficiency in the spring as in the fall. On the other hand, driving piles into frozen ground will be more difficult in the spring when very low ground temperatures, and therefore hard frozen materials, are encountered, especially in the active layer. In such cases, it may be necessary to drill a pilot hole to start the pile.

7.9 Freezeback of Piles

Piles must be well anchored in permafrost before loads are applied. Special attention must therefore be given to the freezeback time, particularly for piles placed in steam-thawed or slurry-backfilled drilled holes, to ensure that adequate adfreeze bond is mobilized to resist the applied loads. Piles placed in the late summer, fall or early winter must also resist uplift due to frost heave as the active layer refreezes, if special measures are not incorporated in the design to prevent or reduce frost-grip (Section 7.3.2). Some increase in the ground temperature can be anticipated immediately adjacent to an augered or bored hole due to the drilling operation; in some cases even a driven pile may have an effect. Large amounts of latent heat may have to be removed during freezeback of the slurry around a pile, especially if the hole has been steam thawed. It is essential that freezeback be monitored by measuring ground temperatures on representative piles, no matter what type of pile or method of installation was used nor what time of year they were placed. The temperature cables can also be used to monitor future performance of the foundation.

Freezeback may occur by natural dissipation of the heat to the surrounding frozen ground or it may have to be assisted by artificial refrigeration methods to ensure rapid and positive refreezing. Whether or not artificial refreezing methods are required will depend primarily on local ground thermal conditions. They may have to be used when permafrost temperatures are warm and the construction period is short. Mechanical refrigeration systems must be used during the summer, since passive cooling devices do not function when air temperatures are warmer than the ground temperature.

Carefully mixed soil slurries properly placed around piles in augered dry holes is the preferred technique commonly used for installing all types of piles. The factors that govern the freezeback time include the ground temperature regime, the volume of slurry per unit length of pile, the latent heat of fusion of the slurry and the spacing of the piles. Under given ground thermal conditions, the freezeback time will be most rapid when the diameter of the hole and thus the volume of slurry is at a minimum, the water content of the slurry is at a minimum and the spacing of the piles is at a maximum.

As a general rule, the annular space around the pile should be at least 2 in. (5 cm) but no more than 4 in. (10 cm) in width; that is the hole diameter should be 4 to 8 in. (10 to 20 cm) greater than the pile diameter (or largest dimension of the pile in the case of an H-section). Difficulties in backfilling and vibrating the slurry may be experienced when the annular space is less than 2 in. (5 cm) wide. The freezeback time may be unduly long if it exceeds 4 in. (10 cm).

The latent heat of fusion of a slurry is governed largely by its water content, which therefore should be kept as low as possible. Three important factors related to the ground temperature and the water content of the slurry must be considered when dealing with the thermal aspects of slurried piles. Initially, latent heat liberated by the slurry as it freezes is absorbed by the surrounding colder permafrost. The larger the water content, therefore, the more latent heat is released. It should be noted that heat exchange cannot take place when the slurry and the surrounding ground are at the same temperature. Secondly, the temperature of the permafrost between piles increases as the latent heat is absorbed. Thirdly, the temperature increase slowly dissipates over a long time period to the surrounding undisturbed permafrost. Installation and freezeback of piles in permafrost by natural and artificial means have been described by Crory (1966), U.S. Army/Air Force (1966c) and Sanger (1969). Based on this work, the freezeback time for slurried piles can be estimated using the expressions and chart given in Fig. 7.43.

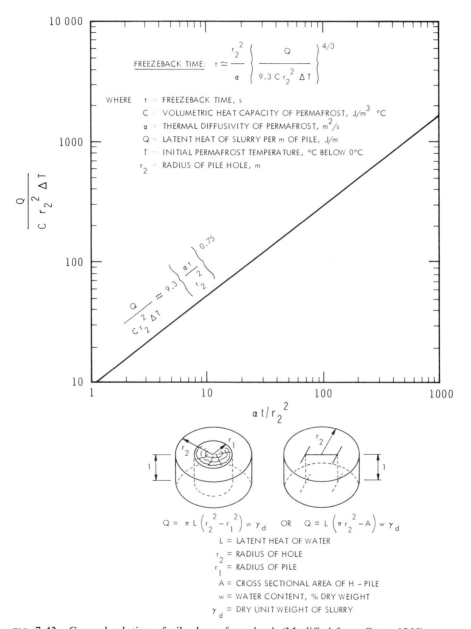

FIG. 7.43   General solution of pile slurry freezeback (Modified from Crory 1966).

Pile spacing depends on freezeback considerations and also on pile group interaction. The minimum spacing to prevent an excessive rise in ground temperature
can be estimated by assuming the heat from the slurry is distributed uniformly
throughout the frozen ground between the piles. The effect of pile spacing on
temperature rise in the surrounding permafrost for a specific slurry is shown in
Fig. 7.44. The temperature rise in the frozen ground around the piles should be
calculated and accounted for in "end-of-construction" pile load design. This
temperature increase may take months or even a year to dissipate. Exact assessment of the post-construction thermal regime requires special analysis if it is
critical to the design. Since no factor of safety is included in calculating the effect
of pile spacing, it is essential that ground temperatures be monitored to confirm
that freezeback has occurred. Heat introduced by driven piles is negligible and
can be neglected.

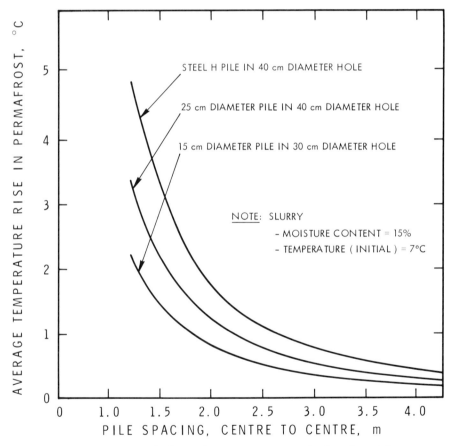

FIG. 7.44   Effect of slurry and pile spacing on temperature rise in adjacent frozen
ground. Note that these curves are examples only and are for a specific pile size, hole
diameter and slurry mix.

When a mechanical refrigeration system is used to promote freezeback of a slurry, it may be necessary to divide the freezing coils wrapped around the piles into two sections so that the bottom portion can be refrozen first and thus provide resistance to frost heave as the upper layers refreeze. Although heat flow will occur in different directions along the pile at different times of the year because of variations in ground temperature with depth, normally it is assumed that heat is conducted in a radial direction. Freezeback of the slurry occurs primarily from the wall of the hole inward toward the pile. If the pile itself is also colder than the slurry, as would be the case when piles are placed during the winter, and particularly for open-end steel pipe piles when cold air can circulate inside the pile, or when a refrigeration system on the pile is used, then freezeback may also occur outward from the pile. As refreezing occurs under either natural or artificial conditions, water removed from the slurry will frequently form an ice layer at the slurry-hole wall interface; this usually is not significant with respect to pile bearing capacity. A similar layer of ice may also form, however, at the pile-slurry interface when the pile is colder than the slurry. When the backfill consists of frost susceptible material, thin, vertically oriented, ice lenses may also form in the slurry parallel to the pile. Unless proved otherwise, it should be assumed that under the above conditions, the face of the pile is coated with a thin layer of ice and that ice lenses form in the slurry (Zhigulskiy 1970). Adfreeze design stresses must therefore take into account these conditions after evaluating the relative long-term strengths of ice and frozen slurry for the critical (warmest) design temperatures.

7.10 Design for Vertical Loads

7.10.1 End Bearing and Adfreeze Strength

Pile foundations in permafrost areas must be designed to support sustained loads without exceeding allowable total or differential settlements and resist heave forces due to frost action in the active layer, short-term loads such as those imposed by wind or dynamic loading and downdrag loads caused by settlement of the soil in a degrading permafrost situation. Typical forces acting on a pile in permafrost are shown in Fig. 7.45. The usual design approach is to predict the loads to be carried and determine the depth to which a pile of a suitable type and size should be embedded in frozen ground to resist them by either adfreeze or end bearing. Vertical pile loadings should not exceed the allowable compressive stress of the pile material. Usually this will not be a problem with steel members but working stresses of 600 to 800 psi (4000 to 5500 kPa) may be applicable for local timber piles.

End bearing is normally taken into account only when a dense competent stratum is encountered and no ice layers exist below the pile. For most piles, where the soil below the tip is the same as that along the pile shaft, adfreeze bond will take most of the load. The contribution of end bearing to the total pile

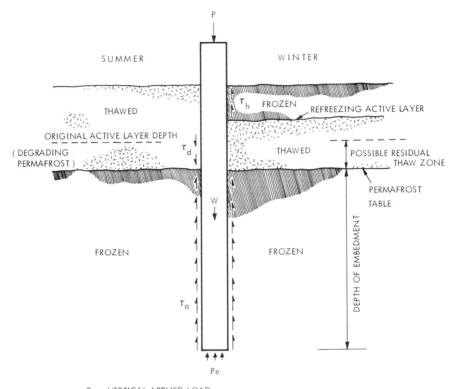

P = VERTICAL APPLIED LOAD
τ_a = STRESS MOBILIZED BETWEEN PILE SHAFT AND FROZEN SOIL
τ_d = DOWNDRAG STRESS DUE TO DEEPENING OF ACTIVE LAYER
W = WEIGHT OF PILE
Pe = MOBILIZED END-BEARING STRESS
τ_h = SEASONAL FROST HEAVE STRESS

FIG. 7.45   Schematic representation of the forces acting on a pile in permafrost.

capacity will usually be relatively small and it is conservative to ignore it (Crory 1966). Where support from the underlying frozen soil might be considered, the relationships for circular footings developed in Section 7.6 can be used to estimate end bearing capacity. In some cases, it may be necessary to enlarge the base of the pile to obtain the desired capacity. Where frozen rock underlies a site, careful investigations are required to ensure it is not just a boulder and to determine the slope of the stratum and whether or not it contains ice lenses. The piles may have to be socketed in the rock.

Frost heave forces have been discussed in Section 7.3. For design purposes, the depth of the active layer that may develop during the service life of the structure to be supported on piles must be estimated. If detailed ground temperature records or previous experience in the area are not available, the depth of the active layer may be calculated using methods outlined in Chapter 4. These should be confirmed, if possible, by probing at the site. When fill is placed on the natural organic surface cover, calculations must take into account the properties of the compacted peat layer and the fill material. In pile design calculations, the estimated active layer depth should be increased by 1 or 2 ft. (0.3 or 0.6 m). This is to account for local natural variations and increased thaw around a pile, caused by the warming effects of solar radiation on unshaded steel piles on the perimeter of a building or under a tower.

The adfreezing strength of frozen soil to timber, steel or concrete is both temperature- and time-dependent. In general, the strength of frozen materials increases with decreasing temperature and they exhibit creep behaviour under loads which are only a fraction of the failure load found by short-term testing procedures. The adfreezing strength used for design is also dependent on a number of other factors, including method of pile placement, properties of the slurry, ground temperatures, type of pile material and nature of its surface, the loading rate and the time during which loads are applied. Some early Soviet data on the short-term tangential adfreeze strength between various soils and wood and concrete are given by Kaplar (1971a) but the reliability of the data is not known because test conditions were not given. The results of some short- and long-term laboratory tests to determine the adfreeze strength of model timber and steel piles frozen in ice are reported by Stehle (1970). When a low moisture content dense sand has been placed properly around a pile in ice-rich permafrost, it is possible that the frozen slurry-pile bond will be much stronger than the slurry-permafrost bond at the wall of the hole. If this is the case, in some situations it may be possible to use the outside diameter of the slurry as the effective diameter of the pile.

There is little long-term load test data on piles in permafrost and, therefore, allowable adfreezing values for various soil types and ice contents are not known exactly. Adfreeze bond strength relationships for short-term and sustained loadings are given in Fig. 7.46; some of the load test data on which the relationships are based are also shown. These indicate the pile shaft stresses that will prevent rupture of the adfreeze bond over short and relatively long time periods. They must be used with caution, however, as they do not take creep settlements into account. These are discussed in the next section.

The warmest ground temperature profile is used for assessing pile capacity based on adfreeze strength. These maximum temperatures might occur soon after placement of the slurry or in the fall or early winter of any subsequent year. Where the temperature varies with depth, the total pile capacity is obtained by integrating the adfreeze strength $\tau(z)$ with depth:

$$P = \pi d \int_0^L \tau(z) dz \qquad (7.8)$$

This can usually be carried out graphically, and the required embedment depth determined for a specified load and safety factor.

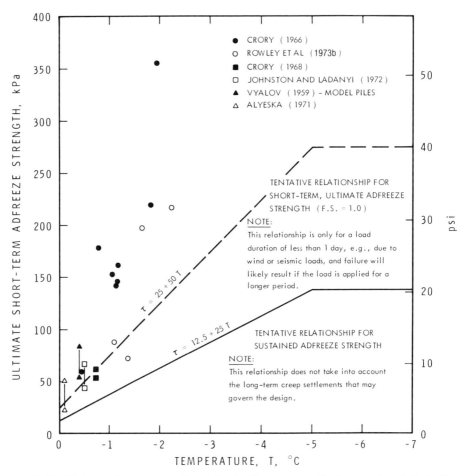

FIG. 7.46 Ultimate short-term and sustained adfreeze strengths for wood and steel piles in frozen clays or silts with ice. Note that the relationships are given in metric units.

7.10.2 Pile Settlements

Permafrost soils with significant excess ice contents have a tendency to creep under sustained loads. Ice is known to creep at a steady rate under low stresses, and it is considered that above a certain ice content the properties of ice will dominate the behaviour of a frozen soil. Undisturbed ice-rich frozen soils have been found to creep at low stresses in a manner similar to ice (Roggensack 1977, McRoberts et al. 1978) as described by Eq. 7.5 (Section 7.6.2).

Piles founded in ice-rich soils can also be expected to creep at a steady rate at stresses below the adfreeze strength. In order to carry out a settlement analysis and limit pile shaft stresses so that long-term pile settlements are maintained within tolerable limits, Nixon and McRoberts (1976) presented a method of predicting pile settlements based on the secondary creep law noted above. The steady pile settlement rate $\dot{u}_a$ can be written as

$$\dot{u}_a = \frac{3^{(n+1)/2}}{n-1} Ba\tau_a^{\,n} \tag{7.9}$$

where a is the pile radius and τ_a is the average applied shaft stress. By rearranging this equation, and having determined the creep constants, B and n, from laboratory tests (Eq. 7.5), the relationship between pile shaft stress and settlement rate can be determined for a given temperature. At other ground temperatures, B and n vary, and different pile shaft stresses will be obtained for a specified settlement rate.

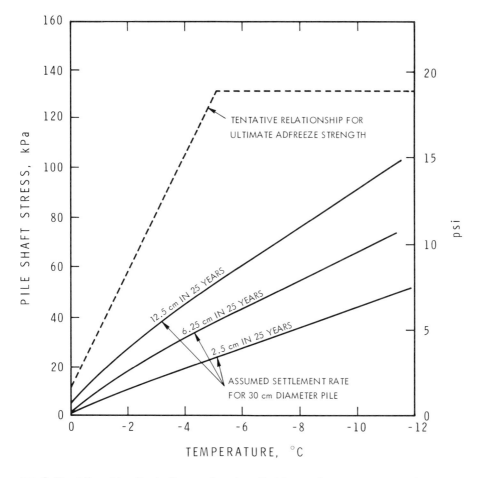

FIG. 7.47 Allowable pile shaft stress based on limiting settlement rate. Note that these curves are based on specific settlement rates and pile size and are presented for illustration purposes only.

Relationships between pile shaft stress and temperature for piles founded in ice or very ice-rich ground are shown in Fig. 7.47. Pile settlement rates of 1, 2.5, and 5 inches (2.5, 6.25 and 12.5 cm) in 25 years have been used for purposes of illustration. The adfreeze relationship given in Fig. 7.46, which does not account for creep, is also shown for comparison. It is seen that, at least in ice-rich soils, pile design based on limiting settlements to tolerable levels will often control the design. The actual settlements and design life selected for a foundation are dependent on tolerances, imposed by the structural designer, that relate to the flexibility of the structure, differential settlements, presence of piping connections, etc. Settlement rates will normally vary during the year and from year to year, depending on the ground temperature regime. Using the warmest temperature profile to estimate settlement rate will over-estimate the average annual settlement, perhaps by as much as a factor of 2. Settlement rates will decrease during the winter when ground temperatures are colder. This should be borne in mind when making estimates of the annual settlement rate.

Settlement analysis for piles in dense, ice-poor soils may be carried out by either (a) obtaining the creep characteristics of the soil in question from a series of laboratory tests, or (b) relating the properties of the frozen soil to the properties of the same soil if it were in the unfrozen state at the same density. This latter concept requires further research, but settlements will probably be limited and decrease with time if the shear stress on the soil around the pile does not exceed the strength of the same soil in the unfrozen state. As a rough guide to pile design in dense, ice-poor soils, allowable shaft stresses might be calculated based on the unfrozen shear strength of the soil thawed under undrained conditions. If this strength is very low or zero, then the soil should be termed "ice-rich," and design should be based on adfreeze strength and limiting settlements as outlined above.

In general, it should be noted that the design of pile foundations for major structures on permafrost requires a careful appreciation of soil, ice and ground thermal conditions, together with proper analysis of bearing capacity and settlement. These have been ignored too often in the past, resulting in serious foundation problems and expensive remedial measures.

7.10.3 Permafrost Thawing and Downdrag

In some areas, and particularly within the discontinuous permafrost zone, disturbance due to construction activity or other factors may initiate a long-term thawing process. A well-ventilated airspace under a structure that shades the ground in summer and reduces snow cover in winter may maintain permafrost conditions in the discontinuous zone. In many cases, however, such as transmission towers or a pile-supported, above-ground pipeline on a cleared right-of-way, it may be assumed that long-term degradation of the permafrost will result. Depending on the vegetation cover and the amount of disturbance, data from Linell (1973a) show that the thaw depth X may be calculated from

$$X = a \sqrt{t} \tag{7.10}$$

where X is in metres, t is the time in years, and the coefficient a can vary from 0.9 to 1.3 m/yr.$^{1/2}$ (See also Section 4.3.3).

The shear stress τ_d on a pile at any depth X can be related to the effective stress $\gamma'X$ by

$$\tau_d = K_o \tan\phi' \cdot \gamma'X \qquad (7.11)$$

where $K_o \tan\phi'$ is often around 0.3 for many soft soils. The total pile load resulting from downdrag effects can be obtained by summing these shear stresses over the predicted depth of thaw.

It will often be found that these downdrag loadings result in excessive increases in the vertical load imposed on the pile and some method, such as the use of insulation or thermal piles, must be employed to reduce the depth of thaw. In addition, as the thaw plane progresses deeper into the ground, the length of pile embedded in permafrost decreases, thereby reducing its vertical support capacity. This concept is illustrated in Fig. 7.48.

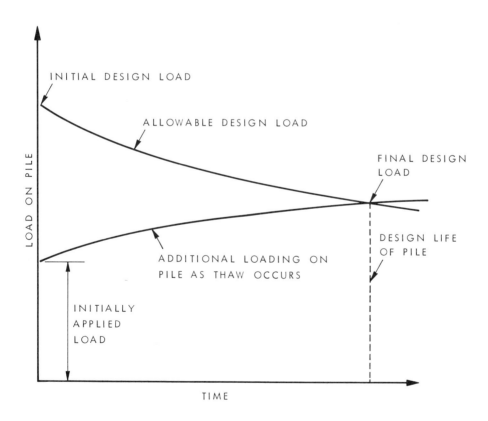

FIG. 7.48   Effect of thawing (downdrag due to permafrost degradation) on pile loading and pile capacity.

7.11 **Lateral Loads on Piles**

The capacity of vertical piles to resist lateral loads may be limited in three ways: large horizontal movements of the piles and failure of the foundation may occur because the ultimate capacity of the soil is exceeded; structural failure of the pile may occur because bending moments have generated excessive bending stresses in the pile material; and unacceptable movements of the superstructure may occur due to very large deflections of the pile heads. The capacity of a laterally loaded vertical pile in frozen ground is very dependent on the duration of the applied load. Therefore, it is important to distinguish between at least three loading durations, some of which may not apply for different facilities: (a) short-term loadings such as those imposed during construction, or by wind or seismic forces; (b) seasonal loadings such as those caused by thermal expansion and contraction of members in a structure. These are typically of a 6 month duration. Those caused by daily temperature fluctuations can be considered as short-term loads; and (c) long-term loadings such as those imposed on pipeline anchors at intermediate points and at bends in the line. These loads would normally be applied for the life of the structure, that is for many years.

Frozen ground around an embedded pile has high strength under rapid rates of loading. Lateral loads on a pile will normally be governed by the strength of the pile section, assuming it to be rigidly embedded at the base of the active layer. It is recommended, however, based on geotechnical considerations and the results of load tests carried out on 12 in. (30 cm) diameter steel pipe and timber piles by Rowley et al. (1973b, 1975), that the short-term lateral load on any pile, not less than 12 in. (30 cm) in diameter and embedded not less than 20 ft. (6 m) in frozen ground, be restricted to 8 t for steel piles and 6 t for timber piles. This restriction should take precedence over any other criterion based on the structural strength of the pile. Only very limited information is currently available and the results of many more load tests are required to improve the basis for design.

Loading criteria for vertical piles subjected to seasonal or long-term lateral loads will probably be governed by creep of the frozen soil around the embedded pile section. The creep of laterally loaded vertical piles requires special analysis, which is not well established at present. Based on limited load test data, however, sustained lateral loads of more than 1 to 3 t will probably cause excessive creep in only a few years, even in relatively ice-poor soils. This would not be tolerable in the long term since, as creep occurs, cavities formed between the frozen ground and the upper part of the embedded piling might cause a serious reduction in vertical load capacity. Extra piles may be installed and rigidly tied together to decrease the load per pile but, in general, sustained lateral loads of any significance should not be resisted by vertical piles, particularly in ice-rich, warm temperature soils.

If sustained loadings exceed the lateral capacities just discussed, it will probably be necessary to install a group of battered piles to attain the desired lateral capacity. Large sustained lateral loads may have to be resisted (for example, at pipe anchorage points, or pipe bends supported on piles). Drilling and backfilling or driving battered piles in frozen ground will clearly be more difficult and costly than for the equivalent vertical piles. It should be possible to drive piles at batter angles of 20° to 30° to the vertical. Although increasing the batter angle increases the lateral resistance of the pile group, it also increases the problem of backfilling the annulus if the pile is placed in a slurry-filled, drilled hole, a factor which should be borne in mind when selecting the batter angle.

A method of determining the capacity of a battered or mixed-pile group is to calculate the axial load transmitted to each pile in the group by graphical force polygon techniques (for example, see U.S. Navy 1971). Once the load on each pile in the axial direction is known, the design criteria for vertically loaded piles can be used to establish the required pile dimensions. A rigid connection must be provided at the head of each battered pile or group of piles to prevent rotation or movement of one or more piles relative to the others. If the head of a battered pile is allowed to displace relative to the other pile or piles, then the beneficial effect of battering may be lost. Field load tests are essential to determine the capacity of either vertical or battered single piles or pile clusters which are to resist large forces without failure.

7.12 Pile Load Tests

Frozen soil tends to creep under loads that are only a fraction of the failure load obtained in short-term loading tests. Few long-term load tests have been carried out on piles in permafrost. Such tests should be conducted whenever possible to verify design parameters used on specific jobs and also are needed to improve design methods in general. Pile load tests are of little value unless the load has been sustained for at least several months. It is usually not considered practicable to perform a cyclic test of the kind generally used for testing piles in unfrozen ground because of the high cost, even when they can be conducted in or near an existing community. It is preferable, therefore, that tests on piles in permafrost be carried out using sustained dead loads left in position for as long a period as possible. Stage loading of piles might also be considered. In this case a load is applied and left on until the secondary (steady) creep rate is established before the next load increment is applied. Analysis of results can be carried out in a manner similar to that used by Johnston and Ladanyi (1972).

The settlement of the pile and ground temperatures can be observed at intervals of one or two months. Considerable effort must be directed towards sheltering instrumentation and the ground surface from wide fluctuations in ambient temperature. It is also suggested that a number of piles of varying length be installed at each site. These piles would be loaded so as to induce pile shaft stresses of varying magnitude. Crory (1966) gives details of test methods used where it is desired to determine the adfreezing strength only.

PART IV—SPECIAL FOUNDATIONS

7.13 Bridges, Wharves and Offshore Structures

The design of foundations for structures that are located adjacent to or in bodies of water in the North must be given special attention. The distribution and properties of perennially frozen soils are of particular concern. Rivers, lakes and the ocean exert a moderating influence on the ground thermal regime, not only under but also adjacent to them. Permafrost is usually absent or there may be an extensive thaw basin beneath large bodies of fresh water that do not freeze to the bottom in winter. River or lake banks may or may not be underlain by permafrost, depending upon their location (discontinuous or continuous permafrost zones), orientation to solar radiation, the effects of erosion due to wind, ice, floods and wave action and the thermal influence of the water body. It is generally found that shorelines subject to active erosion are more likely to contain permafrost than those currently subject to deposition (Mackay 1963c, Lewellen 1973, Newbury et al. 1978, Shah 1978, Scott 1978). A geothermal explanation for this has been presented by Smith and Hwang (1973).

Until recently, little has been known concerning permafrost distribution under Arctic seas. Extensive permafrost has been encountered offshore in the Beaufort Sea and elsewhere, and its presence is usually explained as being either aggradation permafrost due to the below-freezing mean temperature of the saline water or relic permafrost resulting from rapid recession of coastal shorelines (Section 2.1). Permafrost is sometimes encountered at shallow depths below the sea bottom where the ice cover extends to the sea bed during the winter. The permafrost table is depressed very sharply, however, where there is a relatively thick layer of unfrozen water between the ice cover and the sea bed.

In view of the many uncertainties regarding the existence of permafrost and the properties of frozen ground near and under water bodies, it is mandatory that the distribution of permafrost be defined by careful terrain analysis and site investigation, so that an optimum location for structures such as bridges, wharves, water intakes, mooring facilities and drilling platforms can be selected. Hydrological studies to determine tidal limits, peak flood levels and when they occur, water volumes and flow rates, ice conditions, rates of river bank migration and scour depth are also essential for determining the best location for bridge abutments, wharves, approach fills, the need for bank protection and channelization works and to assist in understanding subsurface conditions and choosing appropriate foundation designs and construction methods. Studies of the occurrence, properties and mechanical behaviour of unfrozen and frozen saline soils are particularly important.

7.13.1 Bridge Foundations

The location of bridges and the design of their foundations are usually dictated by foundation soil and permafrost conditions, river flows and ice conditions.

Many northern rivers and streams can be bridged by single-span structures with the abutments placed, sometimes in frozen ground, well back from the high water level to avoid bank erosion, riverbed scour and ice damage. On the other hand, some large rivers will require several spans, and therefore intermediate piers must be constructed within the river.

Caissons, piers, or end-bearing piles may be satisfactory where a competent, strong and stable stratum exists at reasonable depth. Where bedrock is at excessive depths—say greater than 150 ft. (50 m)—consideration may have to be given to other types of foundations. Friction piles may be used where unfrozen ground is encountered. Freezeback piles (perhaps utilizing artificial cooling techniques) may be considered where frozen ground is encountered and excessive permafrost degradation is not anticipated. Large footings or piers may be applicable where either frozen or unfrozen ground underlies the site. In all cases, detailed site information must be obtained so that rational, economic and safe foundations can be designed and construction methods and schedules chosen (Crory 1968, 1975, Beauchamp and Stamer 1971, Hibbert and Beauchamp 1978). For some situations, bank protection and channelization works (such as groynes, rip rap, gabions, dykes and dredging) may be required to prevent damage to the structure and to control and stabilize the river channel.

Footings, piers and freezeback piles are seldom used because of the unstable permafrost conditions that usually exist adjacent to or under water bodies. Footings and piers are normally used only where permafrost is absent, such as in the centre of a river or where the perennially frozen ground is absolutely thaw-stable. Freezeback piles should not be used for bridges in the discontinuous permafrost zone and should be used in the continuous permafrost zone only after a detailed study of the foundation soils and ground thermal regime has shown they will perform satisfactorily. It is imperative that any possible changes in the ground thermal regime that could occur during the life of the structure be predicted with the best possible accuracy so that bearing capacity, frost heave forces, settlement and downdrag loads arising from permafrost degradation and other related considerations can be predicted with confidence. The design of freezeback piles has been discussed in Part III of this chapter.

Driven steel piles, which develop most of their resistance by point bearing in underlying bedrock or other strong stratum, are most suitable for bridge foundations in the discontinuous zone. Experience in the upper Mackenzie Valley and Alaska has shown that heavy steel H piles or open-end pipe piles can be driven satisfactorily through significant depths of warm temperature, frozen fine-grained soils with little risk of pile damage. End bearing piles should be designed for either the structural capacity of the pile as a column or the full projected end bearing capacity of the pile on the bedrock surface, whichever is the least. It is essential that the compressive strength and competence of the bedrock be determined. In many instances, closed-end steel pipe piles seated in bedrock are economical. Installation of this pile type usually requires preboring a hole that is approximately 90% of the pile diameter. The piles should be driven to practical refusal in the bedrock with the minimum penetration being the prebored depth.

The design of piled bridge foundations for highways and railways is described in standard reference manuals for those facilities and in the Canadian Foundation Engineering Manual (Canadian Geotechnical Society 1978). Pile load tests should be conducted whenever possible and should be mandatory for large structures.

The overall construction sequence plays an important part in determining the structural load-carrying capacity of any pile foundation design. Bridge approach fills in permafrost terrain will normally be at least 6 ft. (2 m) and often 10 ft. (3 m) or more in thickness. Bridge abutment piles should be installed through the fill, preferably when fill settlement has ceased, to eliminate the undesirable effects of negative skin friction. Because the time required for settlement to dissipate or become negligible can be several years in cases where thaw subsidence is occurring, it is often impractical to schedule construction activities such that all potential downdrag forces are eliminated. An optimum must therefore be found between the costs of scheduling for minimum pile downdrag and constructing to withstand greater forces.

Although serious difficulties have been experienced due to frost heave (Péwé and Paige 1963) and it cannot be overlooked, it should not be a problem when bridge piles are installed through a fill in the manner just described on sites underlain by permafrost. The active layer is often confined to the approach fill, which is generally constructed of non-frost-susceptible material. At sites where bedrock is deep, the length of pile required to establish end bearing resistance is usually sufficient to provide anchorage against uplift forces caused by tangential adfreezing. Frost heave of piles may become a problem on sites underlain by unfrozen soil, however, if the approach fill is sufficiently thick to cause aggradation of permafrost. Sufficient embedment in the underlying unfrozen or frozen ground is required to provide adequate shaft friction or adfreeze bond to resist the heave forces. Tangential frost heaving forces on piles may be assessed using values given in Section 7.3.

7.13.2 Wharves

Although water transport in the Arctic is generally limited to a relatively short period of the year due to the ice cover, most settlements are located on rivers, lakes or sea coasts for ease of access. The construction of wharves on shorelines containing permafrost has therefore been a common activity throughout the North. On the Mackenzie River, for example, there are docks at all major settlements along the river and also at major oil company base camps and communities in and adjacent to the Mackenzie Delta. For permanent wharves it is common practice to construct a sheet pile bulkhead behind which backfill is placed. The main structure may sometimes consist of a wood deck supported on timber or steel piles. Temporary and older structures are often timber cribs filled with sand and gravel. Only one deep-sea dock, consisting of three circular steel pile cells filled with angular material, a backup area and a causeway, has been built in the Canadian Arctic (Girgrah and Shah 1977). As with bridges, careful site and hydrological investigations are mandatory in order to select an optimum site for a wharf. Particular attention must be given to determining permafrost distribution both on- and off-shore, soil types, depth to bedrock, water levels at spring flood and during the summer and fall, ice movement and the danger of creating an obstruction that would cause ice jams. The irregular distribution of permafrost and warm temperature frozen ground may lead to structure foundation and bank stability problems.

On many rivers in the Arctic, the water level rises rapidly during the spring breakup, sometimes 20 ft. (6 m) or more in a week or two, and the major movement of ice takes place at the peak river stage. It is usually impractical to design a wharf, especially on a large river, to resist the impact forces generated by moving ice or those imposed by ice jams caused by the structure or occurring just downstream. Most wharves are therefore constructed so that they are submerged at high water, allowing the ice to run over them. If it is a "low water" breakup year such that the wharf obstructs ice movement or the water recedes rapidly, it is often necessary to remove stranded pans and piles of ice by blasting and bulldozing and to do minor repairs and replace some of the backfill as part of a regular maintenance program (Fig. 7.49).

A sheet pile bulkhead is generally sufficiently rigid and anchored such that it will resist moderate horizontal and vertical ice forces that occur on rivers during freeze-up in the fall and early winter and during the early stages of breakup in the spring, when the water level is rising and the ice cover is still bonded to the face of

FIG. 7.49   Ice piled up on earthfill wharf that created jam will have to be removed by blasting and bulldozer.

the piles. Nevertheless, these factors must be given attention. Of particular significance to wharves and docks constructed on northern sea shores are the forces acting on the structure due to horizontal movement of pack ice at all seasons of the year and the vertical movements of the ice cover caused by tidal action.

Stability of the bank behind a wharf is often a major consideration in site selection. Frequently, cuts have to be made when access roads are constructed to the wharf and working areas have to be prepared to permit movement of unloading equipment and temporary storage of materials. This may require major construction on the bank adjacent to the wharf; cut and fill operations on the shoreline may induce thermal disturbance and slope instability (Fig. 7.50). This work requires careful attention when planning the layout of a proposed site.

The feasibility of driving sheet piles is completely dependent upon foundation conditions, particularly the distribution of permafrost. Sheet piling cannot be driven through any depth of frozen ground without structural damage or

FIG. 7.50 Bank instability behind wharf was caused by gross disturbance of the area as a result of removal of the organic slope surface cover and excavation of ice-rich soil to enlarge the working and storage area. Unsuccessful attempts were made to construct a retaining wall with 10 m long wood piles, some of which were tied back with cables to piles placed at top of slope. Final solution was to blanket slope with about 0.7 m of peat, improve drainage and prohibit all activity on the slope and at the top of the bank.

FIG. 7.51   Original timber pile bent wharf at Inuvik was replaced by sheet pile structure. Sheet piling has been placed and old structure is being dismantled as shown in (a). Sheet piling was anchored by tie rods seen in (a) and (b) to groups of battered steel H section soldier piles driven into permafrost. The tie rod connection to the soldier piles is shown in (b). The plastic pipe contains a ground temperature cable.

breakage of interlocks. Often the outer line of sheet piling can be positioned so that it is just beyond the permafrost boundary along the shoreline (Fig. 7.51). Pile penetration, section size, and position of tieback systems can be selected based upon conventional design procedures. Frost heave is a consideration when a pile-bent structure is contemplated. Low water levels during the fall and winter may result in deep frost penetration below the bottom. Piles can be subjected to large uplift forces and will heave unless well embedded (Fig. 7.52).

Wharves or docks may cause a scour problem to develop where erodible materials, such as fine sand and silt, extend to considerable depth in a river bottom. As a rough guide, it is suggested that sheet piles should be at least 20% longer than that required for structural purposes, to allow for scour. Scour potential and design depth of sheet piles to account for this should be assessed by personnel experienced in river hydrology in the area. In some instances, severe scour problems can be remedied or controlled by placing cement-enriched sand in bags or other forms of rip-rap protection along the outer edge or upstream of the bulkhead.

Stability of the tieback anchorage system is an important consideration for a sheet pile wall in permafrost regions. The anchor system must not only support the wall (long-term loading) but also resist impact forces (short-term loading) due

FIG. 7.52 Deep frost penetration each season caused frost heave of these 10 to 12 m long timber wharf piles on the Mackenzie River.

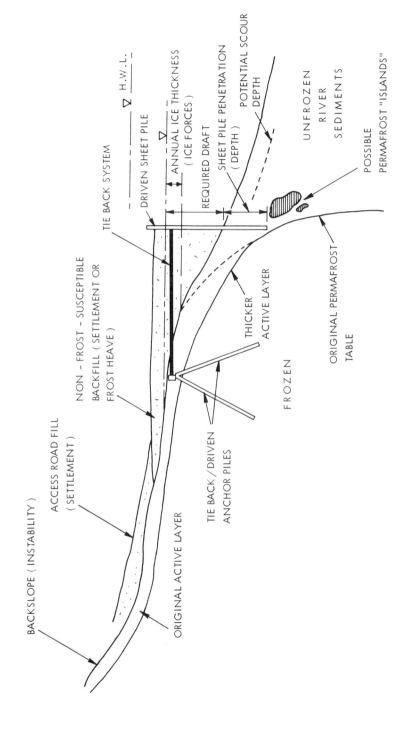

FIG. 7.53 Schematic illustration of a typical wharf facility in a permafrost area and some design considerations.

to vessels and ice striking the structure. Seasonal freezing of the fill behind the wall can also exert large forces on the sheet piles and the anchors. Thaw subsidence as a result of permafrost degradation beneath or around the anchors can result in either loss of support for the wall or overstressing of the tieback system (Fig. 7.53). For this reason, vertical and lateral stability of the tieback system is usually provided by anchor piles placed in competent, usually frozen material on the bank and permafrost degradation prevented.

Anchor piles can usually adequately resist impact forces but their resistance to long-term lateral loading may be quite low, due to the warm permafrost temperatures resulting from the adjacent water body and the potential for creep movements to occur. Evaluation of the existing and future ground thermal regime is most important in assessing the capacity of the tieback system. The steady-state temperature distribution, accounting for the effects of channel migration, should be predicted and confirmed, if at all possible, by field measurements using permanent ground temperature installations.

The project schedule often dictates that a sheet pile wharf be constructed during the late winter or early spring before breakup. The low water conditions are an advantage; the ice cover can be used as a working surface and the facility will be ready for use during the following navigation season. Moderately heavy sheet pile sections can be effectively driven through 6 ft. (2 m) of ice into thawed bottom soils. All of the ice must be removed from within the bulkhead, however, before any fill can be placed. This has occasionally proven troublesome, particularly if the operation is rushed by the impending spring breakup. Good, well-draining backfill material may not be readily available; granular material, for example, may be frozen in stockpiles. Construction can also be undertaken during the summer with driving equipment operating from barges or the shore.

7.13.3 Artificial Islands

Recent discoveries of oil and gas in the Mackenzie Delta have initiated a comprehensive exploration program for hydrocarbons in the shallow waters of Mackenzie Bay and the southern Beaufort Sea. Since 1973 more than fifteen "artificial" earthfill islands have been constructed and used successfully as exploratory drilling platforms in water depths ranging from about 5 to 40 ft. (1.5 to 12 m). The size of the islands varies somewhat but their tops (working surface) are usually about 300 ft. (100 m) in diameter.

Important geotechnical considerations in island design and construction are: availability of suitable borrow material; techniques used to transport and place the fill; sea bottom soil and permafrost conditions (Section 2.1); and vertical and lateral stability of the island and foundation soils to settlement and heave and to ice and wave action. Design and construction procedures are described by Hayley and Sangster (1974), Brown and Barrie (1975), deJong et al. (1975), Croasdale and Marcellus (1978) and Garratt and Kry (1978). It must be noted that these islands are temporary structures for exploratory drilling and are meant to last only a limited time, usually for less than one year.

The main design concerns, with respect to foundation stability when a surcharge load (the island fill) is placed on the seabed, are slope failure, excessive settlement and the possibility of the soils being overstressed. A field investigation must be carried out at the site in order to design and predict the performance of an artificial island. The purpose of a drilling program is to determine water depths and the nature of unfrozen sea bottom sediments (particularly their consistency and density), to obtain undisturbed samples for laboratory testing, to determine if permafrost exists within a critical depth and to assess its potential for thaw settlement and stability problems when the island is constructed. Loose to compact non-plastic silt and silty sand is abundant in the Mackenzie Bay region. Boreholes in unfrozen sea bottom soils slough readily, making downhole sampling and testing difficult. Drilling equipment that has proven adequate to cope with these problems are the hollow stem auger, a rotary drill using drilling mud and casing where required, and a rotary hammer drill using a double wall core tube through which air is circulated to return the cuttings.

Information from field and laboratory testing programs is used to determine if the foundation soil has sufficient bearing capacity to support the island fill and what settlements can be anticipated. When unfrozen materials are being dealt with, fill and seabed soil shear strengths are normally used in conventional slope stability analyses to determine acceptable slope angles. The occurrence, properties and behaviour of saline foundation soils should not be overlooked. An allowance for extra fill can be incorporated into the design to take care of settlements but the height of fill (surcharge load) is limited by the allowable bearing pressure on the seabed soil. If permafrost is encountered, potential thaw settlement problems associated with permafrost degradation must be evaluated. Both one- and two-dimensional thermal calculations may be required to assess the extent of frozen and thawed zones in the interior and perimeter zones of the island. Based on a successful comparison of numerical and analytical solutions, Bafus et al. (1975) concluded that artificial islands are thermally practicable in shallow water.

In the shallow water areas where the islands are located, the ice cover that forms during the winter eventually becomes landfast and subject to only limited motion and therefore the interaction of a wide structure (the island) is mainly with ice sheets, which attain a thickness of 7 ft. (2 m) or more by the end of the winter. Although much progress has been made in recent years, considerable uncertainty surrounds the prediction of ice forces that might act on artificial islands (Croasdale and Marcellus 1978). Ice forces exerted on wide structures arise from the mechanical processes inherent in particular ice failure modes as an ice sheet moves past a structure. Kry (1980) discusses the four primary ice failure modes that can occur against wide structures; flexure, rubble formation, buckling and crushing. For sand or gravel fill islands, failure by lateral movement could occur by shear through soft foundation soils. It is often not possible to design an island having a foundation contact area of less than about 10,000 sq. yd. (8400 m^2) that will resist the forces generated by moving ice.

Observations on the behaviour of ice sheets around an island have shown that an ice rubble field builds up during the early winter due to extensive movements of thin ice, which failed in flexure as it rode up on the sloping sides of the island. During the winter the rubble field becomes very large and the consolidated rubble will prevent or reduce the possibility of the thicker and stronger ice sheet riding up on the island, but it also results in larger forces being exerted on the island due to the increase in effective width against which the ice sheet must fail. Buckling, although not a true failure mode, is indicative of an instability that leads to failure. It is dependent, for example, on the thickness of the ice sheet, the width of the structure and the boundary conditions at the edge of the ice sheet. Crushing results from compressive forces and can be anticipated in late winter, when the ice is sufficiently thick such that failure by buckling is not dominant.

Lateral instability of the artificial fill is of particular concern when oil and gas wells are being drilled. Instrumentation should be installed to monitor any lateral shift. The instruments used are conventional inclinometers modified to include a detection system that will give warning if gross movements occur between each set of readings. A contingency plan is normally developed so that immediate action can be taken to disconnect the drill pipe and abandon the site if the island is apparently unstable.

The islands have been constructed during the summer, utilizing suitable unfrozen sea bottom materials excavated by dredge and transported by barge, and also during the winter, when granular fill, obtained from onshore borrow pits and hauled over ice roads by trucks, is placed through holes cut in the sea ice. If summer construction is anticipated, a suitable sea bottom borrow source must be located and evaluated by a drilling program, usually carried out from the ice surface during the preceding winter. Borrow material must be granular, preferably coarse sand or fine gravel, for the dredge and barge method of construction to function efficiently. The material should be uniform in gradation with at least 50% of the particles retained on a No. 100 sieve to ensure that sedimentation occurs in the barges at a reasonable rate.

Islands have been constructed in the summer with and without a fill-retaining structure of some type. The long, flat underwater slopes that are inevitable on unconfined islands built of fine-grained material make this type of construction uneconomical unless a substantial supply of coarse material is available immediately adjacent to the proposed island site. Recent practice includes construction of a sandbag dike around the perimeter of the proposed fill in order to retain the material. Above the water level, the sandbags are carefully placed, separated from the fill material with a synthetic filter blanket, and tied into the island with wire mesh so that they act as a breakwater to protect the fill against erosion.

Winter construction of islands is necessary in areas where the water is too shallow for barges to operate. The sea ice is removed in stages from the area to be filled, either by ripping when it is frozen to the bottom, or by cutting and remov-ing blocks with a mechanical ditching machine and loader. Clean, well-graded gravel can be placed satisfactorily by end dumping into the water until the fill is at least one foot above ice level. The material is then placed and compacted in lifts until the desired height above high water level is reached.

7.14 Tower Foundations

Several important factors influence the design and construction of towers for power transmission lines, communication antennae, navigation aids, tramlines, cableways or other purposes in the North. In some cases, many towers may have to be erected for facilities that traverse long distances over highly variable terrain and are not readily accessible; in other cases, a single tower may have to be built at a remote location. Power transmission lines and communication systems must be provided to northern communities for living comfort and industrial efficiency, and often actual survival. Design and construction must be such that operation and maintenance problems will not occur or must be kept to an acceptable minimum. Interruption of these services is critical, even for short time periods, and every precaution must be taken to ensure that foundation failures are not the cause of downtime. If failures occur, repair work often has to be carried out dur-ing periods of adverse weather and may require days and weeks because of dif-ficult access to a tower or section of a line and the time needed to mobilize and move heavy equipment and materials to the site.

Foundation conditions can be highly variable, ranging from deep deposits of frozen or unfrozen organic material (muskeg), which frequently occur in low-lying, poorly drained areas, to badly frost-fractured and frozen rock at high elevation. The foundations and anchors for a tower can be subjected to a wide variety of loading conditions acting either separately or in combination and of both long- and short-term duration. These include, in addition to the dead load of the structure, high wind and ice loads acting not only directly on the structure itself but also on the conductors or cables and transmitted to the structure and an-chors, seismic loadings in earthquake zones, frost heave forces in the active layer and thaw settlement due to degradation of permafrost, particularly in the discon-tinuous zone.

The routes and sites for towers must be carefully selected by detailed studies (Chapter 5). Locations for single communications towers can usually be in-vestigated and a suitable foundation selected with little difficulty. For long transmission lines, however, although desirable, it is usually not possible to con-duct a detailed investigation at individual tower sites. Great emphasis must therefore be placed on careful terrain analysis to predict subsurface conditions at each proposed tower location. Frequently, conditions are assessed and a suitable foundation type selected at the time the foundations for a tower are constructed. Although several types of foundations may be considered, it is common practice to choose in advance two or three types that will satisfy most of the conditions that it is anticipated will be encountered on the line. It is not practical to have many kinds of construction equipment moving along a line to install a different foundation type at adjacent towers if foundation conditions vary.

Wood poles set in augered holes or attached to stub piles are often used for power distribution lines (Section 10.4.1). For major transmission lines and heavily loaded structures such as tramways and microwave or radar towers, which have little tolerance to movement, steel guyed or self-supporting towers are normally used. Self-supporting or free-standing towers are usually 4-legged and require four separate foundations, each capable of resisting uplift, horizontal and downward loadings. A guyed structure may consist of a single- or double-mast tower supported by one central foundation, which is subjected to a variety of downward and horizontal loads, and several separate guy anchors to take uplift forces.

Several types of foundations can be considered for the support of each tower leg or mast, depending on site conditions and loads to be carried. Timber, reinforced concrete and steel footings or grillages are often used for transmission line towers but pile foundations are normally chosen for communication towers in

FIG. 7.54   Concrete block footings, 6 m x 6 m x 4.5 m deep, support each leg of this 190 m high communications tower constructed in the continuous permafrost zone. The tower was located on a ridge of frozen sand containing little or no ice. Depth of the active layer was about 1.5 m.

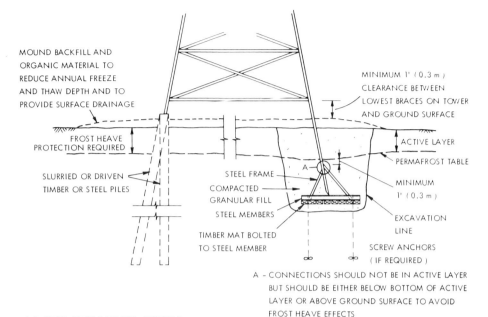

MOUND BACKFILL AND
ORGANIC MATERIAL TO
REDUCE ANNUAL FREEZE
AND THAW DEPTH AND TO
PROVIDE SURFACE DRAINAGE

MINIMUM 1' (0.3 m)
CLEARANCE BETWEEN
LOWEST BRACES ON TOWER
AND GROUND SURFACE

FROST HEAVE
PROTECTION REQUIRED

ACTIVE LAYER

PERMAFROST TABLE

SLURRIED OR DRIVEN
TIMBER OR STEEL PILES

STEEL FRAME

A

COMPACTED
GRANULAR FILL

MINIMUM
1' (0.3 m)

STEEL MEMBERS

EXCAVATION
LINE

TIMBER MAT BOLTED
TO STEEL MEMBER

SCREW ANCHORS
(IF REQUIRED)

A - CONNECTIONS SHOULD NOT BE IN ACTIVE LAYER
BUT SHOULD BE EITHER BELOW BOTTOM OF ACTIVE
LAYER OR ABOVE GROUND SURFACE TO AVOID
FROST HEAVE EFFECTS

(a) SELF-SUPPORTING TOWERS

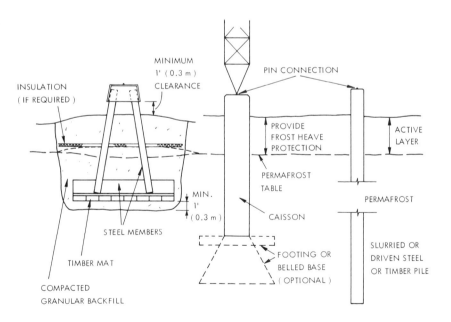

INSULATION
(IF REQUIRED)

MINIMUM
1' (0.3 m)
CLEARANCE

PIN CONNECTION

PROVIDE
FROST HEAVE
PROTECTION

ACTIVE
LAYER

PERMAFROST
TABLE

PERMAFROST

MIN.
1'
(0.3 m)

CAISSON

STEEL MEMBERS

SLURRIED OR
DRIVEN STEEL
OR TIMBER PILE

FOOTING OR
BELLED BASE
(OPTIONAL)

TIMBER MAT

COMPACTED
GRANULAR BACKFILL

(b) GUYED TOWERS

FIG. 7.55 Sketches illustrating several types of foundations for self-standing and guyed towers.

FIG. 7.56   (a) Steel posts embedded about 2.5 m in permafrost were used as foundations for these airfield approach lights. Differential heave (maximum heave is about 45 cm) has occurred due to frost action in 0.7 m thick active layer. (b) Transmission line tower on buried grillage footings has suffered differential movements due to thaw settlement and frost heave. (c) Solution to problem shown in (b) was to excavate and relevel foundations, improve local drainage and place select granular backfill around structure.

(b.)

permafrost areas. For reasons of economy, pile foundations are generally used for transmission line towers only when exceptionally difficult conditions are encountered on tangent sections of the line and at corners where angle towers have to carry heavy loads. Various types of foundations that have been used for towers are described by Nees (1951), Roberts and Cooke (1950), Reinart (1971), Barry and Cormie (1971), MacFarlane (1969), Battle (1971) and Myska and How (1978). Some typical tower foundations are shown in Figs. 7.31, 7.54 and 7.55. Anchorages are discussed in Section 7.15.

Footings and grillages may be used to provide vertical bearing in areas where permafrost will not degrade during the life of the structure. The footing or grillage, similar to those shown in Fig. 7.16, should be placed in a pit excavated below the maximum anticipated depth of the active layer or in a compacted fill on the ground surface, if local materials are available, and select backfill carefully placed. In the continuous permafrost zone the active layer can be expected to deepen by at least 2 ft. (0.6 m) as a result of disturbance due to construction and heat conducted along the steel members. Footings and grillages can also be used in the discontinuous permafrost zone but only where foundation soils are thaw-stable because permafrost degradation will inevitably occur unless special measures are taken as discussed below. Pile foundations can provide stable support for towers throughout the permafrost region. Design and construction considerations are described in Part III of this chapter.

Frost action has caused many tower foundation problems (Fig. 7.56). In some cases, foundation movements, frequently differential on self-supporting towers, have occurred due to a combination of frost heave and thaw settlement. In other cases, where a footing or grillage has provided more than adequate resistance to uplift and allowed no movement to relieve the induced tensile stresses, adfreeze and basal heave forces acting on buried vertical and sloping members and their connections have been so large that the steel angles have been bent and twisted and shear failures have occurred at bolted connections. Special attention must be given to frost action design to ensure that members in the active layer are not subjected to significant frost grip and basal heave forces (Section 7.3).

Insulation placed in the fill and around structural members below ground, as depicted in Fig. 7.57, is an effective method for reducing the depth of the active layer and therefore the potential for frost action and also the footing excavation depth. The use and proper placement of select backfill around tower foundations and careful attention to drainage will alleviate many problems. Passive ground cooling devices or thermal piles can also be used to limit or prevent thawing and reduce frost action effects (Section 7.7.1). Strict control and supervision of construction operations is of prime importance.

7.15 Anchorages

Anchorages are used for many types of structures, including bridges, retaining walls, guyed towers, above-ground and buried oil and gas pipelines, water, sewer

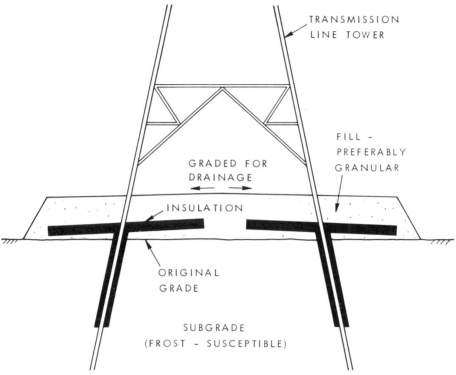

FIG. 7.57   Sketch illustrating scheme for an insulated tower foundation to reduce frost penetration.

and heating lines in utilidors (Section 10.3.2.2) and even small or temporary buildings. The forces to be resisted can vary greatly, both in magnitude and nature, depending on the type of structure and the loading conditions imposed by it on the anchorage. Loadings can by cyclic, dynamic, short-term or sustained. Sustained forces, which can be very large, usually have to be resisted by anchors at bends on large diameter pipelines. On the other hand, sustained loadings on tower guy anchors may not be large but transient wind forces usually require that larger, almost instantaneous, loadings be resisted. The design and installation of anchors in frozen ground, and indeed in unfrozen ground, present complex problems and solutions are not yet well established. A variety of design and construction methods have been used (Hironaka 1974b, Kovacs et al. 1975). Anchors in frozen ground will generally creep in proportion to the magnitude of the applied load. The design and capacity of anchors will therefore be governed to a large extent by the displacements that can be tolerated rather than by uplift or pull-out capacity. Frost heave and thaw settlement also are important considerations.

   Three main types of anchors can be considered for use in permafrost areas: gravity or block anchors, piles and grouted rod anchors (Figs. 7.58 and 7.59).

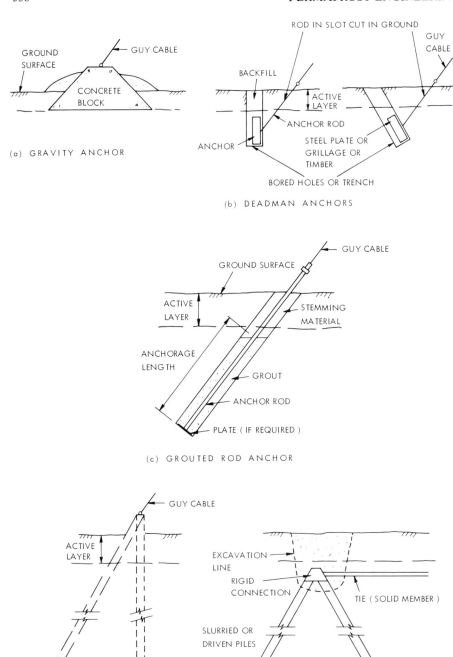

FIG. 7.58   Sketches of several types of anchorages in permafrost.

Gravity or "dead-man" anchors usually consist of a heavy weight, such as a concrete block, placed on or just below the ground surface, or a timber or steel member or system buried in the ground. These normally provide positive anchorage and are relatively free of creep. Heave and settlement of those placed in the active layer may require frequent adjustment of guy wires and tie rods, for example, and may overstress and damage the structure being anchored. They usually perform satisfactorily if they can be embedded in stable permafrost and thawing prevented.

Vertical or battered piles or groups of piles can also be used as anchorages. As discussed in Section 7.11, the capacity of a single vertical pile to resist non-vertical loads is not large and excessive creep may result from low sustained loads. The capacity can be increased by using a battered pile or group of piles. A pair or group of battered piles, tied together with a rigid structural connection at the pile cap, will allow the load to be resolved along the axes of both or all piles in the group and the pair or group can be designed as axially loaded piles (Sections 7.10 and 7.11).

Grouted rod and power-installed screw anchors may also be used. Both these types of anchors should be placed well below the anticipated maximum depth of

FIG. 7.59 Concrete block (dead weight or gravity) guy anchor.

thaw and protection against frost heave provided in the active layer. Grouted rod anchors are formed by drilling a hole in the frozen ground and filling the annulus around a steel reinforcing bar with a cement grout or well-prepared soil slurry (Barry and Cormie 1971, Johnston and Ladanyi 1972). The grout or slurry should be tremied or pumped into the hole. A high early-strength cement should be used and difficulties caused by freezing of cement grouts when placed in a cold environment or thawing of surrounding frozen ground, which may not refreeze, should be taken into consideration. Single- or multi-helix screw anchors can be installed, but with difficulty, in warm temperature, frozen fine-grained soils (Johnston and Ladanyi 1974). Ideally, they should be advanced or "screwed" into the ground so that the frozen soil is not unduly disturbed, physically or thermally. Resistance to uplift is mobilized only after the helix or plate has been significantly displaced. They cannot be installed in hard frozen soils. Installation of both types must be closely supervised.

When the ground thermal regime around a grouted rod anchor has stabilized, pull-out resistance is mobilized by adfreeze bond or friction of the cylindrical grout "pile" with the wall of the hole. Analysis of the short-term adfreeze strength and long-term creep displacements can be carried out using methods described in Section 7.10 for axially loaded piles. Wind and seismic loadings may be based on short-term values with a suitable factor of safety. Ice or other loads imposed for durations longer than 24 hours should be based on long-term values, since creep movements may occur. Allowable stresses due to creep movements can be determined using relationships given in Fig. 7.47 or using analytical methods such as those given by Johnston and Ladanyi (1972) or Nixon and McRoberts (1976). It should be noted that creep movement is proportional to anchor radius and that the curves in Fig. 7.47 apply only for a 1 ft. (30 cm) diameter pile.

A screw anchor may mobilize resistance to pull-out in two ways. If the ground above the helix "heals" and is a well-bonded frozen mass following installation, the plate will probably behave like a circular footing subjected to an upward load. In this case, the capacity can be determined as described in Section 7.6. On the other hand, if the soil above the plate is sufficiently disturbed during installation and the ground does not fully "heal," resistance to pull-out will probably be mobilized by adfreeze or friction between a cylindrical column of soil having the same diameter as the helix, and the wall of the "hole" cut by the helix as it was installed. In this case, the capacity of the soil "pile" above the plate can be determined as for the grouted rod anchor. In both cases, and particularly the latter, however, large displacements can be expected and capacities will undoubtedly be very low depending on how much disturbance was created by installation of the anchor, how well the disturbed soil "healed" and how soon after installation the loads are applied.

Predicted anchor capacities and creep displacements should be confirmed by field load tests of representative anchors at selected typical locations. Johnston and Ladanyi (1972, 1974) describe load testing procedures and methods of

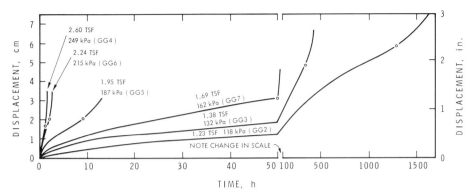

FIG. 7.60   Sustained load, pull-out tests on grouted rod anchors at Gillam, Manitoba
(After Johnston and Ladanyi 1972).

analysis; some typical results are shown in Fig. 7.60. Anchors installed in warm
temperature frozen soils will undoubtedly require periodic maintenance. Preten-
sioning of tower guy wires, for example, may gradually be lost due to creep
displacements and to irreversible displacements due to short-term wind loads.
Subsequent retensioning or installation of additional anchors may be necessary at
relatively frequent intervals to prevent failure of and excessive vibrations in the
structure under wind loads. Records of creep movements of anchors and
maintenance required will provide valuable information for the design of similar
installations in the future.

7.16 Retaining Walls

In general, retaining walls are not common in permafrost areas, but may be required where sloping areas are being developed, on shorelines at wharf sites and
for bridge abutments. They may be constructed of reinforced concrete, timber
piles and planks or cribs, or steel sheet piling. Retaining walls are susceptible to
settlement, frost heave and overturning forces. Basal frost heaving forces on
horizontal foundation surfaces together with tangential adfreeze forces on vertical surfaces are possible. Lateral freezing of the backfill behind the exposed vertical face of the wall may also cause overturning forces and must be controlled by
careful backfilling procedures. Settlement may occur due to thawing of frozen
ground below and behind the wall. A schematic illustration of a wall and relevant
features is given in Fig. 7.61.

The thickness of non-frost-susceptible backfill placed behind the wall should
be equal to the depth of frost and thaw penetration. These may be calculated by
methods outlined in Chapter 4 for 2-layer freezing or thawing, taking into account the thickness of concrete or timber in the wall and the design freezing and
thawing indices. The freezing n-factor for an exposed concrete surface may vary
between 0.7 and 0.9, depending on exposure. The thaw depth calculated for a
saturated granular fill will indicate the thickness of backfill required to prevent

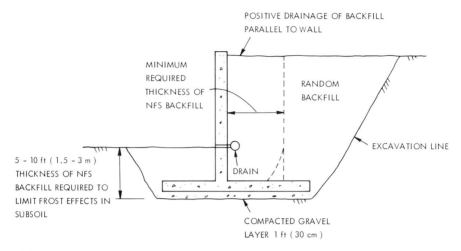

(a) RETAINING WALL CONFIGURATION

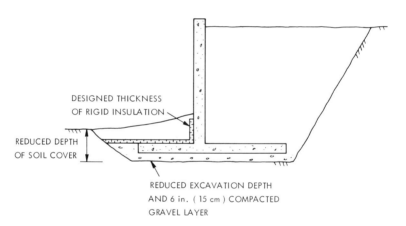

(b) INSULATED RETAINING WALL

FIG. 7.61   Sketches illustrating some features of retaining walls in permafrost areas.

thawing of permafrost in the slope behind the wall, whereas the frost depth calculated gives the backfill thickness required to prevent freezing of unfrozen frost-susceptible soils.

Drains should be installed in the backfill zone that thaws annually to ensure water can escape during the thaw season. In the event that the drain pipes are blocked or frozen for part of the thaw season, however, the wall should be designed to resist a flooded, full hydrostatic water head condition. Positive drainage of the backfill surface must be provided to shed surface water as quickly as possible during the spring snow melt period and during periods of heavy rain.

The natural soil beneath the toe and foundation of the wall must be kept in a frozen condition. Persistent thawing and freezing of the foundation soil will inevitably cause intolerable movements of the structure due to thaw settlement and frost heave. This can be accomplished by providing either a sufficient thickness of soil cover above the toe or a combination of soil and insulation as shown in Fig. 7.61. The thickness and position of the insulation is similar to that required for footings for unheated structures and should be determined from a special study of the particular project. Allowable bearing pressures for frozen foundation soils outlined in Section 7.6 can be used as a guide in selecting appropriate values, provided the ground temperatures and possible changes in them are known.

CHAPTER 8

Roads, Railways and Airfields

(Contributors–G. H. Argue, J. A. Fullerton,
G. H. Johnston and F. L. Peckover)

Design and construction of roads, railways and airfields in the permafrost region are similar in many respects. An embankment placed on the ground surface, for example, is a basic structure that is common to all. Permafrost problems may vary to some extent, depending on the anticipated use of the particular facility and on terrain conditions.

Design and construction standards can vary greatly and depend primarily on the level of service to be provided and an evaluation of capital and subsequent maintenance costs. A "resource" road that is built to provide access for exploration, for example, will be constructed to a lower standard than that of a highway required to carry heavy traffic throughout the year. Similarly, standards may be different for a rail line that carries one mixed train a day than for one carrying several fast unit trains moving heavy tonnages daily. An airfield used only by light planes may be constructed to a lower standard than one intended for jet aircraft.

An embankment can be designed and constructed and will perform satisfactorily provided that the route or site selected has been carefully investigated and that the potential problems posed by frost action, drainage and the ground thermal regime have been given full consideration. Over the years many miles of highway and many airfields have been built successfully in the North. The Inuvik airstrip is an example of a facility that was constructed following a detailed evaluation of all factors and using sound engineering judgment. It has given excellent performance with no more than normal maintenance being required in the past twenty years.

Careful preplanning of all operations and, in particular, the need for detailed route investigations for roads and railways that cross widely varying types of terrain are essential. Selection of the best route is based not only on terrain conditions but also on the availability of suitable construction materials (which can be scarce in many parts of northern Canada) and on the impact on the environment. The same factors apply to the selection of an appropriate site for an airfield although somewhat different constraints or considerations may be involved.

Linell and Johnston (1973) summarize the factors to be considered in the design and construction of embankments and other structures for roads, railways and airfields in permafrost areas and some of the measures or approaches taken to minimize problems and provide satisfactory performance. Frost action (heave and thaw weakening), permafrost degradation (thaw settlement), drainage (including icings), thermal contraction cracking of pavements and earth materials and the stabilization of cut, embankment and natural slopes are important considerations. Charles (1959, 1965), Savage (1965), Quong (1971), Reid (1974) and Huculak et al. (1978) describe some Canadian experience and current U.S. design practices and experience are summarized by Hennion and Lobacz (1973), Berg (1974), Murfitt et al. (1976) and Lobacz and Eff (1978).

8.1 Embankment Design

The most important embankment design and construction objective is to provide a stable roadbed having adequate subgrade bearing capacity and a suitable traffic surface. It is influenced mainly by thermal, frost action and drainage factors. One of three basic approaches is usually followed in the design and construction of embankments for roads, railways and airfields in permafrost areas. Minimal, partial or complete protection may be provided against the detrimental effects of frost action and permafrost degradation.

Provision of minimal protection involves consideration of the reduced strength, heave and settlement that will occur during thaw and freeze periods. A large decrease in bearing capacity, seasonal movements due to frost action, severe settlements due to permafrost degradation, and surface roughness or deterioration of traffic surfaces must be anticipated and accepted. Continuing (and frequently heavy) maintenance will usually be necessary, depending on traffic requirements. This approach is followed when protection against these effects is not needed or is too costly, and is normally used only for secondary structures, such as low-standard roadways carrying light traffic at low or moderate speeds, airfield parking aprons and short railway spurs. It is usually applicable only where isolated islands of frozen ground are found in the discontinuous permafrost zone, in areas of extremely rough topography when cuts and fills are required to achieve desired gradients in both the discontinuous and continuous permafrost zones, and where adequate quantities of good non-frost-susceptible fill materials are not available.

Partial protection is the approach most commonly followed, especially for roadbeds and airfields carrying heavy, high density or high speed traffic. It involves control of subgrade frost penetration and permafrost degradation to eliminate or minimize heave, bearing capacity and settlement problems and to maintain surface roughness characteristics within acceptable limits. It may permit some permafrost degradation, but only at a rate and to a depth that will minimize damage to the roadbed and limit the amount of annual maintenance work required.

In some cases, where environmental regulations, access and construction schedules allow economical stripping of the right-of-way, excavation and establishment of drainage, the perennially frozen foundation soils may be thawed and consolidated or excavated and replaced with non-frost-susceptible materials prior to construction. These latter methods apply mainly to the southern part of the discontinuous zone where permafrost is thin and patchy and to granular soils that will drain readily when thawed. In Canada, this method has been used in relocating existing roads when the new route could be prepared several years in advance of construction. Careful evaluation of subsurface conditions is required, however, to avoid unacceptable subsidence, slope instability and disruption of natural surface and subsurface drainage.

Complete protection against the effects of frost action and especially of permafrost degradation can generally be provided only in the continuous permafrost zone and sometimes in northern areas of the discontinuous zone. This approach is normally applicable where the terrain is fairly level, the climate is sufficiently cold, the thaw period is short and hence the depth of annual thaw is shallow, and large quantities of good quality, non-frost-susceptible borrow materials are readily available. The use of a layer of insulation in the embankment may be considered in cases where ice-rich foundation soils cannot be avoided, thick fills are required to prevent thawing of permafrost and there is a lack of good fill material.

8.1.1 Thermal and Frost Action Considerations

Construction of a fill causes a radical change in the heat exchange at the ground surface and consequently in the previously existing ground thermal regime (Lachenbruch 1960b, Berg and Quinn 1977). In winter the fill and the ground below are generally cooler than the adjacent snow-covered natural ground, because the snow cover on the fill is usually removed by plow or wind or compacted by traffic. Its insulating effect is therefore lost or greatly reduced. The situation is complicated, however, because the snow removed is usually deposited on the side slopes of the fill and the adjacent natural ground at the toe, to a greater depth than that on nearby undisturbed terrain. It thus provides a greater insulating blanket and may cause a somewhat warmer ground thermal regime under the slopes and toe than under the main fill and adjacent undisturbed terrain.

On the other hand, more radiation may be absorbed by the relatively dark surface of a fill during the summer, particularly if it is paved. The cooling effect of evaporation is absent or markedly reduced compared with adjacent vegetation-covered areas, where evaporation and transpiration play a large role in the surface energy exchange. As a result, the fill is usually warmer than the surrounding ground. The increased amplitude of the annual range of surface temperature is reflected in a proportionally larger fluctuation in temperature below the surface. The depth to which this effect penetrates is dependent on the physical and thermal characteristics of the embankment materials. Fine-grained materials with a high moisture content, for example, damp out temperature changes with depth more rapidly than dry granular materials.

Determination of the depths of freeze and thaw in natural, undisturbed terrain, in homogeneous fills and in layered systems (e.g., pavement/embankment/insulation/foundation) is important in the design of earthfill structures for roads, railways and airfields. This problem is quite complex but estimates can be made with reasonable accuracy using methods described in Section 4.3 (See also Brown, W. G. 1964, Sanger 1966, U.S. Army/Air Force 1966c, Aitken and Berg 1968, Nixon and McRoberts 1973).

Relatively thick earth fills, usually exceeding 5 ft. (1.5 m) and frequently greater than 8 ft. (2.5 m) in depth, are often required to prevent permafrost degradation. The construction of thick embankments may not always be practicable, particularly when good fill material is in short supply. In such cases, a layer of synthetic insulation placed in the embankment can be used to prevent or control thaw penetration and reduce the amount of fill required, and may be economical when the costs of obtaining sufficient quantities of good borrow material and of future maintenance and other factors are considered. Recent experience in northern Canada and Alaska indicates that when gravel costs are greater than about $5/yd.^{3} ($6/m^3), it is economical to replace some of the fill by a thermally equivalent thickness of rigid insulation.

Studies by Esch (1973), Esch and Rhode (1977), Berg and Aitken (1973) and Smith, N. et al. (1973) show that in northern permafrost areas, insulation can be used to reduce the thickness of fill required in a ratio that depends on the type of insulation and its thermal conductivity compared to that of the fill material. Various types of insulating materials, ranging from peat and wood chips to synthetic rigid insulations, can be used but great care must be taken in selecting an appropriate type to ensure it will perform satisfactorily, both thermally and structurally, for the life of the embankment. It must be emphasized that absorption of moisture can significantly affect the thermal properties of any type of insulation. Possible deterioration of synthetic materials when they are subjected to wetting, sunlight, freeze-thaw cycles and hydrocarbons should be evaluated (Ankers et al. 1977, Schaefer 1976, Kaplar 1974b, Williams 1971). In marginal permafrost areas and, in general, throughout the discontinuous permafrost zone insulation will reduce the rate of thaw degradation but not prevent it. Studies by Berg and Quinn (1977), Berg and Aitken (1973), Fulwider and Aitken (1962), Wechsler and Glaser (1966) and Kritz and Wechsler (1967) show that painting a pavement surface white can reduce the summer pavement surface temperature by 9°F (5°C) and the thickness of gravel required to preserve the permafrost regime by as much as 35%.

Several factors, including thermal, structural and slope stability must be considered in the design of insulated embankments (Knight and Condo 1971, McDougall 1977, Wellman et al. 1977). Thermal design involves evaluation of the material properties and the surface boundary conditions. Great care must be taken in selecting appropriate values and conditions, particularly with respect to the energy exchange at the air-ground interface. Whenever possible, values obtained from field measurements made at typical locations should be used to improve the reliability of calculations. Layered system problems are usually solved by numerical methods on a computer because of their complexity, which is due to variable material properties and surface temperature conditions (Chapter 4).

Lachenbruch (1959), however, presents a useful analytical solution for two- and three-layer systems subjected to a surface temperature sine wave. It should be noted that the solution is restricted in that it does not take into account a moisture phase change within any of the layers nor any change in the unfrozen water content of the frozen soils. Nevertheless, this method can be used to make preliminary estimates of the thickness of gravel and insulation required to provide complete protection against thawing of the frozen foundation soils; that is, when the permafrost table is to be maintained at the base of or within the fill and when the gravel and insulation can be assumed to be completely dry (Nixon 1979).

Although it is sometimes more expedient to place the layer of insulation on the ground surface, which has to be levelled to provide a good base and prevent breakage of the insulation, normally it is thermally more efficient to place the insulation as high as possible in the embankment. It must be covered with a sufficient thickness of fill so that it is not overstressed, particularly during the construction period, when the heaviest loads are imposed by hauling equipment.

A stress analysis can be carried out when the design wheel loading characteristics have been selected but it is usually sufficient to calculate the elastic stress distribution beneath the wheel load using the Boussinesq theory. The wheel loading can be replaced by a flexible load on a circular area and the stress distribution with depth calculated. Based on the theoretical vertical stress increment induced by a circular load of intensity p, the required depth of cover to limit the compressive stress in the insulation to σ_a (McDougall 1977) is

$$Z = \sqrt{\frac{W/\pi p}{\left(1 - \dfrac{\sigma_a}{p}\right)^{-2/3} - 1}} \qquad (8.1)$$

where Z is the required depth of cover, p is the tire inflation pressure, W is the design wheel load and σ_a is the allowable stress for the type of insulation to be used and the number of repetitive loads to which it will be subjected.

The allowable stress should be selected with care so that it will take into account all anticipated loading situations and therefore allow calculation of the required thickness of cover. It is a good practice to overbuild a gravel surface by 5 or 6 in. (12 or 15 cm) to take care of a reduction in fill height due to maintenance grading. If the design is such that some thawing will be permitted below the embankment, the bearing capacity of the thawing subgrade must be checked by estimating the strength parameters and excess pore pressures that may result on thawing. Methods for determining thaw settlement and consolidation are discussed in Section 3.7. This is particularly critical if the insulation is placed on or just above the ground surface and the foundation soils in the active layer are ice-rich, relatively impermeable and very weak when thawed. In such cases, a minimum total fill thickness of, say, 3 ft. (1 m), is selected to avoid bearing capacity problems and the design should usually not permit thawing to occur below the base of the embankment or the bottom of the insulation, whichever is the lower.

Frequently, embankments have to be constructed across sloping terrain. If thawing of ice-rich soils occurs under thin uninsulated embankments or even under the side slopes of insulated fills and if the permeability and compressibility of the subgrade soils are such that excess pore pressures will develop and be maintained, foundation stability problems may be experienced. As described in Section 3.7.2, the build-up of excess pore pressures in a thawing soil is related to the dimensionless parameter

$$R = a/2\sqrt{c_v} \tag{8.2}$$

where a is a parameter describing the rate of thaw and c_v is the coefficient of consolidation. If the rate of thaw is high and the consolidation coefficient is sufficiently low, then the value of R becomes large and excess pore pressures are maintained.

Although deepening of the active layer may occur under thin gravel fills, the surcharge effect of the fill will be beneficial in that it increases the effective overburden pressure at the thaw front. A layer of insulation also has a beneficial effect by decreasing the rate of thaw. McRoberts and Nixon (1977) present some approximate analytical relationships and examples that indicate the effects of gravel alone and gravel with insulation on the stability of thawing slopes. The factor of safety against sliding is significantly increased over the entire thaw period due to the decreased thaw depth and rate when a layer of insulation is used in a gravel fill. Various combinations of gravel and insulation can improve the stability of shallow sliding surfaces and the relationships derived permit design charts to be prepared for specific situations.

Pufahl and Morgenstern (1979) propose a method for stabilizing or inhibiting the occurrence of planar landslides in permafrost areas using a layer of insulation and a free-draining surcharge load. A measure of the pore pressures considered in the effective stress analysis is obtained by assuming steady-state seepage parallel to the surface and pore water pressures generated during thaw consolidation due to self-weight and the surcharge load. The insulation reduces the rate of thaw and thus the rate at which excess pore water pressures are generated, and the surcharge load increases the effective normal stress disproportionate to any increase in shearing stress. Different design methods are outlined and a series of design charts are presented for rapid computation of the required combination of insulation thickness and surcharge load for a range of typical soil and climatic conditions encountered in the North.

Frost action occurring in the embankment or foundation soils can be a serious problem. Differential heave during the freezing season and loss of shear strength during the thawing season can seriously affect the riding quality and use of trafficable surfaces. The frost action process and methods for identifying frost-susceptible materials are discussed in Section 3.8. A synthesis of available information on the design of roadways in seasonal frost areas was prepared by Johnson et al. (1974).

The approach generally taken to prevent or reduce frost action effects is to eliminate one or more of the three basic conditions causing the growth of ice lenses: freezing temperatures, frost-susceptible soils and a water supply (Section 3.8). Frost heaving of highway and railway roadbeds and airport runways is most commonly prevented by using non-frost-susceptible, well-draining materials for those layers subjected to annual freezing and by providing good drainage to eliminate or reduce the water supply for ice lens growth.

Whenever possible, embankments in permafrost areas should be constructed of non-frost-susceptible materials. When they are available, dry granular materials or quarried rock are frequently the only materials that can be readily excavated and handled, not only during the winter when much of the fill is placed, but also during the summer when final grading is usually carried out. It has been observed, however, that even when frost-susceptible soils such as dirty gravels are used, the rate of frost penetration through the fill may be rapid enough during the short northern fall season, when a rapid change from above- to below-freezing ambient temperatures occurs, that the growth of ice lenses in the embankment is negligible. Nevertheless there are many cases where frost-susceptible fill materials have to be used and freezing and moisture conditions are such that frost action in the embankment is a major problem. Where thawing has penetrated below the original ground surface, heave of the fill may occur (due to formation of ice lenses during freezeback of the underlying thawed, often saturated, layer) if critical frost penetration rates and ground water conditions exist.

In northern areas, thaw softening in the spring and summer may often be a greater source of trouble than heaving. The generation and slow dissipation of excess pore pressures and loss of shear strength due to low or non-existent effective stresses when melting of ice lenses, or even of pore ice in frost-susceptible embankment materials that have not heaved, takes place, may cause a substantial decrease in bearing capacity and stability problems. These are aggravated by the moving and repetitive loads to which embankments are usually subjected. Differential thaw frequently results in irregular settlement of the previously heaved structure and further complicates internal drainage. "Pumping" of frost-susceptible, fine-grained soils into overlying granular base course materials may also occur.

A layer of insulation placed in a fill can be effective in preventing or reducing the depth and rate of freeze and thaw as already noted. The surcharge loading effect of the fill on the ground surface, together with improved drainage, can significantly reduce but not completely eliminate seasonal heaving. Aitken (1966, 1974) reports an average heave reduction of more than 30% with a 2.3 psi (15.9 kPa) surcharge load and about 75% with an 8 psi (55.2 kPa) surcharge load for a silt soil at Fairbanks, Alaska. The encapsulation of fine-grained soils in impermeable membranes to prevent moisture movement and reduce frost heave and thaw effects (Smith and Pazsint 1975, Sayward 1976) and the treatment of soils with additives to modify their frost susceptibility (Lambe and Kaplar 1971) have been studied. Tests indicate they are effective and can be used with good results, but for the present these methods must be considered as impracticable, expensive or only for temporary use in the North.

Embankments may also suffer damage due to thermal contraction cracking resulting from exposure to long periods of very low temperatures. This will most probably be a problem in the continuous permafrost zone. Throughout the permafrost region, however, intense cracking of pavements and wearing surfaces may occur due to thermal shrinkage. Water can enter the cracks and freeze and accumulate in the base course, thus reducing its ability to function as a drainage layer. The thermal coefficients of expansion of ice and asphalt are about 5 and 20 times greater, respectively, than that of mineral particles. Thus, control of moisture and bitumen contents in soils and asphalt pavements is important if the intensity of cracking is to be reduced. Regular grading and sealing of surfaces is usually necessary.

8.1.2 Drainage

Drainage is a most important design consideration for roads, railways and airfields even though precipitation is generally low over much of the Canadian permafrost region. Surface and subsurface drainage problems are obviated as far as possible by proper route and site selection. Large and sudden flows of snow and ice meltwater over the ground surface and in streams and rivers must be handled during the very short spring break-up period. In some areas, heavy runoff from occasional summer storms produces greatly increased flows, particularly in mountain-fed rivers.

Poor natural drainage is typical of many parts of the permafrost region, particularly where the terrain is relatively flat, because of the presence of impervious frozen ground at shallow depths (Fig. 8.1(a)). The active layer consequently is usually saturated. Ponding of water may induce accelerated thawing under and adjacent to embankments. On the other hand, flowing water causes hydraulic erosion, particularly of thawing soils, and can quickly remove large quantities of material and cause stability problems (Fig. 8.1(b)).

Adequate facilities must be provided to accommodate both surface and subsurface movement of water associated with fills under various conditions. Subsurface drains are effective only for the short annual thaw season or where unfrozen zones exist. Excavation of ditches (and cuts in general) in permafrost are avoided whenever possible, particularly in ice-rich materials. When essential, they must be carefully located and designed to prevent increased and unacceptable thaw and erosion, especially if they may affect an embankment or other structures and cause environmental damage.

Icings are a major problem in some areas, tending to block drainage facilities and cause operational problems (Thomson 1966, Carey 1970, 1973, Johnson and

(a.)

FIG. 8.1   (a) Low muskeg areas with a thin active layer are difficult to drain as
shown in this view of a road offtake ditch in the northern part of the discontinuous
permafrost zone, Mackenzie River Valley. (b) Severe ditch erosion in ice-rich materials
(Public Works Canada photograph).

FIG. 8.2 Examples of culvert and road icing: (a) View showing formation of icing at
upstream end of ice-blocked culverts (Environment Canada photograph). (b) View of
outlet of ice-blocked culverts shown in (a) (Environment Canada photograph). (c) View
of outlet of an ice-blocked culvert. Note that because invert is set too high and no
protection has been provided, water flow will cause "plunge pool" to form and
detrimental erosion of embankment slope is certain to occur unless remedial measures
are taken (Environment Canada photograph).

FIG. 8.2   (d) Embankment constructed across small drainage course has obstructed subsurface drainage flow and caused icing which completely blocked road (After Brown 1970a).

Esch 1977) (Fig. 8.2). Laboratory and field studies for developing or improving methods for the control or prevention of culvert icing have been undertaken in Alaska (Gaskin and Stanley 1974, Carey et al. 1975). Recognition and prediction of potential icing locations and conditions are difficult but need careful attention in planning and design. Icings can occur in rivers, streams and small drainage courses, on slopes and in cuts. Although they occur naturally at many locations, they are also frequently initiated because the fill or an inadequate drainage structure has blocked, restricted or disturbed the natural drainage pattern. Icings and methods of dealing with them are discussed in Section 8.2.2.3.

Bridges on transportation routes are usually constructed to cross major streams and rivers at carefully selected locations. Large corrugated steel pipe culverts up to 40 ft. wide by 30 ft. high (12 m by 10 m) are used occasionally in certain situations. Geotechnical investigations for the design of structures are mandatory at all major water crossings. Special attention must be given to preparation of the beds and placement of the backfill for all culverts to ensure satisfactory performance. Settlement, frost heave, lateral movement and even collapse of culverts may result if poor materials within the potential thaw zone are not replaced with good quality materials and the bedding and backfill are not carefully placed and compacted.

Bridges and culverts must be carefully designed and constructed so that stream bed morphology, stream flow, and sedimentation are not seriously changed and fish passage inhibited. Special channelization measures or works may be required upstream and downstream of the structures.

8.2 Roads

To date, most major highways in northern Canada have been constructed within the discontinuous permafrost zone in the Yukon Territory, the Mackenzie District of the N.W.T. and the northern parts of British Columbia and the Prairie Provinces (Fig. 1.11). Except for relatively short stretches in and adjacent to communities, mainly in the lower Mackenzie Valley, and the northern parts of the Dempster and Mackenzie highways, no major highways have been built in the continuous permafrost zone in Canada. Although emphasis is placed on constructing highways quickly and economically to meet traffic needs, special attention must be given to route selection and good design to minimize costs and maintenance problems, obtain a reasonable service life and ensure minimal adverse environmental impact. The same factors must be considered in the design and construction of roads in northern communities.

As in the design of foundations (Section 7.1), there are two principal concepts to be considered with regard to the design and construction of roadbeds on permafrost; the "active" approach, where preservation of permafrost is not possible or practicable and the consequences of thaw are allowed for in the design, and the "passive" approach, where the roadbed is constructed with the intention of preserving the permafrost. Both approaches may be employed on any appreciable length of highway crossing highly variable terrain and also for roads within a community that has islands of permafrost and unfrozen ground.

Factors influencing location, design and construction include topography, soil and rock conditions, permafrost conditions, drainage, economics, scheduling and, last but not least, environmental impact (Reid 1974, Curran and Etter 1976). The design of any road, in addition, is based to some degree on the optimum utilization of available materials with consideration of their construction qualities and the cost of alternate sources. The availability of suitable materials may be a major factor in location and design for permanent construction.

8.2.1 Road Location

The methods used to evaluate terrain conditions and select a suitable route are described in Chapter 5. The shortest route that permits standard alignment and grades and a reasonably economical design, consistent with traffic volume and safety requirements, is naturally preferred. In permafrost terrain, however, favourable foundation and drainage conditions and availability of materials, rather than the most direct route, usually govern.

Route location in permafrost areas is a stage procedure. The first step is the selection of tentative routes based on an examination of topographic maps, air photos and other available information and an initial evaluation of the terrain, including prediction of subsurface conditions, and hydrological and environmental impact studies. Conceptual designs of fills and structures required can be drawn up at the same time to give a preliminary idea of costs and facilitate an economical comparison of alternative route locations. Field investigations then follow to gather the information needed to refine the route location and begin detailed design studies. Geotechnical, hydrological and environmental studies are interdependent and must be developed together.

Potentially thaw-unstable, ice-rich perennially frozen ground and deposits of frost-susceptible materials are to be avoided if at all possible to reduce settlement, stability and frost action problems. Great emphasis must be placed on the assessment of drainage conditions, including surface and subsurface movement of water, detailed surveys of stream flow, bed and bank characteristics, and potential icing hazards. Snow drifting and accumulation patterns must also be noted.

Subsurface investigations must be conducted to determine soil and permafrost conditions, especially the type and distribution of ground ice, in different types of terrain along the route. Special attention should be given to stream crossings and major drainage courses, areas where cuts are proposed or that must carry high fills, potential borrow sites, thermokarst areas and sidehill locations, which may be unstable and subject to slides.

8.2.2 Road Design and Construction

Design and construction techniques used for roadways apply with few exceptions to the design and construction of railway roadbeds. Correspondingly, some of the information given for railway work in Section 8.3.2 will be useful to the highway engineer. Roads are built to various standards depending on traffic requirements. The roadway is normally constructed by placing fill hauled from borrow pits on the undisturbed ground surface. Cuts and ditches are avoided wherever possible so that no attempt is made to balance cut and fill. Flat horizontal and vertical curves and gradients not exceeding 8% are highly desirable. Lack of suitable fill materials can mean long hauls from borrow pits and therefore earthwork is kept to a minimum consistent with geometric and stability requirements. In general, embankments should be at least 4 ft. (1.2 m) thick and very high fills are avoided.

8.2.2.1 Embankments

The right-of-way is usually cleared by hand. The movement of clearing and construction equipment over the natural ground surface should be carefully controlled or prohibited to keep terrain disturbance to a minimum, particularly in environmentally sensitive areas. Thus, the organic mat is preserved and, although it may lose a significant amount of its insulating value due to compression by the fill, it is usually effective during construction when the heaviest loads are imposed by traffic. In forested areas, it is customary to corduroy the embankment area with the trees cut on the right-of-way. Closely packed, cross-laid logs will act as a layer of insulation and will strengthen the organic mat if it thaws. Unless prohibited for environmental reasons, as much as possible of the snow cover is carefully removed before construction of the embankment in a winter operation to reduce settlement of the fill during the thaw period.

Optimum use is made of local materials for construction of the embankment but careful evaluation of their advantages and disadvantages is required based on their properties and potential behaviour as fill, and the problems and costs of excavating, hauling and placing them under either summer or winter conditions. The most desirable materials are clean gravel and well-graded sand. Because of their strength and drainage characteristics they perform well and overcome settlement and frost action problems. They can also be readily placed during winter.

Low ice content glacial tills, quarried rock and clay shales have been used extensively with considerable success in northern Canada, where gravel is in short supply. The shales are subject to mechanical disintegration by weather and traffic, however, and usually require a thick cap or wearing surface of granular material to carry heavy traffic. In southern areas of the discontinuous permafrost zone, cohesive soils are commonly used for embankment construction when they can be obtained from borrow pits in unfrozen areas at suitable moisture contents.

FIG. 8.3 Embankment constructed by end dumping on hand-cleared right-of-way (Public Works Canada photograph).

FIG. 8.4 Construction of embankment on permafrost by end dumping. Note terrain disturbance and ponding of water in ruts caused by tracked vehicles operating on the right-of-way (Transport Canada photograph).

In more northerly areas, cohesive soils are usually frozen, contain much ice and are difficult to excavate, and therefore rarely merit consideration. Sources of suitable materials are frequently widely scattered and may not exist in some areas. As a result, average haul distances are often long and construction costs correspondingly high.

The embankment is constructed by the "overlay" or end dumping method so that the vegetation cover will not be damaged by hauling equipment (Figs. 8.3 and 8.4). A typical fill cross-section for highways constructed in northern Canada is shown in Fig. 8.5. The material brought from borrow pits is dumped on the end of the fill by the hauling equipment and is pushed forward onto the undisturbed terrain by bulldozer, which compacts it as it moves back and forth. Coarse material is usually placed in the initial lifts, which average about 1 ft. (0.3 m) in thickness. A "pioneer" fill, which must be sufficiently thick to carry the heavy construction equipment, is normally pushed through to gain access to borrow pits. During summer construction, pioneer fills are usually about 3 ft. (1 m) thick but in winter when the ground is solidly frozen they may be only 1 ft. (0.3 m) thick. The embankment should be brought up to final grade as soon as possible to

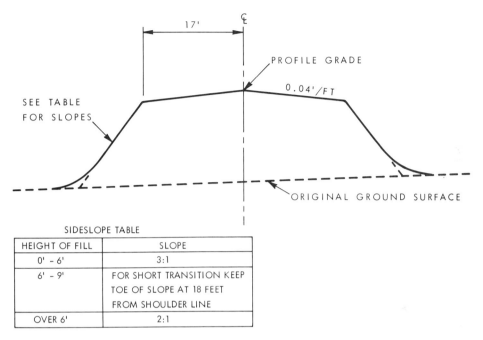

SIDESLOPE TABLE

HEIGHT OF FILL	SLOPE
0' – 6'	3:1
6' – 9'	FOR SHORT TRANSITION KEEP TOE OF SLOPE AT 18 FEET FROM SHOULDER LINE
OVER 6'	2:1

FIG. 8.5   Typical cross section of highway embankment in northern Canada.

prevent excessive thawing. Whether placed in the winter or summer, the design height and side slopes of fills must take into account any settlement that will occur when the thawing active layer and perhaps the thawing permafrost is compressed or displaced. The final design elevation should be sufficient to provide good drainage and easy snow removal. A typical example of a nearly completed fill on permafrost is shown in Fig. 8.6.

The stability of an embankment and its side slopes, particularly those constructed of frozen soil, is directly related to the ice content of the fill material and its behaviour during thaw, and the foundation conditions. Conventional slopes can be constructed if the fill material is dry and relatively well drained and the foundation is stable when thawed. The placement of ice-rich, fine-grained fill in the winter must be avoided since compaction of such soil is largely ineffective and it will usually flow when thawed. Problems in embankment construction are most often associated with inadequacy of either foundation conditions for the fill or the quality of the borrow.

Some cracking and sloughing of the side slopes and the shoulders should be anticipated because the rate and depth of thaw under and at the toe of the slopes will be greater than under the main body of the embankment (Fig. 8.7). In cases where thaw-unstable conditions will occur, the slopes must be flattened, bermed or insulated to ensure that the integrity of the main embankment is maintained. Some possible designs for uninsulated and insulated embankments are presented schematically in Fig. 8.8.

FIG. 8.6   Overlay construction, Dempster Highway, Yukon Territory (Public Works Canada photograph).

FIG. 8.7   Cracking of side slope of road fill due to thawing of permafrost and resulting settlement of ground under slope (Transport Canada photograph).

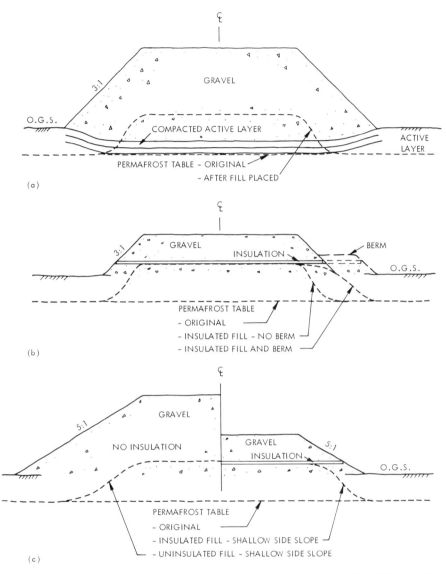

FIG. 8.8 Schematic representation of thermal effect of uninsulated and insulated embankments on permafrost table when frozen condition is to be preserved.

8.2.2.2 *Cuts*

Although it is good practice to avoid cuts in permafrost wherever possible, this is not always practical for roads, railways and other linear structures. Cuts may be required to maintain design gradients when the route crosses long, steep-sided linear topographic features, such as drumlins and terminal moraines. Cuts are

frequently required on the approaches to deeply incised streams, where exceptional measures may be needed for environmental protection. Ditch checks and settling basins, for example, may be necessary to avoid erosion and stream siltation caused by meltwater and normal runoff from the cut.

The behaviour of cuts in frozen ground is intimately related to the nature of the soil and the distribution of ground ice within it. In ice-poor, free-draining material, slopes may be cut at angles comparable to those used in unfrozen soils. The greatest risk of precipitating unstable conditions arises in areas that contain significant deposits of stratified drift in the form of post-glacial lacustrine silts and clays (Fig. 8.9). Extensive movements will also develop in terrain containing ice wedges and other massive ice deposits.

Exposures that do not contain appreciable quantities of massive ice can generally be stabilized more easily because there is sufficient soil in the mass to form a stable active layer. The main concern is to control the rate of melting until a stable active layer develops. When extensive massive ice deposits are encountered, measures must be taken either to prevent any thaw from occurring or to allow the cut face to retreat at an acceptably slow rate (See also Sections 2.5.2 and 8.1.1).

FIG. 8.9 Aerial (a) and ground (b) views of deep highway cut in frozen glacio-lacustrine silts and clays with little excess ice. Note cracking and sloughing along entire face of thawing backslopes and also on roadbed. Sloughing material fills ditches causing ponding of water and soft roadbed. Mackenzie Highway north of Ft. Simpson, N.W.T.

(a)

(b)

FIG. 8.10   Backslope of a cut on the Dempster Highway, Yukon Territory, before (a) and after (b) trimming and placement of a gravel blanket (Public Works Canada photograph).

The need for cut slope stabilization will depend primarily on the amount and type of ground ice, the soil type and the depth of the cut. Other factors, such as the long-term effect on the operation and cost of maintenance of a transportation facility, potential environmental impact and general aesthetics, will also influence the need for and degree of protection required. Many cut slopes will self-stabilize within the first two or three thaw seasons, provided reasonable care has been taken in design and construction to ensure that unacceptable thawing and continuing retreat of the slope does not occur.

Where cuts cannot be avoided, good construction practice normally involves a wide excavation to allow for wide ditches and, in some cases, the construction of low rock revetments at the toe of the backslope. Blanketing slopes with gravel and re-vegetating them to inhibit thermal degradation are usually necessary stabilizing measures (Fig. 8.10). The timing and procedures to follow for an excavation operation will depend on several factors, including the size of the cut, soil conditions and equipment available. The operation is best carried out quickly. It may be essential in some cases that work be started and completed in the winter. Only an absolute minimum area should be opened at any one time. Exposed faces should not be left untouched long enough to allow substantial thaw, sloughing and subsidence, which would interfere with movement of construction equipment. The area that can be worked at any one time depends on the amount and type of equipment provided by the contractor; a 24-hour operation may be necessary to prevent excessive thaw of exposed faces. When the bottom of the excavation is reached, it should be covered immediately with a granular fill of sufficient thickness to minimize thawing of the subgrade and to allow construction equipment to travel over it. The performance of cuts in permafrost is recorded by Smith and Berg (1973), Pufahl et al. (1974), Jackman (1974), Berg and Smith (1976), Murfitt et al. (1976) and Wang et al. (1977).

Cuts in free-draining granular materials, even those which contain a few thin lenses of ice-rich fine-grained soil, can usually be excavated satisfactorily with conventional slopes. They drain and stabilize fairly rapidly. Cohesive soils with moisture contents at or below the plastic limit may be sloped in the conventional manner. The use of excavated, frozen cohesive soils in adjacent fills may not be possible and disposal of the material in carefully chosen areas must be considered in the design and scheduling of construction. If the moisture content is indeed low and the weather suitable, especially if watering is required to reach optimum moisture content, the material may thaw when being compacted but it may be possible to place it in thin layers and obtain the desired density. The use of frozen, high moisture content fine-grained soil in the core of high fills where it will not thaw may be considered. Such material must be capped immediately with suitable material to prevent thawing. This approach must be carefully evaluated to ensure stability of high embankments. The use of such materials is avoided in all cases where it will thaw.

Cuts in ice-rich cohesive soils present a serious problem and a detailed geotechnical investigation is mandatory, especially for deep cuts. Experience has shown that it is good practice to use near-vertical backslopes to reduce the area exposed to thawing and hasten the return to equilibrium. For shallow cuts, 6 ft. (2 m) or less in depth, vertical backslopes may be made at approximately the ditch line. Subsequent thaw along the vertical face commonly results in the organic mat being undercut at the top and collapsing more or less gradually onto the slope. The organic mat usually remains intact and provides insulation, thus promoting stabilization of the slope (Fig. 8.11).

In deeper cuts in ice-rich soils, thermal undercutting of vertical slopes tends to proceed more rapidly because of the larger area exposed to thawing, the overhanging organic mat tends to tear and fall, large quantities of material slide downslope and accumulate at the toe or flow along the ditch and stabilization is slow. Unsightly masses of sliding vegetation, blocked ditches and severe siltation are the result.

In such cases ditches should be at least 12 ft. (3.6 m) wide so that they can be cleared periodically by earth-moving equipment. Backslopes should be no greater than 1:1; experience has shown that 1H:4V backslopes are preferred. A wide ditch will also permit placement of a rock revetment or rock backfill at or against the bottom of the cut slope. These act as a buttress and filter to enhance drainage and promote stabilization. Surface runoff from the slope above the top of a cut should be intercepted and diverted to the side by constructing small dykes (rather than ditches) on the ground surface to prevent water from running down and eroding the face of the cut.

FIG. 8.11 Shallow cut in permafrost on Dempster Highway, Y.T. Note intact vegetation mat on side slopes (Public Works Canada photograph).

The mat of organic material above the cut must not be damaged. Trees should be hand cleared back from the top of the slope to a distance of from one to two times the height of the slope. The stumps, cut no higher than 1 ft. (0.3 m), can be tied together with a coarse wire mesh to prevent or reduce tearing of the organic mat as it collapses onto the slope. The most severe melting and subsidence will occur in the first year or two following excavation, but the rate of degradation decreases steadily. Seeding of the lower portions of the slope should begin as soon as they become relatively stable, followed by progressive seeding of higher areas. Some of these features are shown in Fig. 8.12 and also by Murfitt et al. (1976).

When cuts in terrain that contains extensive deposits of massive ice cannot be avoided, a more positive approach must be taken to prevent uncontrolled and long-term recession of slopes that consist essentially of ice and are not self-healing. The type of slope protection method selected will vary, depending mainly on the slope angle, availability of granular materials, amount of excavation required and severity of erosion. Several possible techniques, suggested by Pufahl (1976), are illustrated in Fig. 8.13. They utilize various combinations of gravel and insulation for stabilizing the cut slopes.

It is essential that any of these approaches provide drainage of melt water at the permafrost table, both on the slope and at the toe. Sufficient strength, flexibility, stability and durability of the cover on the slope and sufficient insulation to prevent thawing or reduce the rate of thaw to an acceptable value must also be provided. Large quantities of granular material and wide excavations are required in most cases. Light-coloured gravels are effective in increasing the reflectivity of a surface. The surface of moderately steep and shallow slopes should be stepped or roughened to provide mechanical interlocking of the gravel cover and frozen face of the cut. It is important that all work be carried out only during the winter, when the ground is completely frozen and air temperatures are below freezing.

The roadway is subexcavated several feet before placing the gravel embankment. The depth of the subcut and the thickness of fill required is based on the ice content of the underlying soil, the insulation value of the backfill material and the anticipated depth of thaw. Usually, at least 2 ft (0.6 m) and possibly as much as 5 ft. (1.5 m) of gravel fill is required. The need for regular grading including cleaning of ditches and perhaps placement of additional fill on the roadway in the cut can be expected during the early years until the foundation stabilizes.

8.2.2.3 *Drainage*

The provision of good drainage in permafrost areas is a major consideration, since the effects of ponding, erosion and icings along the roadway can be far-reaching. Disruption of traffic, environmental damage and high maintenance costs can be expected if drainage problems occur. Ponding may cause degradation of permafrost with resulting formation of thermokarst depressions and settlement or softening of the embankment. In extreme cases, the roadway may suddenly collapse into underlying large caverns formed by thawing or erosion of

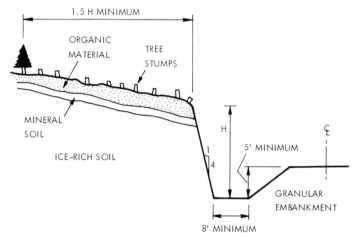

(a)   INITIAL FROZEN CUT PROFILE

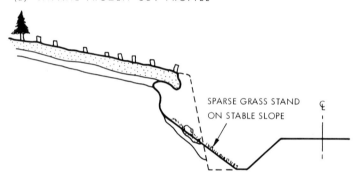

(b)   END OF FIRST THAW SEASON.   SLOPE IS MOSTLY
UNSTABLE AND VERY UNSIGHTLY; DITCH WILL
REQUIRE CLEANING IF MASSIVE ICE IS PRESENT

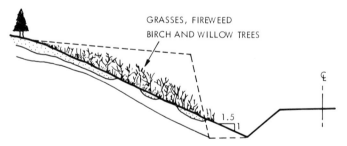

(c)   END OF FIFTH OR SIXTH THAW SEASON.   SLOPE
STABILIZES WITH REDUCED THAW AND VEGETATION
ESTABLISHED

FIG. 8.12   Idealized development of stability in ice-rich cut (After Berg and Smith 1976).

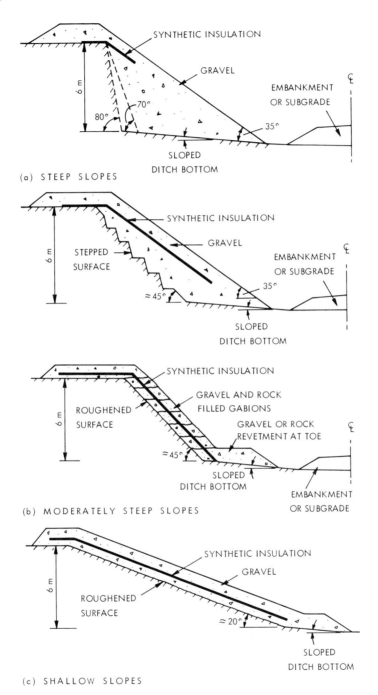

FIG. 8.13 Possible methods for stabilizing cut slopes in terrain containing massive ground ice deposits (After Pufahl 1976).

massive ice, which the relatively rigid fill has bridged for a period of time (Fig. 8.14).

The effects of erosion by runoff are accentuated by the presence of frozen ground (even where the ice content is relatively low) and can result in rapid gullying and detrimental siltation. Icings resulting from restricted movement of groundwater or stream flow and freezing of water on the ground surface from springs that flow the year round present a particularly severe problem. Ice may build up to considerable depths along and over the roadway and in drainage structures, requiring continual maintenance to clear the roadway and ditches, maintain flow in culverts and repair washouts.

(1) Ditching

Excavation of ditches in permafrost is to be avoided wherever possible. Cross drainage should not be diverted or intercepted by the embankment but passed through culverts located at every definable water course and sag in the gradeline. Widespread "sheet" drainage may require the use of a large number of culverts. The culverts should be spaced so that no significant volume of water flows along the toe of the fill. In cases where the gradient is not sufficient to avoid ponding, a berm may be constructed along the embankment toe to guide the flow to the culverts.

FIG. 8.14   Large cavern rapidly developed under road embankment due to erosion of ice wedge. Road collapsed shortly after photo was taken.

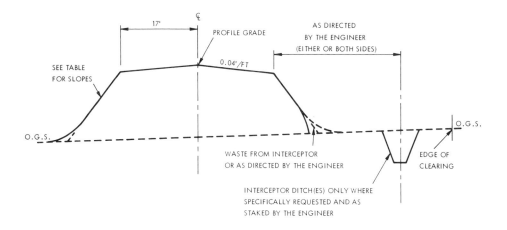

SIDESLOPE TABLE

HEIGHT OF FILL	SLOPE
0' – 6'	3:1
6' – 9'	FOR SHORT TRANSITION KEEP TOE OF SLOPE AT 18 FEET FROM SHOULDER LINE
OVER 6'	2:1

FIG. 8.15 Typical road cross section with interceptor ditch.

The use of interceptor ditches, although generally avoided, may be acceptable if they are constructed at least 20 ft. (6 m) from the roadway and have minimal gradients (Fig. 8.15). In ice-rich soils, special measures may be required to avoid erosion and keep the ditch level in line with culverts and drainage systems generally. These include the use of rip rap on fill slopes, ditch blocks and checks (Fig. 8.16) and lining the ditch with granular materials (Fig. 8.17).

Where roadway cuts are required, roadside ditches may require special treatment, not only to protect the roadway but also to prevent siltation of water courses (Fig. 8.18). In ice-rich cuts and those subject to erosion, the ditches should be excavated and backfilled with granular or rock material. Ditch checks may be required to reduce the water velocity to an acceptable level.

(2) Icings

Icings are difficult to predict and difficult and very costly to correct in many cases. Frequently, in the extreme, relocation of the road is the only solution. River icings occur in shallow braided streams or where rapids and obstructions, including bridges, cause the flow to be dispersed or restricted. Icings are also caused by artesian flow from springs (Fig. 8.19). These areas can often be identified by the absence or sparseness of vegetation cover.

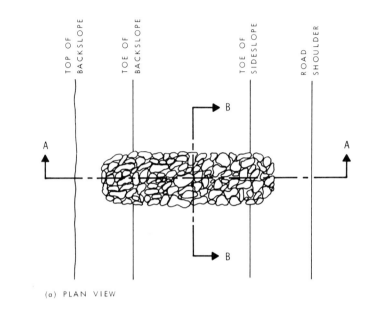

(a) PLAN VIEW

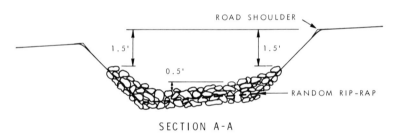

SECTION A-A

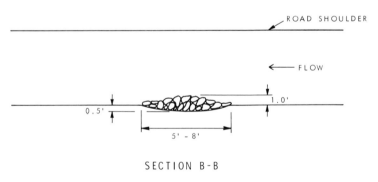

SECTION B-B

(b) CROSS SECTIONS

FIG. 8.16 Typical ditch check in thaw-stable soils. Similar design is used for interceptor ditches.

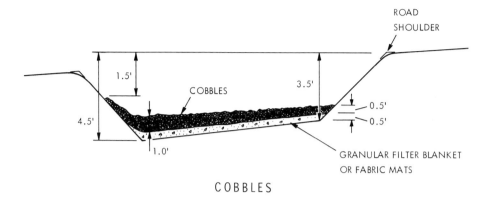

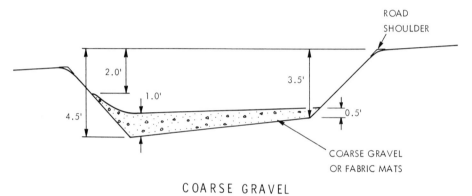

FIG. 8.17   Typical ditch lining to prevent erosion. Similar design is used for interceptor ditches.

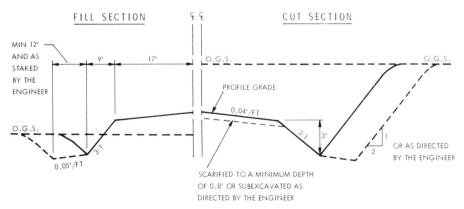

FIG. 8.18   Typical cross sections for "V" and wide ditches in relatively thaw-stable soils.

FIG. 8.19   Views taken in October and May on Canyon Creek, Mackenzie Valley
showing thickness of icing developed during the winter (Transport Canada
photographs).

Bridges should be located in areas where the stream flow is steady and deep to avoid icings. This may be achieved in some cases by channel work to contain the stream or by the removal of obstructions. In most cases channel work is effective but may be temporary and require frequent maintenance. Roads in the vicinity of "icing" streams should be located above the limits of the icing level and should be well protected against erosion by water flowing over the surface of the icing, since extreme changes in the stream direction can be caused by the buildup of ice.

Ground icing is caused by "pinching" or restriction of groundwater flow as the active layer freezes. Since the ground thermal regime is altered by the presence of the embankment, these icings may be induced by the road. Typical areas for such icings are alluvial fans, hanging deltas and seepage zones through muskegs. Icings tend to form more readily in hilly or mountainous terrain. Icings are not necessarily an annual occurrence. They are frequently caused by groundwater movement not evident prior to construction and so they do not exist before the structure creates a disturbance. Thus their occurrence and extent may be difficult to predict. The identification of potential icing sites depends largely on the experience of the location engineer.

Several techniques have been used to prevent icing conditions. Often trial and error is required before a suitable method is found for a particular condition. The principal methods are:

(a) Raising grade: this approach is the simplest but is costly and assumes a knowledge of the limits of icing. Large storage areas for the ice are required and these are rarely available in the steep terrain where icings commonly occur;

(b) Ice fences or dams: permanent earthworks may be constructed some distance upslope to contain or limit the buildup of ice; sufficient storage space to contain the seasonal buildup is required; temporary fences of reinforced paper or burlap are effective in areas where the seepage is slow and in thin layers;

(c) Frost belts: removal of the insulation cover of vegetation and snow at some point above the road will allow rapid freezing of the active layer and start the icing at a point where it is hoped it will not reach the road; this solution is temporary at best but can be effective for one or two seasons;

(d) Staggered culverts: where ice collects behind a roadway embankment and blocks the culverts, auxiliary culverts may be placed above the anticipated ice level to carry spring runoff until the lower culverts are clear (Fig. 8.20);

(e) Application of heat: steam lines and fuel oil heaters (firepots) are commonly used to open up culverts or thaw channels in icings in the spring and, in some cases, during the winter; electrical heating cables have also been used in Alaska;

(f) Insulated subsurface drains: these can be used to intercept groundwater and carry it away from the road; modern filter and insulation materials make such drains possible but, in some cases, expensive;

(g) Road relocation: this is the most extreme solution. Icings of such severity as to require relocation can probably be identified before construction.

Icings and methods of avoiding or controlling them are well described by Carey (1973).

(3) Culverts

Generally, techniques for the design and installation of culverts are similar to good practice in more southerly areas. Although wood would be the preferred material because of its thermal properties, corrugated metal pipe is used almost exclusively. Experience with wooden culverts indicates that the costs of handling and installation do not always warrant their use. Wood stave pipe, nevertheless, is attractive for culverts in icing areas and should be considered where its costs are competitive.

Where large diameter culverts are required on major streams, permafrost is usually absent or at such a depth that the installation is unlikely to cause substantial degradation and settlement that would endanger its structural integrity. Geotechnical investigations are nevertheless required at these sites to confirm foundation conditions. The hydraulic design of large culverts should be conservative to provide ample capacity for the rapid runoff from impermeable permafrost terrain.

Small culverts up to 5 ft. (1.5 m) in diameter may have to be used at sites where the permafrost table is close to the surface and may therefore present some prob-

FIG. 8.20   Staggered culverts through embankment to provide drainage if lower culvert(s) become blocked with ice.

lems in embankment construction. It may be necessary to excavate frozen ground in order to provide adequate bedding and obtain suitable slopes for the culverts. Difficulties with ponding and erosion may arise as a result of differential heave or settlement of the ends or middle of the culvert after the roadbed has been constructed. Culverts placed at locations where water flows are intermittent, such as to take spring runoff only, are particularly susceptible to such problems. Care must be taken to evaluate such possibilities; in some cases it may be advantageous to install the culverts after the embankment is built. Culverts may also be slightly oversized to compensate for subsequent settlement.

Maintenance of culverts is important to ensure their effective operation and to avoid icing. Where culverts are frequently blocked by ice, small diameter pipes can be permanently installed through them so that a steam line can be connected in the spring to melt the ice. Additional culverts may also be placed above the main one to take the flow if the lower pipe is plugged with ice.

8.2.2.4 *Pavement*

Almost all highways in Canadian permafrost areas have a gravel surface. Those that have been paved are located either in areas free of permafrost in the discontinuous zone, in areas where the permafrost had retreated to considerable depth below the surface or on materials that are thaw-stable. It is the usual practice to wait several years after construction of the main gravel-surfaced embankment before placing a pavement, so that major changes in the ground thermal regime, settlement and heave have occurred. Gravel-surfaced embankments that suffer distress can be maintained much easier and at less cost than a paved embankment.

Experience shows that the addition of pavement to a gravel road that has an apparently stabilized thermal regime will result in renewed permafrost degradation, due to the change in surface albedo. The thickness of additional fill required to maintain the existing thermal regime may be estimated but is generally costly for any but short stretches near or in communities. The use of artificial insulation as a replacement for fill under pavements may be an economical alternative (Section 8.1.1). To ensure satisfactory performance of a paved embankment, one or more of the following approaches must be followed:

—locate on thaw-stable subgrades;
—remove permafrost; or
—place sufficient fill or use artificial insulation to maintain the existing ground thermal regime.

8.3 Railways

Of the five railway lines constructed in the Canadian permafrost region (Fig. 1.12), only the Hudson Bay Railway, completed to Churchill in 1929, encountered significant permafrost (Charles 1959). All the others are located within the southern fringe of the permafrost region and experienced few, if any, permafrost problems (Woods et al. 1959, Pryer 1966, Johnston, A. V. 1964, Charles 1965). A thorough conceptual plan, using the best engineering knowledge available, has recently been completed for a major railway to haul oil and gas from the Mackenzie Delta and northern Alaska (Canada Transport 1974, Cornell et al. 1973). The material in this section draws extensively on information gathered during this study.

8.3.1 Railway Location

The criteria for railway location in permafrost areas are similar to those for a road location (Section 8.2.1) but with particular emphasis on minimum gradient and curvature, minimum cost of river crossings and minimum involvement with difficult terrain. The gradient of a main line freight railway should be less than 1% and curvature less than 3 or 4% to minimize the tractive power required and the wear on rails and wheels. In these respects the criteria for railway location are somewhat different than for highways and greatly different than for pipelines. In crossing the same territory each of these transportation modes has an economical route separate from the others; the more rugged the topography, the wider the separation will be.

Rivers in permafrost areas have special characteristics, due to ice cover, spring break-up conditions and the broad, braided channels of meltwater streams emanating from glaciers and mountain regions. Such characteristics require a careful choice of river crossings to ensure integrity and to minimize costs of bridging. Approach cuts and sidehill locations are to be avoided wherever possible for stability and environmental reasons. The flat gradients required do not allow the railway profile to dip down into narrow or deep river valleys. As a result, bridges of unusual length and height, frequently spanning river valleys from crest to crest, may be required. The selection of river crossings may affect the location of a railway route to a major degree.

The effect of topography and soils on both a regional and local scale affect the route to a lesser degree. Rough terrain requiring heavy grading is to be avoided where possible; this is particularly important where permafrost is present and cuts are undesirable. Procedures followed in selecting routes for railways in permafrost areas are similar to those for roads (Section 8.2.1) and methods used are described in Chapter 5.

8.3.2 Railway Design and Construction

Design considerations for a railway are similar to those for a road in many respects but different in others. Major considerations for a railway are the traffic loads to be handled and the reliability, frequency and speeds on which standards of construction are based. A major difference from roads is in the scheduling of railway projects. Since new rail lines are normally built to serve industrial or mining developments, economic factors require a return on the investment as soon as possible. Construction time must be kept to a minimum, with a strict deadline for completion. This practically eliminates the possibility of using stage construction techniques or upgrading a pioneer line as traffic increases. This approach does not necessarily apply, of course, to a development railway built to open up a new territory and financed by public funds. In such a case the construction is planned and scheduled for maximum economy. Subject to the limitations imposed by location as discussed in Section 8.3.1, all important design and construction considerations for roads (Section 8.2.2) apply with equal emphasis to railway roadbeds. Embankment and drainage are planned and built with care and the track is predominantly on fill to avoid cuts.

There are some additional considerations. A track structure can easily be lifted and levelled periodically, and shimmed against temporary unevenness of support. Subsidence is corrected by the addition of select crushed rock ballast material under the track ties. In permafrost terrain, adjustment of the track level to compensate for settlements will be a major part of the maintenance required. For any section of the route, planning and design must compare the cost of such maintenance with the cost of reducing it by using thicker, wider fills and controlled construction techniques in continuous permafrost, or by allowing the permafrost to melt to the maximum possible extent during construction in discontinuous permafrost. In the design of a transportation route running north into permafrost terrain, one of the most important engineering decisions will be estimating the boundary north of which it can be assumed that permafrost can be maintained to a practical degree.

The amount and rate of fill settlement, due to both fill and foundation thaw settlement and consolidation, are of major concern in planning the construction schedule and in estimating maintenance required during operation of a railway. The greatest amount of settlement will normally occur in the first two or three years following construction. It would occur at a greatly decreased rate thereafter and be within tolerable limits or largely complete in about five years. In some locations slow degradation of permafrost over a long period will be unavoidable and maintenance costs will be high (Figs. 8.21 and 8.22).

Where it is intended that permafrost is to thaw and settlement is anticipated, all operations should be scheduled with thermal factors in mind. Clearing, stripping and fill placement are usually done in summer. Where it is intended that permafrost should be preserved to the maximum extent possible, winter construction operations become most important. No stripping or ground travel can be permitted on the right-of-way. All culverts are placed during the winter, when water levels are low. The initial "pioneer" fill is placed directly on undisturbed ground during the winter, when the active layer is completely frozen, minimizing both consolidation of the active layer and degradation of permafrost. The initial layer is placed to the minimum height required to prevent permafrost from thawing during the following summer. This minimum height is based on thermal calculations and can range from 5 ft. (1.5 m) at the southern boundary of continuous permafrost to 8 ft. (2.4 m) in tundra areas, where it is most important to keep massive ground ice from melting. Winter construction decreases the volume of material required and the subsequent settlement of fills (and hence long-term maintenance costs), and also minimizes environmental damage. Placement of fill above the minimum required to preserve permafrost can be completed during the following summer.

Maintenance costs will be minimized if construction of the initial fill can be scheduled sufficiently far ahead of railway operation to allow thermal equilibrium of the embankment-permafrost system to develop as much as possible. As permafrost degradation and settlement occur, periodic regrading of slopes and filling of slope cracks will be necessary.

In areas where permafrost is allowed to thaw, fills may have side slopes of 2:1 or 3:1 unless a geotechnical study of the foundation and fill materials shows that flatter side slopes are required for stability. Where permafrost is to be preserved, fill side slopes should be at least 3:1. Berms are usually required outside this slope, so that thawing and settlement will occur under the outer toe of the berm and the stability of the main embankment will not be adversely affected. Cracking of the outer slopes of the fill or berm caused by thaw settlement is inevitable

FIG. 8.21 Several feet of settlement have occurred and subsidence is continuing due to permafrost degradation on this railway line in a marginal permafrost area in northern Manitoba. Major annual maintenance and "slow train orders" are required to keep this line in operation.

FIG. 8.22   View of abandoned railway spur line showing settlement that has occurred due to permafrost degradation in southern part of discontinuous permafrost zone.

in such cases but will not affect the stability of the roadbed. Some typical railway fill cross-sections are shown in Fig. 8.23.

Either crushed rock or crushed gravel can serve as track ballast but, due to the high cost of track maintenance in northern areas, crushed rock is preferred because of its better performance and longer service life. For a line carrying heavy axle loads a superior quality of rock is highly desirable. As the bedrock types found in parts of the North are not of good quality, long hauls may be necessary or this requirement compromised. The total thickness of ballast and sub-ballast required will depend on the need to adequately spread track loads to the subgrade, limit frost heaving in the active layer and prevent thawing of permafrost. Sub-ballast material should be free-draining and non-weathering gravel and sand. Economics may dictate that crushed rock or gravel be used as sub-ballast in some locations.

8.4 Airfields

Air transportation in northern Canada began more than 50 years ago and was developed almost exclusively to serve military and resource exploration activities at numerous and widely scattered locations throughout the Yukon and Northwest Territories. Prior to 1968, when jet service was begun, piston-engined aircraft

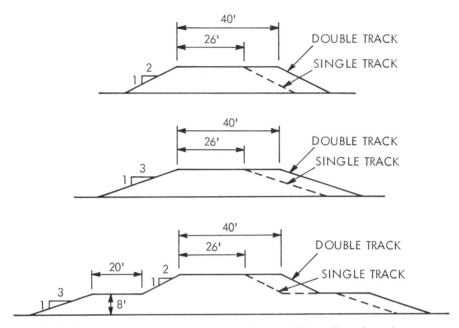

FIG. 8.23 Embankment cross sections proposed for main line railway in various types of permafrost terrain in northern Canada (After Canada Transport 1974).

served the North. The recent rapid increase in mineral and oil exploration activity in the Arctic has spurred the development of northern airports to meet new air technology incorporating larger and heavier aircraft with multi-wheel undercarriages.

At present there are about 40 civil airports in the permafrost region of Canada; 26 are in the Yukon and Northwest Territories. Many other airstrips in the North are built to various standards and operated privately or by the military. Graded earth or turf surfaces generally exist at the smaller, less frequently used sites. A higher frequency of traffic requires "all-weather" gravel surfaces, as operating conditions on earth runways are greatly affected by the weather, particularly during the annual thaw and freeze periods. Jet aircraft operations normally require paved surfaces and the increasing use of such aircraft in the North is creating a demand for paved runway facilities.

8.4.1 Airport Location

A typical layout of a northern Canada airport with a single runway is shown in Fig. 8.24. The airside pavements at an airport are divided into the three operational areas of runway, taxiway and apron. These pavements must meet specified geometrical criteria with respect to longitudinal and transverse grades, vertical curvature and sight distances. Around the perimeter of these pavements is an associated graded area with slopes not exceeding a specified maximum and with no obstructions to aircraft that accidentally run off the pavement surface. There is also a runway strip width in addition to the runway and a graded area width which is kept clear of major obstructions to aircraft such as buildings, trees and sharp changes in ground contours. Geometrical criteria used in Canada for these surfaces are listed in Table 8.1.

Standards for Canadian airport geometric and zoning requirements are given by Canada Transport (1973). Arctic airports in Canada are classified in three categories. Arctic A airports have a paved runway of minimum 6,000 ft. (1830 m) length and 150 ft. (45 m) width. The minimum standards for Arctic B and C airports require a gravel surface, runway lengths of 5,000 and 3,000 ft. (1525 and 915 m) with widths of 150 and 100 ft. (45 and 30 m) respectively. Otherwise, the geometrical criteria listed in Table 8.1 apply.

The factors considered and methods used to select a suitable airfield location in permafrost areas are similar to those for roads and railways. There is usually some latitude in siting an airport within a general geographical area, but a thorough investigation must be carried out to locate an acceptable site. The most important factors, in addition to the geometrical requirements discussed above, include favorable foundation conditions, local climate, topography of the site as it affects access road development, airport grading and drainage, availability of large quantities of fill materials, impact on the environment and distance from the community to be served.

The need for a thorough and comprehensive geotechnical investigation during the planning phase of an airport development in permafrost areas cannot be overemphasized. Major design, construction and maintenance problems can be experienced if structures are placed on ice-rich soils. If the runway, taxiway and

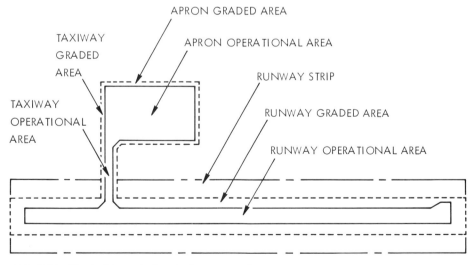

FIG. 8.24 Typical layout of a single runway airport.

TABLE 8.1
Geometrical Requirements for Canadian Airport Pavements

GEOMETRIC REQUIREMENT	DESIGN AIRCRAFT CLASS			
	A	B	C	D
Runways				
minimum length (ft.)	7,000	5,000	3,000	1,500
minimum width (ft.)	200	200	100	75
maximum longitudinal slope G (%)	±1.0	±1.0	±1.0	±2.0
maximum change in longitudinal slope ΔG (%)	±1.5	±1.5	±1.5	±2.0
maximum rate of change in longitudinal slope (% per 100 ft.)	±0.1	±0.1	±0.2	±0.25
minimum dist. between long. slope changes = $\dfrac{\Delta G_1 + \Delta G_2}{100} \times L$, where L =	100,000	100,000	50,000	25,000
maximum transverse slope (%)	±1.5	±1.5	±1.5	±2.0
min. sight distance 10 ft. to 10 ft. above surface	1/2 rny	1/2 rny	1/2 rny	—
7 ft. to 7 ft. above surface	—	—	—	1/2 rny
Runway Graded Area				
minimum width each side of runway centreline—I.F.R. (ft.)	250	250	250	—
—V.F.R. (ft.)	250	250	200	80
minimum length at end of runway (ft.)	200	200	200	100
maximum longitudinal slope (%)	±1.5	±1.75	±1.75	±2.0
maximum transverse slope (%)	±2.5	±2.5	±2.5	±3.0

Runway Strip			
minimum width—I.F.R. runway (ft.)	1,000	1,000	—
—V.F.R. runway (ft.)	500	500	200
minimum length beyond end of runway (ft.)	200	200	100
Taxiways			
minimum width (ft.)	75	75	35
maximum longitudinal slope (%)	±1.5	±1.5	±3.0
maximum rate of change of longitudinal slope (% per 100 ft.)	±1.0	±1.0	±1.25
maximum transverse slope (%)	±1.5	±1.5	±2.0
min. sight dist. 10 ft. to 0 ft. above surface (ft.)	1,000	1,000	—
7 ft. to 0 ft. above surface (ft.)	—	—	800
Taxiway Graded Area			
minimum width on each side of taxiway (ft.)	50	50	20
maximum longitudinal slope (%)	±2.0	±2.0	±3.0
maximum transverse slope (%)	±2.0	±2.0	±3.0
Apron			
maximum slope (%)	±1.0	±1.0	±1.0
Apron Graded Area			
minimum width around apron (ft.)	50	50	20
maximum longitudinal and transverse slope (%)	±3.0	±3.0	±3.0

Note: I.F.R. = instrument flight rules.
      V.F.R. = visual flight rules.

apron pavements (consisting of the wearing surface, base and sub-base courses) and the main fill are constructed on such soils, and permafrost degradation occurs after construction, large settlements and unstable foundation conditions may result. Drainage is most important and adequate facilities must be provided to avoid or reduce the detrimental effects of frost action and thawing caused by ponding of water under or adjacent to the embankment. The construction of airport facilities on ice-free, well-drained granular deposits will minimize these problems.

8.4.2 Airfield Design and Construction

As in the case of roads and railways, several alternative designs may be considered when planning an airfield. At one extreme lies a substantial installation involving high initial costs for construction but requiring little maintenance and having a relatively long service life. At the other extreme is a minimum installation with low initial costs for construction but requiring considerable maintenance and more frequent rehabilitation measures. An economic analysis to determine the net present value of the designs over a period of about 30 years should be prepared as an aid to choosing among alternatives.

The best possible design approach is to preserve the permafrost by constructing a suitably thick granular embankment. With the foundation maintained in a frozen state, the pavement structure will provide more than adequate bearing strength, settlement and frost heave problems will be eliminated and surface roughness characteristics will be acceptable. The thickness of fill required may be estimated by methods outlined in Chapter 4. These predictions should be checked by field test installations whenever possible.

When this approach is not economically feasible or practical because of the large fill thickness required or the scarcity of construction materials, the minimum design thickness is normally governed by the bearing strength of the thawed subgrade. A minimum design may perform adequately if good subgrade materials prevail but experience has shown that unacceptable differential movements frequently result when the subgrade thaws. In this situation, the designer may consider incorporating a layer of artificial insulation in the fill under the runway, taxiway and apron areas to prevent freezing and thawing of the subgrade (Keiner 1969, Esch and Rhode 1977).

Cuts and excavation of frozen ground are avoided by careful site selection and establishing suitable grade lines. Even relatively minor cuts can mean the excavation of large quantities of material because of the runway area width required to satisfy geometrical criteria. Where excavation is necessary, principles similar to those for roads are followed (Section 8.2.2.2). Surface roughness due to differential seasonal movements and, in some cases, permafrost thaw settlement can be corrected relatively easily by regrading when the surface is gravel or earth. Corrective measures are much more difficult and costly when a paved or treated surface is employed. Hence, if operational requirements permit, stage construction should be considered when designing a facility that will ultimately be surfaced with asphaltic concrete (Portland cement concrete surfaces are seldom used in the North for economic reasons). A delay of three to five years before paving will allow time for some stabilization of the subsurface thermal regime and soil conditions. During this period, a liquid asphalt spray can be applied to the gravel surface, so that its albedo will be similar to that of the asphaltic concrete to be placed later.

A typical cross-section for a Transport Canada airfield runway in the North is shown in Fig. 8.25. Embankments should be constructed of ice-free and preferably pervious granular material (Fig. 8.26). The use of impervious fill materials will probably create difficulties with drainage of the pavement base and sub-base. The sub-base and base courses normally consist respectively of selected granular material and densely graded crushed stone or crushed gravel aggregate, capable of withstanding the high shear stresses imposed by aircraft tire pressures. Requirements for the asphaltic concrete surfacing course are also related to stability and durability properties. Typical layer thickness as used in Canada for different aircraft tire pressures are given in Table 8.2.

In the design of flexible pavements for airfields, the subgrade bearing strength is usually evaluated by plate bearing tests. Because of the remoteness of many northern sites, actual plate bearing tests are rarely made and a conservative value must be estimated for design. Estimates may be based on textural soil descriptions, or preferably on other soil strength measurements such as the California Bearing Ratio (CBR) test. Methods for estimating plate bearing strengths are given in Canada Transport (1969), along with a description of design aircraft

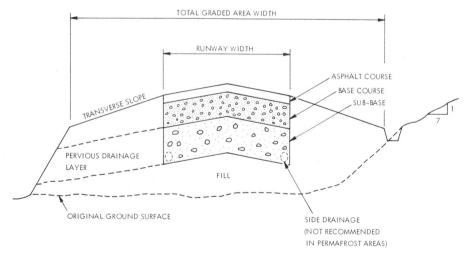

FIG. 8.25 Typical runway cross section.

FIG. 8.26   Airport runway under construction at Inuvik, N.W.T. Initial rock fill was
placed during the winter and additional fill is being placed to bring it to final grade
(After Brown 1970a).

loading groups and the specific types of aircraft assigned to these groups. If insulation is used, it is important that the structural capacity be analyzed to ensure
that it can carry the impact loads and stresses to which it will be subjected, as
discussed in Section 8.1.1.

Close attention to good drainage design is necessary at airfield sites in permafrost areas. Many of the recommendations made for roads (Section 8.2.2.3)
apply equally to airfield installations. U.S. Army/Air Force (1965) gives criteria
for airfield surface drainage.

Surface drainage of airfield pavements involves crowning runways and taxi-
ways at centerline and sloping the adjacent graded area away from the pavements. Surface runoff directed toward the pavement area by site topography is
intercepted by open ditches located at the outer edge of the graded area. Ponding
and erosion in open ditches on the graded area are prevented by setting proper
ditch grades and, in open ditches in the natural terrain, by the use of rip rap,
granular lining and ditch checks. Particular attention must also be given to
drainage at the toe of slopes to prevent ponding of water and increased thaw,
which may lead to slope failures and embankment problems.

The use of culverts under paved areas is to be avoided if possible. Thawing and
settlement of open ditches usually results in the culvert inlet being above the ditch

TABLE 8.2

**Typical layer thicknesses used in Canada
for asphalt, base and sub-base courses**

	Minimum Layer Thicknesses—inches (mm)			
	Design Aircraft Tire Pressure—psi (kPa)			
Layer	< 60 (415)	< 100 (690)	100 to 149 (690 to 1030)	150 to 199 (1035 to 1370)
Asphaltic concrete	2 (50)	2.5 (65)	3.5 (90)	4 (100)
Base	6 (150)	9 (230)	9 (230)	12 (305)
Sub-base	—As necessary to provide adequate bearing strength in flexible pavement.			

invert. When culverts must be used, problems of this nature can be reduced by well-designed impervious cut-off and headwall structures at the end of the pipes, along with impervious blankets on the channel bed and on the slopes adjacent to the inlet and outlet of pipes. Measures must be taken to prevent culverts from becoming blocked with ice during the winter.

In seasonal frost areas, drainage of pavement bases and sub-bases constructed on impervious subgrade soils is effected through subsurface pavement side drains. These installations are not reliable in permafrost areas, due to the short period during the summer when thaw is at or below the drainage level and the drains are operable. At the design stage, therefore, consideration must be given to the placement of pervious fill materials set to predetermined grades to ensure sub-surface pavement drainage. With asphalt pavements, a regular sealing program is needed to prevent access of water to the pavement sub-layers through cracks in the pavement surface.

CHAPTER 9

Dams and Reservoirs

(Contributors–G. H. Johnston and J. G. Macpherson)

9.1 General Considerations

The design and construction of dams and dykes normally require considerable experience to deal with the problems of seepage, settlement, stability, slope protection, construction methods and scheduling. In permafrost areas these become more complex because of the thawing effect of the impounded water on the perennially frozen materials underlying the reservoir and the structures. The great variability in subsurface conditions that can occur within relatively short distances further complicates design.

Earthfill structures are normally built in permafrost areas unless the structural competence of the foundation is altered little by thawing. This is the case with most bedrock foundations, where concrete dams may be justified. As required in standard earthfill dam construction, it is essential that facilities with adequate overflow or discharge capacity be provided to avoid overtopping of the embankments and their subsequent erosion. Suitable measures must also be taken to avoid damage from wave and ice action on the upstream slopes and from erosion on the downstream slopes.

In permafrost areas, special attention must be given to the thermal regime of the foundation and embankment. Thawing may precipitate large differential movements, unacceptable or uncontrolled seepage and unstable conditions, none of which can be tolerated by most hydraulic structures. The need for detailed site investigations and careful assessment of all factors is therefore essential. Suitably conservative factors of safety, based on careful analyses of the best available information, are necessary in design.

The use of the dam will influence its thermal performance and thus its design. For example, the foundations of dams and dykes for hydro-electric complexes, water supply reservoirs, sewage lagoons or mine tailings ponds that impound water over long periods of time may be subjected to significant thawing. Others, used for temporary storage of liquids such as for flood control, mud sumps at drilling sites or to confine spills at petroleum product storage farms, may not be thawed during the relatively short period of impounding. Controlled seepage through and under embankments is usually tolerable but may be unacceptable in certain cases, particularly if toxic wastes are involved.

Examples of dams and dykes constructed on permafrost for hydro-electric developments and water supply reservoirs are given in Section 9.3. Thornton (1974) and Cameron (1976) describe the performance of a sewage lagoon dyke at Inuvik, N.W.T. The design and construction of tailings dams and waste embankments, in general, are discussed by Klohn (1972), Mittal and Morgenstern (1975), Chafet (1975) and Coates and Yu (1977). Studies of tailings dams and ponds in the Great Slave Lake and Great Bear Lake areas in the Northwest Territories are reported by Taylor and Gill (1973), Roy et al. (1973), Berube et al. (1973) and Roy and Vezina (1973).

A review of the state-of-the-art of petroleum product spill containment dykes in northern Canada is presented by Canada Environment (1974c). Tests were conducted at Yellowknife, N.W.T. to evaluate the suitability of four potential liner systems for containment of petroleum products (Canada Environment 1978). These systems included processed bentonite mixed with in situ soils, a rigid liner formed from spray-applied molten sulphur, two urethene coatings spray-applied onto a fabric and two types of urethane foam. These preliminary studies indicated that the urethane coatings and foam liners had some potential for use as liners in petroleum product storage areas. Sheets of impermeable synthetic materials, such as rubber and polyethylene, are receiving increasing use in Canada (including northern areas) to line dykes, ponds, sewage lagoons and reservoirs constructed from soils for water conservation purposes and the storage and control of pollutants (Foster et al. 1979). While special requirements may be necessary for individual cases with respect to dams and reservoirs, only the factors related to permafrost are discussed here.

The effects of impounding on the natural perimeter of a reservoir must be evaluated, in addition to the design of impounding structures. In some cases thaw settlement of low freeboard areas can result in loss of water unless a dyke is constructed. The submergence and subsequent thawing of permafrost-affected river banks may precipitate slides within the reservoir (Section 2.5.2). Such slides can affect the reservoir holding capacity, dyke foundations or outlet works.

9.2 Design and Construction

Two types of earthfill dams can be constructed on permafrost: impervious or semi-pervious. Impervious dams may be designed to maintain the foundation and embankment in a frozen condition, or take into account thawing of the permafrost foundation during construction and during the life of the structure.

A "frozen" dam may be constructed of practically any kind of soil including frozen or unfrozen material. The core of the dam and its foundation are frozen either during or immediately after construction. The fill must be saturated with ice to produce a well-bonded mass and special attention must be given to maintaining the frozen condition for the life of the structure. The high strength and impermeable nature of the frozen ground can thus be utilized. A "thawed" impervious dam must be founded on competent bedrock or incompressible material and have an impermeable core or membrane and appropriate provisions for handling seepage through and under the embankment. The design of semi-pervious dams must take into account thawing of the foundation materials and the potential settlement, seepage and stability problems that may arise, particularly if an ice-rich foundation is involved.

Limited experience to date, in both the USSR and North America, indicates that these various types of dams can be built successfully, but only after careful investigation and assessment of all local factors show that their particular requirements can be met (Bogoslovskiy et al. 1966). Special construction procedures and scheduling of the work are frequently required. The performance of the structure should be carefully monitored by specially installed instrumentation to confirm design predictions and to give warning if remedial work is required (Johnston 1965, Gupta et al. 1973).

In the continuous permafrost zone, where ground temperatures are low and the thawing season is short, low head (< 25 ft.; 8 m), impervious frozen dams may be built by natural freezing of the fill as the material is placed in layers (Fulwider 1973). In most cases, however, and particularly for larger dams, artificial freezing methods (e.g., mechanical refrigeration systems or circulation of cold air through vertical ducts) must be used to create and maintain an impervious frozen core and foundation (Biyanov 1975, Trupak 1970).

In the discontinuous zone, where permafrost temperatures and the climate are warmer, dams must be designed for thawed conditions. Whether or not a semi-pervious or impervious dam will be constructed will depend on local ground conditions (ice-rich vs competent rock foundation materials), availability of fill materials, use of the structure (e.g., dyked water supply reservoirs or sewage lagoons) and cost of the various design alternatives (MacDonald et al. 1960). Effects of seasonal freezing and thawing of the fill must also be considered; deterioration of the core and downstream slopes may increase seepage (Duguid et al. 1973). Thermally induced stresses and growth of ice lenses can result in severe cracking of the core and outer shell. Typical sections indicating critical areas are shown in Fig. 9.1.

At many locations, site access is difficult during summer months and excavation and placement of initial fill can only be carried out successfully during the winter, when heavy equipment can move on the frozen ground surface. This suggests that materials that can be handled in low temperatures should be utilized. Such materials are usually granular and pervious compared to the impermeable types commonly associated with dam construction. The broad cross-sections required for stability on weak foundations also tend to limit seepage due to flat gradients and thus permit the use of pervious fills.

Fine-grained soils required for impermeable cores are not easily obtained at many sites. If they are frozen in situ, they become very wet on thawing because of the high ice content. Special treatment is required to dry them, reduce their frost action characteristics and place them during freezing temperatures. These considerations have been discussed in Chapter 6.

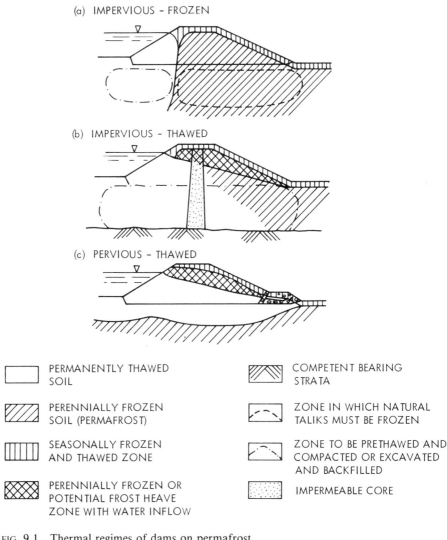

FIG. 9.1   Thermal regimes of dams on permafrost.

9.2.1 Site Conditions

Foundation conditions can be extremely variable at individual dam sites. A thawed zone penetrating through permafrost, or at least to great depth in it, exists under most large rivers and lakes, whereas a closed thaw bulb of limited extent may exist under smaller streams and lakes. Of particular concern in dam design is the location of the permafrost table at the shoreline of water bodies. On land areas, frozen ground may be continuous or occur in scattered patches. Bedrock may be frozen or unfrozen, occur at shallow or great depths, be quite competent or contain many ice-filled fissures (Kagan and Krivonogova 1973). Overburden may consist of a variety of soils (including permeable frozen materials), be relatively ice-free or contain large ice masses irregularly distributed throughout the material.

It is essential, therefore, that as much information as possible be obtained on the nature of the foundation materials before the design of the dam can begin. The effort expended will depend to some extent on the size and importance of the structure, large dams requiring much more detailed investigations. Alternative locations should be evaluated in early phases of the investigation.

Of special importance are the distribution of permafrost, type of soil or rock, ice content, thermal regime, settlement and permeability characteristics in the frozen, thawing and thawed states. The stability of the structure is influenced by the rate of thaw and dissipation of excess pore pressures, differential settlements and percolation of water. Although dense gravels or fissured rock may be quite rigid and stable after thawing, the resulting seepage can be critical. In some cases cut-offs, such as grout curtains, may have to be extended as thawing occurs. Provisions for drainage are essential.

9.2.2 Thermal Conditions

Determination of the thermal regime of dams is a basic requirement for design to ensure long-term satisfactory performance of the structure. Of particular interest are the long-term equilibrium (steady state) condition that will ultimately be reached after the structure is completed, and the transient (non-steady state) conditions that will exist at various times during the life of the structure.

Following disturbance to the existing thermal regime by construction operations and filling of the reservoir, the long-term equilibrium conditions may not be established for perhaps 100 years, even for low head structures. Knowledge of the thermal changes that occur during construction and operation of the dam are of great practical importance, for designs can take these variations into account and measures can be planned to control them to ensure stability of the structure.

These thermal problems are complex, usually requiring two- and three-dimensional analyses (Chapter 4), and are not easily solved. They are complicated by the constantly changing boundary conditions and phase changes (water/ice) at the moving boundary between the thawed and frozen zones. Heat transfer by convection (caused by seepage water) as well as by conduction is usually involved, particularly in the case of pervious materials. In addition, the distribution of ice and unfrozen zones in the foundation cannot be precisely known under the whole length of a structure.

Although rigorous solutions are still being developed for the various types of dam (e.g., semi-pervious, impervious, frozen core, thawed but impermeable core) predictions can be made based on various assumptions that are useful for engineering purposes. For example, Brown and Johnston (1970), using simple one-dimensional heat conduction theory, derive an expression for predicting with reasonable accuracy the depth of thaw under a semi-pervious dyke at any time after the reservoir is filled. Similarly, Soviet investigators have developed methods for determining the depth of thaw and temperature distribution in various types of dams at different times during and following construction (Bogoslovskiy et al. 1966, Semenov 1967, Shugaeva 1976, Tsytovich et al. 1972, Tsytovich 1973). The accuracy of the predictions is significantly affected by the values of the various parameters and boundary conditions used in the calculations. The most important are the values for total moisture content (ice and unfrozen water), thermal properties of the soils (mainly of the unfrozen materials) and ground, water and air temperatures.

Field measurements that show the progression of thaw or the temperature distribution within a structure and foundation during the year and/or over a period of time are of interest (Fig. 9.2). Examples are given by Johnston (1969), Roy et al. (1973) and Fulwider (1973) for low head dams and by Kitze and Simoni (1972), Biyanov (1978), Kamenskiy (1978), Simoni (1975) and Odintsov and Nedosekin (1975) for larger structures.

The progression of thaw below an impervious dam will be quite different from that of a semi-pervious dam. Under a semi-pervious dam, thawing penetrates downward under the whole structure at essentially the same rate as it does under the adjacent reservoir due to the influence of the water in the reservoir and water percolating through the fill. Under an impervious dam with a frozen or unfrozen impermeable core (no seepage), thawing is influenced not only by the water temperature on the upstream face but also by the effects of freezing devices (if any) and the climate over the remainder of the dam surface. Thus, penetration of thaw will be mainly downward only under the reservoir and the upstream slope and laterally into the structure and foundation (Fig. 9.1).

The shape of the thaw front under and adjacent to the dam/water interface may be critical with regard to stability, even for semi-pervious structures, where the rate of thaw beneath the main body of the dam may be somewhat less than that under the toe of the upstream slope and the reservoir. Thawing can greatly reduce the effective strength of materials and differential thaw settlement tends to produce cracking in overlying materials. The combined effects of loss of strength and settlement can lead to failure of the structure or increased seepage.

As discussed previously, many factors (including the type of embankment selected) influence the rate and extent of thawing. During the first year or two after water is impounded, the rate may vary considerably from season to season, being less in the winter than in the summer (Fig. 9.2). Other conditions being equal, this difference will usually be more pronounced in the discontinuous permafrost zone, where the water temperatures will be much warmer for a longer period of time than in the far North. In the continuous permafrost zone, summer thawing is usually slower, and freezeback in the winter is significant; thus, the permanently frozen dam concept becomes feasible. After the initial years, the effect of the annual variation in temperature will diminish greatly and the thaw plane will move according to

$$X = a\sqrt{t} \tag{9.1}$$

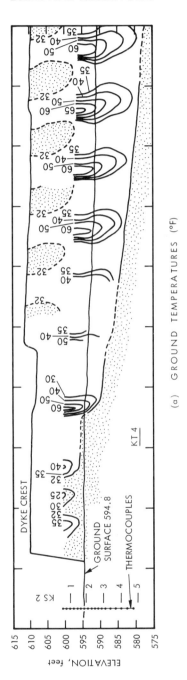

(a) GROUND TEMPERATURES (°F)

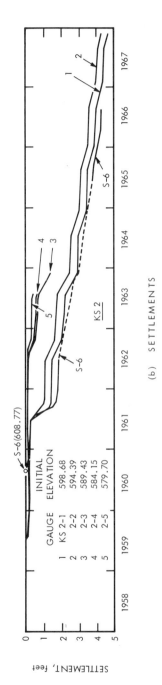

(b) SETTLEMENTS

FIG. 9.2   Dyke observations at Kelsey Generating Station, Manitoba (Modified from Johnston 1969).

where X is the depth to the thaw plane, t is the time and a is a constant (Brown and Johnston 1970, Nixon and McRoberts 1973, see also Chapter 4). After the anticipated shapes of the thaw front at various times have been established, settlements can be evaluated and stability analyses of the embankment can be made utilizing potential failure surfaces related to weak zones.

9.2.3 Settlement

Investigations and observations of existing dams show that most of the total settlement of dams on permafrost foundations results from thawing of the ice inclusions and associated release of water. Recent laboratory testing confirms this and relates it to soil type and initial water-ice contents or, in broad terms, bulk density of the frozen soil. In nature, higher ice contents are usually associated with soils that are also compressible in the unfrozen state. Although these soils consolidate more after thawing than dense, well-graded soils, the initial thaw settlement is still the predominant characteristic (Fig. 9.3). Thaw settlement and consolidation considerations are discussed in Sections 3.7.1 and 3.7.2 respectively.

Variation of both soil types and ice content within the foundation of a dam must be expected, but evaluation of all data may not reveal local irregularities present within short distances under the structure. When thaw progresses laterally and at unequal rates under the dam and adjacent reservoir, or when both unfrozen and frozen materials underlie the structure, significant differential settlements and cracking can be expected (Fig. 9.4). Some differential movement may be tolerated in low to medium head dams as long as the overall stability and seepage control are adequate. Transverse cracks, however, can lead to failures. Although frozen soils are usually considered to be practically incompressible, there is evidence that significant compression can occur, particularly when large areas are heavily loaded (Section 3.4.1.7). Such a situation might arise if a large dam was placed on a foundation maintained in a frozen state.

Settlement limits that should not be exceeded must be established, based on careful evaluation, experience and judgment. Total settlement must be limited to that which still provides adequate freeboard to prevent overtopping. Initially the settlement occurs rapidly, but over the long term, the decreasing rate of settlement provides more time to arrange for and execute repair. The results of differential settlement can often be tolerated if suitable precautions are taken in the initial design and construction. Several alternative methods of avoiding or controlling excessive foundation settlements, including excavation of part or all of the high ice content materials are described by MacDonald et al. (1960) and Macpherson et al. (1970). The example in Fig. 9.5 indicates the depth of excavation required to limit foundation settlement to a preselected value of approximately 5 ft. (1.5 m) if the average ice content of the upper 12 ft. (3.7 m) of foundation was 80% prior to construction and a final void ratio of 0.3 could be expected in the foundation.

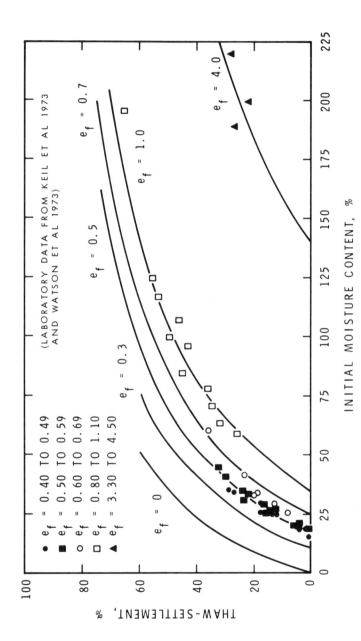

FIG. 9.3   Thaw settlement.

FIG. 9.4   (a) Differential settlement of low, semi-pervious dyke on permafrost
(Manitoba Hydro photograph). (b) Placement of fill on regular maintenance program
maintains freeboard for low dyke on permafrost as it settles due to thawing of ice-rich
foundation soils. Boundary between light and dark coloured materials indicates
approximate magnitude of differential settlements. Maximum settlement experienced
was about 2 m.

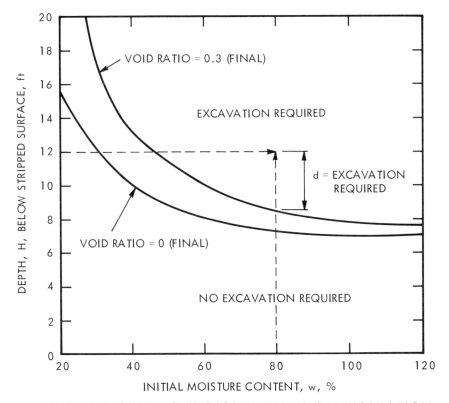

GUIDE CURVES TO INDICATE DEPTH OF EXCAVATION
REQUIRED TO LIMIT THAW SETTLEMENT TO 5 FEET (1.5 m)

FIG. 9.5   Theoretical thaw settlement–final void ratio = 0.3 (After Macpherson et al. 1970).

Semi-pervious materials, such as sands, that can deform and heal cracks as settlement occurs have been used successfully for small dykes (Johnston 1969). Thin zones of selected material should be avoided in the fill, since movements may be large enough to displace and render them ineffective. Over-compaction of fill may make it sufficiently brittle that cracks will not heal, thereby permitting seepage or piping to erode materials quickly. Similarly, failure may occur if "bridging" of the seasonally frozen outer shell allows the underlying material to separate from it by settlement. Access to and along the structure must be maintained so that emergency repairs can be accomplished promptly.

The inclusion in a thawed dam or foundation of a rigid structure, such as a membrane or conduit, should be avoided since it could easily be broken by the relatively large differential movements that can be expected. Under certain circumstances it may even contribute to the differential movements. Thawing and thaw settlement in the vicinity of the downstream toe of the dam may be accelerated if seepage flow is allowed to pond locally in the summer. This may be avoided by drainage of the water away from the toe.

9.2.4 Stability

The stability of the dam and its foundation may be endangered if excess pore pressures are generated and shearing resistance is decreased because the rate of advance of the thaw front is faster than the rate at which the thaw water is expelled. Until recently, little information on thaw strength was available. Earlier estimates of strength were based mainly on observations of natural slopes and, of necessity, led to conservative assumptions for the design of dams. The stability of thawing soils is difficult to analyze, but quantitative stability predictions can be made by considering the important effects of thaw consolidation including rate of thaw and soil permeability parameters as discussed in Section 3.7.2 and associated references. Although good agreement has been obtained between theory and experimental results, further testing and field observations, particularly with regard to the behavior and effects of excess pore pressures, are required to confirm theoretical evaluations.

To evaluate the stability of an embankment under non-permafrost conditions a series of surfaces, expected from experience to be potential failure planes, are selected. The resisting force available in the materials through which the surface passes must adequately exceed the forces tending to cause sliding. Knowing the proposed embankment geometry and the strength parameters of the fill and the foundation, the location of the critical potential failure surfaces and the related factors of safety can be determined for different conditions during the life of the embankment. Adjustments to the proposed configuration are made until adequate safety is attained.

In a permafrost foundation, the resistance to sliding mobilized in the frozen soil will usually decrease on thawing and subsequently recover somewhat as the thawed soil consolidates. If escape of the thaw water is restricted by the impervious nature of the soil, the increase in pore water pressure and the re-orientation of soil particles may significantly reduce the resistance to sliding at the thaw front. Sand drains have been provided to dissipate pore pressures in impervious soils in some cases (MacDonald 1966, Macpherson et al. 1970). A short time after the reservoir is impounded, there will be four areas of differing strength:

—the embankment, the strength characteristics of which are predictable and controllable by selection of materials and placing methods,

—the upper part of the foundation, which has thawed and consolidated, thus regaining some strength,

—the foundation material near the thaw front, whose strength may be significantly reduced by increased pore pressures caused by slow drainage of thaw water, and

—the still frozen and strong foundation beyond the thaw front.

The critical failure surface will probably be associated with the thawed zone immediately adjacent to the advancing thaw front, where pore pressures reduce shear strength. Along such surfaces, the resisting forces in the fill usually do not contribute effectively because of the geometry of the dam and the incompatibility of strains. Therefore, a strong fill is of only limited benefit to stability. In fact, a strong fill may be detrimental to the extent that cracking can occur and lead to internal erosion by seepage. The most sensitive area with regard to stability of a dam on permafrost is under or adjacent to the toe of the upstream slope. Critical conditions can also exist under the downstream slope, particularly if the active layer at and near the toe is increased due to disturbance by construction or ponding of water due to inadequate drainage facilities. The remote possibility of a stability failure in frozen material underlain by a thawed zone (McRoberts and Morgenstern 1974b) should not be overlooked.

If the analyses indicate that stability may be marginal or inadequate, various measures to improve the situation should be assessed. These include adjustments in the loading (embankment configuration), excavation of some or all of the potentially weaker (ice-rich) frozen ground, improved drainage to remove excess water and provisions to reduce the rate of thaw and thus limit pore pressure buildup or to alter the shape of the thaw front to a more advantageous configuration.

9.2.5 Instrumentation

Following construction of a dam or dyke and the impounding of the reservoir, surveillance must be maintained for the life of the structure. In the initial years changes may be relatively active due to the imposition of the new thermal regime as well as the reservoir loading conditions. Provisions to effect rapid remedial measures should be allowed for in the overall program.

During the design stage, inspection and observation programs should be formulated to permit the installation of instrumentation devices during construction to augment visual inspection. Such devices should be simple and dependable in order to function in spite of differential movements. Settlement gauges in the foundation and fill, alignment pins, thermocouples or thermistors and piezometers have been installed in dykes in Manitoba (Johnston 1965, Gupta et al. 1973). With the possible exception of temperature measuring devices, accuracy must be considered as secondary to ruggedness.

9.3 Examples of Dam Construction on Permafrost

In North America only a few small structures have been built on permafrost and these are located primarily in the discontinuous zone. In the Soviet Union a number of large and small structures have been constructed throughout the permafrost region (Biyanov 1975). In total, there are relatively few dams in the world built on permafrost. Apparently no concrete dams have been founded on permafrost-affected soils, and only bedrock or dense till have been utilized for foundations of structures higher than about 60 ft. (20 m). Ice-filled fissures in rock foundations are usually grouted from galleries incorporated in the structure as thawing occurs (Kagan and Krivonogova 1976).

TABLE 9.1

Features of Some Dams Constructed on Permafrost

Project	Location	Temp. (°C) Mean	Min[1]	Max[1]	Found'n	Fill	Type[2]	Slopes U/S	D/S	H[3] (m)	Year[4]	Notes	Reference
North America													
Hess Creek Dam	Alaska 65°+N, 148°+W Hess Creek	−4	—	+15	Silt on 10 m gravel	Hydraulic and rolled fill at crest (5m)	F	1.3:1 2.5:1	1.3:1 2:1	24	1946	6-12 m ice rich excavated from foundation. Steel sheet pile cut-off steamed in and frozen with refrig. system. Fill not frozen after 20 years. Abandoned after 16 years.	Rice and Simoni 1966 Kitze and Simoni 1972 Simoni 1975
Barrow	Alaska 71°+N, 156°W	—	−35	—	Sand bars Silts	Sandy gravel	F	4:1±	4:1±	4	1964	Water supply at sea coast. Fresh water floating on sea water. Concrete filled oil drum rip rap.	Buchanan et al. 1966
Crescent Lake Dam	Thule Greenland 77°−N, 69°W	−11	—	—	Well-graded till	Well-graded till, placed thawed	F	7:1	6±:1	3.6 6 6.25	1952 1955 1959	Water supply. Freeze back first year 3.6 m. Freeze index: 4510. Thaw index: 440.	Fulwider 1973
Kelsey Gen. Sta. Hydro Electric	Manitoba 56°+N, 96°+W Nelson River	−4	−26	+16	Varved clays on till	Sand	T	4:1	3:1	6	1961	Vertical sand drain grid in foundation. Constructed in winter. Permafrost not continuous. Freeze index: 3050. Thaw index: 1830.	MacDonald et al. 1960 MacDonald 1966 Johnston 1969 Brown and Johnston 1970

Name	Location				Foundation	Core	Type			Height	Year	Remarks	References
Kettle Gen. Sta. Hydro Electric	Manitoba 56°+N, 95°−W Nelson River	−5	−26	+15	Silts and clays	Sand	T	4:1	3:1	9	1970	Vertical sand drain grid. Initial construction in winter. Permafrost not continuous.	MacPherson et al. 1970 Gupta et al. 1973
Long Spruce Gen. Sta. Hydro Electric	Manitoba 56°+N, 94°+W Nelson River	−5	−26	+15	Clays, silty clays	Sand	T	4:1	3:1	11	1977	Vertical sand drain grid (partial). No stripping in freeboard areas. Permafrost not continuous.	Keil et al. 1973
Little Chena Dam (Proposed)	Alaska 65°N, 147°W Little Chena River	—	—	—	Silts (Frozen)	Granular (Thawed)	T/F	3:1	2.5:1	31	—	Flood control.	George 1973
USSR													
Thermal Electric	Siberia 69°N, 89°E	—	—	—	Over-burden	Clay. Concrete core	F	—	—	10	1942	Brine circulated in shafts initially. After brine leak, air circulated.	Trupak 1970
Arkagalinsk Myaundzha Thermal Electric	Myaundzha River	−13	−44	+17	Basalt	Loam core 6 m wide	F	3.5:1	1.5:1	11.5	1959	Maximum water temperature 14°. Ammonia and air refrigeration.	Trupak 1970
Irelyakh	Yakutia 64°±N, 113°E Irelyakh River	−8	−34 (−63)	+35	Silty loam core on rock	Loamy sands placed thawed	F	6:1	3:1	20	1964	Water supply for Mirny. Refrigeration with cold air when temperature < −15°C.	Trupak 1970 Semenov 1967 Biyanov 1965 Odintsov and Nedosekin 1975

TABLE 9.1 (Cont'd.)
Features of Some Dams Constructed on Permafrost

Project	Location	Temp. (°C) Mean	Min[1]	Max[1]	Found'n	Fill	Type[2]	Slopes U/S	D/S	H[3] (m)	Year[4]	Notes	Reference
Pevek	Anadyr Pevek River	—	—	—	—	—	F	—	—	—	—	—	Trupak 1970 Smirnov and Vasiliev 1973
Vilyui Hydro Electric	Yakutia 63°±N, 112°±E Vilyui River	−8	−41 (−63)	+36	Diabase. grout curtain from gallery	Sloping core rockfill	T	2.5:1	2:1	74	1969	Thawed core placed in winter. Flood passed over partially completed dam.	Biyanov 1965 Batenchuk et al. 1968
Kolyma Hydro Electric	Magadan 62°±N, 150°±E Kolyma River	−12	−50 (−62)	25-30 (36)	Thin alluvium on granite	Loam core rockfill shells	T	2:1	1.8:1	126	U.C.	Construction started 1970. Grout curtain from gallery after construction. Underground powerhouse.	Biyanov 1975
Dam II	Yakutia Vilyui Basin	—	—	—	Overburden. Core on rock	Crib core. Loam shell	T	2.5:1	2.5:1	12	1960	Failure at crib spillway repaired.	Biyanov 1970b
Dam III	Yakutia Vilyui Basin	—	—	—	Rock	Central core	F	2:1	1.5:1	3	—	Core placed thawed in winter.	Biyanov 1970b
Dam V	Yakutia Vilyui Basin	—	—	—	Loam	Homogeneous silty soil	T	3:1	2.5:1	17	—	Severe permafrost excavated. Remedial blanket and concrete cut-off.	Biyanov 1970b

Dam	Location	Temp.	Extremes	Foundation	Material	Type	U/S slope	D/S slope	Height (m)	Year	Remarks	Reference
Dam VI and VII	Yakutia Vilyui Basin	—	—	Loam marl	Sandy gravel and loam	F	2.5:1	2.5:1	6 8	—	Flood control. Winter construction. Vertical timber diaphragm to rock.	Biyanov 1970b
Ust-Khantaisk Hydro Electric	Siberia 68°±N, 87°±E Khantaika River	8	(−63) (32)	Complex over-burden	Moraine core Gravel shells	T	3.5:1	3:1	65	1970	Severe permafrost excavated. Impervious core placed in winter. Floods passed over partly completed dam.	Biyanov 1975
		—	—	—					30	—	Right bank dam similar. Cofferdam with polyethylene membrane.	Myznikov et al. 1973 Zhilenas et al. 1973
?	Oidur-Yurege River	—	—	—	Silty sandy loam and rocky soil	F	3:1	2:1	13	—	Core placed in summer. 20 m wide crest.	Odintsov and Nedosekin 1975
? Hydro Electric	Sytykan River	—	—	—	Clay core	F	3:1	2:1	20	—	Flood flow over partly completed dam. Refrigeration of core in two months.	Odintsov and Nedosekin 1975
?	?	−10.6	—	Over-burden	Homo-geneous loam	F	—	—	21	1967	City water supply dam. 1970 failure repaired. Construction 1960-1966.	Anisimov and Sorokin 1973

FOOTNOTES:

1. Minimum and maximum months. Extreme temperatures in brackets.
2. Type, F = Frozen, T = Thawed.
3. Height of embankment.
4. Reservoir impounded (U.C. Under Construction).

The majority of dams on permafrost are earth fills because of the technical advantages of flexible structures requiring less strength in the foundations, and the economy in utilizing local materials. Both "frozen" and "thawed" designs are used. In the discontinuous zone, maintaining the dam in a frozen condition is difficult and virtually impossible to achieve economically. Regardless of the nature of the permafrost and climate, broad cross-sections with flat slopes are the rule rather than the exception. Pertinent features of several dams constructed in the permafrost region are given in Table 9.1.

Frozen dams have been constructed in the continuous permafrost zone in the USSR (discussed later), and at least three have been built in the western hemisphere. The Hess Creek Dam (Fig. 9.6), constructed in Alaska in the 1940's to provide water for a summer mining operation, has not been used for some years and did not freeze completely (Kitze and Simoni 1972, Simoni 1975). A short sheet pile cutoff, steamed into foundation silts, was frozen in place by artificial refrigeration and most of the fill was placed by hydraulic methods. Difficulties were experienced in operation of the tunnel-like outlet works and the

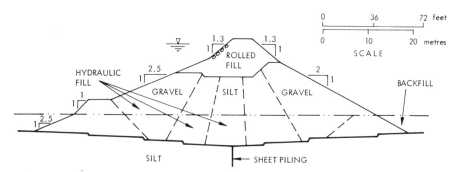

FIG. 9.6   Hess Creek dam, Alaska (After Rice and Simoni 1966).

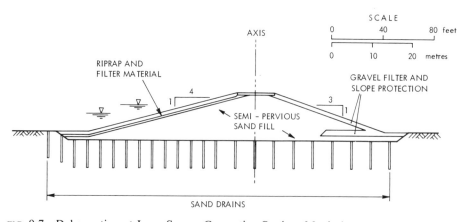

FIG. 9.7   Dyke section at Long Spruce Generating Station, Manitoba.

overflow spillway. Small frozen dams have been constructed at Thule, Greenland (Fulwider 1973) and Point Barrow, Alaska (Buchanan et al. 1966). Stage construction of the former permitted complete freezing and no problems have been reported as reservoir levels have been kept below the active thawed zone to maintain a frozen core.

Thawed dams, constructed in the discontinuous zone, are designed to accommodate limited seepage and settlement. Differential settlements due to thawing of frozen portions of the foundation lead to cracking, which is dealt with by using fill materials of a self-healing nature to prevent serious seepage. The relatively small 20 to 30 ft. (6 to 10 m) high dykes at the Kelsey (MacDonald 1966), Kettle (Macpherson et al. 1970) and Long Spruce Generating Stations (Keil et al. 1973) in northern Manitoba are of this type (Fig. 9.4 and 9.7). The higher embankments at these projects are founded on strong foundations of bedrock or till after excavation of ice-rich permafrost materials. Insulating sand blankets were placed on the slopes of deeper cuts through the permafrost to prevent thaw deterioration during construction. A number of other small structures have been constructed in Canada, but design and performance details are not available in the literature. Many of them experienced some settlement and cracking and required periodic maintenance, usually placement of additional fill.

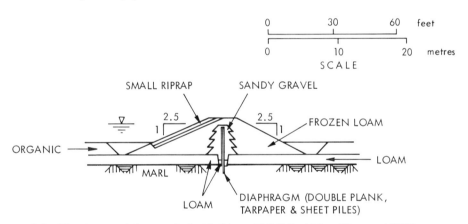

FIG. 9.8   Flood control dam on Irelyakh River, U.S.S.R. (After Biyanov 1970b).

In the USSR thawed dams have been constructed with diaphragms of sheet piling, timber or clay-cement cutoffs through the fill and into a strong foundation material such as bedrock (Fig. 9.8) (Biyanov 1970b, 1975). In some cases, failures have occurred because the cutoff was inadequate in the foundation, resulting in either excessive differential settlement or seepage as thawing took place (Trupak 1970). Larger thawed dams are usually founded on bedrock and have been built under severe winter conditions (Fig. 9.9 and 9.10). It is reported that on small unimportant thawed dams, frozen materials have been used, but with caution, for the shells supporting the impervious diaphragms.

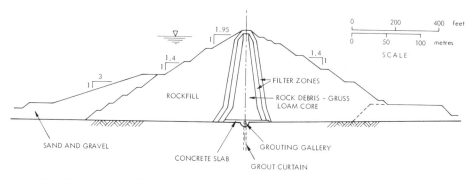

FIG. 9.9   Cross section of dam on Kolyma River, U.S.S.R. (After Evdokimov et al. 1973).

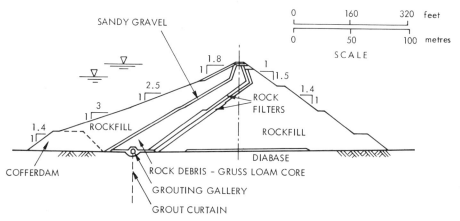

FIG. 9.10   Cross section of dam on Vilyui River, U.S.S.R. (After Batenchuk et al. 1968).

Much of the Soviet literature deals with permanently frozen dams in the continuous permafrost zone (Biyanov 1965, 1975). In a typical case the core is artificially frozen by cooling systems and the downstream slope has been frozen by natural cooling (Fig. 9.11). Soviet practice has been to construct frozen dams on competent foundations following removal of ice-rich material. Sometimes only a core trench is excavated to competent materials in the riverbanks. All of the thawed soil in the riverbed talik is removed from under the dam. The construction schedule is arranged so that the stripped foundation will be well frozen when the initial unfrozen fill is placed.

Fill used for the core of the dam is normally an unfrozen well-graded impervious material, such as till that includes sand and gravel compacted to a density of 95 lb./ft.^{3} (1.5 t/m^3) at optimum water content. Relatively high water contents provide a saturated fill, which is watertight when frozen and reasonably plastic near the crest to avoid cracking. Detailed investigations are conducted to select

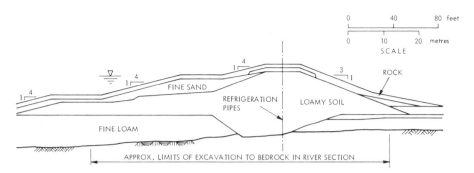

FIG. 9.11   Cross section of dam on Irelyakh River flood plain, U.S.S.R. (After Smirnov and Vasiliev 1973).

methods for treating, handling and placing the fill materials in temperatures as low as $-40°F$ ($-40°C$) (Tsytovich and Kronik 1970, Zhilenas et al. 1973). The materials are specially treated with additives and many other precautions are taken to prevent them freezing in stockpiles and during transport and placement. Such operations are quite expensive (Batenchuk et al. 1968, Biyanov 1970a).

Freezing of the dam is accomplished by circulating cold air through double concentric pipes placed in holes drilled at about 5 ft. (1.5 m) centres along the crest (Biyanov 1965). Cold air is drawn down the annular space between the pipes and up the centre pipe by fans on headers joining several holes. Cooling is done when air temperatures fall below $5°F$ ($-15°C$). Precautions must be taken to prevent clogging of the pipe inlets by snow in the winter and freezing of condensation in the pipes during the summer. If the mean annual air temperature exceeds $23°F$ ($-5°C$), a refrigerant such as brine or freon is circulated. Although heat transfer between a refrigerant and the soil is better than between air and soil, care must be taken to avoid leaks in the piping due to rupture or corrosion; thawed zones may form in the dam or foundation (Anisimov and Sorokin 1975). The use of thermal piles to create frozen membranes in dams is under study (Buchko et al. 1975), but no dams incorporating these devices have yet been constructed. Special precautions are essential to ensure that the dam remains frozen adjacent to the spillway where heat from the water may cause thawing of the core.

Peat moss was used as an insulator on the crests of a few early dams and occasionally on the downstream slope, to reduce thawing during the summer, but it also reduces the effects of natural freezing during the winter. To some extent the orientation of the slope with respect to the sun will influence the decision as to whether or not the slope should be insulated (George 1973).

CHAPTER 10

Utilities

(Contributors–E. I. Carefoot, A. L. Davies, G. H. Johnston,
N. A. Lawrence, P. Lukomskyj and D. E. Thornton)

The same basic engineering principles followed in temperate climates can be applied to the design of water supply, sewage disposal, central heating and power and communication systems in the North. The severe climate and the presence of permafrost complicate matters, however, and must be given special attention to ensure safe and satisfactory performance of the systems. The need to install and maintain services at isolated locations, the lack of skilled operators and high transportation, construction and operating costs pose further problems and introduce serious economic considerations in providing essential services to northern communities (Gamble and Janssen 1974).

Perennially frozen soil, often containing a great deal of ice, and the long periods of extremely low temperatures present such problems as difficult excavation, failure of foundations and utility lines due to frost heaving or thaw settlement of ice-rich soil, poor grounding for electrical equipment and systems, frozen water and sewer lines, slow or virtually no biological action for sewage treatment and freezing of sewage disposal retention ponds, tanks and associated facilities.

To overcome these problems, certain additional features are incorporated in the design of utilities and a thorough thermal analysis must usually be carried out at the design stage. High energy costs demand that a proper economic balance be maintained between energy supply and system losses. Systems must be kept as simple as possible, because spare parts and skilled technicians usually are not readily available. Built-in safety devices and duplication of essential equipment are mandatory if systems are to be kept in operation. Compact water and sewer systems, capable of being thawed, are necessary if they are to be operated economically. Where communities have central heating, the design of heating, electrical power and municipal services systems should be integrated to obtain further economies.

In the design of utility systems, consideration must be given not only to the physical and economic factors, but also to the health and social aspects (i.e., the well-being and satisfaction of the residents). With a greater awareness of environmental impact being required because of the "fragile" nature of northern ecosystems the designer is faced with an even greater challenge. Special attention must be given to disposal of all forms of wastes, to avoid polluting the land, air and bodies of water. A comprehensive design manual for utilities in cold regions has recently been published (Canada Environment 1979).

10.1 **Water Supply**

A safe and adequate supply of water for domestic use is as essential in northern regions as elsewhere. It is also important that sufficient quantities of water be available for fire-fighting. Large quantities of raw or treated water may be needed for industrial processing operations. Water is often difficult to obtain because of the thick ice cover on lakes and rivers and the presence of permafrost, and is usually of poor quality. The need to find a suitable supply at an economic cost is of primary concern.

Careful investigations must be carried out to locate and evaluate potential suitable sources of water. One cannot generalize about this and in the search for a supply each possible source must be considered separately and either proven or rejected, based on information gathered for that particular source. In some cases it may be possible to meet requirements from two different sources. For example, domestic water may be taken from a lake and treated but raw water of inferior but suitable quality for industrial use may be taken from a river.

Various aspects of water supplies and systems for northern communities in Canada and Alaska are discussed by several authors (Grainge 1959, Thomas 1957, Boyd and Boyd 1965, 1967, Owen 1967, Alter 1969a, Heinke 1973, 1974, Hartman and Carlson 1970).

10.1.1 **Surface Water Sources**

Melted snow and ice are the only practical sources of drinking water at some locations. Ice or snow may be stored on the ground during the winter or in insulated shelters during the summer, and melted as required. Collection and storage of large volumes of ice and snow are required (2 ft.^{3} (57 dm^3) of snow $\approx$ 1 gallon (4.5 litres) of water), and protection during storage is essential to prevent contamination. Thus, use of ice and snow under these circumstances will be minimal.

Lakes and rivers provide most of the water used in northern Canada. Numerous lakes dot the landscape, giving the impression that there is an unlimited supply of water. In reality many of them are shallow, become algae-ridden in summer and freeze deeply or to the bottom in winter. As the ice thickness increases in winter the dissolved solids (salt) content increases in the water below and organic taste and odor problems develop. Michel (1971) discusses the winter regime of rivers and lakes.

A 5 to 8 ft. (1.5 to 2.4 m) thick ice cover is not uncommon on small lakes and ponds. Lakes must be at least 10 ft. (3 m) deep, therefore, if they are to provide a reliable year-round source of water. Small or shallow lakes do not usually have an inflow of water during the winter because they are underlain by permafrost or impervious soil or rock or are not connected to a natural drainage system and therefore are recharged each spring from only a small local drainage basin. Supply is limited to that present at the end of the summer season. Typical examples are the small lakes from which the communities of Inuvik and Aklavik get their water. In both cases, a supplementary winter supply is obtained from adjacent rivers and lakes by pumping to the lake, which is used as a storage basin.

Relatively large and deep lakes are normally excellent sources of year-round water supply, but may be affected by the inflow from turbid rivers. In some cases, when the lake is deep enough to allow stratification, it may be possible to obtain water below the thermocline where the temperature is several degrees above freezing. Water temperatures in the water supply lake at Alert on Ellesmere Island are 36°F (2°C) at a depth of approximately 30 ft. (9 m).

Many small streams in the North freeze to the bottom or to a depth that greatly decreases the flow. Use of such streams causes problems, not only because they may freeze to the bottom but also because "frazil" and "anchor" ice may form in them. Frazil ice, which resembles slush, forms in turbulent water when the water cools below the freezing point. Anchor ice forms on the bed of a stream when super-cooled water is prevented from forming an ice cover due to turbulence. In such cases, infiltration galleries or screened inlets normally become plugged by ice. Streams draining muskeg areas will probably be highly organic, affecting taste and colour.

Small streams are not usually a satisfactory source of year-round water supply. On the other hand large streams and rivers usually have sufficient flow and depth that they do not freeze to the bottom and thus will provide an adequate supply of water throughout the year. Many streams and rivers in the North become highly turbid during the spring and may be unsuitable as a water source for a considerable period of time. If a satisfactory continuous water supply is desired, special treatment facilities (such as for sedimentation, flocculation and filtration) must be provided. An alternative is to store water in adjacent lakes or dyked ponds, which are filled during the previous fall or winter and have sufficient capacity to last over the break-up period.

Special attention must be given to the design of water intakes on lakes and rivers to protect them against ice damage and high water levels during the spring, bank erosion and freezing. The distribution of permafrost under and adjacent to the water body, particularly at the shoreline, is also an important factor with regard to the location of pipelines and pumping stations. Permafrost may lie at relatively shallow depth under gently sloping lake and river shorelines where the water freezes to the bottom each winter. As a result of thawing caused by construction activity and/or subsequent movement of warm water through a buried line, bank stability and foundation problems may arise that affect the intake structure and a buried or supported pipeline (Fig. 10.1).

Sea water is a potential source along the Arctic mainland coast and in the Arctic Islands in the continuous permafrost zone but must be desalinized for a domestic water supply. The desalination process is expensive and requires sophisticated equipment and operation. Due to high power costs and lack of skilled operators, this source will probably be used only in isolated special cases. Sea ice that has formed under quiescent conditions is frequently sufficiently low

FIG. 10.1 Water intake on a small northern lake failed due to settlement of the timber crib foundation and is being replaced by a floating structure (Associated Engineering Services Ltd. photograph).

in salt content to provide ice melt water. Towns such as Tuktoyaktuk and Coppermine are able to obtain fresh water in winter from below the sea ice. This fresh water comes from the large rivers entering the sea at these locations and, being lighter than salt water, stratifies under the ice cover and travels long distances without mixing.

Pure, clear ice melted in situ has provided good water from glaciers or ice caps (Schmitt and Rodriquez 1960, Alter 1969a). A pilot hole is drilled with a steam jet to a substantial depth in the ice. Water is collected in a cavern (created by melting ice at the bottom of the hole using steam) and pumped to the surface. This source is limited to glacier and ice cap regions, and the method is expensive and is not in common use. As yet no settlements in northern Canada utilize this water source.

10.1.2 Groundwater Sources

Groundwater has been used successfully at several locations in northern Canada but, in general, sources for a dependable and suitable year-round supply are difficult to find in permafrost areas. Groundwater is sometimes available in limited quantity above permafrost (suprapermafrost water), occasionally in permafrost (intrapermafrost water) and in larger quantity below permafrost (subpermafrost water) (Brandon 1965, 1966, Williams and van Everdingen 1973, van Everdingen 1974, Tolstikhin and Tolstikhin 1974). Typical examples of groundwater sources are indicated in Fig. 2.7. Wells are used in most cases to tap these sources and pumping is required unless artesian conditions exist.

Suprapermafrost water is obtained from an aquifer that may extend into or through the permafrost but the available water lies in the thawed zone above the frozen ground. The recharge period is generally limited to the summer season when surface water is present. Winter recharge may occur when a sufficiently thick and extensive thawed layer exists between the permafrost and seasonally frozen layer. Suprapermafrost water sources are usually not reliable in quantity, quality, or as a year-round supply and are readily subject to surface contamination. Because of the usually shallow depth to water, wells can be hand dug, bored or constructed by driving well points.

The very nature of intrapermafrost water makes its use uncommon. Since it is a water source trapped in layers or in thawed bulbs in the permafrost, it is unlikely to have a dependable recharge source. In some geological formations water may move through a thawed layer of granular material under a hydraulic gradient to eventually escape and provide a surface source.

Subpermafrost water sources provide the best water supply. Water may be found just below or at a substantial depth beneath the bottom of permafrost. Wells developed in shallow permafrost areas may differ little from normal water wells. Heating tapes can be used to prevent freeze-up in the permafrost.

Springs are used to advantage in a few isolated cases but are generally confined to relatively small water supplies. They are not always reliable and sometimes the flow is difficult to collect for pumping. In some cases, spring water is warm and will prevent or reduce freezing of the small streams which they feed (Brandon 1965, van Everdingen 1974).

Information obtained from observations of springs and from chemical analysis of river water in the Mackenzie River Valley indicates that seepage of groundwater to lakes and rivers occurs throughout the region, except in areas of continuous permafrost. South of the Arctic Circle in this area, groundwater moves toward the rivers. Wells drilled through permafrost into the water bearing stratum will yield a supply of water. The temperature of subpermafrost water may be relatively high and is an important consideration in the provision and distribution of water to northern communities. Faro, Y.T. has a well water temperature of 37° to 41°F (2.8° to 4.4°C).

Springs have been reported in a few places within the continuous permafrost zone but field evidence indicates that continuous flow does not always occur or is very limited. The development of groundwater supplies in the continuous permafrost zone is usually impractical, if not impossible. Wells drilled through deep permafrost may bottom in bedrock and groundwater is not usually available in any quantity. In cases where wells have been developed successfully, high mineralization has been encountered.

Drilling and operation of wells through deep permafrost presents some unique problems, including the freezing of water in, the thawing of permafrost around and the rupture or collapse of the well casing. Linell (1973b) describes an interesting situation experienced near Fairbanks, Alaska, where a well ran "wild" due to artesian flow and was only brought under control with great difficulty. In most cases, a plentiful supply of water of low mineral content has been obtained successfully from wells located in the alluvium adjacent to rivers where much of the water is from storage in the aquifer, or by artificially induced infiltration from adjacent streams.

10.1.3 Water Storage

It is often necessary to provide water storage facilities to ensure an adequate off-stream water supply during periods of high turbidity or low flow in streams, for fire fighting purposes in addition to domestic needs, and when treatment processes require relatively long retention periods. Both reservoirs and tanks are used. Reservoirs have been developed by constructing dams across streams, building dykes around an existing lake to increase its storage capacity and by excavating ponds and constructing dykes adjacent to streams to catch and store the spring runoff (Foster et al. 1979). The selection of suitable sites and the design of these facilities are most important. Factors to be considered in the construction of dams and dykes have been discussed in Chapter 9.

The reservoir must be deep enough that an adequate quantity of water is available under the winter ice cover. Thawing of frozen ground under the reservoir and the containing dykes and natural banks will occur. Sites underlain by ice-rich and pervious materials must be avoided so that loss of water by seepage and, more important, unacceptable settlements or failure of the impermeable dykes or dams and associated structures (including intakes and spillways), will not occur. A water supply dam has been successfully constructed on permafrost at the Anvil Mine, located about 12 miles (19 km) from the town of Faro, Y.T.

Wood, steel or concrete tanks are widely used for storage of water in northern Canada. Many are semi-buried to reduce heat loss and prevent freezing or are housed inside a heated building (Fig. 10.2). Above-ground tanks must be insulated. The storage facilities must be designed and built to operate under extremely low temperatures and special consideration must be given to foundation conditions, heat retention, icing in the structure, use of insulation and structural design.

FIG. 10.2   A large water storage tank is completely enclosed in a heated, framed wooden structure. A 3 ft. (1 m) space was left between the tank and the insulated enclosure (Associated Engineering Services Ltd. photograph).

Structures underlain by ice-rich frozen soils must be placed on piles or on vented and insulated granular pads (Fig. 10.3) to prevent or reduce heat loss from the structure and subsequent thawing of the foundation materials (see Chapter 7). Preferably the stored water should be kept warm enough to prevent ice buildup inside the tank. Interior ladders and structural members should be avoided; ice adhering to members can cause failure of the tank when the water level is lowered or raised. Particular care must be taken in the design of venting systems for exposed tanks to prevent them from being blocked by frozen moisture. Negative pressure may cause collapse of the tank when the water level is drawn down.

10.2 Waste Disposal

Waste disposal methods in many northern Canada communities are best described as ''primitive'' and there is a real need to upgrade treatment and disposal facilities (Heinke 1974). Organized waste disposal procedures have been initiated in all except the smallest settlements. Of necessity, the procedures used are simple but form the basis for more complex systems. Snodgrass (1971) and Cameron and

FIG. 10.3 Water storage tank placed on a duct-ventilated gravel pad foundation overlying ice-rich soil in continuous permafrost zone (Associated Engineering Services Ltd. photograph).

Smith (1977) compiled bibliographies on waste disposal and treatment in permafrost areas and Alter (1969b) discusses sewerage and sewage disposal in cold regions. Some examples of solid and liquid waste disposal problems in the northern environment are given in Slupsky (1976). Heinke (1974) reports on waste disposal methods in communities in the Northwest Territories.

10.2.1 Liquid Wastes

Various methods are used to dispose of human wastes. Many homes invariably have pail-type chemical toilets, which are lined with disposable plastic bags, commonly called "wet-bags." Partially filled bags are collected 3 to 6 times per week and deposited at the local "dump" or on the sea or river ice. Household wash water is usually drained onto the ground next to the house; quantities are not large and in winter the resulting ice is soon covered with snow. In summer, however, the combination of broken plastic bags and septic wash water is unsightly and causes serious contamination and health problems. Ponding of water may cause foundation problems due to thawing and frost heave.

The use of a retention tank installed in an insulated and heated space in or below the house to collect all toilet and household waste water is a great improvement. The contents of the tank, which usually has a capacity of from 300 to 1,000 gallons (1,350 to 4,500 litres) are collected once or twice a week by tank truck and disposed of at the dump. Interior plumbing is semi-orthodox with toilets generally being minimum-water-use types.

An innovation is the adoption of a truck-mounted vacuum tank which cuts "pumping" time to a minimum. This method of disposal is much more acceptable to health authorities, because it eliminates open storage in the house and the handling of bags of sewage, which frequently break. Operating costs are in the order of three cents per gallon (4.5 litres) of liquid disposed, with measurements based on water delivery quantities.

Flush toilets and piped collection systems of various kinds are being installed in large communities. Interior plumbing is generally orthodox and 30 to 70 gallons (130 to 320 litres) of water per capita per day are required for flushing. Liquid wastes are collected in piped systems and discharged into convenient small lakes (Ft. McPherson, Yellowknife), excavated or bermed lagoons (Inuvik, Hay River, Edzo, Faro) or directly into rivers (Ft. Simpson, Whitehorse) or the sea (Frobisher Bay, Alert). In all cases increased public pressure is demanding a higher standard of treatment and disposal.

Industrial camps are subject to more stringent regulations than established communities (Canada Environment 1974a, b). Primary treatment of wastes is required for small camps and secondary treatment for larger and permanent camps. This means that mechanical plants using either biological processes or physical-chemical methods of treatment are required. If lagoons are used they must have a one year retention capacity.

Disposal of the effluent from primary plants or single cell lagoons into muskeg or swamp areas is being studied (Dawson and Grainge 1969). Such areas are biologically active and appear to have substantial assimilation capacity. Sludge buildup in lagoons because of slow biological action is a major problem. Reasonable treatment can be obtained if retention periods are in excess of six months. Upgrading of community services and the development of innovative systems is receiving considerable attention. New systems and methods that warrant study include vacuum collection, grinder pump low pressure collection, high temperature incineration and liquid salt bath incineration.

10.2.2 Solid Wastes

Solid wastes are usually disposed of on land. The presence of permafrost does not permit the extensive use of sanitary land fills because of the difficulty of excavating sufficient thawed material for cover, especially during the winter. Wastes are usually collected by truck and burned at an isolated, well-drained area some distance from the community. Poor or difficult access to the dump often leads to scattering of the refuse along the roads.

Depending on the location of the dump, site conditions and quantity of material, part of the wastes may become perennially frozen and remain preserved. Excavation of old covered military dumps in Alaska has confirmed this. Greater attention is being given to cleaning up and confining the dumps. As yet no effort is being made to separate metal wastes for future recycling. Lack of biodegradation of organic materials and retention of liquids within packaged materials means that a high volume of waste has to be handled. This is a major problem in the larger communities. Special plants for incineration of waste materials are usually too costly for most communities. Point Barrow, Alaska is an exception; incineration equipment using local natural gas for fuel has been installed. Alter (1969c) discusses the management of solid wastes in cold regions.

10.2.3 Sewage Treatment and Disposal

Individual septic tanks with tile fields cannot be used in permafrost areas because the perennially frozen ground is impermeable and the active layer is thawed for only a relatively short period of the year. They may be feasible in some parts of the discontinuous zone if installed in permafrost-free areas and below the deep seasonal frost layer. Wet-bags and pump-out tank liquids are disposed of in the same manner and usually in the same place as solid wastes. Ideally, the community dump is located in an isolated but accessible area, which is well drained. Where possible, pits are excavated but small low areas generally serve as disposal sites. Biological degradation is slow and dilution by snow melt is common.

Unfortunately, wastes are often dumped onto the river ice during the winter with the hope that they will disappear at breakup. Debris may be scattered by wind or animals, deposited along the banks near communities downstream, or sink to the bottom creating a health hazard. Similarly, debris from solid wastes dumped on lake or sea ice is very often washed back onto the shore and becomes an eyesore and pollutant. Floating garbage also becomes entangled in fishing nets.

Sewage lagoons are used at several locations in northern Canada. Natural lagoons, such as at Inuvik, Fort McPherson and Yellowknife, are small lakes or sloughs that have been modified by dyking and erection of control structures to receive and retain raw sewage. They are generally shallow and weed grown. The single cell lagoon at Inuvik, N.W.T. has provided reasonable treatment at minimal cost for 15 years in spite of some serious design and construction deficiencies (Miyamoto and Heinke 1979). The raw sewage enters at one end and after retention the effluent is discharged out the other end through a weir, which controls the level in the lagoon, into a small creek which empties into the East Channel. The capacity of the lagoon is sufficient to provide a minimum of 3 months storage, even with maximum ice cover. Natural settling and dilution with groundwater reduces suspended solids in the order of 80%. B.O.D. reduction varies from 30% in winter to 90% in summer. The major drawback is the slow biodegradation of the sludge. Extensive exposed sludge banks create a considerable odor problem, which could be remedied if the lagoon was relocated in a more remote area.

Lagoons formed by berms surrounding low areas or excavated areas are in service at Faro, Y.T. and Edzo, N.W.T., where ground conditions are relatively stable and permit orthodox earthwork construction. Difficulties with thick ice covers are minimized by maintaining water depths greater than 6 ft. (2 m). Inlets and outlets require special attention, including the use of insulation and termination of pipes below the ice inside the lagoon. The Imperial Oil lagoon in Tuktoyaktuk, located in an area of large ground ice deposits, was blasted out of an existing small low area and side berms were constructed of the excavated earth. The piped inlet is mounted on a high trestle to prevent ice buildup on the lagoon surface from blocking the end of it. The capacity of the lagoon provides for approximately 8 months storage. No overflow is provided on the premise that it will be pumped out if it fills to capacity.

At least 6 collection tanks are in use at Norman Wells. Each services a section of the settlement and they have been installed by various industrial or government groups. These provide primary treatment and discharge to the Mackenzie River. This is not considered adequate and a community lagoon located inland from the townsite is being planned.

Only a few mechanical treatment plants, such as at Churchill and Thompson, Manitoba and Carmacks, Y.T., are in service in the Canadian North. There are numerous installations in Alaska serving industrial needs, particularly pipeline, mining and drilling camps. The requirement to house and heat biological plants gives rise to problems of high humidity within buildings. A critical evaluation of extended aeration systems in arctic and subarctic regions was made by Given and Smith (1977).

From the limited experience available it appears that chemical-mechanical "package" plants are more adaptable to temporary or mobile industrial establishments. All solids are chemically precipitated in a tank and suspended solids are removed by filtration. B.O.D. reduction is accomplished by absorption in carbon columns. This is the same process used in treating some domestic water supplies. The sludge and solids removed by the process are dewatered by centrifuging or by filtration, and then discharged into pits or disposed of by incineration. The major advantages of the physical-chemical system are that it requires only a few hours to start up the system, compared to several days or even weeks to get a biological process operating, it is easily controlled by a skilled operator and not easily upset by detergents, bleaches or oils inadvertently dumped into the sewer. The major disadvantage is that the chemicals for precipitation and recharging the carbon columns are costly. Schematic diagrams of physical-chemical and secondary biological treatment plants are shown in Figs. 10.4 and 10.5.

The installation of individual pumpout collection tanks in homes and other buildings, such as nursing stations and schools, has led to the use of several different types of toilets and fixtures. The high cost of trucked water for flushing

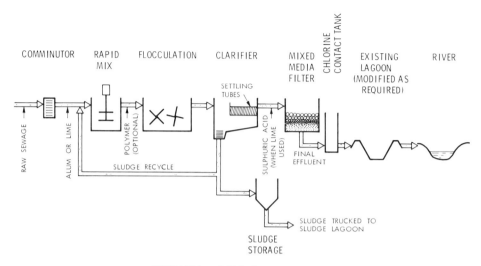

FIG. 10.4   Schematic diagram of a physical-chemical sewage treatment system.

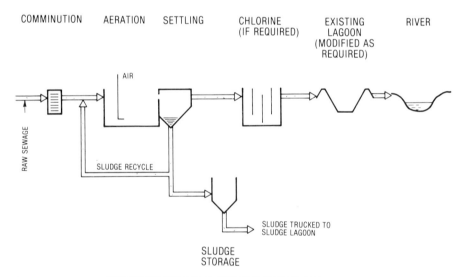

SECONDARY BIOLOGICAL (WITHOUT PRIMARY TREATMENT)

FIG. 10.5   Schematic diagram of a secondary biological (without primary treatment) sewage treatment system.

means that the need to conserve water is very real. Marine type toilets with direct trapped inlets into the retention tanks are in use at various locations. Approximately 1 pint (0.6 litres) of water is required to flush and provide a trap. Monomatic or aircraft-type units are also used. In these units a blue or green bacteriacide dye that prevents or retards bacterial action is introduced into the

holding tanks. Compartment construction of the receiving tank permits the coloured liquid to be pumped back into the bowl for flushing. If the holding capacity of the tank is fairly large and retention periods are long, odor becomes a problem.

Considerable experimentation has been given to boiling off and burning the
domestic wastes inside a toilet unit. Electrical elements and fuel oil fired units
have been tried. Experience has not been satisfactory and odors are the major
problem. The Alaska Village Demonstration Project undertook to treat and recy-
cle "grey" water from the showers and laundry wastes for reuse as laundry water
and for flushing toilets. An elaborate treatment system was evolved and results
show that it can be done, but at high cost. The same costs could provide additional freshwater by storage methods without the operational problems. Recycling of waste water is not recommended for community use. It could be done in
certain cases, but only if carefully controlled and if interested, skilled help is
available on a full-time basis.

10.3 Piping Systems

Municipal piping systems in the North are characterized by special design features
that make them functional under severe climatic and terrain conditions. They
must be designed to prevent water freezing in pipes exposed to low air or ground
temperatures and to ensure the structural integrity of piping where it may be affected by frost action and permafrost degradation in foundation soils. Aside
from adapting them to low temperatures and to difficult foundation conditions,
they do not differ greatly from conventional systems in most other respects.

Insulation of piping and addition of heat are the two basic methods used to
prevent freezing. Structural stability of the piping system is essentially a foundation problem, similar to that of other structures and facilities in permafrost areas.
Heat losses from the piping system must be given special attention, however, to
prevent detrimental thawing of frozen soils and unacceptable movements of the
piping. The use of good bedding and backfill material, insulation, pile foundations, stronger pipe materials or placing the systems above-ground are the usual
methods of dealing with foundation problems. The basic types of water and
sewer systems suitable for northern applications and the primary design considerations, with emphasis on the thermal aspects and including practical examples of thermal calculations, are presented in the following sections.

10.3.1 System Arrangements

Buried or above-ground piping systems are the two basic design alternatives
available to the engineer. Which of these is selected will depend primarily on site
conditions, installation costs and operating requirements. Alter (1969a, b),
Grainge (1969), Cameron (1977) and Dawson and Cronin (1977) discuss the
various factors to be considered in the design and construction of buried and

above-ground utility systems and Heinke (1974) and James (1976) give further examples of systems used in northern Canada.

The use of conventional, bare-pipe buried systems is influenced mainly by minimum ground temperatures, the distribution of permafrost and thaw-stable soils, depth of frost penetration and ease of excavation. In most cases, conventional systems can be used only in areas free of permafrost, where maximum ground temperatures are 30°F (-1°C) or higher and the soils are non-frost-susceptible and relatively easy to excavate. In the southern fringe of the discontinuous zone it may occasionally be possible to trench through relatively thin islands of permafrost and place the lines below the permafrost or backfill the trench with good granular bedding material to pipe grade (Johnston et al. 1963, Klassen 1965). Conventional systems usually require special design features such as deep burial, circulation of heated water and "freeze-proof" appurtenances.

In some cases it may be practicable to install insulated lines in the active layer just above the permafrost table and thus avoid the high cost of deep excavations (Figs. 10.6, 10.7, 10.8 and 10.9). Consideration has to be given to the maximum depth of frost penetration, ground temperatures, frost heave and thaw settlement characteristics of the soils and the ability of the pipe, placed in a shallow trench,

FIG. 10.6 Installation of shallow buried insulated water and sewer mains in discontinuous permafrost zone (Associated Engineering Services Ltd. photograph).

FIG. 10.7   This water main trench excavated in permafrost was not backfilled for more than one month and filled with flowing soil as the frozen ground thawed (Associated Engineering Services Ltd. photograph).

to carry traffic loads where lines are laid under roadways. The ground under roadways or similar snow-cleared areas will freeze more quickly and to a greater depth and be much colder than in adjacent undisturbed areas. Examples of insulated, heat traced water supply lines with and without continuous circulation of water, placed at shallow depth or on the ground surface are given by Cheriton (1966), O'Brien and Whyman (1976) and Heavy Construction News (1977).

Where burial cannot be considered because of foundation stability problems or for other reasons, and the systems will not interfere unduly with traffic, insulated pipes may be installed in berms constructed on the ground surface (Fig. 10.9). This is usually the least expensive method and the services are readily accessible for maintenance and repair. Care must be taken to ensure that surface drainage is not obstructed and the berms must be well designed and constructed so that the pipes will not be exposed due to erosion or experience unacceptable movements caused by frost action or thaw settlement.

In most northern areas, and particularly where permafrost is widespread and thick and the active layer is shallow, services are usually placed in utilidors. Utilidors are containers enclosing any number of pipes. They may carry steam or

FIG. 10.8   Broken asbestos-cement water main taken from a trench backfilled during
the winter with frozen material. The transverse break is typical for this type of pipe
(Associated Engineering Services Ltd. photograph).

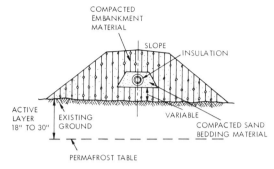

(a) SEWER MAIN INSTALLED IN
     BERM ON GROUND SURFACE
     (EDZO, N.W.T.)

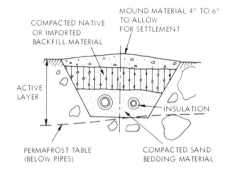

(b) WATER AND SEWER MAINS INSTALLED
     IN COMMON SHALLOW TRENCH
     (EDZO, N.W.T.)

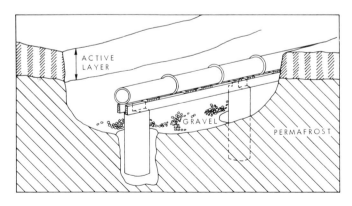

(c) PILE SUPPORT FOR SEWER IN THAW-UNSTABLE PERMAFROST
                                              (After U.S. Navy, 1955)

FIG. 10.9   Sketches of lines installed above and below the ground surface.

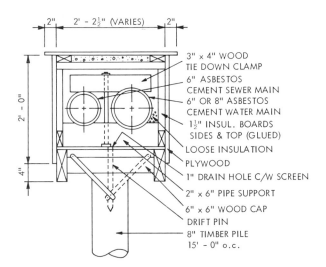

2"   2' – 2½" (VARIES)   2"

3" × 4" WOOD
TIE DOWN CLAMP
6" ASBESTOS
CEMENT SEWER MAIN
6" OR 8" ASBESTOS
CEMENT WATER MAIN
1½" INSUL. BOARDS
SIDES & TOP (GLUED)
LOOSE INSULATION
PLYWOOD
1" DRAIN HOLE C/W SCREEN
2" × 6" PIPE SUPPORT
6" × 6" WOOD CAP
DRIFT PIN
8" TIMBER PILE
15' – 0" o.c.

2' – 0"

4"

(a) PLYWOOD BOX UTILIDOR
(INUVIK, N.W.T.)

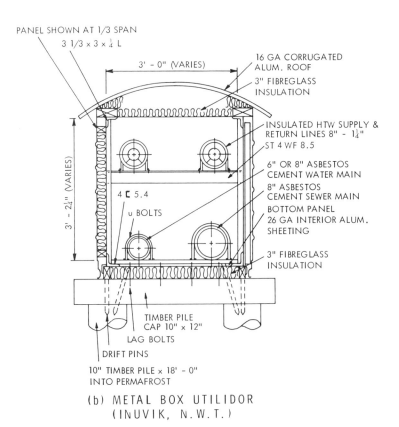

PANEL SHOWN AT 1/3 SPAN
3 1/3 × 3 × ¼ L

3' – 0" (VARIES)

16 GA CORRUGATED
ALUM. ROOF
3" FIBREGLASS
INSULATION

INSULATED HTW SUPPLY &
RETURN LINES 8" – 1¼"
ST 4 WF 8.5

6" OR 8" ASBESTOS
CEMENT WATER MAIN
8" ASBESTOS
CEMENT SEWER MAIN
BOTTOM PANEL
26 GA INTERIOR ALUM.
SHEETING

3" FIBREGLASS
INSULATION

3' – 2¼" (VARIES)

4 C 5.4

u BOLTS

TIMBER PILE
CAP 10" × 12"
LAG BOLTS
DRIFT PINS

10" TIMBER PILE × 18' – 0"
INTO PERMAFROST

(b) METAL BOX UTILIDOR
(INUVIK, N.W.T.)

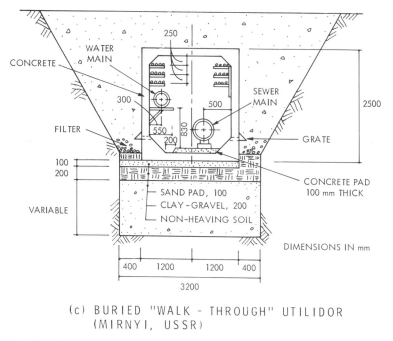

(c) BURIED "WALK - THROUGH" UTILIDOR
(MIRNYI, USSR)

FIG. 10.10 Sketches of typical above-ground and buried utilidors.

hot water heating pipes, fuel distribution lines and electrical cables in addition to sewer and water mains. They may be constructed of wood, metal or precast concrete sections and may range in size from a small corrugated metal pipe or wood box carrying a single service line to a walk-through tunnel or hall carrying a large number of pipes and cables. All or none of the pipes may be insulated; in some cases the utilidor shell is insulated, in others the utilidor is filled with insulation. Utilidors may be installed either above or below ground, the choice depending on local site conditions, economic limitations and operating requirements. Some typical examples of utilidors are shown in Figs. 10.10, 10.11 and 10.12. Others are given by Alter (1969a, b), U.S.S.R. (1970), Hoffman (1971), Tobiasson (1971), Heinke (1974), Gamble and Lukomskyj (1975), and O'Brien and Whyman (1976).

Above-ground utilidors are more elaborate and usually more expensive than conventional buried pipe systems and for this reason are normally used in areas where excavation would be very costly or where detrimental permafrost degradation will occur. To minimize permafrost disturbance, utilidors installed on piles or gravel pads are most suitable. These structures, however, are exposed to extreme air temperatures and may obstruct traffic, require raised building foundations to provide gravity sewer flow, be subject to mechanical damage and vandalism and are unsightly (Figs. 10.13, 10.14 and 10.15). It is common practice to keep the utilidor size to a minimum in order to reduce heat losses and costs.

FIG. 10.11   Metal box utilidor at Inuvik, N.W.T. carrying water, sewer and central heating piping. Enclosure with door houses valves and fittings and protruding box protects a hydrant. For details of utilidor see Fig. 10.10b (Associated Engineering Services Ltd. photograph).

The disadvantages of above-ground utilidors can be overcome by burying them in shallow trenches when subsurface conditions permit; usually in the active layer or in thaw-stable perennially frozen materials (Fig. 10.16). Although they are in a less severe temperature environment, they must be specially designed to prevent undue thermal disturbance of the surrounding frozen ground if high maintenance and operating costs are to be avoided. They must be carefully constructed to prevent infiltration of ground or surface water, which may cause icing problems or wetting of insulation. Selection of suitable materials for the enclosure and insulation is therefore important. Provision should be made to ensure proper drainage of groundwater and water from leaking joints or broken lines, circulation of warm air for drying (if necessary) and access for maintenance work. They can be

FIG. 10.12   View of metal box utilidor under construction showing concrete anchor block and expansion joints on hot water piping. Compare with Figs. 10.10b and 10.11 (Associated Engineering Services Ltd. photograph).

FIG. 10.13   A typical utilidor overpass (in Inuvik, N.W.T.), which is required at all street crossings to accommodate traffic. Note that precast concrete piles support the bridge (Associated Engineering Services Ltd. photograph).

FIG. 10.14 View of main utilidor and "utilidettes" that provide services to housing, Inuvik, N.W.T. (Montreal Engineering Company Ltd. photograph).

FIG. 10.15 View of wood box utilidor carrying water and steam lines on gravel berm. Construction activity, poor drainage and steam leaks caused permafrost degradation and differential movements along utilidor. Also note leaning power poles caused by frost heave and thaw settlement.

FIG. 10.16   Electrically heat-traced cast iron pipe installed in a buried box filled with loose insulation (Associated Engineering Services Ltd. photograph).

very useful in high density, built-up areas but care must be taken to ensure that foundations of buildings to which they are providing services, or other adjacent structures such as roads, bridges and buildings, are not adversely affected. In other words, the foundation designs must be thermally compatible.

An alternative applicable to a limited number of pipes is to install underground utilidors completely filled with rigid hydrophobic insulation. There are no air spaces in these conduits and the possibility of groundwater infiltration is reduced or eliminated. It is advantageous to install these conduits near the ground surface in berms or shallow trenches to facilitate access to the pipes. In difficult areas these utilidors may require pile foundations to eliminate movements caused by thaw settlement or frost heave.

10.3.1.1 *Water Distribution Systems*

To prevent freezing, five basic systems for distributing water can be considered. Two are conventional systems with deep burial or bleeding, two rely on continuous circulation of water and the last employs intermittent flow to prevent freezing of the water. All have limitations and advantages depending on site, climate and geotechnical conditions.

As already noted, conventional buried, uninsulated water systems, placed below the seasonal frost line to prevent freezing, are only practical in areas free of permafrost. They frequently must be buried at great depth. At some locations the depth of seasonal frost penetration may exceed the economical depth of trenching, so that deep burial alone does not provide a solution. Where buried lines may freeze, heat must be added to the water. This will normally prevent freezing of major lines, but problems may develop in outlying small-diameter mains because heated water may never reach them due to low usage of water. In remote portions of a system the mains should be buried deeply if freezing is to be avoided.

Where water mains cannot be economically placed below the seasonal frost line, a conventional system may be installed within the active layer provided continuous flow of water can be maintained. Bleeding water into the sewer line from each service connection and at the end of each main will provide sufficient flow to keep the system in operation. Systems of this type may require 5 to 10 times the normal domestic demand for water, however, and where pumping and extensive treatment are required the cost may be prohibitive. Large quantities of water also cause sewage treatment problems due to dilution and, in addition, piping and associated equipment have to be increased in size to carry the increased flows.

Water mains and all services can also be protected from freezing by continuous circulation of water through a dual-main system. This type of system consists of two parallel water mains each operating at a different pressure. Heated water circulates through service lines from a high pressure supply main, passes through a pressure reducing valve in the building, and then returns to the pumphouse through a low pressure main. The water may be reheated at the pumphouse before being recirculated in the system. The dual-main circulation system can be used in utilidors as well as for buried, bare or insulated pipes. This system does not waste any water, but it does require more piping and more extensive pressure control and pumping facilities than other systems.

FIG. 10.17   Unheated utilidor on piles carrying water and sewer mains in an insulated
corrugated metal pipe enclosure. Water temperature is maintained by heating at the
pumphouse and continuous circulation (single main circulation system) (Associated
Engineering Services Ltd. photograph).

Water can also be continuously circulated through a single main system that is
designed to form a loop or a series of loops starting and terminating at the pumphouse, where heat is added (Fig. 10.17). Freezing of service lines is prevented by
using electrical heat tracing cables (Fig. 10.18), by maintaining circulation using a
pump located in each building or by a device known as "pitorifice" which incorporates the principles of both the Pitot tube and the orifice (Lawrence 1969). The
pitorifice is inserted in the pipe at the corporation stop and flow is maintained in
the service lines by utilizing the velocity head in the water main. In the latter case,
two lines, which generally should not exceed 50 feet in length from the main to
the building, are required; heat-traced services require only one service line and

are practically not limited in length. Where conventional systems are not practicable, the usual solution is to install a buried single-main circulating system at
shallow depth, unless severe ground conditions require a utilidor. The same type
of circulation system is usually used in utilidors unless the lines are heat traced or
the conduit is heated by other means, and continuous circulation is not required.

FIG. 10.18 Domestic insulated service pipes connection to mains in a common trench.
The water service has a return line for recirculation and a heating cable for emergency
thawing (Associated Engineering Services Ltd. photograph).

Sometimes a system similar to a single-main circulating system but utilizing a small-diameter return line is used to maintain circulation in a dead-end water main. This is frequently the most economical method of serving outlying areas of a settlement, but it is the one most vulnerable to freeze-up if circulation is not maintained. The small-diameter return line, containing a relatively small volume of water compared to the larger diameter main line, will usually freeze several times faster than the main line. To overcome return line freezing, it is sometimes installed inside the main line. Alternatively, the return line is eliminated and the main line is heat traced electrically. Heat tracing not only maintains a desired water temperature, but also provides a ready means of thawing in the event of a freeze-up.

Intermittent pumping may be used in systems that would freeze if water was left in the lines for long periods of time. Water is pumped only at predetermined times and, after each consumer fills his tank, the system is drained. This procedure is used during the winter only; during the summer the system may be operated in a conventional manner. Bare pipe, above-ground systems that operate only during the summer can also be used. The system is drained during the fall and water is delivered by truck during the winter. This type of system has application in northern communities where roads are poor and difficult to maintain during the summer. Intermittent pumping is usually only practical in small communities, although it can be designed to serve larger ones. Intermittent pumping can also be used on supply lines used to fill a storage tank from a well, river or lake. In cold weather the line may be preheated by an electrical cable or by circulating hot air before pumping water.

10.3.1.2 *Sewage Collection Systems*

Piped sewage collection systems in the North generally present fewer freezing problems than water systems because the sewage is warmer than the water in the water mains. Sewers usually freeze in branch lines having very low flows or in lines that have sagged so that the sewage collects or blocks the line at the low points. Most sewer lines built in the North, whether buried or above-ground in utilidors, are gravity flow systems and can be called "modified conventional" since they employ only a few special design features such as insulation. Considerations with respect to freezing and stability of the piping and buried vs above-ground systems are essentially the same for sewer lines as for water lines.

Buried sewer lines may be insulated or they may be installed in the same trench as the water main. Common-trench installation allows considerable cost savings in excavation but health regulations usually require that the sewer be constructed using pressure-type pipe. On buried systems, frost covers are usually installed in the manholes to prevent freezing due to natural circulation of cold air. Tee or Y-type cleanouts are normally used on lines in above-ground utilidors.

Intermittent flow systems can be used where the flow is always too low to keep the sewer main open. In such cases the system is designed to carry periodic high flows. The system operates in a manner similar to a septic tank. The sewage is collected in a tank and discharged into the main only when a sufficient quantity has accumulated such that a high flow rate can be maintained in the line for a long enough time period to remove any ice which might have formed on the inside of the main. The flow into the sewer pipe can be controlled by a siphon outlet or by a float-controlled pump. As in the case of intermittent flow water mains, the pipe may be preheated, but a well-designed sewage line normally should not require preheating.

Vacuum and pressure sewage systems can be considered where the water supply is limited and installation of gravity lines presents problems (Averill and Heinke 1974, Rogness and Ryan 1977, Ryan and Rogness 1977). The vacuum system has not as yet found wide application in the North, but in communities where water is not available in sufficient quantity for gravity waste disposal, this type of system may be an economic alternative. Pressure systems involve the installation of grinding and pumping equipment in each building. Sewage is discharged under pressure from each building into the main collector sewer. This type of system may be installed in areas where gravity mains are not practical and where, rather than constructing a gravity collection sewer (flowing opposite to the desired direction) with a lift station and pressure main, only the pressure main is constructed.

Both the vacuum and pressure systems present possible solutions to problems posed by community layout restrictions, deep cuts in permafrost, or shortages of water. These systems do not have to be considered as solutions to sewage system problems in entire communities. Vacuum and pressure sewage systems are in fact most adaptable as parts of overall systems in specific areas where services cannot be provided by gravity flow.

10.3.2 Design Considerations

10.3.2.1 *Site and Foundation Conditions*

It is most important that site investigations be carried out so that suitable piping system layouts, designs and construction methods can be selected. In addition to collecting information on the topography, drainage, snow cover and other terrain factors, it is essential that climatic and geotechnical studies be conducted. Climatic conditions usually vary over a reasonably predictable range and, if necessary, can be estimated from nearby weather stations. Subsurface conditions, on the other hand, are frequently highly variable and present much greater potential for difficulties. In most cases, therefore, assumptions and extrapolations are inadvisable. Attention given to collection of site information has to be consistent with the attention paid to subsequent thermal calculations and to structural design. Foundation problems are equal in importance to heat loss considerations and detailed investigations, using methods described in Chapter 5, must be conducted to obtain information on subsurface conditions.

Prevention of movements caused by frost heave and thaw settlement of soils is the prime consideration in the design of foundations for northern piping systems; the load bearing capacity of the soil is usually of secondary interest. Buried systems present more complex problems in most northern areas. If it is proposed that uninsulated pipelines be installed in the active layer or permafrost, the zone of thermal influence, which will extend downward and laterally several times farther than the depth to the pipe, must be known. Preliminary thermal calculations are necessary to determine the extent of soil exploration required and ensure that thaw-unstable materials are not involved. Similarly, if underground piping and utilidors are to be supported on piles in a trench, the extent of the ultimate thaw bulb must be determined so that piling of sufficient length can be installed to ensure positive and permanent support.

A warm buried system, which allows a large thaw zone to develop in an attempt to provide protection against freezing, will make the system vulnerable to instability and settlement problems associated with permafrost degradation. Frequently, complete failure of the piping system will occur where excessive thawing and settlement take place. The damage can extend to adjacent structures as thawing progresses and is accelerated by leaks which eventually develop in the piping system. Flow of groundwater along the piping may cause erosion and further complications. Where adverse conditions can develop thawing cannot be permitted. Two design alternatives are possible. Either the pipes must be covered with a sufficient thickness of insulation such that the $32°F$ ($0°C$) isotherm will always be maintained within or just next to the insulation or the systems have to be installed above ground in a utilidor.

Pile foundations are widely used for above-ground utilidors and their design does not differ from building foundation design (Chapter 7). Piles subjected to lateral loads, such as at pipe anchor points or where changes in alignment or grade occur, must be given special attention.

10.3.2.2 *Thermal Considerations*

Thermal aspects are critical in the design and operation of all northern piping systems. The primary areas of concern in piping design are failures resulting from thermal and structural stresses and strains in the pipelines and appurtenances caused by freezing of water within the mains, thawing and settlement of ice-rich foundation soils and heaving of frost-susceptible soils. Heat loss calculations affecting the water in the pipes and foundation soils are usually based on steady-state analysis and are discussed in Section 10.3.3.

When the anticipated rates of heat loss are known, the required thickness of insulation, circulation pump capacity, heater size, fuel storage requirements and other associated components of a system can be selected. The capacities of all circulation pumps and heaters are designed for the maximum rate of heat loss, while total energy requirements in terms of fuel or electrical power are estimated on the basis of total heat losses calculated for the portion of the year when heating is required.

The most severe conditions have to be considered when estimating the minimum time to freeze-up, which is the safe period a system may be left inoperational before freezing commences. The design time to freeze-up should be sufficiently long to permit repairs or drainage of the system and depends primarily on the availability of maintenance personnel and equipment. In smaller communities, the design time to freeze-up might have to be several days, while in larger centres it may be less than 24 hours.

The latent heat in water provides a considerable factor of safety against freeze-up. It is a misconception, however, to assume that freezing will not occur until all the latent heat in the system is lost. In actual fact, as soon as the water temperature drops below $32°F$ ($0°C$), ice formation may start somewhere in the system, particularly on metal valves and fittings. Ice plugs that prevent water circulation can form long before the entire system freezes, so designs should not allow the temperature to drop below about $32.5°F$ ($0.3°C$).

Excessive heat gains also have to be considered in addition to heat losses. Within utilidors carrying hot water or steam lines, heat sometimes may be permitted to escape in order to prevent water and sewer lines from freezing during the coldest weather. This arrangement frequently causes undesirable overheating of the potable water and sewage during warm weather, as well as wasting energy. Experience has shown that the performance of a utilidor can be improved by insulating the domestic water lines.

Insulation and heating are the two primary and complementary methods of preventing freezing. To obtain an optimum thermal design, an acceptable balance has to be reached between the reduction of heat losses by insulation and the addition of heat to the system. Well-insulated systems are preferred since they require a minimum of heating and provide a longer freeze-up period and therefore are less vulnerable. A similar argument favours the use of buried systems compared to exposed utilidors; the soil cover will damp out the large transient ground surface temperature fluctuations and moderate the subsurface thermal regime.

For underground systems, simple theoretical calculations of the ground temperature near the pipe are possible using meteorological and geotechnical data (Nixon and McRoberts 1973). The influence and variability of the large number of factors involved, such as snow depth, soil type and moisture content and surface vegetation usually cannot be accurately estimated and contribute to the uncertainty of the calculated results. Actual ground temperature measurements provide a more reliable design base.

Utility systems in cold regions are normally designed to have a fairly high factor of safety against freezing. A high factor of safety is used under average conditions due to the extreme variability in thermal properties of insulating materials and because the worst conditions that will cause freezing, such as rupture of a pipe or failure of a pump or heating system, are assumed to occur simultaneously, even though this seldom happens.

The absorption of moisture by porous materials such as some types of artificial insulation, wood and soils is a most important factor, since it can drastically reduce their resistance to heat flow. Upon freezing a further significant decrease will occur. A comparison of the thermal conductivities of unfrozen and frozen soils at various moisture contents illustrates the changes that can be expected (see Section 3.5, Table 3.8 and Figs. 3.17 to 3.20). Thermal conductivity values for several types of wood and commercial insulations are also given in Table 3.8. Insulation values for many types of loose-fill insulation can be seriously affected if they become wet. Most types of rigid plastic foam insulation are relatively resistant to excessive moisture absorption. Some deteriorate significantly when exposed to sunlight, freeze-thaw cycles and hydrocarbons. These drastic changes in the insulating values due to moisture absorption and freezing dictate that all designs consider the worst possible conditions.

Values for the thermal conductivity of compacted, saturated and frozen backfill soils should be used in design since their conductivity increases with density, degree of saturation and freezing. The use of manufactured hydrophobic insulating materials for piping is preferred to avoid having to design for increased conductivity due to water saturation and freezing. In practice, the freezing of saturated insulation is the most frequent cause of system freeze-up problems.

When calculating heat losses from piping systems, adequate allowance must be made for poorly insulated or exposed sections of pipe, valves, fittings, couplings, service connections, hydrants and other appurtenances. On a typical water system, losses at such points, if poorly insulated, can be as high as 50% of the total loss from the system. To calculate these losses the area of the exposed portions should be estimated. This area can be converted to an equivalent length of bare, straight pipe and the losses computed. For example, an uninsulated 6 in. (150 mm) gate valve is estimated to have an exposed area equivalent to 3 ft. (1 m) of bare pipe. If this valve is left exposed it will lose as much heat as about 200 ft. (60 m) of 6 in. (150 mm) diameter pipe insulated with 2 in. (50 mm) of polyurethane rigid foam. This points to the danger of restricting heat loss considerations to straight pipe sections only and emphasizes the importance of adequate design of insulation for all appurtenances. As a general rule of thumb it is suggested that the insulation around appurtenances should be 1.5 times thicker than that around connecting pipe lengths.

Thermal stresses and strains must also be taken into account in the design of water and sewerage piping. The two factors that must be considered are the maximum unrestrained movement of a pipe due to temperature changes and the maximum stress in the pipe and resultant loads to be taken by anchors, assuming movement is restrained. These can be computed using the following equations

$$e = lc\Delta T \qquad\qquad\qquad (10.1)$$

$$f = Ec\Delta T \qquad\qquad\qquad (10.2)$$

where e is the total change in length, l the total length of pipe subject to change, c the coefficient of thermal expansion per unit length, ΔT the change in

temperature, f the stress and E is the modulus of elasticity. Consistent units, of
course, must be used in these equations.

As an example, 1,000 ft. (305 m) of steel pipe, with $c = 0.64 \times 10^{-5}$
ft./ft.°F (1.15×10^{-5} cm/cm· °C), when subjected to a 100°F (56°C) temperature
change will change in length by 0.64 ft. (195 mm). Assuming movement is completely restrained, the stress in the pipe will be 19,200 psi (132.38 MPa) when
$E = 30 \times 10^{6}$ psi (206 843 MPa). For a 12 in. (30 cm) diameter standard steel
pipe (Schedule 40) the total load to be restrained, therefore, is 147 tons (1308 kN).

In the above example, and in most practical cases, it is more economical to
allow maximum movement rather than provide restraint. On municipal systems
these movements are accommodated by using compression or sleeve-type couplings and by expansion joints. This approach is applied to standard pipe materials
such as steel, ductile and cast iron, asbestos cement, concrete, wood and clay
pipe.

On the other hand, a different approach is necessary if plastic pipes are used,
because of their high coefficient of thermal expansion and low tensile strength
(e.g., 3,000 psi; 20.68 MPa for polyethylene pipe). With plastic pipe the thermal
forces are tolerable while thermal movements are not and it is usually possible to
provide anchorage and eliminate movements.

For example, an unrestrained polyethylene pipe 1,000 ft. (305 m) long subjected to a temperature change of 100°F (56°C) will change in length by 9 ft.
(2.7 m). Typical values of c and E for polyethylene pipe are 9×10^{-5} ft./ft.°F
(16.2×10^{-5} cm/cm·°C) and 60,000 psi (413.69 MPa) respectively. Assuming
total restraint, the stress in this pipe is 540 psi (3.72 MPa) and for a 6 in. (15 cm)
diameter Series 100 polyethylene pipe the corresponding total load is about 2.5
tons (22.2 kN). A load of this magnitude can be restrained only by anchoring the
line.

Thermal movements of plastic pipe can be restrained in three ways. The pipe
can be anchored in solid concrete blocks or secured to steel anchors. A second
method is to enclose the pipe in rigid insulation and a rigid casing, which are not
affected by extreme thermal movements. Anchorage depends in this case on the
shear strength of the insulation and its bond to the pipe and to the rigid exterior
casing. Burial is the third method for reduction or prevention of movement, but
this depends on whether or not the friction coefficient and the soil weight are adequate to provide sufficient reaction and prevent slippage.

10.3.2.3 *System Materials, Equipment and Details*

Piping, insulation and heating equipment must be carefully selected to overcome
or reduce thermal and foundation problems. Many types of pipe, including steel,
cast iron, asbestos cement, plastic and wood stave pipe, have been used in northern Canada. All have advantages and limitations, which must be taken into account. High coefficient of expansion, poor structural strength, heavy weight and
high thermal conductivity are properties usually considered undesirable for a
northern piping system.

FIG. 10.19   Ice build-up under a utilidor caused by a very small leak in a water main illustrates the importance of selecting pipe with leakproof joints for all utilidor piping (Associated Engineering Services Ltd. photograph).

Jointing is a critical factor (Fig. 10.19). Flexible joints, which permit lateral and some longitudinal movement of pipes, are favoured for both underground systems and those in above-ground utilidors. By selecting a suitable jointing method it is generally possible to avoid incorporating special measures for thermal expansion. Where rigid joints, such as welds or bolted flanges, are used allowances have to be made for all anticipated stresses and strains. In the case of fused-joint plastic pipes, movement may be prevented by anchorage. On the other hand, welded steel pipe requires expansion joints, which must operate satisfactorily under severe conditions. Sleeve-type expansion joints may cease to function when coated with ice on the inside while flexible, bellows-type joints, which have no sliding parts, generally provide better service. Sleeve-type compression couplings, rather than welded joints, are frequently used to avoid expansion problems. Since most types of joint couplings will not take any longitudinal forces, adequate blocking and anchorage are required.

Insulation that absorbs little or no moisture is preferred for a piping system. Polystyrene and polyurethane rigid foam insulations are practically hydrophobic and, therefore, are commonly used. It is essential that consideration be given to the possible deterioration of insulating materials when they are exposed to wetting, freezing, sunlight, hydrocarbons or other undesirable conditions during the normal life of a municipal system (say 20 to 40 years). A reduction in insulating value may be tolerated under certain circumstances provided heat can be added to the system.

Heat can be added to a system in various ways to prevent freezing. It is possible to heat the water entering the mains, to heat the water in the pipe, to heat the exterior of the pipe or, in the case of utilidors, to heat the air around the pipe. Although water lines are the most critical, heat may also have to be added to sewer lines in some situations such as long outfall lines.

Boilers and heat exchangers are commonly employed to heat water entering the mains; continuous circulation of water throughout the system is required to distribute the heat. Where circulation is not possible or intermittent, such as at dead ends and house connections, heat may be added by installing electrical heating cables inside or outside the pipes. In-line cables are more efficient than external cables, but problems arise in maintaining continuity where valves or other similar restricting appurtenances are installed in the line. Various electrical heating cables are now available to suit most purposes. Heat tracing with hot water or steam lines is also possible. Hot air can be circulated in utilidors using fans or, if heating lines are included, heat from the hot pipes can maintain a warm environment in the utilidor.

Several products have been specially developed in recent years for use in northern utility systems. These range from preformed pipe insulation sections to prefabricated utilidors intended for above- and below-ground installations (Fig. 10.20). The suitability of these products for any specific application should always be carefully appraised with respect to their ability to perform satisfactorily. In particular, the type of piping, method of jointing, type of insulation and provisions for heating, where applicable, should be evaluated.

Special attention must be given to detailing on northern systems. Insufficient standards or codes have been developed to date to allow standard design approaches to be used. Site conditions often dictate the use of unique and innovative designs, which, together with new materials and equipment, usually require the development of new details and the preparation of an above-average number of carefully detailed drawings. A well designed and detailed system makes installation easier and faster—a crucial factor in northern areas where logistics, weather and access plus a short construction season pose difficult problems. When preparing design details for a northern system the engineer should keep in mind the primary concerns regarding heat losses, foundations and detailing of system connections and appurtenances. An inadequate design or lack of attention to details may very easily result in a poor installation with subsequent operating difficulties, high maintenance costs and even failure.

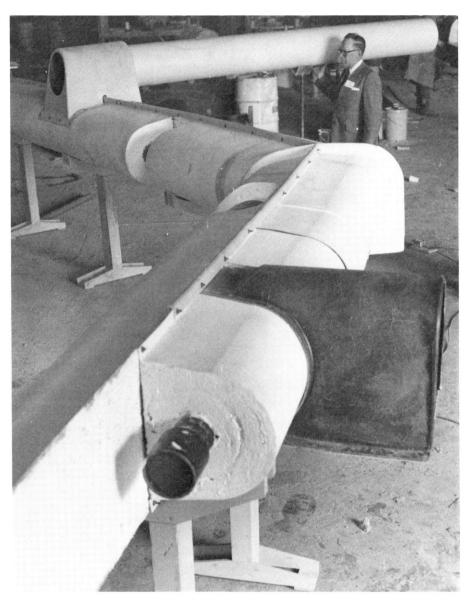

FIG. 10.20 A prefabricated utilidor prototype constructed of fibreglass reinforced materials and assembled for display purposes. First utilidors of this type were constructed in Canada in 1976 (Associated Engineering Services Ltd. photograph).

10.3.3 Thermal Calculations

The second order differential equation which describes the conduction of heat (the diffusion equation) succumbs to only a limited number of closed-form solutions. These generally relate to geometrically simple boundaries and relatively homogeneous materials (Carslaw and Jaeger 1959). Such solutions are particularly useful since their explicit nature permits relatively easy numerical computation and gives a quantitative insight into heat-flow problems. An important sub-set of these closed-form solutions, the time-independent, steady-state solutions, describe the long-term (strictly infinite) heat flow in a region with constant boundary conditions. This section is concerned with the use of certain of these results to aid in the design of utility piping systems in permafrost regions.

TABLE 10.1

Symbols and Subscripts used in Figs. 10.21, 10.22, 10.23 and 10.24

(a) *Symbols*

$c = \sqrt{H^2 - r^2}$, ft. (m)
$d =$ fluid density, lb./ft.^{3} (kg/m^3)
$D =$ length scaling parameter, ft. (m)
$h =$ thermal film coefficient (or surface conductance), Btu/hr. ft.^{2} °F (W/m^2·K)
$H =$ depth of bury, ft. (m)
$k =$ thermal conductivity, Btu/hr. ft. °F (W/m·K)
$L =$ latent heat, Btu/lb. (J/kg)
$l =$ pipe length, ft. (m)
$P =$ mean perimeter, ft. (m)
$Q =$ rate of heat loss per unit longitudinal length, Btu/hr. ft. (W/m)
$r =$ radius, ft. (m)
$R =$ thermal resistance of unit longitudinal length, hr. ft. °F/Btu (m·K/W)
$S =$ fluid specific heat, Btu/lb. °F (J/kg·K)
$t =$ thickness, ft. (m)
$T =$ temperature, °F (K)
$V =$ velocity, ft./hr. (m/s)

(b) *Subscripts*

A — refers to air
C — refers to conduit
E — refers to exterior casing of utilidor
f — refers to frozen soil
G — refers to ground surface
I — refers to insulation around pipe
j — denotes 1, 2, 3 . . .
L — refers to thermal lining of utilidor
O — refers to freezing point of water
p — refers to pipe
S — refers to soil (general)
t — refers to thawed (unfrozen) soil
U — refers to utilidor
W — refers to water (fluid) within the pipe
z — refers to zone of thaw

Relevant formulae and computational procedures for the thermal design of a variety of utility distribution systems in northern areas are given in condensed form in Fig. 10.21A, B and C. Symbols and subscripts used in these figures are listed in Table 10.1.

Figure 10.21A deals with above-ground pipe systems including heat flows from a bare pipe, an insulated pipe, a single pipe utilidor and a multiple pipe utilidor. In each case, some of the major approximations, in addition to the implied time-independent, steady-state assumption, are indicated and comments, intended to facilitate application of the formulae, are included. Figure 10.21B gives similar information pertaining to uninsulated and insulated buried pipes. For each of these cases, thawing around the pipe is considered, and formulae for calculating the dimensions of the resulting thaw bulb are included. Formulae for estimating the temperature drop (or rise) along a pipeline system and expressions relating to freeze-up times under no-flow conditions, are given in Fig. 10.21C.

To simplify computation, numerical values for certain stages of some of the calculations may be read directly from Figs. 10.22, 10.23 and 10.24. These curves summarize information pertaining to the thermal resistance of a hollow cylinder (insulation shell or pipe), the thermal resistance of a soil mass covering a pipe, and the physical dimensions of a thaw cylinder around a pipe buried in permafrost, respectively.

The methods of calculation presented in this section are based upon time-independent solutions to the heat conduction equation. The transient temperature variations which occur at the ground surface, however, although damped with depth, propagate into the soil and the longer period ones, particularly the annual periodic variations, make a significant contribution to the thermal regime at typical pipe burial depths. Long-term thawing around a warm buried pipe in permafrost will be most extensive during that period when the ground temperatures are at a maximum in similar but undisturbed permafrost. An estimate of the highest soil temperatures in the disturbed permafrost, can be obtained using the following equation:

$$T(X,Y) = T_G + (T_o - T_G) \exp[B(Y-A)] + (T_W - T_G) \frac{\ln\left(\frac{X^2 + (c+Y)^2}{X^2 + (c-Y)^2}\right)}{2\ln\left(\frac{H_p + r_p + c}{H_p + r_p - c}\right)}$$

[for $Y \geqslant A$] (10.3)

Here, A denotes the maximum depth of the active layer, X and Y are cartesian co-ordinates (see Fig. 10.21B) for any point when $Y \geqslant A$, and $B = \sqrt{\pi C_f/k_f y}$, where y is the time period of one year (in appropriate units), C_f is the volumetric heat capacity of frozen soil in Btu/°F ft.^{3} (J/°C·m^3) and the remaining symbols are defined in Table 10.1. It should be noted that $\ln[H_p + r_p + c/H_p + r_p - c]$ is equal to arccosh H_p/r_p. For an insulated pipe, T_w should be replaced by T_I (as given in Fig. 10.21B3) and r_p should be replaced by r_I. The maximum depth of the active layer (A) may be taken directly from field measurements or estimated using methods outlined in Chapter 4.

	A1 BARE PIPE	A2 INSULATED PIPE	A3 SINGLE PIPE UTILIDOR	A4 MULTIPLE PIPE UTILIDOR
SKETCH				
ASSUMPTIONS	THIN WALLED PIPE (i.e. $r_i < 2 r_w$) R_W IS NEGLIGIBLE, h_A CALCULATION ASSUMES FREE CONVECTION. $R_p < R_A$.	ALL THERMAL RESISTANCES EXCEPT THAT OF THE INSULATION ARE NEGLECTED.	AS A1 OR A2. CONVECTION ENSURES THE TEMPERATURE INSIDE THE UTILIDOR, T_U, IS UNIFORM. UTILIDOR AIR FILMS NEGLIGIBLE.	SAME AS A3
THERMAL RESISTANCE	✳ $$R_p = (r_p - r_w)/(r_p + r_w)\pi k_p$$ $$h_A = N\left(\frac{T_w - T_A}{r_p}\right)^{0.25}$$ $$R_A = 1/2\pi r_p h_A$$ $$R_C = R_p + R_A$$ WHERE: $N = 0.23$ Btu/hr ft$^{7/4}$ · °F$^{5/4}$ OR $N = 1.12$ J/s · m$^{7/4}$ · °C$^{5/4}$	✳ $$R_C = R_I = \frac{\ln(r_I/r_p)}{2\pi k_I}$$ $$\approx \left(\frac{r_I - r_p}{r_I + r_p}\right)/\pi k_I \text{ IF } r_I < 2 r_p$$ GIVEN r_I/r_p AND k_I READ OFF R_I FROM FIG. 10.22	✳ CALCULATE R_C, THE THERMAL RESISTANCE OF THE INTERIOR CONDUIT BY: USING A2 IF INSULATED OR USING A1 IF BARE AND REPLACING T_A IN THE FORMULA FOR h_A BY <u>AN ESTIMATE</u> FOR T_U ($\leq T_W$) $$R_L = t_L/p_L k_L \qquad R_E = t_E/p_E k_E$$ $$R_U = R_L + R_E$$ $$R = R_C + R_U$$ $$T_U = \frac{(T_W/R_C) + (T_A/R_U)}{(1/R_C) + (1/R_U)}$$ IF BARE INTERIOR PIPE, ITERATE T_U	✳ CALCULATE R FOR EACH PIPE AS IN A3 TO GET R_j, ($j = 1, 2, 3, \ldots\ldots$) CALCULATE R_U AS IN A3 $$T_U = \frac{\sum_j (T_j/R_j) + (T_A/R_U)}{\sum_j (1/R_j) + (1/R_U)}$$ IF BARE PIPES PRESENT, ITERATE T_U

RATE OF HEAT LOSS	$Q = (T_W - T_A)/R_C$ *	$Q = (T_W - T_A)/R_I$	$Q = (T_W - T_A)/R$ *	$Q_j = (T_j - T_U)/R_j$ (PER PIPE) $Q = \Sigma_j Q_j = (T_U - T_A)/R_U$ *
INSULATION THICKNESS (Given Q)	N/A	$r_I - r_p = r_p \{ \exp[2\pi k_I (T_W - T_A)/Q] - 1 \}$ $\cong \pi k_I (T_W - T_A) Q$ IF $r_I < 2 r_p$, READ OFF r_I/r_p FROM GIVEN R_I & k_I, READ OFF r_I/r_p FROM FIG. 10.22	OBTAIN R_E AND R_C AS ABOVE $t_L = P_L L_L \left[\dfrac{(T_W - T_A)}{Q} - R_E - R_C \right]$ IF BARE INTERIOR PIPE, ITERATE T_U, R_C AND HENCE t_L	GIVEN ACCEPTABLE Q_j, CALCULATE R_j AS ABOVE AND EVALUATE $T_U = T_j - R_j Q_j$ FOR EACH PIPE FOR WHICH Q IS KNOWN. USING THE MAXIMUM T_U FOUND, CALCULATE NEW Q_j AS ABOVE. USING THESE Q_j AND THE SAME T_U, EVALUATE $t_L = P_L L_L \left[\dfrac{(T_U - T_A)}{\Sigma Q_j} - R_E \right]$ IF BARE PIPES PRESENT, ITERATE T_U, R_j AND HENCE t_L
COMMENTS	OFTEN, FOR METAL PIPES, R_P MAY BE NEGLECTED. IF R_P IS SIGNIFICANT, THE EXPRESSION ABOVE FOR h_A WILL GENERATE AN OVERESTIMATE OF Q. IF $T_A > T_W$ SWITCH T_A AND T_W IN THE EXPRESSION FOR h_A. FORMULAE FOR h_W (AND FOR R_A UNDER FORCED CONVECTION) MAY BE FOUND IN THE CHEMICAL ENGINEERS' HANDBOOK, McGRAW-HILL, 5TH ed. SEC. 10	THE NEGLECTED THERMAL RESISTANCES GIVEN IN A1 MAY BE INCLUDED IF DESIRED.	THE VALUE OF h_A, AND HENCE R_A, IS FAIRLY INSENSITIVE TO THE CHOICE OF T_U, AND SO ONE ITERATION ON T_U IS USUALLY SUFFICIENT. OFTEN R_E MAY BE NEGLECTED. SIMILAR CALCULATIONAL PROCEDURE MAY BE PERFORMED FOR UTILIDORS OF DIFFERENT CROSS-SECTION.	AS A3. IF IT IS CLEAR THAT ONE PIPE DOMINATES THE HEAT LOSS PROCESS, A3 MAY BE USED TO ESTIMATE T_U. IT IS WISE TO CONSIDER THE HEAT LOSS FROM THE VARIOUS PIPES IF CERTAIN OTHER PIPES CEASE TO FUNCTION.

* ILLUSTRATED IN EXAMPLE PROBLEMS IN TEXT

FIG. 10.21(a) Condensed thermal design procedures—above-ground pipes.

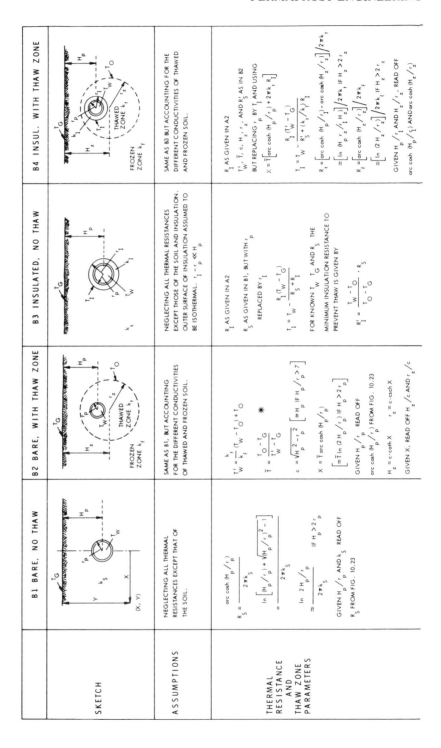

RATE OF HEAT LOSS	$$Q = \frac{T_W - T_G}{R_S}$$	FROM FIG. 10.24 (IF X << 0.2 USE $H_z/c = r_z/c = 1/X$) R_t, r_f AND R_S $(= R_t + R_f)$ AS GIVEN IN B4, BUT WITH r_I REPLACED BY r_p. * $$Q = \frac{T'_W - T_G}{R'_S} \quad \text{WHERE}$$ $$R'_S = \frac{\text{arc cosh}(H_p/r_p)}{2\pi k_f}$$ TO EVALUATE R'_S USE FIG. 10.23	* $$Q = \frac{T_W - T_G}{R_I + R_S}$$	FROM FIG. 10.23 $$R_S = R_f + R_I$$ $$Q = \frac{T'_W - T_G}{R'_S + (k_t/k_f)R_I}$$
INSULATION THICKNESS	N/A	THE THAWED ZONE IS A CIRCLE (IN CROSS-SECTION)	FOR NO THAWING OUTSIDE THE INSULATION THE MINIMUM INSULATION THICKNESS IS $r_I - r_p = r_p \left[\exp(2\pi k_f R'_I) - 1 \right]$ GIVEN R'_I AND k_f READ OFF r_I/r_p FROM FIG. 10.22	GIVEN H_z OR r_z CALCULATE H_z/c OR r_z/c AND USE FIG. 10.24 TO EVALUATE X. THEN USE FIG. 10.23 FOR arc cosh (H_p/r_I) $$R_I = \left[X/\overline{7} + \text{arc cosh}(H_p/r_I) \right] / 2\pi k_t$$ $r_I - r_p$ AS B3 WITH R'_I REPLACED BY R_I
COMMENTS	MAY BE USED TO APPROXIMATE B2 IF $k_t = k_f$ AND/OR $r \simeq r_p$ AND THE THAW ZONE PARAMETERS ARE NOT REQUIRED. FOR AN UPPER LIMIT ON THE AVERAGE HEAT LOSS USE $k_s = k_f$, OTHERWISE USE $k_s = (k_f + k_t)/2$		MAY BE USED TO APPROXIMATE B4 IF $k_t = k_f$ AND/OR $r \simeq r_I$ AND THAW ZONE PARAMETERS ARE NOT REQUIRED. $k_s = k_f$ OR $(k_f + k_t)/2$ AS B1	THE ABOVE EXPRESSIONS FOR R_I, R_f AND R_S OFTEN ARE NOT REQUIRED.

* ILLUSTRATED IN EXAMPLE PROBLEMS IN TEXT

FIG. 10.21(b) Condensed thermal design procedures—buried pipes.

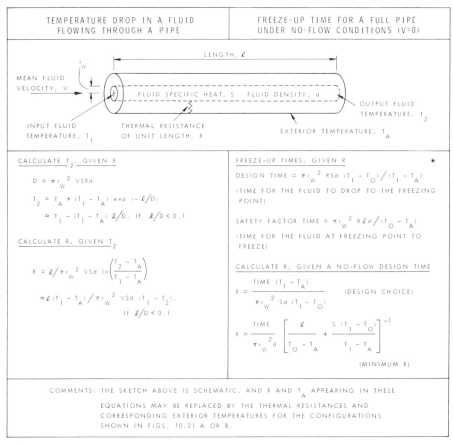

FIG. 10.21(c)   Condensed thermal design procedures for utility distribution systems in northern areas—temperature drop and freeze-up times in pipes.

Equation 10.3 is based on a number of simplifying assumptions, which have been selected so that it predicts greater thaw around the pipe than would occur in practice for the same boundary conditions. The equation is particularly suited for an evaluation of temperatures on a grid pattern, using only a small programmable calculator. The important temperatures along the axis of symmetry, and particularly those below the pipe, may be evaluated quite quickly, even manually, because, in this case, $X = 0$, thus simplifying the equation.

It is also possible to obtain an approximate description of the time-dependent thawing around a warm pipeline using steady-state results, by using the quasi-static approximation. Steady-state solutions are utilized in the thawed and frozen zones, but the thaw interface moves with time. The technique is similar to the well-known Stefan approximation for estimating thaw rates in one dimension. Approximate time-dependent solutions for uninsulated and insulated pipes for a

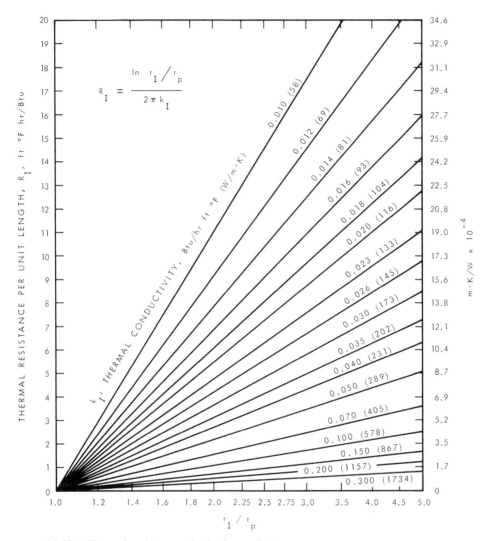

FIG. 10.22   Thermal resistance of a hollow cylinder.

range of pipe size and burial depths are given by Thornton (1976). These and other solutions are compared in Section 4.3.

It should be pointed out that boundary temperatures in the field vary continuously with both random and periodic components, and are often a result of complex heat exchange effects. Materials encountered in practice, in addition, are frequently not homogeneous, isotropic media. Soil, for example, is a complex, multi-phase, heterogeneous medium, the behaviour of which is further complicated by the water component, which undergoes phase transitions when freezing or thawing occurs. Some of these complexities may be taken into account by

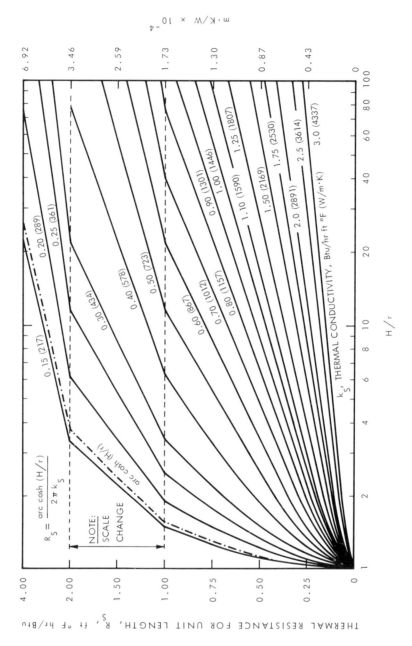

FIG. 10.23   Thermal resistance of a soil mass covering a pipe.

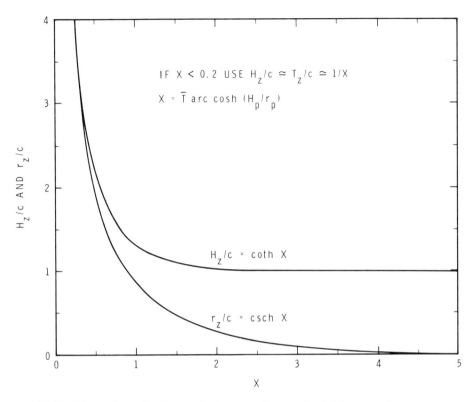

IF X < 0.2 USE $H_z/c \simeq T_z/c \simeq 1/X$

$X = \bar{T}$ arc cosh (H_p/r_p)

$H_z/c =$ coth X

$r_z/c =$ csch X

FIG. 10.24   Dimensions of a thaw cylinder around a pipe buried in permafrost.

using strictly numerical techniques to solve the appropriate differential equations, but even the most sophisticated methods still incorporate many restrictive approximations. The use of such numerical methods may often only be warranted for large design projects because of the associated high manpower and computing costs.

In summary, the procedures presented in this section, based mainly upon time-independent, steady-state solutions to the heat conduction equation are, of necessity, highly idealized and calculations made using them should be considered only as as guide to engineering design rather than as rigorous solutions. The sample problems which follow will illustrate the computational procedures given in Fig. 10.21.

PROBLEM 1: Calculate the rate of heat loss (per unit length) from a metal pipe
of outside diameter 0.152 m, encased in 0.076 m of polyurethane
foam of thermal conductivity 0.024 W/m·K when the pipe contains water at 10.0°C and the exterior is exposed to a temperature
of $-45.6°C$.

(From Fig. 10.22)

SOLUTION: r_p = 0.076 m
r_I = 0.152 m
T_W = 10.0°C
T_A = $-45.6°C$
k_I = 0.024 W/m·K

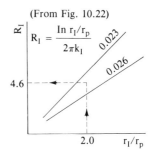

$\therefore r_I/r_p = 0.152/0.076 = 2.0$

From Fig. 10.22

$$R_I = 4.6 \text{ m·K/W}$$

$$\therefore Q = \frac{T_W - T_A}{R_I} = \frac{10.0 - (-45.6)}{4.6} = \frac{55.6}{4.6} = 12.1 \text{W/m}$$

NOTE: In this case, since $r_I/r_p = 2$, the following approximate relation
could have been used to evaluate R_I

$$R_I = \left(\frac{r_I - r_p}{r_I + r_p}\right)\bigg/ \pi k_I$$

PROBLEM 2: Calculate the interior temperature and rate of heat loss (per unit length) from the plywood box utilidor sketched below, which contains a 6-inch nominal diameter, class 150 asbestos cement pipe. Temperatures and dimensions are shown below.

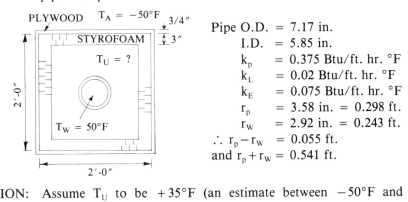

Pipe O.D. = 7.17 in.
I.D. = 5.85 in.
k_p = 0.375 Btu/ft. hr. °F
k_L = 0.02 Btu/ft. hr. °F
k_E = 0.075 Btu/ft. hr. °F
r_p = 3.58 in. = 0.298 ft.
r_W = 2.92 in. = 0.243 ft.
∴ $r_p - r_W$ = 0.055 ft.
and $r_p + r_W$ = 0.541 ft.

SOLUTION: Assume T_U to be +35°F (an estimate between −50°F and +50°F)

$$R_p = \frac{0.055}{0.541 \times \pi \times 0.375} = 0.086 \text{ hr. ft. °F/Btu}$$

$$h_A = 0.23 \left(\frac{50-35}{0.298}\right)^{0.25} = 0.613 \text{ Btu/hr. ft.}^2 \text{ °F}$$

$$\therefore R_A = 1/(2\pi \times 0.298 \times 0.613) = 0.872 \text{ hr. ft. °F/Btu}$$

and $R_C = 0.086 + 0.872 = 0.958 \approx 0.96 \text{ hr. ft. °F/Btu}$
$P_E = 4(2.0 + 0.75/12) = 8.25 \text{ ft.}$
$\therefore R_E = 0.75/12/8.25 \times 0.075 = 0.101 \text{ hr. ft. °F/Btu}$
$P_L = 4(2.0 - 3/12) = 7.0 \text{ ft.}$
$\therefore R_L = 3/12/7.0 \times 0.02 = 1.786 \text{ hr. ft. °F/Btu}$
$\therefore R_U = 0.101 + 1.786 = 1.887 = 1.89 \text{ hr. ft. °F/Btu}$

$$T_U = \frac{(50/0.96) - (50/1.89)}{(1/0.96) + (1/1.89)} = 16.3°F$$

Iterate (use the new value of T_U and repeat the calculation)

$$h_A = 0.23 \left(\frac{50-16.3}{0.298}\right)^{0.25} = 0.75 \text{ Btu/hr. ft.}^2 \text{ °F}$$

$$\therefore R_A = 1/(2\pi \times 0.298 \times 0.75) = 0.712 \text{ hr. ft. °F/Btu}$$
and $R_C = 0.086 + 0.712 = 0.798 \approx 0.80 \text{ hr. ft. °F/Btu}$

$$T_U = \frac{(50/0.80) - (50/1.89)}{(1/0.80) + (1/1.89)} = 20.3°F$$

Thus $T_U \approx 20°F$

                    (another iteration gives a value of T_U = 19.7°F)

Hence $Q = \dfrac{50 - (-50)}{0.80 + 1.89} = 37.2 \approx 37 \text{ Btu/hr. ft.}$

PROBLEM 3: The same as Problem 2 but the utilidor also contains a 2 in. O.D. steam pipe encased within 1-1/2 in. of asbestos fibre (conductivity 0.03 Btu/hr. ft. °F)

SOLUTION: As in Problem 2, R_U = 1.89 hr. ft. °F/Btu.
To evaluate the thermal resistance per unit length of the insulation encasing the steam pipe, use Fig. 10.22 with r_1/r_p = 2.5 and k_1 = 0.03 Btu/hr. ft. °F.
This gives R_2 = 4.9 hr. ft. °F/Btu
(The contributions from the steam pipe itself and the air film adjacent to the insulation are neglected.)

Begin by again assuming T_U = 35°F (since part of the calculation has already been completed in problem 2).

$$\text{Thus } R_1 = 0.96 \text{ hr. ft. °F/Btu (for the water conduit)}$$
$$\therefore \ \Sigma T_j/R_j = 212/4.9 + 50/0.96 = 95.3 \text{ Btu/hr. ft. °F}$$
$$\text{and } \Sigma 1/R_j = 1/4.9 + 1/0.96 = 1.24 \text{ Btu/hr. ft. °F}$$

$$\therefore \ T_U = \frac{95.3 - 50/1.89}{1.24 + 1/1.89} \approx 39°F$$

(Another iteration gives T_U = 38.4°F)

For the steam pipe: $Q_1 = \dfrac{212 - 39}{4.9}$ = 35.3 ≈ 35 Btu/hr. ft.

For the water pipe: $Q_2 = \dfrac{50 - 39}{0.96}$ = 11.5 ≈ 12 Btu/hr. ft.

NOTE: If the steam pipe ceases to function, the rate of heat loss from the water pipe becomes that calculated in Problem 2 (37 Btu/hr. ft.).

PROBLEM 4: A copper pipe of outside diameter 5-1/2 in. is buried 6 ft. below grade in a soil of mean surface temperature 20°F and thermal conductivity 0.60 and 1.0 Btu/hr. ft. °F when thawed and frozen, respectively. What is the mean size of the thawed zone and average rate of heat loss if water at 50°F is circulated through the pipe?

SOLUTION: $r_p = 5.5$ in./2 = 2.75 in. = 0.229 ft.
The thermal resistance per unit length of the pipe is negligible.
$$T'_w = (0.60/1.0)(50-32) + 32 = 42.8°F$$
$$\bar{T} = (32-20)/(42.8-20) = 0.526$$
$$c = \sqrt{6^2-0.229^2} = 6 \text{ ft.}$$
$H_p/r_p = 6/0.229 = 26.2$
Given $H_p/r_p = 26.2$, read off arccosh 26.2 from Fig. 10.23
arccosh 26.2 = 4.0
$\therefore X = 0.526 \times 4 = 2.1$
From Fig. 10.24, using X = 2.1
$H_z/c = 1.03$
$r_z/c = 0.25$
$\therefore H_z = 1.03 \times 6 = 6.18$ ft. $\approx$ 6 ft. 2 in.
and $r_z = 0.25 \times 6 = 1.5$ ft. = 1 ft. 6 in.

Hence, the thawed zone will be present within a cylinder parallel to the pipe, of radius 1-1/2 ft. and with its axis approximately 2 in. below the pipe axis.

From Fig. 10.23, with H/r ($= H_p/r_p$) = 26.2 and
k_S ($= k_f$) = 1.0 Btu/hr. ft. °F, we have
$R'_S = 0.63$ hr. ft. °F/Btu
and $Q = \dfrac{42.8-20}{0.63} = 36.2 \approx 36$ Btu/hr. ft.

PROBLEM 5: A metal pipe of external diameter 0.152 m is buried in permafrost (k_f = 1.73 W/m·K) with its axis 1.22 m below the ground surface whose mean temperature is $-2.5°C$. What is the minimum thickness of polyurethane foam insulation (k_1 = 0.024 W/m·K) which will maintain the soil in a frozen state (on average) if water flowing through the pipe has a mean temperature of 7.2°C? What is the average rate of heat loss if this insulation thickness is used?

SOLUTION: To evaluate R_S use Fig. 10.23 with
$$H/r = 1.22/0.076 = 16 \text{ and } k_S (= k_f) = 1.73 \text{ W/m·K}$$
Then R_S = 0.32 m·K/W
$$R_1' = \frac{(7.2-0)}{0-(-2.5)} \times 0.32 = \frac{7.2 \times 0.32}{2.5} = 0.92 \text{ m·K/W}$$
To evaluate r_1/r_p use Fig. 10.22 with
$$R_1 = 0.92 \text{ m·K/W and } k_1 = 0.024 \text{ W/m·K}$$
Then $r_1/r_p \approx 1.15$
$$\therefore r_1 - r_p = (1.15-1) \times 0.076 = 0.011\text{m} = 1.1 \text{ cm}$$
$$Q = \frac{7.2-(-2.5)}{0.92+0.32} = \frac{9.7}{1.24} = 7.8 \text{ W/m}$$

NOTE: (1) To design for the worst conditions, in order to minimize the thaw zone during the fall when the soil is relatively warm, the calculation for the insulation thickness should be repeated using the *maximum* temperature attained by the undisturbed permafrost at the depth of bury, rather than the mean surface temperature, T_G.

              (2) To estimate the maximum rate of heat loss, the calculation should be repeated using the selected thickness of insulation and the *minimum* temperature attained by the undisturbed permafrost at the depth of bury, rather than the mean surface temperature, T_G.

PROBLEM 6: What is the design freeze-up time and safety factor time for the utilidor design and temperatures used in Problem 2? (For water: d = 62.4 lb./ft.^{3}, S = 1 Btu/lb. °F, L = 144 Btu/lb.)

SOLUTION: R = 0.80 + 1.89 = 2.69 hr. ft. °F/Btu
             (Pipe and air film + utilidor)
             $\therefore$ Design Time
                  = π (0.243)^2 × 62.4 × 2.69 × 1 × [50−32]/[50−(−50)]
                  = 5.6 hr.
                  $\approx$ 5-1/2 hr.
             Safety Factor Time
                  = π (0.243)^2 × 2.69 × 62.4 × 144/[32−(−50)]
                  = 54.7 hr.
                  $\approx$ 55 hr.

10.4 Electrical Power and Communication Systems

In the North electrical power is obtained from hydro, diesel or turbine (steam or gas) generating plants. Communication facilities range from the standard telephone and telegraph land systems to the more sophisticated microwave and satellite transmitting and receiving stations. Power and local communication services are usually carried on overhead lines within communities and over longer distances. Cables are usually buried in special situations such as airports.

Construction and operating problems caused by the northern climate, including thick ice covers and formation of frazil ice on rivers and reservoirs at hydro sites, accumulation of ice and rime on towers, lines and structures and performance of materials and equipment at low temperature, are similar to those experienced in southern Canada. They are of greater concern, however, because of the long period of extreme cold and the very strong winds that occur in many northern areas.

Special attention must be given to permafrost and frost action foundation problems because most power and communications structures and equipment can tolerate very little movement. Interruption of service due to failure of structures or malfunctioning of equipment is most undesirable and subsequent maintenance and repair can be costly because locations are usually isolated and not readily accessible. Furthermore, the extremely high resistivity of frozen ground makes grounding of electrical equipment and systems a difficult problem. Route and site selection and assessment of foundation conditions in permafrost areas are most important, therefore, to ensure safe and reliable operation.

The special thaw settlement and stability foundation problems associated with the design and construction of dams and dykes for hydro-electric power generating stations have been discussed in Chapter 9. The foundations for structures housing central heating equipment and thermal or diesel power generating plants must be designed and constructed to take into account the special thermal and structural loads, which are usually larger than those on most other structures. Boiler foundations should be isolated from the building foundations and floor slabs to allow for thermal expansion and contraction. Power generating equipment also should be isolated to reduce or avoid transmitting vibrations to the building and other equipment. The effect of the transmission of heat and dynamic loads on foundations embedded in permafrost must be critically assessed. Similarly, the effects of frost heave and thaw settlement on the performance of isolated, unheated structures, such as power and communication tower foundations and anchors and switchyard equipment and transformers, are important considerations. The design of foundations for these types of structures are discussed in Chapter 7.

10.4.1 Distribution Systems

Power and communication cables are usually placed above the ground surface. Occasionally, short, temporary lines (used for a few days or weeks) may be laid directly on the unprepared ground surface. Permanent installations on the ground surface, however, are subject to lateral and vertical displacements resulting from frost heave, thaw settlement, solifluction or other slope movements, drainage and moisture problems, damage by off-the-road vehicles and vandalism.

Cables are normally buried only in special situations. Buried cables are used extensively around airports, for example, mainly for runway lighting and navigation systems. In this case, they are usually placed inside plastic conduits in a 1 to 2 ft. (0.3 to 0.7 m) deep trench excavated in the non-frost-susceptible, coarse-grained and well-draining, base course material (Fig. 10.25). Few difficulties are experienced with these installations. Because the area will be kept clear of snow, however, the cables are exposed to wide temperature fluctuations and provision must be made for expansion and contraction of the cables. If, in addition, local drainage and weather conditions are such that these normally free-draining materials become saturated and freeze, "frost-grip" of the material to the conductors or conduit may induce high tensile stresses and cause the conduit to rupture. Entrance and freezing of moisture resulting in damage and deterioration of the insulation and conductor with subsequent electrical problems is also a

FIG. 10.25   Power cables laid in shallow trench on airfield.

possibility. Thermal contraction cracking of the ground may also complicate matters. To help alleviate the problem, cables can be coated to reduce frost-grip and slack should be left in the lines by "snaking" them when they are laid in the trench.

Similar but much more severe problems will be experienced if cables are to be buried in frost-susceptible soils and poorly drained areas. Under such conditions, cables should be placed in a trench excavated at least 2 ft. (0.7 m) below the permafrost table or the maximum depth of seasonal frost penetration. A major

FIG. 10.26   Power pole supported by rock-filled timber crib.

disadvantage of buried systems is that they are not readily accessible for maintenance work. Soviet experience with buried systems is described by Boychenko (1971). Most power and communication cables are placed above-ground in permafrost areas. They may be placed within or attached to the outside of utilidors in communities having this facility. By far the most common method used, particularly for distribution of high voltage power within communities and over long distances, is to string the lines overhead on wood poles or steel towers.

In areas where frost heave is not a problem, conventional practice can be followed and lines are carried on wood poles set in drilled holes. Where frost heave or thaw settlement are problems, lines which carry a few light conductors and can tolerate some movement may be carried on single wood poles set in rock-filled cribs on the ground surface or on wood pole tripods (Figs. 10.26 and 10.27). Where stability is required, the wood poles are strapped to "stub" piles well embedded in permafrost to resist frost heave forces in the active layer (Fig. 10.28). For major transmission lines which cross widely varied and difficult terrain and are subjected to heavy wind and ice loads, steel guyed or self-supporting towers are normally used (Crowley 1977). Various types of foundations described in Chapter 7 are used depending on local conditions.

10.4.2 Electrical Grounding

Effective grounding of electrical circuits and equipment is not easily accomplished in permafrost areas because of the extremely high resistivity of frozen soil

FIG. 10.27   Power or communication lines can be supported by wood pole tripods.

FIG. 10.28   Power poles strapped to wood piles set in permafrost.

(see Section 3.4) and the consequent difficulty of making good contact with permanent earth moisture. The very high resistivity affects electrical plant design for generating stations, switching stations, substations and associated equipment and power transmission lines in several ways. Personnel safety (involving both step potential and touch potential), station ground grid design, choice of system grounding method and protective relaying are important considerations. Grounding is required to protect equipment and personnel, not only from system malfunctions but also from lightning strikes on towers and buildings.

Good grounding can usually be obtained in the southern parts of the discontinuous permafrost zone, where large unfrozen areas having a high water table occur. Special attention must be given to areas of deep seasonal frost penetration. Grounding becomes more difficult further north in the discontinuous zone, where permafrost is more widespread and thicker, and in the continuous permafrost zone. Grounding may occasionally be possible if an unfrozen zone exists between the bottom of the active layer and the permafrost table. The only solution in many cases is to extend ground buses to nearby lakes or streams or to cased water wells.

Satisfactory grounding is an important consideration in selecting sites for switching stations and substations and routes for transmission lines. Transmission lines should be routed, if possible, near lakes and rivers that do not freeze to the bottom during the winter and have a substantial thaw basin beneath them. Improved grounding can be obtained by connecting the line ground wire system to auxiliary electrodes installed in the water bodies. They should avoid crossing gravel pads and roads where very high ground resistance values can occur due to deep ground freezing or a high permafrost table.

The generally high ground resistivity can vary appreciably from place to place locally and also be subject to seasonal variations. Field tests should be carried out to establish the local variability and magnitude of resistivity under both winter and summer conditions. Arcone (1977) gives a computer program developed for rapidly calculating the resistance to ground of simple electrodes, either a vertical rod or a horizontal wire, for a one- or two-layered earth model.

Within relatively confined areas where an equipotential grid can be established, a conventional, effectively grounded electrical distribution system can be used. For those systems where power is to be transmitted for greater distances and a grounding grid of practical size is not possible, the choice of a system grounding method and its protective relaying equipment is more difficult.

Each of the generally recognized system grounding methods may have application for a specific area or system design. Under conditions of extreme cold and probable high ground resistance, high resistance, low current faults such as those caused by a broken conductor lying on snow or frozen tundra must be considered a reasonable possibility. A grounding method based on having sufficient current for selective relaying may therefore work satisfactorily under most conditions but may not be capable of selectively relaying all faults. Other methods (for example a negative sequence current) may have to be considered for either tripping or alarm function to detect faults such as an open conductor. Special line construction using interconnected grounding hardware designed to make contact with a falling broken conductor and ensure reasonable currents for relaying is another method that has been used for increased selective relaying coverage in areas of high resistivity.

Special care must be exercised in the selection of instrument transformers and especially the current transformers, to permit low ground fault currents to be detected so that they will not be subject to saturation on higher current faults. Potential transformer selection and the method of its connection requires more than usual care, depending on the form of system grounding selected, especially if it is other than effectively grounded. North American instrument transformer standards for other than line to line connection of high voltage potential transformers make provision for very limited time of operation at the higher voltages that could be encountered.

Multigrounding and the use of a common primary and secondary neutral in conjunction with common grounding facilities can increase grounding efficiency on distribution lines. Interconnection of individual grounds at services, transformers and other equipment to distribution circuit neutrals can assist in providing grounding system effectiveness and protection of personnel and equipment. Multigrounded networks in built up areas usually involve a large number of grounds, many of which can be made effective by connection to water pipes. Where services are provided from a central plant, an additional ground from each building can be connected to the steel water line providing there are no discontinuities such as insulating connections and gaskets in the line. Adequate ground connections can be made at the central plant between the piping system and the generating equipment. Local conditions must be carefully assessed, however, before water lines are used for grounding. Bennett et al. (1977) describe an unusual form of corrosion of the water system at Faro, Y.T. due to uncertain electrical grounds and the superimposition of radio-frequency currents on the metallic portions of the distribution system. Good grounding in isolated areas must be obtained by other methods, such as drilling wells through the permafrost or extending ground buses to satisfactory grounding beds under bodies of water or in unfrozen ground.

The results of field tests conducted to obtain information for the design of a power system in northern Alaska, including the determination of the best methods of grounding and protection, are described by Sturton et al. (1973). The design of circular earth electrodes for the Nelson River Transmission System consisting of ±450 kV bipolar hvdc circuits of overland transmission lines is described by Shemie and Simons (1971). Earth electrodes were required to carry the normal out-of-balance dc current and, during transient and emergency monopolar operation, the full load current of 1800 A. Frozen ground was considered but was not a problem because of local site conditions in this particular case. Cherney (1975) draws attention to the problems that may arise when buried or above-ground pipelines are constructed adjacent to power transmission lines in southern areas. The very-high-fault currents and the possible voltage levels involved may be significant factors in the design of proper grounding systems in permafrost areas for safety and to prevent undue damage to pipelines during fault conditions. Peabody (1976) describes the cathodic protection system used on the trans-Alaska oil pipeline to overcome currents produced by galvanic or other electrical phenomena that would cause corrosion of the pipe. Peabody (1979) also discusses corrosion problems and their control on both warm and cold pipelines in the North, with emphasis being placed on the effects of induced direct currents caused by variations in the earth's magnetic field (telluric currents).

CHAPTER 11

Operation, Maintenance and Performance of Structures

(Contributor–G. H. Johnston)

11.1 Operation and Maintenance

In the preceding chapters, the main factors influencing the distribution and existence of permafrost, the properties and the behaviour of frozen, freezing, thawing and thawed ground and the design and construction of various types of structures and facilities in permafrost have been described and emphasized. The need to recognize and understand the influence or effects of these factors on foundation and structure performance does not end, however, when construction is completed. It is equally important and essential that they be considered during the operating and maintenance phases to ensure satisfactory performance of structures and facilities. The purpose of this chapter is to stress the importance of some of the more critical factors that must be considered during the period the structure or facility is in use.

The need for regular inspection and maintenance programs cannot be overemphasized. Furthermore, it is essential that complete and accurate records be kept of terrain changes, structural performance, problems experienced, failures that occur, remedial work carried out and costs. Only with this kind of information can future problems be anticipated, failures prevented, new criteria developed, designs improved and construction and maintenance costs decreased.

If a structure or facility constructed on permafrost is to perform satisfactorily, it is absolutely essential that those responsible for operation and maintenance are fully familiar with the site conditions, the basis for design and construction procedures used and are aware of the consequences if important factors are overlooked in operating and maintaining the structure or facility. Reports containing complete details of site investigations, including the results of field and laboratory studies and information collected on site conditions, not only prior to but also during the construction phase must be available. The approach taken (active or passive) and parameters and methods of analysis used in design, including field changes made as a result of new information obtained during construction, must be known. It is mandatory that every detail of the structure or facility, including a description of construction methods, equipment and materials used and, most important, a complete record of the final "as built" drawings must be available in report or manual form.

473

Such documents should always emphasize important features of the site conditions and structure or facility design that must always be given special consideration during regular inspection surveys and describe operating procedures that should be followed and given special attention during its service life. They should also contain a detailed description of all instrumentation installed to monitor performance and a recommended schedule to be used in making observations. The consequences of incorrect operation or use of a structure or facility, lack of proper and regular maintenance and inability to correctly interpret warning signs of impending problems noted during inspections can be disastrous. Damage or failure may occur quickly and remedial work, much of which may have to be carried out without delay and frequently under adverse conditions, may be extremely expensive if the structure or facility is to be kept safe and operational.

Inspections should be carried out regularly throughout the year. In some cases, signs of impending trouble will be noted during the thaw season. For example, subsidence of fills, leaning trees, sloughing of natural and man-made slopes, settlement of foundations, differential movement of structures, ponding of water, ventilation ducts left open, cracking of the ground and water flowing from under a fill usually indicate potential thawing, frost action and drainage problems and slope or foundation instability. Similarly, various clues and signs of possible difficulty will also be noted during the winter. Examples of what should be carefully noted are heave of foundations or fills, culverts blocked by ice, icings forming along fills and embankments or in streams near bridges, undesirable accumulations of snow that block air spaces or ventilating ducts in a fill and thermal contraction cracking of the ground under buildings or in other snow-cleared areas such as airfields and roads. Many indicators of impending problems can be seen during a visual examination, others will be picked up only by regular observations on instrumentation specially installed to monitor ground temperatures, vertical and horizontal movements and groundwater levels and flows. Some signs will immediately indicate that maintenance should be carried out as soon as possible; others are more subtle and require careful analysis of all information to determine what and how serious the problem is or will be.

The most important factor influencing the performance of structures and facilities in permafrost areas is the ground thermal regime. It is a basic consideration in the design, construction and operation of any structure or facility and is affected in many ways by the works of man. It is most important that a structure or facility be operated and maintained in a manner that will not detrimentally disturb the ground thermal regime under or adjacent to it.

Many structures, particularly in the continuous permafrost zone, are designed and constructed to maintain the foundation materials in a perennially frozen condition at or lower than the temperature existing in the undisturbed or natural state (that is, prior to construction). Other designs may permit an increase in ground temperature and allow thawing to occur, with subsequent anticipated settlements, but at a controlled rate. Most of the more difficult engineering problems are experienced in the discontinuous permafrost zone because of the irregular distribution and near-thawing temperature of the perennially frozen ground. It must be recognized that the effects of construction will probably alter the ground surface temperature conditions. Consequently, the thickness of the active layer, the depth to the permafrost table and drainage conditions may change and may ultimately affect even the existence of permafrost. Regular and systematic inspections and monitoring are required to ensure that the ground thermal regime and the structure are reacting as predicted by the designer. If not, appropriate investigations and remedial measures should be undertaken as soon as possible to avoid major and costly maintenance and perhaps failure at a later date.

Although thorough site investigations may have been carried out and the information collected carefully analyzed to select appropriate sites or routes and designs and layouts for structures, it is possible that prominent and potential sources of trouble may have been overlooked. Such situations will arise more frequently on routes or sites for linear structures, such as dykes, roads or railroads, or where larger areas are used, such as for airfields, large single buildings or building complexes. Large isolated ground ice masses and groundwater flows in relatively narrow thawed zones that were not picked up in site surveys and unanticipated changes in snow drifting and accumulation patterns and drainage, due to erection of a structure, are examples of situations or conditions that are found or occur after construction is completed and that may contribute to unsatisfactory performance.

Similarly, improper use of the site during and following construction may have detrimental results. Destruction of the natural ground surface cover under and adjacent to building fill pads or embankments by construction equipment and other vehicles, storage or disposal of materials on the natural ground surface adjacent to or in the air space under a building and neglect of maintenance grading of fill pads and embankment surfaces may interfere with or disrupt air flow and drainage. Accumulation of snow may or may not be an advantage, depending on the situation. Maintenance work must ensure that snow drifts do not block roads, access to buildings, culverts and air spaces and ventilating ducts under buildings. Fences, barriers or deflectors may have to be erected. Snow should be disposed of in carefully selected locations. Because snow is a good insulator and will inhibit deep ground freezing or cause frozen ground temperatures to rise, it should not be allowed to accumulate or be disposed of in areas where it will adversely affect the design ground thermal regime and thus foundation or structure performance. On the other hand, snow can be used to advantage to prevent or control the rate and depth of frost penetration and lowering of permafrost temperatures, such as around tower foundations, at proposed or operating borrow pits, in stockpiles of granular materials and on drainage courses.

Special attention must be given to changes in the natural surface and subsurface drainage in the vicinity of structures and the conditions resulting from construction of drainage ditches and structures. Disruption of drainage that causes ponding of water or increased flows can rapidly and significantly alter permafrost conditions due to changes in the ground thermal regime and to erosion. It may also introduce or increase the potential for frost action. Changes in drainage, therefore, may detrimentally affect structures and the environment. Fills or embankments may block natural drainage courses, causing surface water to pond, seep under or through the fill or be diverted along new channels. Settlement and sloughing of slopes and foundation pads or embankments due to thawing, and movement of material by erosion must be corrected immediately by appropriate maintenance measures.

Large areas can be affected by thawing and large quantities of material can be moved quickly by erosion, blocking ditches and culverts and depositing material in streams to the detriment of fish and wildlife habitats, of structures such as bridges and wharves, and the use of navigable waterways. The formation of icings, whether in streams or on land surfaces, must be anticipated and controlled, for they can be the cause of serious problems. Maintenance programs must be prepared to deal with them, particularly during the spring break-up period, so that surface run-off from melting snow and icings and springs is not hindered. All drainage and hydraulic structures (culverts, bridges, ditches, dykes, dams) should be inspected periodically and problems arising due to settlement, heave, erosion and poor performance corrected as soon as possible.

Changes in subsurface drainage cannot always be identified easily and are often the cause of serious problems. Groundwater flows may be obstructed, for example, by aggradation of permafrost under an embankment, which results in ponding or subsurface diversion of the water. Subsequent settlement, frost action and erosion effects can be severe and unexpected. Subterranean caverns and channels can be created rapidly in areas underlain by ice wedges and massive ground ice deposits, with little obvious change in the ground surface. Sudden collapse of undermined embankments and cut and fill slopes often results. Similarly, a rise in the water table may cause increased frost action with significant heaving and softening of the subgrade occurring in areas previously unaffected or subject only to minor problems.

Special attention must also be given to proper construction and use of a structure or facility. Building foundation designs are based on a certain amount of heat loss from the structure. If design heat losses are exceeded due to building design changes made during or following construction, poor workmanship, insufficient insulation, changes in the intended use of the building that increase the heat load, etc., then problems should be anticipated. Disposal of industrial and human wastes, water and other liquids onto the ground under and adjacent to buildings should be prohibited, not only for foundation performance but also for pollution, health and aesthetic reasons. Although precipitation is generally light over much of the North, adequate provisions for interception, collection and disposal of rainfall and snow meltwater from buildings may be an important consideration in some areas. Mechanical equipment associated with foundations (such as fans and refrigeration systems) and passive cooling devices used to maintain the ground thermal regime within specified limits must be operated properly and checked and maintained at regular intervals to ensure they are performing their intended function. In general, "good housekeeping" of the building or facility and the surrounding area is essential.

Deterioration of steel, concrete, timber, plastic and other construction materials, especially when exposed to long periods of cold temperatures and freeze-thaw cycling, may ultimately affect the performance of a foundation or structure. Their condition should be assessed when making inspections. Wood will decay when subjected to repeated wetting and drying, especially in the active layer and at the groundline. At low temperatures, wet, frozen timber may fail suddenly under load. Similarly, steel and plastic members or coatings may shatter or fracture at low temperatures when subjected to stresses, particularly impact, that would be safe at normal temperatures. Freezing of precast and cast-in-place concrete when setting and curing will result in a poor quality and often unacceptable material for foundations because of low strength, spalling and rapid deterioration when exposed to the local environment. Many insulation materials used in buildings and in the ground are adversely affected when exposed to moisture, freeze-thaw cycling, solar radiation and hydrocarbons. The condition of all materials used for foundations and associated components should always be evaluated so that appropriate remedial action can be undertaken as soon as unacceptable deterioration or performance is noted.

In summary, there is no substitute for regular and thorough inspection and maintenance programs if structures and their foundations are to perform satisfactorily under the severe, and frequently unusual, climate and terrain conditions experienced in the North. Detailed records of all construction, inspection and maintenance work carried out are of equal importance and every effort should be made to document and report the performance of all structures and facilities so that the information is available to others. The high costs associated with every aspect of all northern engineering works, from site investigations to operation of the completed structure, make it mandatory that good records be kept so that design, construction and maintenance procedures can be improved and safe, economical structures and facilities provided.

11.2 Monitoring Performance

Proper maintenance will generally prevent major problems and failures from occurring. Much evidence of deteriorating terrain, foundation and structure conditions can be obtained from periodic visual examinations and remedial work carried out if it is interpreted correctly. Although regular maintenance and visual inspections are essential, they will not always pick up potentially destructive trends that may be occurring over a period of time, perhaps for several years, before a foundation or structure is visibly in distress. Ground temperatures may slowly increase or settlements and heave occur at imperceptible rates without any apparent detrimental effects until a point is reached where severe damage can rapidly occur. In such cases, the availability of appropriate instrumentation, with observations being made at regular intervals, will allow trends to be detected and corrective measures to be taken before damage results. Information obtained will also permit the cause of a problem to be evaluated, should distress have already occurred, an important factor when dealing with the unique terrain and foundation conditions encountered in permafrost areas. A well-organized program for collection and analysis of information should be established during the construction period and continued, perhaps with some later modification and expansion, with reports being prepared periodically.

Basic instrumentation, including ground temperature cables, frost tubes, bench marks, air temperature, precipitation and wind instruments, groundwater gauges or wells and other devices, should be installed, whenever possible, during the course of a site investigation prior to construction. These will provide information on original, undisturbed conditions, which is useful not only for design but, if the devices are suitably located, will also provide a reference for the evaluation of subsequent trends or changes that occur during and after construction. Additional instrumentation should be installed during construction specifically to monitor the performance of the structure and foundation.

The type and number of instruments or devices to be installed and the observation programs required will depend on the project and the type of structure or facility constructed. In most cases, the instrumentation should be simple and rugged so that it will stand up under the usually severe field conditions. Difficulties are frequently experienced with the operation and servicing of sophisticated electrical and mechanical devices in remote areas. Photographs taken before, during and after construction provide an excellent record for performance evaluation.

The most important parameters to be measured in most cases, in addition to weather data, are ground temperatures and vertical and lateral movements. Measurement of groundwater levels and flows may also be desired, particularly when hydraulic structures, general drainage and subsurface sources of water supply are being monitored. Geophysical techniques (Section 5.4) may be employed occasionally, to determine changes in the distribution of permafrost.

The use of temperature sensors and equipment, including frost tubes, for observing the ground thermal regime are outlined in Section 5.5.4. Copper-constantan thermocouples and interchangeable ($\pm 0.1°C$) precision thermistors having a common calibration are the sensors normally used for measurement of ground temperatures. Thermocouples are ideal for measuring temperatures to an accuracy of about $\pm 0.2°C$ and for determining temperature gradients. Individually calibrated precision thermistors should be used if very precise temperature measurements (an absolute accuracy of $\pm 0.1°C$ or better) and temperature difference resolution to several millidegrees are required. In all cases, great care must be taken in fabricating and installing the probes and all components of the circuitry, including connectors and switches, and in selecting and using the read-out equipment. Particular attention should be given to ensuring all cables are moisture-proofed.

Multiconductor cables containing a number of sensors at preselected intervals or individual sensors may be installed in boreholes or test pits, which must be carefully backfilled, particularly near the surface, to prevent disturbance caused by percolating water. Temperature cables may also be placed on piles and other types of foundations, in embankments and wells and below water bodies. A reference mark, usually indicating the ground surface, should be placed on the cable so that the subsequent position of the sensors can be established should movements occur due to frost action or thaw settlement.

Sensors are usually spaced in the ground at intervals of 0.25 to 0.5 m in the upper 3 to 4 m and from 1 to 2.5 m apart at greater depths. Ground temperatures in the upper 1 to 2 m may change hourly or daily in response to air or other temperatures imposed on the ground surface and measurements should be made frequently if useful records are to be obtained. Lead wires should be buried well below the ground surface and brought up some distance, say 3 m, away from the cable location to reduce or eliminate heat conduction along the lead wires, which can seriously affect temperatures measured at shallow depths.

Various types of read-out equipment, ranging from simple manually-operated instruments to sophisticated automatic data acquisition systems, are available. The type selected will depend mainly on project requirements. Many portable instruments contain temperature sensitive components, which seriously affect the operation and reliability of the instruments when used in the field at ambient temperatures below about 7°C. The more sophisticated instruments and systems must be installed in shelters where temperatures are maintained between 20 and 30°C.

Various devices and methods are used to measure vertical and lateral movements caused by frost action, thaw settlement, consolidation of foundation soils and slope instability. Stable permanent points or marks should be attached to or placed on foundation units such as piles, posts and concrete floors. It is suggested that numerous points be established initially and surveyed at frequent intervals. Thus, if some are destroyed or are not accessible at a later date, sufficient will remain to follow movements that occur. Depending on results obtained and the magnitude of movements measured, it may be possible to reduce the number of points to be surveyed and the frequency of observations.

To measure movements occurring in embankments and underlying frozen, thawing or thawed foundation soils, metal or plastic plates and concrete blocks can be embedded at different levels and placed on top of the fill. If the plates are at a relatively shallow depth, say less than 2 to 3 m, holes can be drilled and surveys made directly on the plates. Plates placed at greater depths should have rods extending to the ground surface so that elevations can be established and movements measured by surveys. Spiral foot or similar gauges can also be installed in boreholes to monitor movements at various levels. Alignment pins, inclinometers and similar devices can be used to monitor lateral movements. Conventional engineering survey methods are normally used; liquid filled devices may freeze or not function properly.

Groundwater levels and flows and pore water pressures in the active layer, thawing permafrost, taliks and below the permafrost are often of interest.

Various methods and equipment can be used, including simple observation wells (standpipes), piezometers and dyes inserted in the groundwater. Special precautions must be taken to prevent freezing of liquids and instruments and frost heave.

The vertical and horizontal location of all instrumentation must be tied into stable, permanent reference points that are absolutely free from movements due to frost heave or lateral instability. Tree stumps or short wood or metal stakes

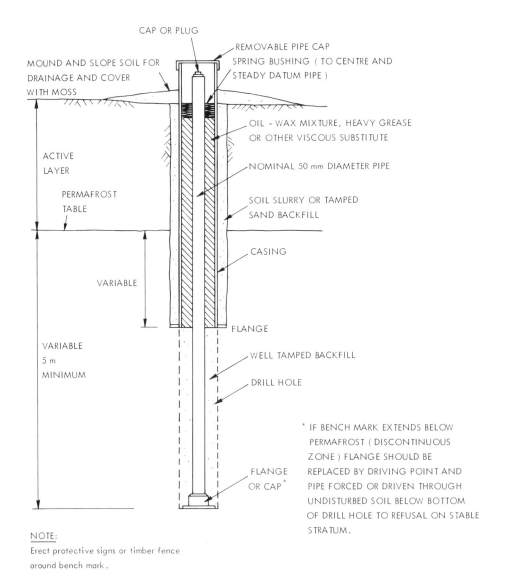

FIG. 11.1   Typical permanent bench mark for permafrost areas.

driven into the active layer or permafrost, or marks established on rock outcrops that are frost shattered, are not reliable. Permanent marks can be placed in competent bedrock, but in its absence special bench marks and reference points that are not affected by frost action must be installed to provide a datum for establishing and checking elevations, centrelines and marker alignments. A typical bench mark or reference point used in permafrost areas is shown in Fig. 11.1.

In many cases, instrumentation used for monitoring construction and the performance and behaviour of structures, foundations and foundation soils in non-permafrost areas (Hanna 1974, Bozozuk 1976) can be modified for use in permafrost areas. In other cases, new instrumentation may have to be developed or installation methods changed to suit the conditions encountered in the North. References describing methods and equipment used in the field for the measurement of ground temperatures are given in Section 5.5.4. Examples of some instrumentation used for monitoring ground, foundation and structure movements, groundwater and pore pressures on various engineering projects in permafrost areas are described by Johnston (1962), Bozozuk et al. (1963), Johnston (1965), Slusarchuk et al. (1973), Gupta et al. (1973) and Guther (1972).

11.3 Conclusion

The design and construction of a variety of engineering structures and facilities have been successfully undertaken in the North in recent years. Much experience has been gained in overcoming the obstacles and problems posed by the hostile northern terrain and climate conditions and the need to construct in remote areas. More complex and challenging projects are proposed and will be undertaken in the future as development of the North and its resources proceeds.

Anything can be built and will perform satisfactorily under any soil and permafrost conditions encountered in northern areas, provided that the required information is obtained from thorough site investigations, basic principles are understood and followed and sound engineering judgment is used in the design, construction, operation and maintenance of structures and facilities. More information is needed to fill in the gaps in our knowledge and to guide those engaged in future engineering works in permafrost areas so that design and construction methods can be improved and the high costs of construction and maintenance can be reduced. Every effort should be made to record and publish the experience obtained on completed projects. Only in this way can advances be made and benefits realized in the development of the North.

REFERENCES

AAMOT, H.W.C. 1966. Dynamic foundation measurements, Barter Island, Alaska. U.S. Army, CRREL, Spec. Rpt. 75, 32 p.

ADAMS, J.I. and BAZETT, D.J. 1963. Till cofferdam dumped in water. Engineering Journal, Oct., pp. 51-56.

ADAMS, K.M. 1978. Building and operating winter roads in Canada and Alaska. Canada, Dept. of Indian and Northern Affairs, Environment Division, Environmental Studies 4, 221 p.

AITKEN, G.W. 1966. Reduction of frost heave by surcharge loading. Proc. International Conference on Permafrost (1963), Lafayette, IN, U.S. National Academy of Sciences, Publ. 1287, pp. 319-324.

AITKEN, G.W. 1970. Transport of frozen soil. Proc. Vermont Conference on Winter Construction (1969), Univ. of Vermont, pp. 50-68.

AITKEN, G.W. 1974. Reduction of frost heave by surcharge stress. U.S. Army, CRREL, Tech. Rpt. 184, 29 p.

AITKEN, G.W. and BERG, R.L. 1968. Digital solution of modified Berggren equation to calculate depth of freeze or thaw in multilayered systems. U.S. Army, CRREL, Spec. Rpt. 122, 18 p.

AKILI, W. 1971. Stress strain behaviour of frozen fine-grained soils. U.S. Highway Research Board, Record 360, pp. 1-9.

ALDRICH, H.P. 1956. Frost penetration below highway and airfield pavements. U.S. Highway Research Board, Bull. 135, pp. 124-149.

ALKIRE, B.D. and ANDERSLAND, O.B. 1973. The effect of confining pressure on the mechanical properties of sand-ice materials. J. of Glaciology, Vol. 12, No. 66, pp. 469-481.

ALKIRE, B.D., HAAS, W.M. and KADERABEK, T.J. 1975. Improving low temperature compaction of a granular soil. Can. Geotech. J., Vol. 12, No. 4, pp. 527-530.

ALTER, A.J. 1969a. Water supply in cold regions. U.S. Army, CRREL, Monograph MIII-C5a, 91 p.

ALTER, A.J. 1969b. Sewerage and sewage disposal in cold regions. U.S. Army, CRREL, Monograph MIII-C5b, 110 p.

ALTER, A.J. 1969c. Solid waste management in cold regions. Alaska, Dept. of Health and Welfare, Alaska Water Laboratory, College, AK, Scientific Research, Data and Reports, Vol. 2, No. 2, 122 p.

ALYESKA PIPELINE SERVICE COMPANY. 1976. Heat pipes. Data Sheet C-2, 1 p.

ANDERSLAND, O.B. and AL NOURY, I. 1970. Time dependent strength behaviour of frozen soils. ASCE, J. Soil Mech. Found. Div., Vol. 96, No. SM4, pp. 1249-1265.

ANDERSLAND, O.B. and ANDERSON, D.M. (ed.) 1978. Geotechnical engineering for cold regions. McGraw-Hill, New York, NY, 576 p.

ANDERSON, D.M. and MORGENSTERN, N.R. 1973. Physics, chemistry and mechanics of frozen ground: a review. Proc. 2nd International Conference on Permafrost, Yakutsk, U.S.S.R., North American Contribution, U.S. National Academy of Sciences, pp. 257-288.

ANDERSON, D.M. and TICE, A.R. 1972. Predicting unfrozen water contents in frozen soils from surface area measurements. U.S. Highway Research Board, Record 393, pp. 12-18.

ANDERSON, D.M., TICE, A.R. and McKIM, H.L. 1973. The unfrozen water and the apparent specific heat capacity of frozen soils. Proc. 2nd International Conference on Permafrost, Yakutsk, U.S.S.R., North American Contribution, U.S. National Academy of Sciences, pp. 289-295.

ANISIMOV, V.A. and SOROKIN, V.S. 1975. Repair work on a frozen dam. Hydrotechnical Construction (U.S.S.R.), No. 6, pp. 5-7, Transl. by Consultants Bureau, New York, NY, for ASCE.

ANKERS, J.W., ANTONIADES, E.P., CAMPBELL, R.W. and WOO, G.L. 1977. Sulphur foams for permafrost protection. Proc. International Conference on Materials Engineering in the Arctic (1976), St. Jovite, Que. (M.B. Ives, ed.), Amer. Soc. for Metals, pp. 42-48.

ANNAN, A.P., DAVIS, J.L. and SCOTT, W.J. 1976a. Impulse radar profiling in permafrost. Geol. Surv. Can., Paper 75-1C, pp. 343-351.

ANNAN, A.P., DAVIS, J.L. and SCOTT, W.J. 1976b. Impulse radar wide angle reflection and refraction sounding in permafrost. Geol. Surv. Can., Paper 75-1C, pp. 335-342.

APTIKAEV, F.F. 1964. Temperature field effect on the distribution of seismic velocities in the permafrost zone. In: Akad. Nauk S.S.S.R., Sibjrskoe otd—ie. Inst. Merzlotovedeniia. Teplovye protsessy v merzlykh porod, pp. 190-199. (In Russian.)

ARAKAWA, K. 1966. Theoretical studies of ice segregation in soil. J. of Glaciology, Vol. 6, No. 44, pp. 255-260.

ARCONE, S.A. 1977. A computer program to determine the resistance of long wires and rods to nonhomogeneous ground. U.S. Army, CRREL, Rpt. 77-2, 20 p.

ARVIDSON, W.D. and MORGENSTERN, N.R. 1974. Water flow induced by soil freezing. Proc. 27th Can. Geotech. Conference, Edmonton, Alta., Preprint vol., pp. 137-143.

ASCE. 1977. Application of soil dynamics in cold regions. Fall Convention (Oct. 17-21, 1977), San Francisco, CA, Conference preprint 3011, 8 papers, 312 p.

ASHRAE. 1977. Design heat transfer coefficients. American Society Heating, Refrigerating and Air-Conditioning Engineers Handbook, Fundamentals vol., Chap. 22, pp. 22-1 to 22-28.

ASTM. 1964. Procedure for testing soils. (4th ed.) ASTM, Philadelphia, PA., 535 p.

ASTM. 1970. Special procedures for testing soil and rock for engineering purposes. ASTM, Philadelphia, PA, Spec. Tech. Publ. 479, 630 p.

ASTM. 1975. Standard recommended practice for investigating and sampling soil and rock for engineering purposes. 1975 Annual Book of ASTM Standards, Part 19, Standard D420-69, pp. 60-64.

ATKINS, R.T. 1979. Determination of frost penetration by soil resistivity measurements. U.S. Army, CRREL, Spec. Rpt. 79-22, 12 p.

ATLAS COPCO. 1964. Permafrost overburden exploration. Compressed Air Comments, Vol. 7, No. 1, pp. 8-9.

AULD, R.G., ROBBINS, R.J., ROSENEGGER, L.W. and SANGSTER, R.H.B. 1978. Pad foundation design and performance of surface facilities in the Mackenzie Delta. Proc. 3rd. International Conference on Permafrost, Edmonton, Alta., Canada, National Research Council, Vol. 1, pp. 765-771.

AVERILL, D.W. and HEINKE, G.W. 1974. Vacuum sewer systems and their possible Canadian applications. Can. J. Civil Eng., Vol. 1, No. 1, pp. 50-61.

AYERS, A.D. and CAMPBELL, R.B. 1951. Freezing point of water in a soil as related to salt and moisture contents of the soil. Soil Science, Vol. 72, Sept., pp. 201-208.

BABB, A.L., CHOW, D.M., GARLID, K.L., POPOVICH, R.P. and WOODRUFF, E.M. 1971. The thermo tube, a natural convection heat transfer device for stabilization of arctic soils in oil producing regions. Presented at the 46th Annual Fall Meeting (Oct.), New Orleans, LA, Society of Petroleum Engineers, AIME, Paper SPE 3618, 12 p.

BAFUS, G.R., GUYMAN, G.L. and CARLSON, R.F. 1975. Some results of a thermal analysis of offshore artificial islands. Proc. 3rd International Conference on Port and Ocean Engineering Under Arctic Conditions, Fairbanks, AK, Vol. II, pp. 967-985.

BAKAKIN, V.P. and ZELENIN, A.N. 1966. Excavation of frozen soils. Proc. International Conference on Permafrost (1963), Lafayette, IN, U.S. National Academy of Sciences, Publ. 1287, pp. 395-399.

BAKER, T.H.W. 1976. Transportation, preparation and storage of frozen soil samples for laboratory testing. ASTM, Spec. Tech. Publ. 599, pp. 88-112.

BALKWILL, H.R., ROY, K.J. and HOPKINS, W.S. 1974. Glacial features and pingos, Amund Ringnes Island, Arctic Archipelago. Can. J. Earth Sci., Vol. 11, No. 9, pp. 1319-1325.

BANIN, A. and ANDERSON, D.M. 1974. The effects of salt concentration changes during freezing on the unfrozen water content of frozen porous materials. Water Resources Research, Vol. 10, No. 1, pp. 124-128.

BANNER, J.A. and VAN EVERDINGEN, R.O. 1979. Frost gauges and freezing gauges. Canada, Dept. of Environment, Inland Waters Directorate, National Hydrology Research Institute, IWD Tech. Bull. 10, NHRI Paper 3, 18 p.

BARNES, D.F. 1966. Geophysical methods for delineating permafrost. Proc. International Conference on Permafrost (1963), Lafayette, IN, U.S. National Academy of Sciences, Publ. 1287, pp. 349-355.

BARNETT, D.M., EDLUND, S.A., DREDGE, L.A., THOMAS, C.D. and PREVETT, L.S. 1975. Terrain classification and evaluation: Eastern Melville Island, N.W.T. Geol. Surv. Can., Open File 252.

BARRY, B.L. and CORMIE, J.G. 1971. Constructional aspects of the ± 450 HVDC Nelson River transmission line. Proc. Manitoba Power Conference EHV-DC, Winnipeg, Man., pp. 459-492.

BARSVARY, A.K., KLYM, T.W. and FRANKLIN, J.A. 1980. List of terms, symbols and recommended S.I. units and multiples for geotechnical engineering. Can. Geotech. J., Vol. 17, No. 1, pp. 89-96.

BASHAM, P.W., FORSYTH, D.A. and WETMILLER, R.J. 1977. The seismicity of northern Canada. Can. J. Earth Sci., Vol. 14, No. 12, pp. 1646-1667.

BATENCHUK, E.M., BIYANOV, G.F., TOROPOV, L.N. and MYZNIKOV, Yu.N. 1968. Placing cohesive soils in winter in the far North. Canada, National Research Council, Tech. Transl. 1501 (1972), 119 p.

BATTLE, J.B. 1971. Wrapped H-piles help beat permafrost. Heavy Construction News, Oct. 11, pp. 4-6.

BAUER, A., CALDER, P.N., MACLACHLAN, R.R. and HALUPKA, M. 1973. Cratering and ditching with explosives in frozen soils. Canada, Defense Research Board, Report DREV R-699/73, 123 p.

BAUER, A., HARRIS, G.R., LANG, L., PREZIONI, P. and SELLECK, D.J. 1965. How 10c puts crater research to work. Engineering and Mining, Vol. 166, No. 9, pp. 117-121.

BEAUCHAMP, J.C. and STAMER, S. 1971. Northern bridge construction. Proc. Roads and Transportation Association of Canada Convention, Vancouver, B.C., pp. 83-96.

BEISTLINE, E.H. 1966. Placer mining in frozen ground. Proc. International Conference on Permafrost (1963), Lafayette, IN, U.S. National Academy of Sciences, Publ. 1287, pp. 463-467.

BELCHER, D.J., COSTELLO, R.B., FALLON, G.J., HODGE, R.J., LADENHEIM, H.C., LUEDER, D.R. and MOLLARD, J.D. 1951. Cornell Univ., Landform Series, Vols. 1 to 6, Ithaca, NY.

BENDZ, J. 1977. Permafrost problems beaten in pile driving research. Western Construction, Vol. 52, No. 11, pp. 16, 18, 34, 35.

BENNETT, F.L. 1975. A half-century of cold-regions construction. ASCE, J. Const. Div., Vol. 101, No. CO4, pp. 839-851.

BENNETT, W.F., HOLLER, A.C. and HURST, W.D. 1977. An unusual form of corrosion. J. Amer. Water Works Assoc., Vol. 69, No. 1, pp. 26-30.

BERG, R.L. 1974. Design of civil airfield pavements for seasonal frost and permafrost conditions. U.S. Federal Aviation Agency, Research and Development, Rpt. FAA-AD-74-30, 98 p.

BERG, R.L. and AITKEN, G.W. 1973. Some passive methods of controlling geocryological conditions in roadway construction. Proc. 2nd International Conference on Permafrost, Yakutsk, U.S.S.R., North American Contribution, U.S. National Academy of Sciences, pp. 581-586.

BERG, R.L., GARTNER, K.E. and GUYMON, G.L. 1977. A mathematical model to predict frost heave. Proc. International Symposium Frost Action in Soils, Univ. of Luleå, Sweden, Vol. 2, pp. 93-109.

BERG, R.L. and QUINN, W.F. 1977. Use of a light-coloured surface to reduce seasonal thaw penetration beneath embankments on permafrost. Proc. 2nd International Symposium on Cold Regions Engineering (1976), Fairbanks, AK, Univ. of Alaska, Dept. Civil Eng., pp. 86-99.

BERG, R.L. and SMITH, N. 1976. Observations along the pipeline haul road between Livengood and the Yukon River. U.S. Army, CRREL, Spec. Rpt. 76-11, 83 p.

BERNELL, L. 1965. Properties of frozen granular soils and their use in dam construction. Proc. 6th International Conference on Soil Mechanics and Foundation Engineering, Vol. 2, pp. 451-455.

BERUBE, Y., FRENETTE, M., GILBERT, R. and ANCTIL, C. 1973. Studies of mine waste containment at two mines near Yellowknife, N.W.T. Canada, Dept. of Indian and Northern Affairs, ALUR Rpt. 72-73-32, 192 p.

BESKOW, G. 1935. Soil freezing and frost heaving. Swedish Geol. Soc., Ser. C, No. 375, 26th Year, Book 3, Transl. by J.O. Osterberg, The Technological Institute, Northwestern Univ., Evanston, IL. (1947), 145 p.

BIA, P., and COMBARNOUS, M. 1970. Measurement of the thermal conductivity and thermal diffusivity of natural rocks at low temperature. J. of Physics (E): Scientific Instruments, Vol. 3, pp. 536-540.

BIRD, J.B. 1967. The physiography of Arctic Canada. The Johns Hopkins Press, Baltimore, MD, 336 p.

BIRD, J.B. 1972. The physical characteristics of northern Canada. In: Studies in Canadian Geography: The North (W.C. Wonders, ed.), Univ. of Toronto Press, for the 22nd International Geographical Congress, Montreal, Que., pp. 1-24.

BIYANOV, G.F. 1965. Construction of a water storage dam on permafrost. Canada, National Research Council, Tech. Transl. 1353, 30 p.

BIYANOV, G.F. 1970a. Construction of a rockfill dam for the Vilyui Hydroelectric Project. Hydrotechnical Construction (U.S.S.R.), No. 2, pp. 125-133, Transl. by Consultants Bureau, New York, NY, for ASCE.

BIYANOV, G.F. 1970b. Experience in construction and operation of low-head dams on permafrost soils. Hydrotechnical Construction (U.S.S.R.), No. 9, pp. 12-17, Transl. by Consultants Bureau, New York, NY, for ASCE.

BIYANOV, G.F. 1975. Dams on permafrost. U.S. Army, CRREL, Draft Transl. TL 555, 234 p.

BIYANOV, G.F. 1978. Experience on constructing dams on permafrost in Yakutia. Proc. 2nd International Conference on Permafrost (1973), Yakutsk, U.S.S.R., U.S.S.R. Contribution, U.S. National Academy of Sciences, pp. 594-598.

BLACK, R.F. 1954. Permafrost: a review. Geol. Soc. Amer. Bull., Vol. 65, pp. 839-856.

BLISS, L.C. and WEIN, R.W. 1971. Changes in the active layer caused by surface disturbance. Proc. Seminar on the Permafrost Active Layer, Canada, National

Research Council, Associate Committee Geotechnical Research, Tech. memo. 103, pp. 37-46.

BLOUIN, S.E., CHAMBERLAIN, E.J., SELLMAN, P.V. and GARFIELD, D.E. 1979. Penetration tests in subsea permafrost, Prudhoe Bay, Alaska. U.S. Army, CRREL, Rpt. 79-7, 45 p.

BOGOSLOVSKIY, P.A., VESELOV, V.A., UKHOV, S.B., STOTSENKO, A.V. and TSVID, A.A. 1966. Dams in permafrost regions. Proc. International Conference on Permafrost (1963), Lafayette, IN, U.S. National Academy of Sciences, Publ. 1287, pp. 450-455.

BOYCHENKO, V.I. 1971. Underground cable systems in permafrost soil. Biblioteka Elektromontera, No. 341, pp. 3-56. U.S. Air Force, Foreign Tech. Div., Transl. FTD-HC-23-1419-74, Aug. 1974, 71 p.

BOYD, D.W. 1973. Normal freezing and thawing degree-days for Canada, 1931-1960. Canada, Dept. of Environment, Atmospheric Environment Service, Publ. CL1 4-73, 38 p.

BOYD, D.W. 1975. Climatic information for building design in Canada. Canada, National Research Council, Paper NRC 13986, 47 p.

BOYD, D.W. 1976. Normal freezing and thawing degree-days from normal monthly temperatures. Can. Geotech. J., Vol. 13, No. 2, pp. 176-180.

BOYD, W.L. and BOYD, J.W. 1965. Water supply and sewage disposal developments in the far North. J. Amer. Water Works Assoc., Vol. 57, No. 7, pp. 858-868.

BOYD, W.L. and BOYD, J.W. 1967. Microbiological studies of aquatic habitats of the area of Inuvik, Northwest Territories. Arctic, Vol. 20, No. 1, pp. 27-41.

BOYDELL, A.N., DRABINSKY, K.A. and NETTERVILLE, J.A. 1974. Legend to accompany maps of Boothia Peninsula and Simpson Peninsula, N.W.T. Geol. Surv. Can., Open File 285.

BOZOZUK, M. 1976. Field instrumentation for foundation soils and buildings. In: Analysis and Design of Building Foundations (Hsai-Yang Fang, ed.), Envo Publishing, Lehigh Valley, PA, pp. 181-208.

BOZOZUK, M., JOHNSTON, G.H. and HAMILTON, J.J. 1963. Deep bench marks in clay and permafrost areas. In: Field Testing of Soils, ASTM, Spec. Tech. Publ. 322, pp. 265-275.

BRANDON, L.V. 1965. Groundwater hydrology and water supply in the District of Mackenzie, Yukon Territory and adjoining parts of British Columbia. Geol. Surv. Can., Paper 64-39, 102 p.

BRANDON, L.V. 1966. Evidences of groundwater flow in permafrost regions. Proc. International Conference on Permafrost (1963), Lafayette, IN, U.S. National Academy of Sciences, Publ. 1287, pp. 176-177.

BRESLER, E. and MILLER, R. 1975. Estimation of pore blockage induced by freezing of unsaturated soil. Proc. Conference on Soil-Water Problems in Cold Regions, Calgary, Alta., pp. 161-175.

BREWER, M.C. 1958a. The thermal regime of an Arctic lake. Trans. Amer. Geophys. U., Vol. 39, April, pp. 278-284.

BREWER, M.C. 1958b. Some results of geothermal investigations of permafrost in northern Alaska. Trans. Amer. Geophys. U., Vol. 39, Feb., pp. 19-26.

BRIDGES, L. 1978. Monster trenchers tackle tough pipeline jobs. Engineering and Contract Record, Feb. pp. 20-21.

BRODSKAYA, A.G. 1962. The creep of polycrystalline ice. U.S.S.R. Academy of Sciences, Moscow. (In Russian.)

BROMS, B.B. and YAO, L.Y. 1964. Shear strength of a soil after freezing and thawing. ASCE, J. Soil Mech. Found. Div., Vol. 90, pp. 1-25.

BROWN, A.D. 1976. Building islands in the Beaufort Sea. Geos, Spring, pp. 19-20.

BROWN, A.D. and BARRIE, K.W. 1975. Artificial island construction in the shallow

Beaufort Sea. Proc. 3rd International Conference on Port and Ocean Engineering Under Arctic Conditions, Fairbanks, AK, Vol. II, pp. 705-717.

BROWN, I.C. (ed.) 1967. Groundwater in Canada. Geol. Surv. Can., Economic Geology
Rpt. 24, 242 p.

BROWN, R.J.E. 1964. Permafrost investigations on the Mackenzie Highway in Alberta
and Mackenzie District. Canada, National Research Council, Division Building
Research, Tech. Paper 175, 67 p.

BROWN, R.J.E. 1965. Permafrost investigations in Saskatchewan and Manitoba.
Canada, National Research Council, Division Building Research, Tech. Paper
193, 73 p.

BROWN, R.J.E. 1966a. Relation between mean annual air and ground temperatures in the
permafrost region of Canada. Proc. International Conference on Permafrost
(1963), Lafayette, IN, U.S. National Academy of Sciences, Publ. 1287, pp.
241-246.

BROWN, R.J.E. 1966b. Influence of vegetation on permafrost. Proc. International Conference on Permafrost (1963), Lafayette, IN, U.S. National Academy of
Sciences, Publ. 1287, pp. 20-25.

BROWN, R.J.E. 1967a. Permafrost investigations in British Columbia and Yukon Territory. Canada, National Research Council, Division Building Research, Tech.
Paper 253, 115 p.

BROWN, R.J.E. 1967b. Permafrost in Canada. Canada, National Research Council, Division Building Research, Map NRC 9769, and Geol. Surv. Can., Map 1246A.

BROWN, R.J.E. 1968. Permafrost investigations in northern Ontario and northeastern
Manitoba. Canada, National Research Council, Division Building Research,
Tech. Paper 291, 75 p.

BROWN, R.J.E. 1969. Factors influencing discontinuous permafrost in Canada. In: The
Periglacial Environment: Past and Present (T.L. Péwé, ed.), Proc. Alaska Field
Symposium, VII INQUA Congress (1965), pp. 11-53.

BROWN, R.J.E. 1970a. Permafrost in Canada: its influence on northern development.
Univ. of Toronto Press, Toronto, Ont., 246 p.

BROWN, R.J.E. 1970b. Permafrost as an ecological factor in the subarctic. Proc. Symposium on Ecology of Subarctic Regions (1966), Helsinki, Finland, UNESCO,
Paris, France, pp. 129-140.

BROWN, R.J.E. 1971. Characteristics of the active layer in the permafrost region of
Canada. Canada, National Research Council, Associate Committee Geotechnical
Research, Tech. memo. 103, pp. 1-7.

BROWN, R.J.E. 1972. Permafrost in the Arctic archipelago. Zeitschrift fur Geomor-
phologie, Suppl. 13, pp. 102-130.

BROWN, R.J.E. 1973a. Influence of climatic and terrain factors on ground temperatures
at three locations in the permafrost region of Canada. Proc. 2nd International
Conference on Permafrost, Yakutsk, U.S.S.R., North American Contribution,
U.S. National Academy of Sciences, pp. 27-34.

BROWN, R.J.E. 1973b. Ground ice as an initiator of landforms in permafrost regions. In:
Research in Polar and Alpine Geomorphology, Proc. 3rd Guelph Symposium on
Geomorphology, Guelph, Ont., pp. 25-42.

BROWN, R.J.E. 1974. Some aspects of airphoto interpretation of permafrost in Canada.
Canada, National Research Council, Division Building Research, Tech. Paper
409, 34 p.

BROWN, R.J.E. 1975. Permafrost investigations in Quebec and Newfoundland
(Labrador). Canada, National Research Council, Division Building Research,
Tech. Paper 449, 99 p.

BROWN, R.J.E. 1978. Influence of climate and terrain on ground temperature in the continuous permafrost zone of northern Manitoba and Keewatin District, Canada.

Proc. 3rd International Conference on Permafrost, Edmonton, Alta., Canada, National Research Council, Vol. 1, pp. 15-21.

BROWN, R.J.E. and JOHNSTON, G.H. 1964. Permafrost and related engineering problems. Endeavour, Vol. XXIII, No. 89, pp. 66-72.

BROWN, R.J.E. and KUPSCH, W.O. 1974. Permafrost terminology. Canada, National Research Council, Associate Committee Geotechnical Research, Tech. Memo. 111, 62 p.

BROWN, R.J.E. and PEWE, T.L. 1973. Distribution of permafrost in North America and its relationship to the environment: a review, 1963-1973. Proc. 2nd International Conference on Permafrost, Yakutsk, U.S.S.R., North American Contribution, U.S. National Academy of Sciences, pp. 71-100.

BROWN, W.G. 1962. Bendix G-15 "ALGO" computer programme for calculating the steady temperature under arbitrary areas on the surface of a semi-infinite solid. Canada, National Research Council, Division Building Research, Computer Programme 14.

BROWN, W.G. 1963a. The temperature under heated or cooled areas on the ground surface. Trans. Engineering Institute, Canada, Vol. 6, No. B-14, 10 p.

BROWN, W.G. 1963b. Graphical determination of temperature under heated or cooled areas on the ground surface. Canada, National Research Council, Division Building Research, Tech. Paper No. 163, 38 p.

BROWN, W.G. 1964. Difficulties associated with predicting depth of freeze or thaw. Can. Geotech. J., Vol. 1, No. 4, pp. 215-226.

BROWN, W.G. and JOHNSTON, G.H. 1970. Dikes on permafrost: predicting thaw and settlement. Can. Geotech. J., Vol. 7, No. 4, pp. 365-371.

BROWN, W.G., JOHNSTON, G.H. and BROWN, R.J.E. 1964. Comparison of observed and calculated ground temperatures with permafrost distribution under a northern lake. Can. Geotech. J., Vol. 1, No. 3, pp. 147-154.

BUCHANAN, R.D., DUDLEY, R.A. and PEOPLES, H. 1966. Ice core for a pervious earth dam north of the Arctic Circle. Civil Engineering, Vol. 36, No. 12, pp. 48-50.

BUCHKO, N.A., KUZENTSOV, A.L., SILOLOV, V.S. and TSORKURENKO, K.M. 1975. Use of thermal piles for creating frozen cut-off curtains. Hydrotechnical Construction (U.S.S.R.), No. 5, pp. 21-31, Transl. by Consultants Bureau, New York, NY, for ASCE.

BUDHIA, H. and KREITH, F. 1973. Heat transfer with melting or freezing in a wedge. International J. Heat Mass Transfer, Vol. 16, pp. 195-211.

BURNS, B.M. 1973. The climate of the Mackenzie Valley-Beaufort Sea. Environment Canada, Climatological Studies 24, Vol. 1 (1973), 227 p., and Vol. 2 (1974), 239 p.

CAILLEUX, A. 1971. Lacs en ourson, cernes et thermokarst (Bear cub and marginate lakes and thermokarst). Cahiers Geogr. Québec, Vol. 15, No. 34, pp. 131-138.

CAMERON, J.J. 1976. Waste impounding embankments in permafrost regions: the sewage lagoon embankment, Inuvik, N.W.T. In: Some Problems of Solid and Liquid Waste Disposal in the Northern Environment, Environment Canada, Environmental Protection Service, Rpt. EPS-4-NW-76-2, pp. 141-230.

CAMERON, J.J. 1977. Buried utilities in permafrost regions. Proc. Symposium on Utilities Delivery in Arctic Regions, Edmonton, Alta., Environment Canada, Environmental Protection Service, Rpt. EPS-3-WP-77-1, pp. 151-200.

CAMERON, J.J. and SMITH, D.W. 1977. Annotated bibliography on northern environmental engineering, 1974-75. Environment Canada, Environmental Protection Service, Rpt. EPS-3-WP-77-6, 154 p.

CAMPBELL, K.J. and ORANGE, A.S. 1974. A continuous profile of sea-ice and fresh water ice thickness by impulse radar. Polar Record, Vol. 17, No. 106, pp. 31-41.

CANADA ENERGY, MINES AND RESOURCES. 1976-77. Pit slope manual. Chap. 1 Summary, CANMET Rpt. 76-22, 65 p., Chap. 2 Structural geology, CANMET Rpt. 77-41, 123 p., Chap. 3 Mechanical properties, CANMET Rpt. 77-12, 87 p., Chap. 4 Groundwater, CANMET Rpt. 77-13, 240 p., Chap. 5 Design, CANMET Rpt. 77-5, 126 p., Chap. 6 Mechanical support, CANMET Rpt. 77-3, 111 p., Chap. 7 Perimeter blasting, CANMET Rpt. 77-14, 82 p., Chap. 8 Monitoring, CANMET Rpt. 77-15, 188 p., Chap. 9 Waste embankments, CANMET Rpt. 77-1, 137 p., Chap. 10 Environmental planning, CANMET Rpt. 77-2, 93 p.

CANADA ENVIRONMENT. 1971. Atlas of climatic maps. Atmospheric Environment Service, Toronto, Ont., 10 maps.

CANADA ENVIRONMENT. 1973. Canadian normals: 1941-70, Vol. 1 Temperature, Vol. 2 Precipitation, Vol. 3 Wind. Atmospheric Environment Service, Toronto, Ont.

CANADA ENVIRONMENT. 1974a. Guidelines for effluent quality and waste-water treatment at federal establishments. Environmental Protection Service, Ottawa, Ont.

CANADA ENVIRONMENT. 1974b. Interim guidelines for waste-water disposal in northern Canadian communities. Environmental Protection Service, Ottawa, Ont., Rpt. EPS-2-WP-74-1, 10 p.

CANADA ENVIRONMENT. 1974c. Review of petroleum product spill containment dykes in the North. Imperial Oil Limited, Environmental Protection Service, Rpt. EPS 3-EE-74-1, 56 p.

CANADA ENVIRONMENT. 1978. Performance assessment of test liners for petroleum product storage areas in northern Canada. EBA Engineering Consultants Ltd., Environmental Protection Service, Ottawa, Ont., Rpt. EPS 4-EC-78-6, 66 p.

CANADA ENVIRONMENT. 1979. Cold climate utilities delivery design manual. Environmental Protection Service, Edmonton, Alta., Rpt. EPS 3-WP-79-2, 644 p.

CANADA NATIONAL RESEARCH COUNCIL. 1965. Climatic information for building design in Canada. Supplement No. 1 to the National Building Code of Canada. Associate Committee on the National Building Code, Ottawa, Ont., 41 p.

CANADA NATIONAL RESEARCH COUNCIL. 1980a. National Building Code of Canada. Associate Committee on the National Building Code, Ottawa, Ont., 547 p.

CANADA NATIONAL RESEARCH COUNCIL. 1980b. The Supplement to the National Building Code of Canada. Associate Committee on the National Building Code, Ottawa, Ont., 293 p.

CANADA TRANSPORT. 1967a. The climate of the Canadian Arctic. Meteorological Branch, Ottawa, Ont., 32 p.

CANADA TRANSPORT. 1967b. Atlas of climatic maps. Meteorological Branch, Ottawa, Ont.

CANADA TRANSPORT. 1969. Engineering planning, design and construction manual, Section 1, Design and evaluation of flexible and rigid pavements. Construction Engineering and Architecture Branch, Ottawa, Ont., July.

CANADA TRANSPORT. 1971. Proc. Arctic transportation conference (Dec. 1970), Yellowknife, N.W.T. Sponsored by Ministry of Transport and Dept. of Indian and Northern Affairs, Ottawa, Ont., 3 Volumes, 1100 p.

CANADA TRANSPORT. 1973. Aerodrome standards, physical characteristics and zoning requirements. Airways Section, Flight Standards and Regulations Division, Ottawa, Ont., Dec.

CANADA TRANSPORT. 1974. Arctic oil and gas by rail. Study by Canadian National

Railways and Canadian Pacific Limited for Ministry of Transport, Transportation Development Agency, Ottawa, Ont., 6 Volumes.

CANADIAN GEOTECHNICAL SOCIETY. 1978. Canadian foundation engineering manual. Part 1 properties of soil and rock, 88 p., Part 2 Shallow foundations, 104 p., Part 3 Deep foundations, 114 p., Part 4 Excavations and retaining structures, 72 p.

CAREY, K.L. 1970. Icing occurrence, control and prevention: an annotated bibliography. U.S. Army, CRREL, Spec. Rpt. 151, 59 p.

CAREY, K.L. 1973. Icings developed from surface water and ground water. U.S. Army, CRREL, Monograph MIII-D3, 67 p.

CAREY, K.L., HUCK, R.W. and GASKIN, D.A. 1975. Prevention and control of culvert icing: summary report on studies 1966-70. U.S. Army, CRREL, Spec. Rpt. 224, 82 p.

CARSLAW, H.S. and JAEGER, J.C. 1959. Conduction of heat in solids. (2nd ed.) Oxford Univ. Press, Oxford, England, 510 p.

CARY, J.W. and MAYLAND, H.F. 1972. Salt and water movement in unsaturated frozen soil. Proc. Soil Sci. Amer., Vol. 36, No. 4, pp. 549-555.

CASAGRANDE, A. 1932. A new theory of frost heaving: discussion. Proc. U.S. Highway Research Board, Vol. 11, Part I, pp. 168-172.

CASS, J.R. 1959. Subsurface explorations in permafrost areas. ASCE, J. Soil Mech. Found. Div., Vol. 85, No. SM5, pp. 31-41. Discussions by G.H. Johnston, G.R. Lange, H.W. Stevens and W.P. Verville in 1960, Vol. 86, No. SM3, pp. 63-67.

CHAFET, A.B. 1975. Guidelines for designing, constructing and operating tailings dams and ponds. Engineering and Mining J., Vol. 176, No. 12, pp. 89-90.

CHAMBERLAIN, E., GROVES, C. and PERHAM, R. 1972. The mechanical behaviour of frozen earth materials under high pressure triaxial test conditions. Geotechnique, Vol. 22, No. 3, pp. 469-483.

CHANDLER, R.J. 1970. Solifluction on low angle slopes in Northamptonshire. Quarternary J. Engineering Geology, Vol. 3, pp. 65-69.

CHARLES, J.L. 1959. Permafrost aspects of the Hudson Bay Railroad. ASCE, J. Soil Mech. Found. Div., Vol. 85, No. SM6, pp. 125-135.

CHARLES, J.L. 1965. The Great Slave Lake Railway. J. Eng. Inst. Canada, May, pp. 15-19.

CHARLWOOD, R.G. and SVEC, O. 1972. Northern pipelines: an application for numerical analysis, Part II. Proc. Symposium on Applications of Solid Mechanics, Univ. of Waterloo, Waterloo, Ont., pp. 65-80.

CHERITON, W.R. 1966. Electrical heating of a water supply pipeline under Arctic conditions. J. Eng. Inst. Canada, Sept., pp. 31-35.

CHERNEY, E.A. 1975. Voltages induced on pipelines near power transmission lines. Ontario Hydro Research Quarterly, Vol. 27, No. 1, pp. 1-6.

CHURCH, M. 1977. River studies in northern Canada: reading the record from river morphology. Geoscience Canada, Vol. 4, No. 1, pp. 4-12.

CHYURLIA, J. 1973. Stability of river banks and slopes along the Liard River and Mackenzie River, N.W.T. Canada, Dept. of Indian and Northern Affairs, Environmental-Social Program, Northern Pipelines, Rpt. 73-3, pp. 111-152.

CIHLAR, J. 1976. Thermal infrared remote sensing: a bibliography. Canada Centre for Remote Sensing, Res. Rpt. 76-1, 48 p.

COATES, D.F. and YU, U.S. (ed.) 1977. Pit slope manual, Chap. 9 Waste embankments. Canada, Dept of Energy, Mines and Resources, Canadian Centre for Mineral and Energy Technology, CANMET Rpt. 77-1, 137 p.

CODE, J.A. 1973. The stability of natural slopes in the Mackenzie Valley. Canada, Dept.

of Indian and Northern Affairs, Environmental-Social Program, Northern Pipelines, Rpt. 73-9, 18 p.

COLLET, L.S. 1974. Geophysical parameters of permafrost. Proc. Symposium on Permafrost Geophysics, Canada, National Research Council, Associate Committee Geotechnical Research, Tech. Memo. 113, pp. 1-16.

COOK, F.A. 1958. Temperatures in permafrost at Resolute, N.W.T. Geographical Bull., No. 12, pp. 5-18.

COOK, J.C. 1960. RF electrical properties of salty ice and frozen earth. J. Geophys. Res., Vol. 65, No. 6, pp. 1767-1771.

CORNELL, E.R., LAW, C.E. and LAKE, R.W. 1973. The Arctic railway: environmental aspects. J. Eng. Inst. Canada, March, pp. 23-27.

COUCH, E.J., KELLER, H.H. and WATTS, J.W. 1970. Permafrost thawing around producing oil wells. J. Can. Petrol. Tech., Vol. 9, No. 2, pp. 107-111.

CRAIG, B.G. 1959. Pingo in the Thelon Valley, Northwest Territories: radio-carbon age and historical significance of the contained organic material. Geol. Soc. Amer. Bull., Vol. 70, pp. 509-510.

CRAMPTON, C.B. and RUTTER, N.W. 1973. A geoecological terrain analysis of discontinuously frozen ground in the upper Mackenzie River Valley, Canada. Proc. 2nd International Conference on Permafrost, Yakutsk, U.S.S.R., North American Contribution, U.S. National Academy of Sciences, pp. 101-105.

CROASDALE, K.R. and MARCELLUS, R.W. Ice and wave action on artificial islands in the Beaufort Sea. Can. J. Civil Eng., Vol. 5, No. 1, pp. 98-113.

CROCKER, C.R. 1971. Winter construction in Canada. Build International, Vol. 4, No. 6, pp. 326-330.

CRONIN, J.E. 1977. A liquid natural convection concept for building subgrade coding. Proc. 2nd International Symposium on Cold Regions Engineering (1976), Fairbanks, AK, Univ. of Alaska, Dept. Civil Eng., pp. 26-41.

CRORY, F.E. 1965. Pile foundations in discontinuous permafrost areas. Proc. Can. Regional Permafrost Conference (1964), Edmonton, Alta., Canada, National Research Council, Associate Committee on Soil and Snow Mechanics, Tech. Memo. 86, pp. 58-76.

CRORY, F.E. 1966. Pile foundations in permafrost, Proc. International Conference on Permafrost (1963), Lafayette, IN, U.S. National Academy of Sciences, Publ. 1287, pp. 467-476.

CRORY, F.E. 1968. Bridge foundations in permafrost areas: Goldstream Creek, Fairbanks, Alaska. U.S. Army, CRREL, Tech. Rpt. 180, 33 p.

CRORY, F.E. 1973a. Settlement associated with the thawing of permafrost. Proc. 2nd International Conference on Permafrost, Yakutsk, U.S.S.R., North American Contribution, U.S. National Academy of Sciences, pp. 599-607.

CRORY, F.E. 1973b. Installation of driven test piles in permafrost at Bethel Air Force Station, Alaska. U.S. Army, CRREL, Tech. Rpt. 139, 22 p.

CRORY, F.E. 1975. Bridge foundations in permafrost areas: Moose and Spinach Creeks, Fairbanks, Alaska. U.S. Army, CRREL, Tech. Rpt. 266, 36 p.

CRORY, F.E. 1978. The Kotzebue Hospital: a case study. Proc. Conference on Applied Techniques for Cold Environments, Anchorage, AK, ASCE, Vol. 1, pp. 342-359.

CRORY, F.E. and REED, R.E. 1965. Measurement of frost heaving forces on piles. U.S. Army, CRREL, Tech. Rpt. 145, 27 p.

CROWLEY, V.F. 1977. Material selection and design practices for electric power systems in the Arctic. Proc. International Conference on Materials Engineering in the Arctic (1976), St. Jovite, Que. (M.B. Ives, ed.), Amer. Soc. for Metals, pp. 71-77.

CURRAN, H.J.B. and ETTER, H.M. 1976. Environmental design for northern road developments. Environment Canada, Rpt. EPS-8-EC-76-3, 89 p.

DAVIDSON, D.W., EL-DEFRAWY, M.K., FUGLEM, M.O. and JUDGE, A.S. 1978. Natural gas hydrates in northern Canada. Proc. 3rd International Conference on Permafrost, Edmonton, Alta., Canada, National Research Council, Vol. 1, pp. 937-943.

DAVIS, J.L. 1973. The problem of depth sounding of temperate glaciers. M.Sc. Thesis, Cambridge Univ., Cambridge, England.

DAVIS, R.M. and KITZE, F.F. 1967. Soil sampling and drilling near Fairbanks, Alaska: equipment and procedures. U.S. Army, CRREL, Tech. Rpt. 191, 50 p.

DAVISON, B.E., ROONEY, J.W. and BRUGGERS, D.E. 1978. Design variables influencing piles driven in permafrost. Proc. Conference on Applied Techniques for Cold Environments, Anchorage, AK. ASCE, Vol. 1, pp. 307-318.

DAWSON, R.N. and CRONIN, K.J. 1977. Trends in Canadian water and sewer systems serving northern communities. In: Proc. Symposium on Utilities Delivery in Arctic Regions, Edmonton, Alta., Environment Canada, Environmental Protection Service, Rpt. EPS-3-WP-77-1, pp. 1-17.

DAWSON, R.N. and GRAINGE, J.W. 1969. Proposed design criteria for waste-water lagoons in Arctic and subarctic regions. Water Pollution Control Federation, Washington, DC, pp. 237-246.

DAY, J.H., NOWOSAD, F.S. and COOPER, D.J. 1961. Note on improved soil borer for sampling in permafrost. Can. J. Soil Sci., Vol. 41, No. 1, pp. 138-139.

DEJONG, J.J.A., STIGTER, C. and STEYN, B. 1975. Design and building of temporary artificial islands in the Beaufort Sea. Proc. 3rd International Conference on Port and Ocean Engineering Under Arctic Conditions, Fairbanks, AK, Vol. II, pp. 753-789.

DEMERS, J. (ed.) 1974. Permafrost hydrology. Proc. Workshop Seminar, Calgary, Alta., Environment Canada, The International Hydrological Decade, Canadian National Committee, The Secretariat, 109 p.

DEMPSEY, B.J. and THOMPSON, M.R. 1970. A heat transfer model for evaluating frost action and temperature-related effects in multilayered pavement systems. U.S. Highway Research Board, Rpt. 342, pp. 39-56.

DEO, P., WOOD, L.E. and LOVELL, C.W., Jr. 1974. Use of shale in embankments. U.S. Transportation Research Board, Spec. Rpt. 148, pp. 87-96.

DEVRIES, D.A. 1952. Het Warmtegeleidingsvermejen van Grond (The thermal conductivity of soil). Madedelingen van de Landouwhogeschool te Wageningen, Vol. 52, No. 1, pp. 1-73, Transl. U.K., DSIR, Building Research Station Library Communication 759.

DICKENS, H.B. and GRAY, D.M. 1960. Experience with a pier-supported building over permafrost. ASCE, J. Soil Mech. Found. Div., Vol. 86, No. SM5, pp. 1-14.

DILLON, H.B. and ANDERSLAND, O.B. 1966. Predicting unfrozen water contents in frozen soils. Can. Geotech. J., Vol. 3, No. 2, pp. 53-60.

DIRKSEN, C. and MILLER, R.D. 1966. Closed-system freezing of unsaturated soils. Proc. Soil Sci. Soc. Amer. Vol. 30, No. 2, pp. 168-173.

DOHERTY, P.C. 1970. Hot pipe. U.S. Geol. Surv., Computer contribution 4, Computer Centre Division, Menlo Park, CA.

DUBNIE, A. 1972. Northern mining problems with particular reference to unit operations in permafrost. Canada, Dept. of Energy, Mines and Resources, Ottawa, Ont., Tech. Bull. TB 148, 20 p.

DUFFY, P.J.B. 1975. Special considerations must be given to major projects in various geographic regions. Canadian Consulting Engineer, July, pp. 24-30.

DUGUID, D.R., REYNOLDS, J.H. and ROBINSON, A.D.G. 1973. Control of frost heave cracking in a zoned earth dyke. Proc. Canada/U.S.S.R. Seminar on Civil and Mechanical Engineering Aspects of the Electrical Power Industry, Moscow, Vol. 2, 35 p.

DYER, D.F. and SUNDERLAND, J.E. 1971. Freeze-drying of bodies subject to radiation boundary conditions. ASME, J. Heat Transfer, Nov., pp. 427-431.

DZHURIK, V.I. and LESHCHIKOV, F.N. 1978. Experimental investigations of seismic properties of frozen soils. Proc. 2nd International Conference on Permafrost (1973), Yakutsk, U.S.S.R., U.S.S.R. Contribution, U.S. National Academy of Sciences, pp. 485-488.

ECKEL, E.B. (ed.) 1958. Landslides and engineering practice. U.S. Highway Research Board, Spec. Rpt. 29, 232 p.

EIKMEIER, J.R., ERSOY, D. and RAMEY, H.J. 1970. Wellbore temperatures and heat losses during production or injection operations. J. Can. Petrol. Tech., April-June, pp. 115-121.

EL'CHANINOV, E.A., SHOR, A.I. and ROZENBAUM, M.A. 1980. The stability of underground workings in permafrost. Proc. 3rd International Conference on Permafrost (1978), Edmonton, Alta., Canada, National Research Council, Translations, Part II, pp. 321-337.

ENGINEERING AND CONTRACT RECORD. 1975. Protecting Manic 3 against frost. Feb., pp. 14-15.

ENGINEERING NEWS-RECORD. 1967. Outardes 4: grab bag of ideas for dam builders. May 25, pp. 94-96.

ESCH, D.C. 1973. Control of permafrost degradation beneath a roadway by subgrade insulation. Proc. 2nd International Conference on Permafrost, Yakutsk, U.S.S.R., North American Contribution, U.S. National Academy of Sciences, pp. 608-622.

ESCH, D.C. and RHODE, J.J. 1977. Kotzebue Airport runway insulation over permafrost. Proc. 2nd International Symposium on Cold Regions Engineering (1976), Fairbanks, AK, Univ. of Alaska, Dept. Civil Eng., pp. 44-61.

ESSOGLOU, M.E. 1957. Piling operations in Alaska. The Military Engineer, Vol. 49, No. 330, pp. 282-287.

EVDOKIMOV, P.D. 1970. Design and construction of earth and rockfill dams in the U.S.S.R. Trans. 10th International Congress on Large Dams, Montreal, Que., Vol. 1, pp. 137-149.

EVDOKIMOV, P.D. et al. 1973. Studies of foundations of earth and rockfill dams under severe climatic conditions. In: Proc. Canada/U.S.S.R. Seminar on Civil and Mechanical Engineering Aspects of the Electrical Power Industry, Moscow, Vol. 1.

EVERETT, D.H. 1961. The thermodynamics of frost action in porous solids. Trans. Faraday Society, Vol. 57, pp. 1541-51.

EVERETT, D.H. and HAYNES, J.M. 1965. Capillary properties of some model pore systems with reference to frost damage. RILEM Bull., New Series, Vol. 27, pp. 31-38.

FERRIANS, O.J., Jr. and HOBSON, G.D. 1973. Mapping and predicting permafrost in North America: a review, 1963-1973. Proc. 2nd International Conference on Permafrost, Yakutsk, U.S.S.R., North American Contribution, U.S. National Academy of Sciences, pp. 479-498.

FERRIANS, O.J., Jr., KACHADOORIAN, R. and GREENE, G.W. 1969. Permafrost and related engineering problems in Alaska. U.S. Geol. Surv., Prof. Paper 678, 41 p.

FIFE, J.A. 1960. Refrigerant piping system supports Arctic radar sites. Heating, Piping and Air Conditioning, Vol. 32, No. 12, pp. 112-118.

FINN, W.D. and YONG, R.N. 1978. Seismic response of frozen ground. ASCE, J. Geotech. Eng. Div., Vol. 104, No. GT10, pp. 1225-1241.

FINN, W.D., YONG, R.N. and LEE, K.W. 1978. Liquefaction of thawed layers in frozen soil. ASCE, J. Geotech. Eng. Div., Vol. 104, No. GT10, pp. 1243-1255.

FLETCHER, R.J. 1964. The use of aerial photographs for engineering soil reconnaissance in Arctic Canada. Photogrammetric Engineering, Vol. 30, No. 2, pp. 210-219.

FLETCHER, R.J. and YOUNG, G. 1976. Climate of Arctic Canada in maps. Univ. of Alberta, Boreal Institute for Northern Studies, Edmonton, Alta., Occasional Publ. 13, 48 p.

FOSTER-MILLER ASSOCIATES. 1965. Final phase I report of an investigation of methods of conveying snow, ice and/or frozen ground from an excavation to a disposal area. U.S. Army, CRREL, Internal Rpt., IR 23, 101 p.

FOSTER-MILLER ASSOCIATES. 1973a. Fundamental concepts for the rapid disengagement of frozen soil—phase I. U.S. Army, CRREL, Tech. Rpt. 233, 148 p.

FOSTER-MILLER ASSOCIATES. 1973b. Fundamental concepts for the rapid disengagement of frozen soil—phase II. U.S. Army, CRREL, Tech. Rpt. 234, 112 p.

FOSTER, R.R., PARENT, T.J. and SOROKOWSKI, R.A., 1979. The Eskimo Point water supply program. Can. J. Civil Eng. Vol. 6, No. 3, pp. 413-422.

FRASER, D.C. and HOEKSTRA, P. 1976. Permafrost and gravel delineation using airborne resistivity maps from a multicoil electromagnetic system. Presented at 46th Annual Meeting, Society of Exploration Geophysicists (Oct.), Houston, TX.

FRASER, W.C. 1964. A study of winds and blowing snow in the Canadian Arctic. Environment Canada, Atmospheric Environment Service, Toronto, Ont., CIR-4162, 47 p.

FRENCH, H.M. 1975a. Man-induced thermokarst, Sachs Harbour airstrip, Banks Island, Northwest Territories. Can. J. Earth Sci., Vol. 12, No. 2, pp. 132-144.

FRENCH, H.M. 1975b. Pingo investigations and terrain disturbance studies, Banks Island, District of Franklin. Geol. Surv. Can., Paper 75-1, Part A, pp. 459-464.

FRENCH, H.M. 1976. Geomorphological process and terrain disturbance studies, Banks Island, District of Franklin. Geol. Surv. Can., Paper 76-1A, pp. 289-292.

FRENCH, H.M. AND EGGINTON, P. 1973. Thermokarst development, Banks Island, western Canadian Arctic. Proc. 2nd International Conference on Permafrost, Yakutsk, U.S.S.R., North American Contribution, U.S. National Academy of Sciences, pp. 203-212.

FROST, R.E. 1950. Evaluation of soils and permafrost conditions in the Territory of Alaska by means of aerial photographs. U.S. Army, CRREL (ACFEL), Tech. Rpts. 34-1 (163 p.) and 34-2 (166 p.).

FROST, R.E. 1952. Interpretation of permafrost features from airphotos. In: Frost Action in Soils: A Symposium, U.S. Highway Research Board, Spec. Rpt. 2, pp. 223-246.

FROST, R.E., MCLERRAN, J.H. and LEIGHTY, R.D. 1966. Photo-interpretation in the Arctic and subarctic. Proc. International Conference on Permafrost (1963), Lafayette, IN, U.S. National Academy of Sciences, Publ. 1287, pp. 343-348.

FROST, R.E. and MINTZER, O.W. 1950. Influence of topographic position in airphoto identification of permafrost. In: Soil Exploration and Mapping, U.S. Highway Research Board, Bull. 28, pp. 100-121.

FRYER, M.W. 1970. The buried pipe problem (quick solutions to selected problems in heat transfer). Univ. of Alaska, Institute Arctic Environmental Engineering, Fairbanks, AK, Bull. 7002, 15 p.

FULLER, W. 1971. Construction problems on the north slope. Proc. Symposium on Cold Regions Engineering, ASCE and Univ. of Alaska, Dept. Civil Eng., Vol. 2, pp. 398-404.

FULWIDER, C.W. 1973. Thermal regime in an Arctic earthfill dam. Proc. 2nd International Conference on Permafrost, Yakutsk, U.S.S.R., North American Contribution, U.S. National Academy of Sciences, pp. 622-628.

FULWIDER, C.W. and AITKEN, G.W. 1962. Effect of surface colour on thaw penetration beneath an asphalt surface in the Arctic. Proc. International Conference on the Structural Design of Asphalt Pavements, Univ. of Michigan, Ann Arbor, MI, pp. 605-610.

FULWIDER, C.W. and STEARMAN, J.H. 1968. A bibliography on winter construction: 1940-1967. (rev. ed.) U.S. Army, CRREL, Spec. Rpt. 83, 84 p.

GAL'PERIN, M.I., TORGONENKO, E.A. and DEGTIAREV, A.P. 1955. Excavation of frozen ground. U.S. Army, CRREL (SIPRE), Transl. TL 53, 5 p.

GAMBLE, D.J. and JANSSEN, C.T.L. 1974. Evaluating alternative levels of water and sanitation service for communities in the Northwest Territories. Can. J. Civil Eng., Vol. 1, No. 1, pp. 116-128.

GAMBLE, D.J. and LUKOMSKYJ, P. 1975. Utilidors in the Canadian North. Can. J. Civil Eng., Vol. 2, No. 2, pp. 162-168.

GANDAHL, R. 1963. Determination of the ground frost line by means of a simple type of frost depth indicator, Transl. and rev. by P.T. Hodgins, National Swedish Road Research Institute, Stockholm, Sweden, Rpt. 30A.

GARG, O.P. 1973. In situ physicomechanical properties of permafrost using geophysical techniques. Proc. 2nd International Conference on Permafrost, Yakutsk, U.S.S.R., North American Contribution, U.S. National Academy of Sciences, pp. 508-517.

GARG, O.P. and DEVON, J.W. 1978. Practical applications of recently improved pit slope design procedures at Schefferville. Bull. Can. Institute of Mining, Sept., pp. 68-72.

GARG, O.P. and KALIA, T. 1975. Slope stability studies in the Schefferville area. Proc. 10th Canadian Rock Mechanics Symposium, Kingston, Ont., Queen's Univ., Dept. of Mining Eng., Vol. 1, pp. 447-472.

GARRATT, D.H. and KRY, P.R. 1978. Construction of artificial islands as Beaufort Sea drilling platforms. J. Can. Petrol. Tech., April-June, pp. 73-79.

GASKIN, D.A. and STANLEY, L.E. 1974. Application of electrical energy to culvert icing problems: a laboratory study. U.S. Army, CRREL, Tech. Rpt. 248, 41 p.

GEIGER, R. 1965. The climate near the ground. (rev. ed.). Transl. by Scripta Technica, Harvard Univ. Press, Cambridge, MA, 611 p.

GEORGE, W. 1973. Analyses of the proposed Little Chena River, earthfill nonretention dam, Fairbanks, Alaska. Proc. 2nd International Conference on Permafrost, Yakutsk, U.S.S.R., North American Contribution, U.S. National Academy of Sciences, pp. 636-648.

GERDEL, R.W. 1969. Characteristics of the cold regions. U.S. Army, CRREL, Monograph MI-A, 51 p.

GILL, D. 1972. Modification of levee morphology by erosion in the Mackenzie River Delta, N.W.T. In: Polar Geomorphology (R. Price and D. Sugden, ed.), Institution of British Geographers, Spec. Publ. 4, pp. 123-138.

GILLOTT, J.E. and SWENSON, E.G. 1973. Some unusual alkali-expansive aggregates. Engineering Geology, Vol. 7, pp. 181-195.

GIRGRAH, M. and SHAH, V.K. 1977. Construction of a deep-sea dock in the Arctic. Proc. 4th International Conference on Port and Ocean Engineering under Arctic Conditions (POAC 77), St. John's, Nfld., pp. 370-381.

GIVEN, P.W. and SMITH, D.W. 1977. Critical evaluation of extended aeration systems in Arctic and subarctic regions. Environment Canada, Environmental Protection Service, Rpt. EPS 3-WP-77-10, 69 p.

GLEN, J.W. 1952. Experiments on the deformation of ice. J. of Glaciology, Vol. 2, Nov., pp. 111-114.

GLEN, J.W. 1955. The creep of polycrystalline ice. Proc. Royal Society A228, pp. 519-538.

GLUSKIN, Yu.E. and ZISKOVICH, V.Ye. 1978. Construction of dams from local materials in the Soviet North. Proc. 2nd International Conference on Permafrost (1973), Yakutsk, U.S.S.R., U.S.S.R. Contribution, U.S. National Academy of Sciences, pp. 591-594.

GOLD, L.W. 1964. Analysis of annual variations in ground temperature at an Ottawa site. Can. J. Earth Sci., Vol. 1, No. 2, pp. 146-157.

GOLD, L.W. 1967. Influence of surface conditions on ground temperature. Can. J. Earth Sci., Vol. 4, No. 2, pp. 199-208.

GOLD, L.W., JOHNSTON, G.H., SLUSARCHUCK, W.A. and GOODRICH, L.E. 1972. Thermal effects in permafrost. Proc. Canadian Northern Pipeline Research Conference, Canada, National Research Council, Associate Committee Geotechnical Research, Tech. Memo. 104, pp. 25-45.

GOLD, L.W. and LACHENBRUCH, A.H. 1973. Thermal conditions in permafrost: a review of North American literature. Proc. 2nd International Conference on Permafrost, Yakutsk, U.S.S.R., North American Contribution, U.S. National Academy of Sciences, pp. 3-25.

GOODMAN, M.A. 1977-78. Arctic well completion series. (8 parts) World Oil, Vol. 185, No. 5, pp. 107-112, Vol. 185, No. 6, pp. 95, 96, 98, 102, 106, 108, 110, Vol. 185, No. 7, pp. 81, 82, 84, 86, 90, Vol. 186, No. 1, pp. 93-99, Vol. 186, No. 2, pp. 44-48, 60, Vol. 186, No. 4, pp. 60, 63, 65, 66, 69, 70, Vol. 186, No. 5, pp. 71-76 and Vol. 186, No. 6, pp. 90-95.

GOODRICH, L.E. 1973. Computer simulation. Appendix to: Thermal Conditions in Permafrost: A Review of North American Literature, L.W. Gold and A.H. Lachenbruch. Proc. 2nd International Conference on Permafrost, Yakutsk, U.S.S.R., North American Contribution, U.S. National Academy of Sciences, pp. 23-25.

GOODRICH, L.E. 1976. A numerical model for assessing the influence of snow cover on the ground thermal regime. Ph.D. Thesis, McGill Univ., Montreal, Que., 538 p.

GOODRICH, L.E. 1978. Some results of a numerical study of ground thermal regimes. Proc. 3rd International Conference on Permafrost, Edmonton, Alta., Canada, National Research Council, Vol. 1, pp. 24-34.

GOUGHNOUR, R.R. and ANDERSLAND, O.B. 1968. Mechanical properties of a sand-ice system, ASCE, J. Soil Mech., Vol. 94, No. SM4, pp. 923-950.

GRAINGE, J.W. 1959. Water supplies in the central and western Canadian North. J. Amer. Water Works Assoc., Vol. 51, No. 1, pp. 55-66.

GRAINGE, J.W. 1969. Arctic heated pipe water and waste water systems. In: Water Research, Pergamon Press, New York, NY, Vol. 3, pp. 47-71.

GUPTA, R.C., MARSHALL, R.G., and BADKE, D. 1973. Instrumentation for dykes on permafrost, Kettle generating station. Can. Geotech. J., Vol. 10, No. 3, pp. 410-427.

GUTHER, H.H. 1972. Bentonite seals for piezometers in frozen soils. Can. Geotech. J., Vol. 9, No. 1, pp. 115-116.

GUYMON, G.L. and BERG, R.L. 1976. Galerkin finite element analog of frost heave. Proc. 2nd Conference on Soil-Water Problems in Cold Regions, Edmonton, Alta., pp. 111-113.

GUYMON, G.L. and LUTHIN, J.N. 1974. A coupled heat and moisture transport model for Arctic soils. Water Resources Research, Vol. 10, No. 5, pp. 995-1001.

HAAS, W.M., ALKIRE, B.D. and KADERABEK, T.H. 1978. Increasing the effectiveness of soil compaction at below-freezing temperatures. U.S. Army, CRREL, Spec. Rpt. 78-25, 68 p.

HABIB, I.S. 1973. Solidification of a semitransparent cylindrical medium by conduction and radiation. ASME, J. Heat Transfer, Feb. pp. 37-41.

HALEY, W.A. 1959. Rippers speed winter earth moving. Excavating Eng., Vol. 53, Part 1, pp. 37-39.

HAMELIN, L.E. and CAILLEUX, A. 1969. Les palses dans le bassin de la Grande-Rivière de la Baleine. Rev. Géogr. Montréal, Vol. 23, No. 3, pp. 329-337.

HAMELIN, L.E. and COOK, F.A. 1967. Le pèriglaciaire par l'image: illustrated glossary of periglacial phenomena. Presses de l'Université Laval, Québec, P.Q., Centre d'Etudes Nordiques, Travaux et Documents 4, 237 p.

HANNA, T.H. 1974. Foundation instrumentation. Trans. Tech. Publications, Rockport, MA, Series on Rock and Soil Mechanics, Vol. 1, No. 3, 372 p.

HANSEN, B.L. 1966. Instruments for temperature measurements in permafrost. Proc. International Conference on Permafrost (1963), Lafayette, IN, U.S. National Academy of Sciences, Publ. 1287, pp. 356-358.

HARDING, R.G. 1962. Foundation problems at Fort McPherson, N.W.T. Proc. 1st Canadian Conference on Permafrost, Canada, National Research Council, Associate Committee Geotechnical Research, Tech. Memo. 76, pp. 159-166.

HARDY, R.M. and MORRISON, H.A. 1972. Slope stability and drainage considerations for Arctic pipelines. Proc. Canadian Northern Pipeline Research Conference, Canada, National Research Council, Tech. Memo. 104, pp. 249-267.

HARE, F.K. 1968. The Arctic. Royal Meteorological Society Quart. J., Vol. 94, No. 402, pp. 439-59.

HARE, F.K. and THOMAS, M.K. 1974. Climate Canada. Wiley, Toronto, Ont., 256 p.

HARLAN, R.L. 1973. Analysis of coupled heat-fluid transport in partially frozen soil. Water Resources Research, Vol. 9, No. 3, pp. 1314-1323.

HARRIS, C.M. and CREDE, C.E. (ed.) 1961, 1976. Shock and vibration handbook. McGraw-Hill, New York, NY, 1st cd. 3 vols., 2nd ed. 1 vol.

HARRIS, S.A. and BROWN, R.J.E. 1978. Plateau Mountain: a case study of alpine permafrost in the Canadian Rocky Mountains. Proc. 3rd International Conference on Permafrost, Edmonton, Alta., Canada, National Research Council, Vol. 1, pp. 385-391.

HARTMAN, C.W. and CARLSON, R.F. 1970. Bibliography of Arctic water resources. Univ. of Alaska, Institute of Water Resources, 344 p.

HARWOOD, T.A. 1966. Dew Line site selection and exploration. Proc. International Conference on Permafrost (1963), Lafayette, IN, U.S. National Academy of Sciences, Publ. 1287, pp. 359-363.

HATHERTON, T. 1960. Electrical resistivity of frozen earth. J. Geophys. Res., Vol. 65, No. 9, pp. 3023-3024.

HAVERS, J.A. and MORGAN, R.M. 1972. Literature survey of cold weather construction practices. U.S. Army, CRREL, Spec. Rpt. 172, 173 p.

HAYLEY, D.W. and SANGSTER, R.H.B. 1974. Geotechnical aspects of Arctic offshore drilling islands. Proc. 27th Can. Geotech. Conference (Nov.), Edmonton, Alta., Preprint vol., pp. 129-135.

HAYNES, F.D., KARALIUS, J.A. and KALAFUT, J. 1975. Strain rate effect on the strength of frozen silt. U.S. Army, CRREL, Res. Rpt. 350, 27 p.

HEAVY CONSTRUCTION NEWS. 1977. Insulated pipe proves ideal for North. May, p. 10.

HEGINBOTTOM, J.A. 1973. Some effects of surface disturbance on the permafrost active layer at Inuvik, N.W.T., Canada. Proc. 2nd International Conference on Permafrost, Yakutsk, U.S.S.R., North American Contribution, U.S. National Academy of Sciences, pp. 649-657.

HEGINBOTTOM, J.A. 1974. The effects of surface disturbance on ground ice content and distribution. Geol. Surv. Can., Paper 74-1A, p. 273.

HEILAND, C.D. 1940. Geophysical exploration. Prentice Hall, New York, NY, 1013 p.

HEINER, A. 1972. Strength and compaction properties of frozen soil. National Swedish Institute for Building Research, Document D11:1972, 116 p.

HEINKE, G.W. 1973. Bibliography of Arctic environmental engineering. Canada, Dept. of Indian and Northern Affairs, Northern Science Research Group, Publ. QS-1516-000-EE-A1, 164 p.

HEINKE, G.W. 1974. Report on municipal services in communities of the Northwest Territories. Canada, Dept. of Indian and Northern Affairs, Northern Science Research Group, Rpt. NSRG 73-1, 165 p.

HENDERSON, D.H. 1959. Refrigerated foundations in permafrost. The Military Engineer, Vol. 51, No. 340, pp. 118-119.

HENDERSON, J. and HOEKSTRA, P. 1977. Electromagnetic methods for mapping shallow permafrost. Proc. Symposium on Permafrost Geophysics (1976), Vancouver, B.C., Canada, National Research Council, Associate Committee Geotechnical Research, Tech. Memo. 119, pp. 16-24.

HENNION, F.B. and LOBACZ, E.F. 1973. Corps of engineers technology related to design of pavements in areas of permafrost. Proc. 2nd International Conference on Permafrost, Yakutsk, U.S.S.R., North American Contribution, U.S. National Academy of Sciences, pp. 658-664.

HEUER, C.E. 1979. The application of heat pipes on the Trans-Alaska Pipeline. U.S. Army, CRREL, Spec. Rpt. 79-26, 33 p.

HIBBERT, G.S. and BEAUCHAMP, J.C. 1978. Effects of a cold environment on the design and construction of Eagle River Bridge. Proc. Conference on Applied Techniques for Cold Environments, Anchorage, AK, ASCE, Vol. 1, pp. 134-145.

HIGHTER, W.H., ALTSHAEFFL, A.G. and LOVELL, C.W. 1970. Low temperature effects on the compaction and strength of a sandy clay. U.S. Highway Research Board, Record 304, pp. 45-51.

HIRONAKA, M.C. 1974a. Trenching on shore and in the ocean in Arctic regions: State-of-the-art survey. U.S. Navy, Civil Eng. Lab., Naval Construction Battalion Centre, Port Hueneme, CA, Tech. Note N-1335, 52 p.

HIRONAKA, M.C. 1974b. Anchoring in snow, ice and permafrost. U.S. Navy, Civil Eng. Lab., Naval Construction Battalion Centre, Port Hueneme, CA, Tech. Note N-1344, 44 p.

HNATIUK, J. and RANDALL, A.G. 1977. Determination of permafrost thickness in wells in northern Canada. Can. J. Earth Sci., Vol. 14, No. 3, pp. 375-383.

HO, D.M., HARR, M.E. and LEONARDS, G.A. 1970. Transient temperature distribution in insulated pavements: predictions vs. observations. Can. Geotech. J., Vol. 7, No. 3, pp. 275-284.

HODGSON, D.A. 1975. The terrain mapping and evaluation system adopted for the eastern Queen Elizabeth Islands. Geol. Surv. Can., Paper 75-1C, pp. 95-100.

HOEKSTRA, P. 1965. Conductance of frozen bentonite suspensions. Proc. Soil Sci. Amer., Vol. 29, Sept.-Oct., pp. 519-522.

HOEKSTRA, P. 1966. Moisture movement in soils under temperature gradients with the cold-side temperature below freezing. Water Resources Research, Vol. 2, No. 2, pp. 241-250.

HOEKSTRA, P. 1969. The physics and chemistry of frozen soils. U.S. Highway Research Board, Spec. Rpt. 103, pp. 78-90.

HOEKSTRA, P. and CHAMBERLAIN, E. 1964. Electro-osmosis in frozen soils. Nature, Vol. 203, Sept., pp. 1406-1407.

HOEKSTRA, P., CHAMBERLAIN, E. and FRATE, T. 1965. Frost heaving pressures. U.S. Army, CRREL, Res. Rpt. 176, 16 p.

HOEKSTRA, P. and DELANEY, A. 1974. Dielectric properties of soil at UHF and microwave frequencies. J. Geophys. Res., Vol. 79, No. 11, pp. 1699-1708.

HOEKSTRA, P. and KEUNE, R. 1967. Pressure effects on the conductance of frozen montmorillonite suspensions. In: Clays and Clay Minerals, Pergamon Press, New York, NY, Vol. 15, pp. 215-225.

HOEKSTRA, P. and O'BRIEN, H.W. 1969. The dielectric properties of clay suspensions in the frequency range from 50 Hz to 20 kHz. U.S. Army, CRREL, Res. Rpt. 266, 15 p.

HOEKSTRA, P., SELLMAN, P.V. and DELANEY, A.J. 1974. Airborne resistivity mapping of permafrost near Fairbanks, Alaska. U.S. Army, CRREL, Res. Rpt. No. 324, 49 p.

HOFFMAN, C.R. 1971. Aboveground utilidor piping systems for cold-weather regions. U.S. Navy Civil Engineering Laboratory, Port Hueneme, CA, Tech. Rpt. R734, 61p.

HOOKE, R.LeB., DAHLIN, B.B. and KAUPER, M.T. 1972. Creep of ice containing dispersed fine sand. J. of Glaciology, Vol. 11, No. 63, pp. 327-336.

HORA, Z.D. and STEPANEK, M. 1977. Terrain typing for engineering and environmental studies. Proc. 30th Canadian Geotech. Conference, Saskatoon, Sask., Preprint vol., pp. III-28 to III-42.

HORSLEY, T.L. 1965. Drilling and blasting at the Cassiar Mine. Can. Mining and Metallurgical Bull., Vol. 58, No. 638, pp. 625-627.

HOW, T.G. 1975. Methods of transportation by land, sea and air. In: Arctic Oil & Gas: Problems and Possibilities. Proc. 5th International Congress of the Foundation Francaise d'Etudes Nordiques (May 1973), Le Havre, France, Contributions du Centre d'Etudes Arctiques XII, Vol. 1, pp. 405-431.

HUCULAK, N.A., TWACH, J.W., THOMSON, R.S. and COOK, R.D. 1978. Development of the Dempster Highway north of the Arctic Circle. Proc. 3rd International Conference on Permafrost, Edmonton, Alta., Canada, National Research Council, Vol. 1, pp. 799-805.

HUGHES, O.L. 1969. Distribution of open-system pingos in central Yukon Territory with respect to glacial limits. Geol. Surv. Can., Paper 69-34, 8 p.

HUGHES, O.L. 1972. Surficial geology and land classification, Mackenzie Valley transportation corridor. Proc. Canadian Northern Pipeline Research Conference, Canada, National Research Council, Associate Committee Geotechnical Research, Tech. Memo. 104, pp. 17-24.

HUGHES, O.L. and TERASMAE, J. 1963. SIPRE ice-corer for obtaining samples from permanently frozen bogs. Arctic, Vol. 16, No. 4, pp. 270-272.

HUGHES, O.L. et al. 1970-75. Surficial geology and geomorphology maps, Mackenzie Valley and northern Yukon Territory. Geol. Surv. Can., Open Files 26, 97, 108 and 294.

HULT, J.A. 1966. Creep in engineering structures. Blaisdell, Waltham, MA, 115 p.

HUNTER, J.A. 1973. The application of shallow seismic methods to mapping of frozen surficial materials. Proc. 2nd International Conference on Permafrost, Yakutsk, U.S.S.R., North American Contribution, U.S. National Academy of Sciences, pp. 527-535.

HUNTER, J.A., JUDGE, A.S., MACAULEY, H.A., GOOD, R.L., GAGNE, R.M. and BURNS, R.A. 1976. Permafrost and frozen sub-seabottom materials in the southern Beaufort Sea. Environment Canada, Beaufort Sea Project, Tech. Rpt. 22, 177 p.

HUSSEY, K.M. 1962. Ground patterns as keys to photointerpretation of Arctic terrain. Iowa Academy of Science, Proc. 69, pp. 332-341.

HVORSLEV, J.J. and GOODE, T.B. 1966. Core drilling in frozen ground, Proc. International Conference on Permafrost (1963), Lafayette, IN, U.S. National Academy of Sciences, Publ. 1287, pp. 364-370.

HWANG, C.T. 1976. Predictions and observations on the behaviour of a warm gas pipeline on permafrost. Can. Geotech. J., Vol. 13, No. 4, pp. 452-480.

HWANG, C.T. 1977a. On quasi-static solutions for buried pipes in permafrost. Can. Geotech. J., Vol. 14, No. 2, pp. 180-192.

HWANG, C.T. 1977b. Frost heave design of a chilled gas pipeline. Proc. 30th Can. Geotech. Conference, Saskatoon, Sask., Preprint vol., pp. V59-V87.

HWANG, C.T., MURRAY, D.M. and BROOKER, E.W. 1972. A thermal analysis for structures on permafrost. Can. Geotech. J., Vol. 9, No. 1, pp. 33-46.

INGERSOLL, L.R., ZOBEL, O.J. and INGERSOLL, A.C. 1954. Heat conduction with engineering, geological and other applications. Univ. of Wisconsin Press, Madison, WI, 325 p.

ISAACS, R.M. and CODE, J.A. 1972. Problems in engineering geology related to pipeline construction. Proc. Canadian Northern Pipeline Research Conference, Canada, National Research Council, Tech. Memo. 104, pp. 147-178.

IVES, J.D. 1962. Iron mining in permafrost: Central Labrador-Ungava. Geographical Bull. No. 17, pp. 66-77.

JACKMAN, A.H. 1974. Highway cut stabilization in areas of permafrost and ground ice. Proc. Amer. Assoc. Geogr., Vol. 6, pp. 29-32.

JAHNS, H.O., MILLER, T.W., POWER, L.D., RICKEY, W.P., TAYLOR, T.P. and WHEELER, J.A. 1973. Permafrost protection for pipelines. Proc. 2nd International Conference on Permafrost, Yakutsk, U.S.S.R., North American Contribution, U.S. National Academy of Sciences, pp. 673-684.

JAMES, F.W. 1976. Buried pipe systems in Canada's Arctic. The Northern Engineer, Vol. 8, No. 1, pp. 4-11.

JENNESS, J.L. 1949, Permafrost in Canada. Arctic, Vol. 2, No. 1, pp. 13-27.

JESSBERGER, H.L. 1970. Ground frost: a listing and evaluation of more recent literature dealing with the effect of frost on the soil. U.S. National Technical Information Services, Springfield, VA, Document AD 865 128, 494 p.

JESSOP, A.M. 1971. The distribution of glacial perturbation of heat flow in Canada. Can. J. Earth Sci., Vol. 8, No. 2, pp. 162-166.

JOHNSON, A.W. 1952. Frost action in roads and airfields: a review of the literature. U.S. Highway Research Board, Spec. Rpt. 1, 300 p.

JOHNSON, E.G. and ESCH, D.C. 1977. Investigation and analysis of the Paxson Roadway icing. Proc. 2nd International Symposium on Cold Regions Engineering (1976), Fairbanks, AK, Univ. of Alaska, Dept. Civil Eng., pp. 100-126.

JOHNSON, P.L. 1970. Remote sensing as an ecological tool. Proc. Symposium on Ecology of Subarctic Regions (1966), Helsinki, Finland, UNESCO, Paris, France, pp. 169-185.

JOHNSON, P.R. 1971. Empirical heat transfer rates of small, Long and Balch thermal piles and thermal convection loops. Univ. of Alaska, Institute of Arctic Environmental Engineering, Fairbanks, AK, Rpt. 7102, 60 p.

JOHNSON, T.C., BERG, R.L., CAREY, K.L. and KAPLAR, C.W. 1974. Roadway design in seasonal frost areas. U.S. Army, CRREL, Tech. Rpt. TR 259, 104 p.

JOHNSTON, A.V. 1964, Some economic and engineering aspects of the construction of new railway lines in northern Canada, with particular reference to the Great Slave Railway. Proc. Inst. Civil Eng., Vol. 29, pp. 571-588. Discussion Vol. 32, Sept. 1965, pp. 135-147.

JOHNSTON, G.H. 1962. Bench marks in permafrost areas. The Canadian Surveyor, Vol. 16, No. 1, pp. 32-41.

JOHNSTON, G.H. 1963. Instructions for the fabrication of thermocouple cables for measuring ground temperatures. Canada, National Research Council, Division Building Research, Tech. Paper 157, 11 p.

JOHNSTON, G.H. 1964. Soil sampling in permafrost areas. Eng. Institute of Canada, Geotech. Div., Paper EIC-64, GEOTECH 1, Vol. 2, No. 1, 8 p.

JOHNSTON, G.H. 1965. Permafrost studies at the Kelsey Hydro-Electric Generating Station: research and instrumentation. Canada, National Research Council, Division Building Research, Tech. Paper 178, 57 p.

JOHNSTON, G.H. 1966a. Engineering site investigations in permafrost areas. Proc. International Conference on Permafrost (1963), Lafayette, IN, U.S. National Academy of Sciences, Publ. 1287, pp. 371-374.

JOHNSTON, G.H. 1966b. Pile construction in permafrost. Proc. International Conference on Permafrost (1963), Lafayette, IN, U.S. National Academy of Sciences, Publ. 1287, pp. 477-481.

JOHNSTON, G.H. 1969. Dykes on permafrost, Kelsey Generating Station, Manitoba. Can. Geotech. J., Vol. 6, No. 2, pp. 139-157.

JOHNSTON, G.H. 1973. Ground temperature measurements using thermocouples. Proc. Seminar on the Thermal Regime and Measurements in Permafrost, Canada, National Research Council, Associate Committee Geotechnical Research, Tech. Memo. 108, pp. 1-12.

JOHNSTON, G.H. and BROWN, R.J.E. 1964. Some observations on permafrost distribution at a lake in the Mackenzie Delta, N.W.T., Canada. Arctic, Vol. 17, No. 3, pp. 162-175.

JOHNSTON, G.H. and BROWN, R.J.E. 1966. Occurrence of permafrost at an Arctic lake. Nature, Vol. 211, No. 5052, pp. 952-953.

JOHNSTON, G.H., BROWN, R.J.E. and PICKERSGILL, D.N. 1963. Permafrost investigations at Thompson, Manitoba: terrain studies. Canada, National Research Council, Division Building Research, Tech. Paper 158, 96 p.

JOHNSTON, G.H. and LADANYI, B. 1972. Field tests of grouted rod anchors in permafrost. Can. Geotech. J., Vol. 9, No. 2, pp. 176-194.

JOHNSTON, G.H. and LADANYI, B. 1974. Field tests of deep power-installed screw anchors in permafrost. Can. Geotech. J., Vol. 11, No. 3, pp. 348-358.

JOY, A. 1973. Arctic pipeline ditcher prototypes engage in severe tests. Heavy Construction News, May 28, pp. 16-18.

JUDD, D.A.W. 1973. Developments in federal policies and regulations for northern Canada, 1968-72. Polar Record, Vol. 16, No. 103, pp. 583-590.

JUDGE, A.S. 1973a. Deep temperature observations in the Canadian North. Proc. 2nd International Conference on Permafrost, Yakutsk, U.S.S.R., North American Contribution, U.S. National Academy of Sciences, pp. 35-40.

JUDGE, A.S. 1973b. The prediction of permafrost thickness. Can. Geotech. J., Vol. 10, No. 1, pp. 1-11.

JUDGE, A.S. 1973c. The thermal regime of the Mackenzie Valley. Canada, Dept. of Indian and Northern Affairs, Environmental-Social Committee, Northern Pipelines, Rep. 73-38, 177 p.

JUDGE, A.S. 1973d. Ground temperature measurements using thermistors. Proc. Seminar on the Thermal Regime and Measurements in Permafrost, Canada, National Research Council, Associate Committee Geotechnical Research, Tech. Memo. 108, pp. 13-22.

JUDGE, A.S. 1974. Occurrence of offshore permafrost in northern Canada. In: The Coast and Shelf of the Beaufort Sea (J.C. Reed and J.E. Sater, ed.), Proc. Symposium (Jan. 1974), San Francisco, CA, Arctic Institute of North America, pp. 427-437.

JUMIKIS, A.R. 1977. Thermal geotechnics. Rutgers Univ. Press, New Brunswick, NJ, 375 p.

JUMIKIS, A.R. and SLUSARCHUK, W.A. 1974. Electrical parameters of some frost-prone soils. In: Advanced Concepts and Techniques in the Study of Snow and Ice Resources, U.S. Contribution to the IHD, U.S. National Academy of Sciences, pp. 765-781.

KACHADOORIAN, R. and FERRIANS, O.J., Jr. 1973. Permafrost-related engineering geology problems posed by the Trans-Alaska Pipeline. Proc. 2nd International Conference on Permafrost, Yakutsk, U.S.S.R., North American Contribution, U.S. National Academy of Sciences, pp. 684-687.

KAGAN, A.A. and KRIVONOGOVA, N.F. 1973. Methods and principles of engineering geological investigations of permafrost foundations for hydraulic structures. Proc. Canada/U.S.S.R. Seminar on Civil and Mechanical Engineering Aspects of the Electrical Power Industry, Moscow, Vol. 1.

KAGAN, A.A. and KIRVONOGOVA, N.F. 1976. Characteristics of the engineering-geologic conditions of hydraulic structure construction in permafrost regions. Hydrotechnical Construction (U.S.S.R.), No. 7, pp. 16-18, Transl. by Consultants Bureau, New York, NY, for ASCE.

KAMENSKIY, R.M. 1978. Thermal regime of the base and core of the dam at the Vilyuy hydroelectric power plant. Proc. 2nd International Conference on Permafrost (1973), Yakutsk, U.S.S.R., U.S.S.R. Contribution, U.S. National Academy of Sciences, pp. 661-665.

KANE, D.L. 1974. Review of dam construction techniques in permafrost regions. The Northern Engineer, Vol. 6, No. 1, pp. 25-29.

KANE, D.L., LUTHIN, J.N. and TAYLOR, G.S. 1975. Physical transfer processes in subarctic soils influenced by forest fires. Proc. Conference on Soil-Water Problems in Cold Regions, Calgary, Alta., pp. 128-147.

KAPLAR, C.W. 1969. Laboratory determination of dynamic moduli of frozen soils and of ice. U.S. Army, CRREL, Res. Rpt. 163, 45 p.

KAPLAR, C.W. 1971a. Some strength properties of frozen soil and effect of loading rate. U.S. Army, CRREL, Spec. Rpt. 159, 25 p.

KAPLAR, C.W. 1971b. Experiments to simplify frost susceptibility testing of soils. U.S. Army, CRREL, Tech. Rpt. 223, 21 p.

KAPLAR, C.W. 1974a. Freezing test for evaluating relative frost susceptibility of various soils. U.S. Army, CRREL, Tech. Rpt. TR250, 36 p.

KAPLAR, C.W. 1974b. Moisture and freeze-thaw effects on rigid thermal insulations. U.S. Army, CRREL, Tech. Rpt. 249, 31 p.

KAPLAR, C.W. and METRISH, R.M. 1974. Bibliography on winter construction: 1967-1971. U.S. Army, CRREL, Spec. Rpt. 204, 79 p.

KATASONOV, E.M. 1961. Composition and cryogenic structure of permafrost. In: Permafrost Investigations in the Field, Part 1, Chap. II, Canada, National Research Council, Tech. Transl. 1348 (1969), pp. 25-36.

KAY, B.C., SHEPPARD, M.I. and LOCH, J.P.G. 1977. A preliminary comparison of simulated and observed water redistribution in soils freezing under laboratory and field conditions. Proc. International Symposium Frost Action in Soils, Univ. Luleå, Sweden, Vol. 1, pp. 29-41.

KAZEMI, H. and PERKINS, T.K. 1971. Mathematical model of freeze-thaw cycles beneath drilling rigs and production platforms in cold regions. J. Petrol. Tech., March, pp. 381-390.

KEIL, L.D., NIELSEN, N.M. and GUPTA, R.C. 1973. Thaw-consolidation of permafrost dyke foundations at Long Spruce generating station, Manitoba. Proc. 26th Can. Geotech. Conference, Toronto, Ont., Preprint vol. pp. 134-141.

KEINER, E.P. 1969. Insulated and improved subgrade for eliminating frost heave. ASCE, Civil Engineer, Vol. 39, No. 2, pp. 38-89.

KELLER, G.V., LEVEL, A.B. and AVSMAN, F.L. 1970. Evaluation of airborne electromagnetic surveying for mapping variations in rock strength. Colorado School of Mines, Air Force Cambridge Research Laboratories, Contract Rpt. F19628-69-C-0281.

KERFOOT, D.E. 1973. Thermokarst features produced by man-made disturbances to the tundra terrain. In: Research in Polar and Alpine Geomorphology, Proc. 3rd. Guelph Symposium on Geomorphology, pp. 60-72.

KERSTEN, M.S. 1949. Thermal properties of soils. Univ. of Minnesota, Engineering Experiment Station, Bull. 28, 227 p.

KING, M.S., BAMFORD, T.S. and KURFURST, P.J. 1974. Ultrasonic velocity measurements on frozen rocks and soils. Proc. Symposium on Permafrost Geophysics, Canada, National Research Council, Associate Committee Geotechnical Research, Tech. Memo. 113, pp. 35-42.

KINOSITA, S. 1967. Heaving force of frozen soils. Proc. International Conference Low Temperature Science, Vol. 1, pp. 1345-1350.

KINOSHITA, S. and ONO, T. 1963. Heaving force of frozen ground: 1. mainly on the results of field researches. Canada, National Research Council, Tech. Transl. TT 1246 (1966), 30 p.

KISELEV, M.F. 1974. Standard values of specific tangential forces of frost heaving of soils. J. Soil Mech. Found. Eng. (U.S.S.R.), No. 3, pp. 41-43, Transl. by Consultants Bureau, New York, NY.

KITZE, F.F. 1956. Some experiments in drive sampling of frozen ground. U.S. Army, CRREL (ACFEL), Misc. Paper 16, 22 p.

KITZE, F.F. 1957. Installation of piles in permafrost. U.S. Army, CRREL (ACFEL), Misc. Paper 18, 34 p.

KITZE, F.F. and SIMONI, O.W. 1972. An earth fill dam on permafrost, Hess Creek Dam, Livengood, Alaska. U.S. Army, CRREL, Tech. Rpt. 196, 56 p.

KLASSEN, H.P. 1965. Public utilities problems in the discontinuous permafrost areas. Proc. Canadian Regional Permafrost Conference, Edmonton, Alta., Canada, National Research Council, Associate Committee on Soil and Snow Mechanics, Tech. Memo. 86, pp. 106-118.

KLASSEN, R.W. and NETTERVILLE, J.A. 1973-74. Surficial geology and photo mosaic maps, northern Manitoba. Geol. Surv. Can., Open Files 134, 142, 150, 186, 217 and 241.

KLOHN, E.J. 1972. Design and construction of tailings dams. Trans. Can. Inst. Mining, Vol. LXXV, pp. 50-66.

KNIGHT, G.R. and CONDO, A.C. 1971. Design and evaluation of insulated and uninsulated roadway embankments for the Arctic. Proc. Symposium on Cold Regions Engineering, ASCE and Univ. of Alaska, Dept. Civil Eng., pp. 195-226.

KONOVALOV, A.A. and ROMAN, L.T. 1973. The thermophysical properties of peat soils. J. Soil Mech. Found. Eng. (U.S.S.R.), No. 3, pp. 21-22, Transl. by Consultants Bureau, New York, NY.

KOVACS, A., BLOUIN, S., MCKELVY, B. and COLLIGAN, H. 1975. On the theory of ground anchors. U.S. Army, CRREL, Tech. Rpt. 258, 77 p.

KOVACS, A. and MICHITTI, F. 1970. Pile driving by means of longitudinal and torsional vibrations. U.S. Army, CRREL, Spec. Rpt. 141, 17 p.

KRITZ, M.A. and WECHSLER, A.E. 1967. Surface characteristics, effects on thermal regime: phase II. U.S. Army, CRREL, Tech. Rpt. 189, 40 p.

KRY, P.R. 1980. Ice forces on wide structures. Can. Geotech. J., Vol. 17, No. 1, pp. 97-113.

KUDRYAVTSEV, V.A. (ed.) 1977. Fundamentals of frost forecasting in geological engineering investigations. U.S. Army, CRREL, Draft Transl. 606, 489 p.

KURFURST, P.J. 1976. Ultrasonic wave measurements on frozen soils at permafrost temperatures. Can. J. Earth Sci., Vol. 13, No. 11, pp. 1571-1576.

KURFURST, P.J., ISAACS, R.M., HUNTER, J.A. and SCOTT, W.J. 1974. Permafrost studies in the Norman Wells Region, Northwest Territories. Proc. Symposium on the Geology of the Canadian Arctic, Saskatoon, Sask., Geol. Assoc. Can. and Can. Soc. Pet. Geol. (joint publishers), pp. 277-299.

LACHENBRUCH, A.H. 1957a. Thermal effects of the ocean on permafrost. Geol. Soc. Amer. Bull., vol. 68, pp. 1515-1530.

LACHENBRUCH, A.H. 1957b. A probe for measurement of thermal conductivity of frozen soils in place. Trans. Amer. Geophys. U., Vol. 38, pp. 691-697.

LACHENBRUCH, A.H. 1957c. Three dimensional heat conduction in permafrost beneath heated buildings. U.S. Geol. Surv., Bull. 1052-B, 19 p.

LACHENBRUCH, A.H. 1959. Periodic heat flow in a stratified medium with application to permafrost problems. U.S. Geol. Surv., Bull. 1083-A, pp. 1-36.

LACHENBRUCH, A.H. 1960a. Thermal contraction cracks and ice wedges in permafrost. U.S. Geol. Surv., Prof. Paper 400-B, pp. B404-406.

LACHENBRUCH, A.H. 1960b. Some geothermal effects of a roadway on permafrost, U.S. Geol. Surv., Prof. Paper 400-D, pp. B141-144.

LACHENBRUCH, A.H. 1961. Depth and spacing of tension cracks. J. Geophys. Res., Vol. 66, No. 12, pp. 4273-4292.

LACHENBRUCH, A.H. 1962. Mechanics of thermal contraction cracks and ice-wedge polygons in permafrost. Geol. Soc. Amer., Spec. Paper 70, 69 p.

LACHENBRUCH, A.H. 1970. Some estimates of the thermal effects of a heated pipeline in permafrost. U.S. Geol. Surv., Circ. 632, 23 p.

LACHENBRUCH, A.H. and BREWER, M.C. 1959. Dissipation of the temperature effect of drilling a well in Arctic Alaska. U.S. Geol. Surv., Bull. 1083-C, 36 p.

LACHENBRUCH, A.H., GREENE, G.W. and MARSHALL, B.V. 1966. Permafrost and geothermal regimes. In: Environment of Cape Thomson Region, Alaska, U.S. Atomic Energy Commission, pp. 149-163.

LACHENBRUCH, A.H. and MARSHALL, B.V. 1969. Heat flow in the Arctic. Arctic, Vol. 22, No. 3, pp. 300-311.

LADANYI, B. 1972. An engineering theory of creep of frozen soils. Can. Geotech. J., Vol. 9, No. 1, pp. 63-80.

LADANYI, B. 1976. Use of the static penetration test in frozen soils. Can. Geotech. J., Vol. 13, No. 2, pp. 95-110.

LADANYI, B. and JOHNSTON, G.H. 1973. Evaluation of in situ creep properties of frozen soils with the pressure meter. Proc. 2nd International Conference on Permafrost, Yakutsk, U.S.S.R., North American Contribution, U.S. National Academy of Sciences, pp. 310-317.

LADANYI, B. and JOHNSTON, G.H. 1974. Behaviour of circular footings and plate anchors embedded in permafrost. Can. Geotech. J., Vol. 11, No. 4, pp. 531-553.

LAMBE, T.W. and KAPLAR, C.W. 1971. Additives for modifying the frost susceptibility of soils. U.S. Army, CRREL, Tech. Rpt. 123, Part 1, March, 41 p.; Part 2, Oct., 41 p.

LAMBE, T.W. and WHITMAN, R.V. 1969. Soil Mechanics. Wiley, New York, NY, 566 p.

LANG, L.C. 1966. Blasting frozen iron ore at Knob Lake. Canadian Mining Journal, August, pp. 49-53.

LANG, L.C. 1976. New permafrost blasting method developed at Asbestos Hill. Canadian Mining Journal, March, pp. 48-53.

LANGE, G.R. 1966. Refrigerated fluids for drilling and coring in permafrost. Proc. International Conference on Permafrost (1963), Lafayette, IN, U.S. National Academy of Sciences, Publ. 1287, pp. 375-380.

LANGE, G.R. 1973. An investigation of core drilling in perennially frozen gravels and rock. U.S. Army, CRREL, Tech. Rpt. 245, 31 p.

LANGE, G.R. and SMITH, T.K. 1972. Rotary drilling and coring in permafrost. In: Deep Core Drilling, Core Analysis, and Borehole Thermometry at Cape Thomson, Alaska, Part III, U.S. Army, CRREL, Tech. Rpt. 95 III, 25 p.

LARKIN, B.S. 1971. An experimental study of the two-phase thermosiphon tube. Trans. Eng. Inst. of Canada, Vol. 14, No. B-6, Aug./Sept., 8 p.

LARKIN, B.S. and JOHNSTON, G.H. 1974. An experimental field study of the use of two-phase thermosiphons for the preservation of permafrost. Engineering Journal, May/June, pp. 33-37.

LAWRENCE, N.A. 1969. Utilities systems in northern Canada. The Northern Engineer, Vol. 1, No. 5, pp. 4-7.

LEGGET, R.F., BROWN, R.J.E. and JOHNSTON, G.H. 1966. Alluvial fan formation near Aklavik, Northwest Territories, Canada. Geol. Soc. Amer. Bull., Vol. 77, pp. 15-30.

LETTAU, H. 1954. Improved models of thermal diffusion in the soil. Trans. Amer. Geophys. U., Vol. 35, No. 1, pp. 121-132.

LEVITIN, L.E. 1957. Cutting as a method of working frozen ground. Mekhanizatsiia Stroitel'stva, Vol. 14, No. 4, pp. 6-9 (In Russian), English abstract in U.S. Army, CRREL (SIPRE) Biblio. No. 15579.

LEWELLEN, R.I. 1973. The occurrence and characteristics of nearshore permafrost, Northern Alaska. Proc. 2nd International Conference on Permafrost, Yakutsk, U.S.S.R., North American Contribution, U.S. National Academy of Sciences, pp. 131-136.

LIGUORI, A., MAPLE, J.A. and HEUER, C.E. 1979. The design and construction of the Alyeska Pipeline. Proc. 3rd International Conference on Permafrost (1978), Edmonton, Alta., Canada, National Research Council, Vol. 2, pp. 151-157.

LIN, C.J. and WHEELER, J.D. 1978. Simulation of permafrost thaw behaviour at Prudhoe Bay. J. Petrol. Tech., March, pp. 461-467.

LINELL, K.A. 1973a. Long-term effects of vegetative cover on permafrost stability in an area of discontinuous permafrost. Proc. 2nd International Conference on Permafrost, Yakutsk, U.S.S.R., North American Contribution, U.S. National Academy of Sciences, pp. 688-693.

LINELL, K.A. 1973b. Risk of uncontrolled flow from wells through permafrost. Proc. 2nd International Conference on Permafrost, Yakutsk, U.S.S.R., North American Contribution, U.S. National Academy of Sciences, pp. 462-468.

LINELL, K.A. and JOHNSTON, G.H. 1973. Engineering design and construction in permafrost regions: a review. Proc. 2nd International Conference on Permafrost, Yakutsk, U.S.S.R., North American Contribution, U.S. National Academy of Sciences, pp. 553-575.

LINELL, K.A. and KAPLAR, C.W. 1959. The factor of soil and material type in frost action. U.S. Highway Research Board, Bull. 225, pp. 81-126.

LINELL, K.A. and KAPLAR, C.W. 1966. Description and classification of frozen soils. Proc. International Conference on Permafrost (1963), Lafayette, IN, U.S. National Academy of Sciences, Publ. 1287, pp. 481-487.

LINELL, K.A. and LOBACZ, E.F. 1978. Some experiences with tunnel entrances in permafrost. Proc. 3rd International Conference on Permafrost, Edmonton, Alta., Canada, National Research Council, Vol. 1, pp. 813-819.

LITVINOV, A.Ya. 1966, Determination of the overall moisture content of frozen ground with thick streaks of ice. J. Soil Mech. Found. Eng. (U.S.S.R.), May-June, pp. 184-185, Transl. by Consultants Bureau, New York, NY.

LIVINGSTON, C.W. 1956. Excavations in frozen ground, Part I, explosion tests in Keweenaw silt. U.S. Army, CRREL (SIPRE) Tech. Rpt. TR 30, 97 p.

LIVINGSTON, C.W. 1960. Fundamentals of Arctic blasting. ASCE, J. Const. Div., Vol. 86, No. C01, pp. 1-9.

LIVINGSTON, C.W. and MURPHY, G. 1959. Excavations in frozen ground. Part. II, explosion tests in frozen glacial till, Ft. Churchill. U.S. Army, CRREL (SIPRE), Tech. Rpt. TR 30, 19 p.

LOBACZ, E.F. and EFF, K.S. 1978. Storm drainage design considerations in cold regions. Proc. Conference on Applied Techniques for Cold Environments, Anchorage, AK, ASCE, Vol. 1, pp. 474-489.

LOBACZ, E.F. and QUINN, W.F. 1966. Thermal regime beneath buildings constructed on permafrost. Proc. International Conference on Permafrost (1963), Lafayette, IN, U.S. National Academy of Sciences, Publ. 1287, pp. 247-252.

LOCK, G.S.H., GUNDERSON, J.R., QUON, D. and DONNELLY, J.K. 1969. A study of one-dimensional ice formation with particular reference to periodic growth and decay. International J. Heat Mass Transfer, Vol. 12, pp. 1343-1352.

LONG, E.L. 1966. The Long thermopile. Proc. International Conference on Permafrost (1963), Lafayette, IN, U.S. National Academy of Sciences, Publ. 1287, pp. 487-491.

LOVELL, C.H. and OSBORNE, A.N. 1968. Feasibility of cold weather earthwork. U.S. Highway Research Board, Record 248, pp. 18-27.

LOW, P.F., ANDERSON, D.M. and HOEKSTRA, P. 1968. Some thermodynamic relationships for soils at or below the freezing point, 2. effect of temperature and pressure on unfrozen soil water. Water Resources Research, Vol. 4, No. 5, pp. 541-544.

LOW, W.I. and LYELL, A.P. 1967. Portage Mountain Dam, III: development of construction control. Can. Geotech. J., Vol. 4, No. 2, pp. 184-228.

LUNARDINI, V.J. 1977. Thawing of permafrost beneath a buried pipe. Proc. 6th Canadian Congress Applied Mechanics (CANAM 77), Univ. of British Columbia, Vancouver, B.C., Vol. 2, pp. 813-814.

LUNARDINI, V.J. 1978. Theory of n-factors and correlation of data. Proc. 3rd International Conference on Permafrost, Edmonton, Alta., Canada, National Research Council, Vol. 1, pp. 41-46.

LUNDQVIST, J. 1969. Earth and ice mounds: a terminological discussion. In: The Periglacial Environment (T.L. Péwé, ed.), McGill-Queen's Univ. Press, Montreal, Que., pp. 203-215.

LUSCHER, U. and AFIFI, S.S. 1973. Thaw consolidation of Alaskan silts and granular soils. Proc. 2nd International Conference on Permafrost, Yakutsk, U.S.S.R., North American Contribution, U.S. National Academy of Sciences, pp. 325-333.

LUSCHER, U., BLACK, W.T. and NAIR, K. 1975. Geotechnical aspects of Trans-Alaska Pipeline. ASCE, J. Transportation Engineering Div., Vol. 101, No. TE4, pp. 669-680.

MACDONALD, D.H. 1966. Design of Kelsey Dykes. Proc. International Conference on Permafrost (1963), Lafayette, IN, U.S. National Academy of Sciences, Publ. 1287, pp. 492-496.

MACDONALD, D.H., PILLMAN, R.A. and HOPPER, H.R. 1960. Kelsey Generating Station Dam and Dykes. Engineering Journal, Vol. 43, No. 10, pp. 87-98.

MACFARLANE, I.C. (ed.) 1969. Muskeg engineering handbook. Univ. of Toronto Press, Toronto, Ont., 320 p.

MACKAY, D.K. 1970. Electrical resistivity measurements in frozen ground, Mackenzie Delta area, Northwest Territories. In: Hydrology of Deltas, International Association of Scientific Hydrology, Proc. of the Bucharest Symposium (May 1969), UNESCO, Vol. 2, pp. 363-375.

MACKAY, J.R. 1962. Pingos of the Pleistocene Mackenzie Delta area. Geographical Bull., No. 18, pp. 21-63.

MACKAY, J.R. 1963a. The Mackenzie Delta area, N.W.T. Dept. Mines Tech. Survey, Geogr. Branch, Ottawa, Ont., Memoir 8, 202 p.

MACKAY, J.R. 1963b. Origin of the pingos of the Pleistocene Mackenzie Delta area. Canada, National Research Council, Associate Committee on Soil and Snow Mechanics, Tech. Memo. 76, pp. 27-83.

MACKAY, J.R. 1963c. Notes on the shoreline recession along the coast of the Yukon Territory. Arctic, Vol. 16, No. 3, pp. 195-197.

MACKAY, J.R. 1966a. Segregated epigenetic ice and slumps in permafrost, Mackenzie Delta area, N.W.T. Geogr. Bull., No. 8, pp. 59-80.

MACKAY, J.R. 1966b. Pingos in Canada. Proc. International Conference on Permafrost (1963), Lafayette, IN, U.S. National Academy of Sciences, Publ. 1287, pp. 71-76.

MACKAY, J.R. 1967. Permafrost depths, lower Mackenzie Valley, Northwest Territories. Arctic, Vol. 20, No. 1, pp. 21-26.

MACKAY, J.R. 1971. The origin of massive icy beds in permafrost, western Arctic coast, Canada. Can. J. Earth Sci., Vol. 8, No. 4, pp. 397-422.

MACKAY, J.R. 1972a. The world of underground ice. Annals Association American Geographers, Vol. 62, pp. 1-22.

MACKAY, J.R. 1972b. Offshore permafrost and ground ice, southern Beaufort Sea, Canada. Can. J. Earth Sci., Vol. 9, No. 11, pp. 1550-1561.

MACKAY, J.R. 1973a. Problems in the origin of massive icy beds, western Arctic coast, Canada. Proc. 2nd International Conference on Permafrost, Yakutsk, U.S.S.R., North American Contribution, U.S. National Academy of Sciences, pp. 223-228.

MACKAY, J.R. 1973b. The growth of pingos, western Arctic coast, Canada. Can. J. Earth Sci., Vol. 10, No. 6, pp. 979-1004.

MACKAY, J.R. 1973c. A frost tube for the determination of freezing in the active layer above permafrost. Can. Geotech. J., Vol. 10, No. 3, pp. 392-396.

MACKAY, J.R. 1974a. Measurement of upward freezing above permafrost with a self-positioning thermistor probe. Geol. Surv. Can., Paper 74-1, Part B, pp. 250-251.

MACKAY, J.R. 1974b. Reticulate ice veins in permafrost, northern Canada. Can. Geotech. J., Vol. 11, No. 2, pp. 230-237.

MACKAY, J.R. 1974c. The rapidity of tundra polygon growth and destruction, Tuktoyaktuk Peninsula-Richards Island area, N.W.T. Geol. Surv. Can., Paper 74-1, Part A, pp. 391-392.

MACKAY, J.R. 1974d. Seismic shot holes and ground temperatures, Mackenzie Delta area, Northwest Territories. Geol. Surv. Can., Paper 74-1, Part A, pp. 389-390.

MACKAY, J.R. 1975a. The stability of permafrost and recent climate change in the Mackenzie Valley, N.W.T. Geol. Surv. Can., Paper 75-1B, pp. 173-176.

MACKAY, J.R. 1975b. Relict ice-wedges, Pelly Island, N.W.T. Geol. Surv. Can., Paper 75-1, Part A, pp. 469-470.

MACKAY, J.R. 1975c. The closing of ice-wedge cracks in permafrost, Garry Island, Northwest Territories. Can. J. Earth Sci., Vol. 12, No. 9, pp. 1668-1674.

MACKAY, J.R. 1976. Ice segregation at depth in permafrost. Geol. Surv. Can., Paper 76-1A, pp. 287-288.

MACKAY, J.R. 1977a. Changes in the active layer from 1968 to 1976 as a result of the Inuvik fire. Geol. Surv. Can., Paper 77-1B, pp. 273-275.

MACKAY, J.R. 1977b. Probing for the bottom of the active layer. Geol. Surv. Can., Paper 77-1A, pp. 327-328.

MACKAY, J.R. 1979. Pingos of the Tuktoyaktuk Peninsula area, Northwest Territories. Géogr. phys. Quat., Vol. 33, No. 1, pp. 3-61.

MACKAY, J.R. and BLACK, R.F. 1973. Origin, composition, and structure of perennially frozen ground and ground ice: a review. Proc. 2nd International Conference on Permafrost, Yakutsk, U.S.S.R., North American Contribution, U.S. National Academy of Sciences, pp. 185-192.

MACKAY, J.R. and LAVKULICH, L.M. 1975. Ionic and oxygen isotopic fractionation in permafrost growth. Geol. Surv. Can., Paper 74-1, Part B, pp. 255-256.

MACKAY, J.R. and MACKAY, D.K. 1974. Snow cover and ground temperatures, Garry Island, N.W.T. Arctic, Vol. 27, No. 4, pp. 287-296.

MACKAY, J.R. and MACKAY, D.K. 1976. Cryostatic pressures in nonsorted circles (mud hummocks), Inuvik, Northwest Territories. Can. J. Earth Sci., Vol. 13, No. 7, pp. 889-897.

MACKAY, J.R. and MATHEWS, W.H. 1973. Geomorphology and quaternary history of the Mackenzie River Valley near Fort Good Hope, N.W.T. Can. J. Earth Sci., Vol. 10, No. 1, pp. 26-41.

MACKAY, J.R. and STAGER, J.K. 1966. Thick tilted beds of segregated ice, Mackenzie Delta area, N.W.T. Biuletyn Peryglacjalny, Vol. 15, pp. 39-43.

MACPHERSON, J.G., WATSON, G.H. and KOROPATNICK, A. 1970. Dikes on permafrost foundations in northern Manitoba. Can. Geotech. J., Vol. 7, No. 4, pp. 356-364.

MCANERNEY, J.M. 1967. Experiments in excavating frozen silt underground. Presented at Alaska Minerals Conference, Univ. of Alaska, College, AK, 18 p.

MCANERNEY, J.M. HAWKES, I. and QUINN, W.F. 1969. Blasting frozen ground with compressed air. Proc. 3rd Canadian Conference on Permafrost, Canada, National Research Council, Associate Committee Geotechnical Research, Tech. Memo. 96, pp. 39-58.

MCCOY, J.E. 1965. Excavations in frozen ground, Alaska, 1960-1961. U.S. Army, CRREL, Tech. Rpt. TR120, 10 p.

MCCULLOUGH, C.R. 1958. Review of frozen ground excavation methods. U.S. Army, CRREL (SIPRE), Tech. Rpt. 51, 9 p.

MCDOUGALL, J.C. 1977. The Beaufort Gas Project surface facilities. Proc. 2nd International Symposium on Cold Regions Engineering (1976), Fairbanks, AK, Univ. of Alaska, Dept. Civil Eng., pp. 383-400.

MCGINNIS, L.D. and JENSEN, T.E. 1971. Permafrost-hydrogeologic regimen in two ice-free valleys, Antarctica, from electrical depth sounding. J. Quat. Res., Vol. 1, No. 3, pp. 389-409.

MCKAY, A.S. and O'CONNELL, L.P. 1975. Permafrost density logger. Presented at 26th Annual Technical Meeting (June), Petroleum Society, Can. Institute of Mining, Banff, Alta.

MCKEOWN, J.D. and MATHESON, D.S. 1977. Use of glacial till and outwash silty sand as construction material for dam cores at Long Spruce Generating Station. Proc. 30th Can. Geotech. Conference, Saskatoon, Sask., Preprint vol., pp. VI-61 to VI-82.

MCQUILLAN, A.K. 1975a. The value of remote sensing in Canadian frontier petroleum operations. Canada Centre for Remote Sensing, Res. Rpt. 75-4AJ.

MCQUILLAN, A.K. 1975b. Benefits of remote sensing in Canadian northern resource development. Canada Centre for Remote Sensing, Res. Rpt. 75-6AX.

MCROBERTS, E.C. 1973. Stability of slopes in permafrost. Ph.D. Thesis, Univ. of Alberta, Dept. Civil Eng., Edmonton, Alta.

MCROBERTS, E.C., LAW, T.C. and MURRAY, T.K. 1978. Creep tests on undisturbed ice-rich silt. Proc. 3rd International Conference on Permafrost, Edmonton, Alta., Canada, National Research Council, Vol. 1, pp. 539-545.

MCROBERTS, E.C. and MORGENSTERN, N.R. 1973. Landslides in the vicinity of the Mackenzie River, Mile 205 to 660. Canada, Dept. of Indian and Northern Affairs, Environmental-Social Program, Northern Pipelines, Report 73-35, 96 p.

MCROBERTS, E.C. and MORGENSTERN, N.R. 1974a. The stability of thawing slopes. Can. Geotech. J., Vol. 11, No. 4, pp. 447-469.

MCROBERTS, E.C. and MORGENSTERN, N.R. 1974b. Stability of slopes in frozen soil, Mackenzie Valley N.W.T. Can. Geotech. J., Vol. 11, No. 4, pp. 554-573.

MCROBERTS, E.C. and MORGENSTERN, N.R. 1975. Pore water expulsion during freezing. Can. Geotech. J., Vol. 12, No. 1, pp. 130-141.

MCROBERTS, E.C. and NIXON, J.F. 1975. Reticulate ice veins in permafrost, northern Canada: discussion. Can. Geotech. J., Vol. 12, No. 1, pp. 159-166.

MCROBERTS, E.C. and NIXON, J.F. 1977. Extensions to thawing slope stability theory. Proc. 2nd International Symposium on Cold Regions Eng. (1976), Fairbanks, AK, Univ. of Alaska, Dept. Civil Eng., pp. 262-276.

MELLOR, M. 1965. Blowing snow. U.S. Army, CRREL, Monograph MIII-A3c, 79 p.

MELLOR, M. 1972a. Jet cutting in frozen ground. Proc. 1st. International Symposium on Jet Cutting, Coventry, England, 10 p.

MELLOR, M. 1972b. Cutting frozen ground with milling drums. U.S. Army, CRREL, Tech. Note, Aug.

MELLOR, M. 1972c. Design parameters for a rotary excavating attachment. U.S. Army, CRREL, Tech. Note, Sept., 28 p.

MELLOR, M. 1975a. Cutting frozen ground with disc saws. U.S. Army, CRREL, Tech. Rpt. TR 261, 65 p.

MELLOR, M. 1975b. Mechanics of cutting and boring, Part I: kinematics of transverse rotation machines. U.S. Army, CRREL, Spec. Rpt. 226, 33 p.

MELLOR, M. 1975c. Controlled perimeter blasting in cold regions. U.S. Army, CRREL, Tech. Rpt. TR 267, 24 p.

MELLOR, M. 1976a. Mechanics of cutting and boring, Part II: kinematics of axial rotation machines. U.S. Army, CRREL, Rpt. 76-16, 53 p.

MELLOR, M. 1976b. Mechanics of cutting and boring, Part III: kinematics of continuous belt machines. U.S. Army, CRREL, Rpt. 76-17, 33 p.

MELLOR, M. 1977. Mechanics of cutting and boring, Part IV: dynamics and energetics of parallel motion tools. U.S. Army, CRREL, Rpt. 77-7, 96 p.

MELLOR, M. 1978. Undersea pipelines and cables in polar waters. U.S. Army, CRREL, Rpt. 78-22, 36 p.

MELLOR, M. and SELLMAN, P.V. 1970. Experimental blasting in frozen ground. U.S. Army, CRREL, Spec. Rpt. SR 153, 37 p.

MELLOR, M. and SELLMAN, P.V. 1975. General considerations for drill system design. U.S. Army, CRREL, Tech. Rpt. TR 264, 41 p.

MICHEL, B. 1971. Winter regime of rivers and lakes. U.S. Army, CRREL, Monograph III-Bla, 139 p.

MICHEL, F.A. and FRITZ, P. 1978. Environmental isotopes in permafrost related waters along the Mackenzie Valley corridor. Proc. 3rd International Conference on Permafrost, Edmonton, Alta., Canada, National Research Council, Vol. 1, pp. 207-211.

MILLER, J.M. 1971. Pile foundations in thermally fragile frozen soils. Proc. Symposium on Cold Regions Engineering (1970), ASCE and Univ. of Alaska, Dept. Civil Eng., Vol. 1, pp. 34-72.

MILLER, R.D. 1970. Ice sandwich: functional semi-permeable membrane. Science, Vol. 169, pp. 584-585.

MILLER, R.D. 1978. Frost heaving in non-colloidal soils. Proc. 3rd International Conference on Permafrost, Edmonton, Alta., Canada, National Research Council, Vol. 1, pp. 707-713.

MILLER, R.D., LOCH, J.P.G. and BRESLER, E. 1975. Transport of water and heat in a frozen permeameter. Proc. Soil Sci. Soc. Amer., Vol. 39, No. 6, pp. 1029-1036.

MITTAL, H.K. and MORGENSTERN, N.R. 1975. Parameters for the design of tailings dams. Can. Geotech. J., Vol. 12, No. 2, pp. 235-261.

MIYAMOTO, H.K. and HEINKE, G.W. 1979. Performance evaluation of an Arctic sewage lagoon. Can. J. Civil Eng. Vol. 6, No. 2, pp. 324-328.

MOHAN, A. 1973. Finite element analysis of heat flow around buried pipes. Ph.D. thesis, Purdue Univ., Dept. Civil Eng., Lafayette, IN, 242 p.

MOLLARD, J.D. 1960. Guides for the interpretation of muskeg and permafrost conditions from aerial photographs. Oilweek, July 23, 8 p.

MOLLARD, J.D. 1968. The role of photographic interpretation in northern route and site surveys. Presented at 61st Annual Meeting (Jan.), Can. Inst. of Surveying, Edmonton, Alta.

MOLLARD, J.D. 1972. Airphoto terrain classification and mapping for northern pipeline feasibility studies. Proc. Canadian Northern Pipeline Research Conference, Canada, National Research Council, Associate Committee Geotechnical Research, Tech. Memo. 104, pp. 105-127.

MOLLARD, J.D. 1975. Landforms and surface materials of Canada: a stereoscopic airphoto atlas and glossary. (4th ed.) 667 stereograms, 1573 contact airphotos, map of Canada, 13 chapters, 2500-term glossary, 336 p. Available from J.D. Mollard, 815 McCallum Hill Building, Regina, Sask.

MOLLARD, J.D. and PIHLAINEN, J.A. 1966. Airphoto interpretation applied to road selection in the Arctic. Proc. International Conference on Permafrost (1963), Lafayette, IN, U.S. National Academy of Sciences, Publ. 1287, pp. 381-387.

MONROE, R.L. 1972-74. Terrain classification and sensitivity maps, Mackenzie Valley and northern Yukon Territory. Geol. Surv. Can., Open Files 117, 120, 121, 125, 131, 132, 144, 145, 157 and 210.

MORGENSTERN, N.R. and NIXON, J.F. 1971. One-dimensional consolidation of thawing soils. Can. Geotech. J., Vol. 8, No. 4, pp. 558-565.

MORGENSTERN, N.R. and NIXON, J.F. 1975. An analysis of the performance of a warm-oil pipeline in permafrost, Inuvik, N.W.T. Can. Geotech. J., Vol. 12, No. 2, pp. 199-208.

MORGENSTERN, N.R. and SMITH, L.B. 1973. Thaw consolidation tests on remoulded clays. Can. Geotech. J., Vol. 10, No. 1, pp. 25-40.

MORGENSTERN, N.R., THOMSON, S. and MAGEAU, D. 1978. Explosive cratering in permafrost: state of the art. Canada, Dept. of National Defence, Defence Research Establishment Suffield, Ralston, Alta., Contract 8SU77-00015, 420 p.

MOULTON, L.K. 1969. Prediction of the depth of frost penetration: a review of literature. West Virginia Univ., Morgantown, WV, 115 p.

MÜLLER, F. 1959. Beobachturger uber pingos (Observations of pingos). Medd. om Gronland, 153, Canada, National Research Council, Tech. Transl. 1073, 117 p.

MULLER, S.W. 1947. Permafrost or permanently frozen ground and related engineering problems. J.W. Edwards, Ann Arbor, MI, 231 p.

MUNN, R.E. 1966, Descriptive micrometeorology. Academic Press, New York, NY, Advances in Geophysics, Suppl. 1, 245 p.

MURFITT, A.W., MCMULLEN, W.B., BAKER, M. and MCPHAIL, J.F. 1976. Design and construction of roads on muskeg in Arctic and subarctic regions. Proc. 16th Muskeg Research Conference (1975), Canada, National Research Council, Associate Committee Geotechnical Research, Tech. Memo. 116, pp. 152-185.

MUSCHELL, F.E. 1970. Pile tips and barbs prevent ice uplift. Civil Engineering, Vol. 40, No. 6, pp. 41-43.

MYERS, G.E. 1971. Analytical methods in conduction heat transfer. McGraw-Hill, New York, NY, 508 p.

MYSKA, A.D. and HOW, G.T.S. 1978. Installation of pile foundations for a microwave tower system, Gillam-Churchill, Manitoba. Proc. 3rd International Conference on Permafrost, Edmonton, Alta., Canada, National Research Council, Vol. 1, pp. 826-832.

MYZNIKOV, Y.N., ZHILENAS, S.V. and TEN, N.A. 1973. Construction of the right-bank dam at Ust'-Khantaisk hydroelectric plant. Hydrotechnical Construction (U.S.S.R.), No. 4, pp. 309-318, Transl. by Consultants Bureau, New York, NY, for ASCE.

NAKANO, Y. and BROWN, J. 1971. Effect of a freezing zone of finite width on the thermal regime of soils. Water Resources Research, Vol. 7, No. 5, pp. 1226-1233.

NAKANO, Y. and BROWN, J. 1972. Mathematical modeling and validation of the thermal regimes in tundra soils, Barrow, Alaska. Arctic and Alpine Research, Vol. 4, No. 1, pp. 19-38.

NAKANO, Y. and FROULA, N.H. 1973. Sound and shock transmission in frozen soils. Proc. 2nd International Conference on Permafrost, Yakutsk, U.S.S.R., North American Contribution, U.S. National Academy of Sciences, pp. 359-369.

NALEZNY, C.L. 1971. Cutting rock or frozen soil with a circular saw. J. of Terra Mechanics, Vol. 8, No. 1, pp. 23-40.

NAYSMITH, J.K. 1971. Canada North: man and the land. Canada, Dept. of Indian and Northern Affairs, 44 p.

NAYSMITH, J.K. 1975. Land use and public policy in northern Canada. Canada, Dept. of Indian and Northern Affairs, 218 p.

NEES, A. 1951. Pile foundations for large towers on permafrost. ASCE, Proc., Vol. 77, No. 103, 10 p.

NERSESOVA, Z.A. and TSYTOVICH, N.A. 1966. Unfrozen water in frozen soils. Proc. International Conference on Permafrost (1963), Lafayette, IN, U.S. National Academy of Sciences, Publ. 1287, pp. 230-234.

NETTERVILLE, J.A., DYKE, A.S., THOMAS, R.D. and DRABINSKY, K.A. 1976. Surficial geology and geomorphology maps of Somerset and Prince of Wales Islands. Geol. Surv. Can., Open File 357.

NEUBER, H. and WOLTERS, R. 1970. Mechanical behaviour of frozen soils under triaxial compression. Fortsch. Geol. Rheinld. u. Westfallen, Krefeld, Germany, Vol. 17, pp. 499-536, Canada, National Research Council, Transl. TT 1902, 25 p.

NEWBURY, R.W., BEATY, K.G. and MCCULLOUGH, G.K. 1978. Initial shoreline erosion in a permafrost affected reservoir, southern Indian Lake, Canada. Proc. 3rd International Conference on Permafrost, Edmonton, Alta., Canada, National Research Council, Vol. 1, pp. 833-839.

NICHOLSON, F.H. 1976. Permafrost thermal amelioration tests near Schefferville, Quebec. Can. J. Earth Sci., Vol. 13, No. 12, pp. 1694-1705.

NICHOLSON, F.H. 1978. Permafrost distribution and characteristics near Schefferville, Quebec: recent studies. Proc. 3rd International Conference on Permafrost, Edmonton, Alta., Canada, National Research Council, Vol. 1, pp. 427-433.

NICHOLSON, F.H. and GRANBERG, H.B. 1973. Permafrost and snow-cover relationships near Schefferville, Quebec. Proc. 2nd International Conference on Permafrost, Yakutsk, U.S.S.R., North American Contribution, U.S. National Academy of Sciences, pp. 151-158.

NICHOLSON, F.H. and THOM, B.G. 1973. Studies at the Timmins 4 permafrost experimental sites. Proc. 2nd International Conference on Permafrost, Yakutsk, U.S.S.R., North American Contribution, U.S. National Academy of Sciences, pp. 159-166.

NIKIFOROV, V.V. 1968. Earth-fill work in the winter on the Saratov hydroelectric stations. Hydrotechnical Construction (U.S.S.R.), No. 7, pp. 577-579, Transl. by Consultants Bureau, New York, NY, for ASCE.

NIXON, J.F. 1973a. The consolidation of thawing soil. Ph.D. Thesis, Univ. of Alberta, Dept. Civil Eng., Edmonton, Alta.

NIXON, J.F. 1973b. Thaw consolidation of some layered systems. Can. Geotech. J., Vol. 10, No. 4, pp. 617-631.

NIXON, J.F. 1978a. Geothermal aspects of ventilated pad design. Proc. 3rd International Conference on Permafrost, Edmonton, Alta., Canada, National Research Council, Vol. 1, pp. 840-846.

NIXON, J.F. 1978b. First Canadian geotechnical colloquium: foundation design approaches in permafrost areas. Can. Geotech. J., Vol. 15, No. 1, pp. 96-112.

NIXON, J.F. 1979. Some aspects of road and airstrip pad design in permafrost areas. Can. Geotech. J., Vol. 16, No. 1, pp. 222-225.

NIXON, J.F. and MCROBERTS, E.C. 1973. A study of some factors affecting the thawing of frozen soils. Can. Geotech. J., Vol. 10, No. 3, pp. 439-452.

NIXON, J.F. and MCROBERTS, E.C. 1976. A design approach for pile foundations in permafrost. Can. Geotech. J., Vol. 13, No. 1, pp. 40-57.

NIXON, J.F. and MORGENSTERN, N.R. 1973a. The residual stress in thawing soils. Can. Geotech. J., Vol. 10, No. 4, pp. 571-580.

NIXON, J.F. and MORGENSTERN, N.R. 1973b. Practical extensions to a theory of consolidation for thawing soils. Proc. 2nd International Conference on Permafrost, Yakutsk, U.S.S.R., North American Contribution, U.S. National Academy of Sciences, pp. 369-376.

NIXON, J.F. and MORGENSTERN, N.R. 1974. Thaw consolidation tests on undisturbed fine-grained permafrost. Can. Geotech. J., Vol. 11, No. 1, pp. 202-214.

NORTHERN MINER. 1974. Federal government backing Baffin Island's first mine. Vol. 60, No. 15, pp. 1-2.

O'BRIEN, E.T. and WHYMAN, A.D. 1976. Polyethylene piping system for remote cold regions. Engineering Digest, June, pp. 41-45.

ODINTSOV, A.K. and NEDOSEKIN, A.S. 1975. Temperature conditions of dams constructed on a permafrost foundation. Hydrotechnical Construction (U.S.S.R.), No. 6, pp. 5-7, Transl. by Consultants Bureau, New York, NY, for ASCE.

OGILVIE, R.T. and BAPTIE, B. 1967. A permafrost profile in the Rocky Mountains of Alberta. Can. J. Earth Sci., Vol. 4, No. 4, pp. 744-745.

OGILVY, A.A. 1967. Geophysical studies in permafrost regions in the U.S.S.R. Geol. Surv. Can., Economic Geology Report 26: Mining and Groundwater Geophysics, pp. 641-650.

OILWEEK. 1976. Artificial islands, drillships: current Beaufort, Delta techniques. Dec., pp. 47-50.

OLHOEFT, G.R. 1977. Electrical properties of natural clay permafrost. Can. J. Earth Sci., Vol. 14, No. 1, pp. 16-24.

ORLOV, V.O. 1974. Concerning M.F. Kiselev's article "Standard values of specific tangential forces of frost heaving of soils". J. Soil Mech. Found. Eng. (U.S.S.R.), No. 3, pp. 44-45, Transl. by Consultants Bureau, New York, NY.

OSTERKAMP, T.E. and HARRISON, W.D. 1976a. Subsea permafrost: its implications for offshore resource development. The Northern Engineer, Vol. 8, No. 1, pp. 31-35.

OSTERKAMP, T.E. and HARRISON, W.D. 1976b. Subsea permafrost at Prudhoe Bay, Alaska: drilling report and data analysis. Univ. of Alaska, Geophysical Institute, Rpt. R-245, 69 p.

OUTCALT, S.I. 1972. The development and application of a simple digital surface-climate simulator. J. Applied Meteorology, Vol. VII, pp. 629-636.

OUTCALT, S.I. 1976. A numerical model of ice lensing in freezing soils. Proc. 2nd Conference on Soil-Water Problems in Cold Regions, Edmonton, Alta., pp. 63-74.

OUTCALT, S.I. 1977. Numerical modelling of the ice lensing processes. Proc. International Symposium Frost Action in Soils, Univ. of Luleå, Sweden, Vol. 2, pp. 75-91.

OUTCALT, S.I. and CARLSON, J.H. 1975. A coupled soil thermal regime energy budget simulator. Proc. Conference on Soil-Water Problems in Cold Regions, Calgary, Alta., pp. 1-32.

OUTCALT, S.I., GOODWIN, C., WELLER, G. and BROWN, J. 1975. Computer simulation of the snowmelt and soil thermal regime at Barrow, Alaska. Water Resources Research, Vol. 11, No. 5, pp. 709-715.

OWEN, E.B. 1967. Northern hydrogeological region. Geol. Surv. Can., Economic Geology Rpt. 24, Chap. VIII, pp. 173-194.

PAIGE, R.A. and O'BRIEN, J.A. 1972. Floor foundation stabilization in permafrost at Barrow, Alaska. Proc. 10th Annual Symposium on Engineering Geology and Soils Engineering, pp. 287-299.

PALMER, A.C. 1978. Thawing and differential settlement of ground around oil wells in permafrost. Proc. 2nd International Conference on Permafrost (1973), Yakutsk, U.S.S.R., U.S.S.R. Contribution, U.S. National Academy of Sciences, pp. 619-624.

PARAMESWARAN, V.R. 1978. Adfreeze strength of frozen sand to model piles. Can. Geotech. J., Vol. 15, No. 4, pp. 494-500.

PARKHOMENKO, E.I. 1967. Electrical properties of rocks. Transl. from Russian by G.V. Keller, Plenum Press, New York, NY, 314 p.

PAVLOVA, K.K. 1970. Phase composition of water and thermo-physical characteristics of frozen peat in the study of infiltration. In: Soviet Hydrology: Selected Papers, Issue 4, pp. 361-378.

PEABODY, A.W. 1976. Special challenge: cathodic protection on Trans-Alaska Pipeline. Pipeline and Gas J., Dec., pp. 40-43.

PEABODY, A.W. 1979. Preventing corrosion on Arctic pipelines. Pipeline and Gas J., Vol. 206, No. 11, pp. 28-42.

PEDROSO, R.I. and DOMOTO, G.A. 1973. Inward spherical solidification solution by the method of strained coordinates. International J. Heat Mass Transfer, Vol. 16, pp. 1037-1043.

PENNER, E. 1959. The mechanism of frost heaving in soils. U.S. Highway Research Board, Bull. 225, pp. 1-22.

PENNER, E. 1960. The importance of freezing rate in frost action in soils. ASTM Proc., Vol. 60, pp. 1151-1165.

PENNER, E. 1970a. Thermal conductivity of frozen soils. Can. J. Earth Sci., Vol. 7, No. 3, pp. 982-987.

PENNER, E. 1970b. Frost heaving forces in Leda clay. Can. Geotech. J., Vol. 7, No. 1, pp. 8-16.

PENNER, E. 1972. Influence of freezing rate on frost heaving. U.S. Highway Research Board, Record 393, pp. 56-64.

PENNER, E. 1973. Frost heaving pressures in particulate materials. OECD Symposium on Frost Action on Roads, Paris, France, Vol. 1, pp. 379-385.

PENNER, E. 1974. Uplift forces on foundations in frost heaving soils. Can. Geotech. J., Vol. 11, No. 3, pp. 323-338.

PENNER, E. and GOLD, L.W. 1971. Transfer of heaving forces by adfreezing to columns and foundation walls in frost-susceptible soils. Can. Geotech. J., Vol. 8, No. 4, pp. 514-526.

PENNER, E. and IRWIN, W.W. 1969. Adfreezing of Leda clay to anchored footing columns. Can. Geotech. J., Vol. 6, No. 3, pp. 327-337.

PENNER, E., JOHNSTON, G.H. and GOODRICH, L.E. 1975. Thermal conductivity laboratory studies of some Mackenzie Highway soils. Can. Geotech. J., Vol. 12, No. 3, pp. 271-288.

PENNER, E. and UEDA, T. 1977. The dependence of frost heaving on load application. Proc. International Symposium on Frost Action in Soils, Univ. of Luleå, Sweden, Vol. 1, pp. 92-101.

PEPLER, S.W.E. and MACKENZIE, I.D. 1976. Glacial till in winter dam construction. Glacial Till Conference, Ottawa, Ont., Royal Society of Canada, Spec. Publ. 12, pp. 381-390.

PERKINS, T.K. and RUEDRICH, R.A. 1973. The mechanical behaviour of synthetic permafrost. AIME, J. Society Petroleum Eng., Vol. 13, No. 4, pp. 211-220.

PETTIBONE, H.C. 1973. Stability of an underground room in frozen gravel. Proc. 2nd International Conference on Permafrost, Yakutsk, U.S.S.R., North American Contribution, U.S. National Academy of Sciences, pp. 699-706.

PEWE, T.L. 1966. Ice-wedges in Alaska: classification, distribution, and climatic significance. Proc. International Conference on Permafrost (1963), Lafayette, IN, U.S. National Academy of Sciences, Publ. 1287, pp. 76-81.

PEWE, T.L. and PAIGE, R.A. 1963. Frost heaving of piles with an example from Fairbanks, Alaska. U.S. Geol. Surv., Bull. 1111-I, pp. 333-407.

PHILBERTH, K. and FEDERER, B. 1971. On the temperature profile and the age profile in the central part of cold ice sheets. J. of Glaciology, Vol. 10, No. 58, pp. 3-14.

PIHLAINEN, J.A. 1959. Pile construction in permafrost. ASCE., J. Soil Mech. Found. Div., Vol. 85, No. SM6, Part I, pp. 75-95.

PIHLAINEN, J.A., BROWN, R.J.E. and LEGGET, R.F. 1956. Pingo in the Mackenzie Delta, N.W.T. Geol. Soc. Amer. Bull., Vol. 67, pp. 1119-1122.

PIHLAINEN, J.A. and JOHNSTON, G.H. 1954. Permafrost investigations at Aklavik (drilling and sampling) 1953. Canada, National Research Council, Division Building Research, Tech. Paper 16, 47 p.

PIHLAINEN, J.A. and JOHNSTON, G.H. 1963. Guide to a field description of permafrost. Canada, National Research Council, Associate Committee on Soil and Snow Mechanics, Tech. Memo. 79, 23 p.

PISSART, A. 1967. Les pingos de l'Ile Prince Patrick (76°N-120°W). Geogr. Bull. (Canada), Vol. 9, pp. 189-217.

PISSART, A. and FRENCH, H.M. 1976. Pingo investigations, north-central Banks Island, Canadian Arctic. Can. J. Earth Sci., Vol. 13, No. 7, pp. 937-946.

PODKOPAEV, A.A. 1973. Experience in the construction of loam and clay dams and canal embankments on the Irtysh-Karaganda Canal during the winter. Hydrotechnical Construction (U.S.S.R.), No. 2, pp. 114-115, Transl. by Consultants Bureau, New York, NY, for ASCE.

PORKHAYEV, G.V. 1966. Temperature fields in foundations. Proc. International Conference on Permafrost (1963), Lafayette, IN, U.S. National Academy of Sciences, Publ. 1287, pp. 285-291.

PREST, V.K., GRANT, D.R. and RAMPTON, V.N. 1968. Glacial map of Canada. Geol. Surv. Can., Map 1253A.

PRICE, L.W. 1971. Vegetation, microtopography, and depth of active layer on different exposures in subarctic alpine tundra. Ecology, Vol. 52, No. 4, pp. 638-647.

PRYER, R.W.J. 1966. Mine railroads in Labrador-Ungava. Proc. International Conference on Permafrost (1963), Lafayette, IN, U.S. National Academy of Sciences, Publ. 1287, pp. 503-508.

PUFAHL, D.E. 1976. The behaviour of thawing slopes in permafrost. Ph.D. Thesis, Univ. of Alberta, Dept. Civil Eng., 345 p.

PUFAHL, D.E. and MORGENSTERN, N.R. 1979. Stabilization of planar landslides in permafrost. Can. Geotech. J., Vol. 16, No. 4, pp. 734-747.

PUFAHL, D.E., MORGENSTERN, N.R. and ROGGENSACK, W.D. 1974. Observations on recent highway cuts in permafrost. Canada, Dept. of Indian and Northern Affairs, Environmental-Social Program, Northern Pipelines, Rpt. 74-32, 53 p.

PUI, N.K. and KLJUCEC, N.M. 1977. Permafrost melting predictions match logs. Oil and Gas J., Vol. 75, No. 33, pp. 66-70.

QUONG, J.Y.C. 1971. Highway construction and permafrost with special reference to the active layer. Proc. Seminar on the Permafrost Active Layer, Vancouver, B.C., Canada, National Research Council, Associate Committee Geotechnical Research, Tech. Memo. 103, pp. 50-53.

RADD, F.J. and OERTLE, D.H. 1973. Experimental pressure studies of frost heave mechanisms and the growth-fusion behaviour of ice. Proc. 2nd International Conference on Permafrost, Yakutsk, U.S.S.R., North American Contribution, U.S. National Academy of Sciences, pp. 377-384.

RADFORTH, N.W. 1961. Distribution of organic terrain in northern Canada. Proc. 7th Muskeg Research Conference, Canada, National Research Council, Associate Committee on Soil and Snow Mechanics, Tech. Memo. 71, pp. 8-11.

RADFORTH, N.W. and BRAWNER, C.O. (ed.) 1977. Muskeg and the northern environment in Canada. Univ. of Toronto Press, Toronto, Ont., 410 p.

RAILTON, J.E. and SPARLING, J.H. 1973. Preliminary studies on the ecology of palsa mounds in northern Ontario. Can. J. Botany, Vol. 51, pp. 1037-1044.

RAMPTON, V.N. 1973. The influence of ground ice and thermokarst upon the geomorphology of the Mackenzie Beaufort region. In: Research in Polar and Alpine Geomorphology, Proc. 3rd Guelph Symposium on Geomorphology, Guelph, Ont., pp. 43-60.

RAMPTON, V.N. and MACKAY, J.R. 1971. Massive ice and icy sediments throughout the Tuktoyaktuk Peninsula, Richards Island, and nearby areas, District of Mackenzie. Geol. Surv. Can., Paper 71-21, 16 p.

RAMPTON, V.N. and WALCOTT, R.I. 1974. Gravity profiles across ice-cored topography. Can. J. Earth Sci., Vol. 11, No. 1, pp. 110-122.

RATHJEN, K.A. and JIJI, L.M. 1971. Heat condition with melting or freezing in a corner. ASME, J. Heat Transfer, Feb., pp. 101-109.

RAY, R.G. 1960. Aerial photographs in geologic interpretation and mapping. U.S. Geol. Surv., Prof. Paper 373, 230 p.

RAYNER, J. 1976. Freezing the foundation eliminates pile-driving. Engineering and Contract Record, May, p. 30.

REED, R.E. 1966. Refrigeration of a pipe pile by air circulation. U.S. Army, CRREL, Tech. Rpt. 156, 19 p.

REID, G.D. 1974. The impact of the northern environment on highway construction. Bull. American Association of Cost Engineers, Vol. 16, No. 2, pp. 43-47.

REID, R.L., TENNANT, J.S. and CHILDS, K.W. 1975. The modelling of a thermosyphon type permafrost protection device. ASME, J. Heat Transfer, August, pp. 382-386.

REINART, I. 1971. Nelson River HVDC transmission line foundation design aspects. Proc. Manitoba Power Conference EHV-DC, Winnipeg, pp. 422-440.

RICE, E. 1973. Northern construction: siting and foundations, The Northern Engineer, Vol. 5, No. 1, pp. 11-18.

RICE, E.F. and SIMONI, O.W. 1966. The Hess Creek Dam. Proc. International Conference on Permafrost (1963), Lafayette, IN, U.S. National Academy of Sciences, Publ. 1287, pp. 436-439.

RICHART, F.E., HALL, J.R., Jr. and WOODS, R.D. 1970. Vibrations of soils and foundations. Prentice-Hall, Englewood Cliffs, NJ, 414 p.

RICKARD, W. and BROWN, J. 1972. The performance of a frost-tube for the determination of soil freezing and thawing depth. Soil Science, Vol. 113, No. 2, pp. 149-154.

RIDDOCH, R.G. 1979. Cratering and ditching in frozen soils. M. Eng. Thesis, The Royal Military College of Canada, Dept. Civil Eng. Kingston, Ont. 213 p.

RILEY, J.G. 1976. The construction of artificial islands in the Beaufort Sea. J. Petrol. Tech., April, pp. 365-371.

RINKER, J.N. and FROST, R.E. 1969. Application of remote sensing to Arctic environmental studies. Proc. Alaska Remote Sensing Symposium, Alaska, Dept. of Economic Development, pp. 105-116.

ROADS AND STREETS, 1972. Tractor rippers can handle deep frost. Vol. 102, Part 1, pp. 90-91.

ROBERTS, P.W. and COOKE, F.A. 1950. Arctic tower foundations frozen into permafrost. Engineering News-Record, Vol. 114, No. 6, pp. 38-39.

ROBERTS, W.S. 1976. Regionalized feasibility study of cold weather earthwork. U.S. Army, CRREL, Spec. Rpt. 76-2, 214 p.

ROBINSKY, E.I. and BESPFLUG, K.E. 1973. Design of insulated foundations. ASCE, J. Soil Mech. Found. Div., Vol. 99, No. SM 9, pp. 649-667.

ROETHLISBERGER, H. 1972. Seismic exploration in cold regions. U.S. Army, CRREL, Monograph MII-A2a, 139 p.

ROGGENSACK, W.D. 1977. Geotechnical properties of fine-grained permafrost soils. Ph.D. Thesis, Univ. of Alberta, Dept. Civil Eng., Edmonton, Alta., 423 p.

ROGGENSACK, W.D. 1979. Techniques for core drilling in frozen soils. Proc. Symposium on Permafrost Field Methods and Permafrost Geophysics (Oct. 1977), Saskatoon, Sask., Canada, National Research Council, Associate Committee Geotechnical Research, Tech. Memo. 24, pp. 14-24.

ROGGENSACK, W.D. and MORGENSTERN, N.R. 1978. Direct shear tests on natural fine-grained permafrost soils. Proc. 3rd International Conference on Permafrost, Edmonton, Alta., Canada, National Research Council, Vol. 1, pp. 728-735.

ROGNESS, D.R. and RYAN, W.L. 1977. Vacuum sewage collection in the Arctic, Noorvik, Alaska: a case study. Proc. Symposium on Utilities Delivery in Arctic Regions, Edmonton, Alta., Environment Canada, Environmental Protection Service, Rpt. EPS-3-WP-77-1, pp. 505-522.

ROMANOFF, M. 1969. Corrosion evaluation of steel test piles exposed to permafrost soils. Proc. 25th Conference of National Association of Corrosion Engineers, Houston, TX, pp. 6-13.

ROONEY, J.W., NOTTINGHAM, D. and DAVISON, B.E. 1977. Driven H-pile foundations in frozen sands and gravels. Proc. 2nd International Symposium on Cold Regions Engineering (1976), Fairbanks, AK, Univ. of Alaska, Dept. Civil Eng., pp. 169-188.

ROWE, J.S. 1972. Forest regions of Canada. Environment Canada, Canadian Forestry Service, Publ. 1300, 171 p.

ROWLEY, R.K., WATSON, G.H., AULD, R.G. and WILSON, T.M. 1973a. Performance of a 48 inch warm-oil pipeline supported on permafrost. Can. Geotech. J., Vol. 10, No. 2, pp. 282-303.

ROWLEY, R.K., WATSON, G.H. and LADANYI, B. 1973b. Vertical and lateral pile load tests in permafrost. Proc. 2nd International Conference on Permafrost, Yakutsk, U.S.S.R., North American Contribution, U.S. National Academy of Sciences, pp. 712-721.

ROWLEY, R.K., WATSON, G.H. and LADANYI, B. 1975. Prediction of pile performance in permafrost under lateral load. Can. Geotech. J., Vol. 12, No. 4, pp. 510-523.

ROY, M., LAROCHELLE, P. and ANTIL, C. 1973. Stability of dyke embankments at mining sites in the Yellowknife area. Canada, Dept. of Indian and Northern Affairs, ALUR Rpt. 72-73-31, 78 p.

ROY, M. and VEZINA, S. 1973. Studies of mine waste containment at mining sites on Great Bear Lake. Canada, Dept. of Indian and Northern Affairs, ALUR Rpt. 72-73-33, 93 p.

RYAN, W.L. and ROGNESS, D.R. 1977. Pressure sewage collection systems in the Arctic. Proc. Symposium on Utilities Delivery in Arctic Regions, Edmonton, Alta., Environment Canada, Environmental Protection Service, Rpt. EPS-3-WP-77-1, pp. 523-552.

SAGER, R.C. 1951. Aerial analyses of permanently frozen ground. Photogrammetric Engineering, Vol. XVII, No. 4, pp. 551-571.

SAMSON, L. and TORDON, F. 1969. Experiences with engineering site investigations in northern Quebec and northern Baffin Island. Proc. 3rd Canadian Conference on Permafrost, Canada, National Research Council, Associate Committee Geotechnical Research, Tech. Memo. 96, pp. 21-38.

SANGER, F.J. 1966. Degree-days and heat conduction in soils. Proc. International Conference on Permafrost (1963), Lafayette, IN, U.S. National Academy of Sciences, Publ. 1287, pp. 253-263.

SANGER, F.J. 1969. Foundations of structures in cold regions. U.S. Army, CRREL, Monograph MIII-C4, 91 p.

SANGREY, D.A. 1974. Geotechnical engineering problems of the Arctic ocean bottom. Proc. 12th Annual Symposium on Engineering Geology and Soils Engineering (L.F. Erickson, ed.), pp. 149-161.

SATER, B.F. (ed.) 1969. Arctic and middle North transportation. Proc. Arctic Institute of North America Symposium (Mar. 1969), Montreal, Que., 208 p.

SAVAGE, J.E. 1965. Location and construction of roads in the discontinuous permafrost zone, Mackenzie District, Northwest Territories. Proc. Canadian Regional Permafrost Conference (1964), Edmonton, Alta., Canada, National Research Council, Associate Committee Soil and Snow Mechanics, Tech. Memo. 86, pp. 119-131.

SAYLES, F.H. 1966. Low temperature soil mechanics. U.S. Army, CRREL, Tech. Note, 15 p.

SAYLES, F.H. 1968. Creep of frozen sands. U.S. Army, CRREL, Tech. Rpt. 190, 54 p.

SAYLES, F.H. 1973. Triaxial and creep tests on frozen Ottawa sand. Proc. 2nd International Conference on Permafrost, Yakutsk, U.S.S.R., North American Contribution, U.S. National Academy of Sciences, pp. 384-391.

SAYLES, F.H. and HAINES, D. 1974. Creep of frozen silt and clay. U.S. Army, CRREL, Tech. Rpt. 252, 54 p.

SAYWARD, J.M. 1976. Evaluation of MESL membrane-puncture, stiffness, temperature, solvents. U.S. Army, CRREL, Rpt. 76-22, 65 p.

SCHAEFER, D. 1976. Water absorption of insulation in protected membrance roofing systems. U.S. Army, CRREL, Rpt. 76-83, 21 p.

SCHMITT, R.P. and RODRIQUEZ, P. 1960. Glacial water supply system. The Military Engineer, Vol. 52, No. 349, pp. 382-383.

SCHNEIDER, P.J. 1955. Conduction heat transfer. Addison-Wesley, Cambridge, MA, 395 p.

SCOTT, K.M. 1978. Effects of permafrost on stream channel behaviour in Arctic Alaska. U.S. Geol. Surv., Prof. Paper 1068, 19 p.

SCOTT, R.F. 1964. Heat exchange at the ground surface. U.S. Army, CRREL, Monograph MII-A1, 49 p.

SCOTT, R.F. 1969. Freezing process and mechanics of frozen ground. U.S. Army CRREL, Monograph MII-D1, 65 p.

SCOTT, W.J., CAMPBELL, K.J. and ORANGE, A.S. 1974. EM pulse survey method in permafrost. Proc. Symposium on Permafrost Geophysics, Calgary, Alta., Canada, National Research Council, Associate Committee Geotechnical Research, Tech. Memo. 113, pp. 92-96.

SCOTT, W.J. and HUNTER, J.A. 1977. Applications of geophysical techniques in permafrost regions. Can. J. Earth Sci., Vol. 14, No. 1, pp. 117-127.

SCOTT, W.J. and MACKAY, J.R. 1977. Reliability of permafrost thickness determination by DC resistivity sounding. Proc. Symposium on Permafrost Geophysics (1976), Vancouver, B.C., Canada, National Research Council, Associate Committee Geotechnical Research, Tech. Memo. 119, pp. 25-38.

SEDZIAK, H.P., SHIELDS, J.K. and JOHNSTON, G.H. 1973. Condition of timber foundation piles at Inuvik, N.W.T. Environment Canada, Forestry Service, Information Rpt. OP-X-67, 27 p.

SELLMAN, P.V. and BROWN, J. 1965. Coring of frozen ground, Barrow, Alaska. U.S. Army, CRREL, Spec. Rpt. 81, 8 p.

SELLMAN, P.V., LEWELLEN, R.I., UEDA, H.T., CHAMBERLAIN, E. and BLOUIN, S.E. 1976. Operational report: 1976 U.S. Army CRREL-USGS subsea permafrost program, Beaufort Sea, Alaska. U.S. Army, CRREL, Spec. Rpt. 76-12, 25 p.

SELLMAN, P.V., MCNEILL, J.D. and SCOTT, W.J. 1974. Airborne E-phase resistivity surveys of permafrost, central Alaska and Mackenzie River areas. Proc. Symposium on Permafrost Geophysics, Calgary, Alta., Canada, National Research Council, Associate Committee Geotechnical Research, Tech. Memo. 113, pp. 67-71.

SEMENOV, N.G. 1967. Construction of a dam in the permafrost zone. Hydrotechnical Construction (U.S.S.R.), No. 9, pp. 14-15, Transl. by Consultants Bureau, New York, NY, for ASCE.

SERGEEV, A.I. 1961. Digging in frozen ground. U.S. Army, CRREL (SIPRE), Transl. TL 65, 5 p.

SHAH, V.K. 1978. Protection of permafrost and ice rich shores, Tuktoyaktuk, N.W.T., Canada. Proc. 3rd International Conference on Permafrost, Edmonton, Alta., Canada, National Research Council, Vol. 1, pp. 870-876.

SHEARER, J.M., MACNAB, R.F., PELLETIER, B.R. and SMITH, T.B. 1971. Submarine pingos in the Beaufort Sea. Science, Vol. 174, pp. 816-818.

SHEMIE, R.K. and SIMONS, D.S. 1971. Ground current return electrode design. Proc. Manitoba Power Conference EHV-DC (1971), Winnipeg, Man., pp. 617-649.

SHEPPARD, M.I., KAY, B.D. and LOCK, J.P.G. 1978. Development and testing of a computer model for heat and mass flow in freezing soils. Proc. 3rd International Conference on Permafrost, Edmonton, Alta., Canada, National Research Council, Vol. 1, pp. 75-81.

SHILTS, W.W. 1973. Drift prospecting: geochemistry of eskers and till in permanently frozen terrain, District of Keewatin, Northwest Territories. Geol. Surv. Can., Paper 72-45, 34 p.

SHILTS, W.W. 1974. Physical and chemical properties of unconsolidated sediments in permanently frozen terrain, District of Keewatin. Geol. Surv. Can., Paper 74-1, Part A, pp. 229-235.

SHILTS, W.W. and DEAN, W.E. 1975. Permafrost features under Arctic lakes, District of Keewatin, Northwest Territories. Can. J. Earth Sci., Vol. 12, No. 4, pp. 649-662.

SHUGAEVA, R.T. 1976. Calculations of the thermal regime of earthen dams considering their construction by layers. U.S. Army, CRREL, Draft Transl. 565, 10 p.

SHUMSKIY, P.A. 1964. Principles of structural glaciology. Transl. from Russian by D. Kraus, Dover, New York, NY, 497 p.

SHUMSKIY, P.A. and VTYURIN, B.I. 1966. Underground ice. Proc. International Conference on Permafrost (1963), Lafayette, IN, U.S. National Academy of Sciences, Publ. 1287, pp. 108-113.

SHUSTER, J.A. 1971. Laboratory testing and characterization of permafrost for foundation uses. Proc. Symposium on Cold Regions Engineering, ASCE and Univ. of Alaska, Dept. Civil Eng., Vol. 1, pp. 73-118.

SIMONI, O.W. 1975. Construction and performance of the Hess Creek earth fill dam, Livengood, Alaska. The Northern Engineer, Vol. 7, No. 3, pp. 23-35.

SIPLE, P.A. 1945. Measurements of dry atmospheric cooling in subfreezing temperatures. Proc. American Philosophical Society, Vol. 89, pp. 177-199.

SKEMPTON, A.W. and HUTCHINSON, J.N. 1969. Stability of natural slopes and embankment foundations. Proc. 7th International Conference Soil Mech. and Found. Eng., State-of-the-Art Vol., pp. 291-340.

SKUBA, V.N. 1974. Investigation of the stability of mine workings under permafrost conditions. Published by Nauka, Novosibirsk, U.S.S.R., 120 p. (In Russian.)

SLOCUM, B.F. 1972. Arctic logistics support technology. Proc. Symposium (Nov. 1971), Hershey, PA., Arctic Institute of North America, 288 p.

SLUPSKY, J.W. (ed.) 1976. Some problems of solid and liquid waste disposal in the northern environment. Environment Canada, Environmental Protection Service, Rpt. EPS-4-NW-76-2, 230 p. (Series of 4 reports.)

SLUSARCHUK, W.A. and FOULGER, P.H. 1973. Development and calibration of a thermal conductivity probe apparatus for use in the field and laboratory. Canada, National Research Council, Division Building Research, Tech. Paper 388, 18 p.

SLUSARCHUK, W.A. and WATSON, G.H. 1975. Thermal conductivity of some ice-rich permafrost soils. Can. Geotech. J., Vol. 12, No. 3, pp. 413-424.

SLUSARCHUK, W.A., WATSON, G.H. and SPEER, T.L. 1973. Instrumentation around a warm oil pipeline buried in permafrost. Can. Geotech. J., Vol. 10, No. 2, pp. 227-245.

SMIRNOV, E.A. and VASILIEV, A.F. 1973. Design and construction of earth and rockfill dams under severe climatic conditions. In: Proc. Canada/U.S.S.R. Seminar on Civil and Mechanical Engineering Aspects of the Electrical Power Industry, Moscow, Vol. 1.

SMITH, G.W. and REMPEL, G. 1974. Review of problems of exploration geophysics in permafrost. Proc. Symposium on Permafrost Geophysics, Calgary, Alta., Canada, National Research Council, Associate Committee Geotechnical Research, Tech. Memo. 113, pp. 72-79.

SMITH, M.W. 1975a. Microclimatic influences of ground temperatures and permafrost distribution, Mackenzie Delta, Northwest Territories. Can. J. Earth Sci., Vol. 12, No. 8, pp. 1421-1438.

SMITH, M.W. 1975b. Numerical simulation of microclimatic and active layer regimes in a high Arctic environment. Canada, Dept. of Indian and Northern Affairs, Arctic Land Use Research Program, Rpt. ALUR 74-75-72, 29 p.

SMITH, M.W. 1976. Permafrost in the Mackenzie Delta, Northwest Territories. Geol. Surv. Can., Paper 75-28, 41 p.

SMITH, M.W. 1977. Computer simulation of microclimatic and ground thermal regimes: test results and program description. Canada, Dept. of Indian and Northern Affairs, Arctic Land Use Research Program, Rpt. ALUR 75-76-72, 74 p.

SMITH, M.W. and HWANG, C.T. 1973. Thermal disturbance due to channel shifting, Mackenzie Delta, N.W.T., Canada. Proc. 2nd International Conference on Permafrost, Yakutsk, U.S.S.R., North American Contribution, U.S. National Academy of Sciences, pp. 51-60.

SMITH, M.W. and TVEDE, A. 1977. The computer simulation of frost penetration beneath highways. Can. Geotech. J., Vol. 14, No. 2, pp. 167-179.

SMITH, N. and BERG, R.L. 1973. Encountering massive ground ice during road construction in central Alaska. Proc. 2nd International Conference on Permafrost, Yakutsk, U.S.S.R., North American Contribution, U.S. National Academy of Sciences, pp. 730-736.

SMITH, N., BERG, R.L. and MULLER, L. 1973. The use of polyurethane foam plastics in the construction of expedient roads on permafrost in central Alaska. Proc. 2nd International Conference on Permafrost, Yakutsk, U.S.S.R., North American Contribution, U.S. National Academy of Sciences, pp. 736-745.

SMITH, N. and PAZSINT, D.A. 1975. Field test of a MESL (membrane-enveloped soil layer) road section in central Alaska. U.S. Army, CRREL, Tech. Rpt. 260, 40 p.

SMITH, W.S., NAIR, K. and SMITH, R.E. 1973. Sample disturbance and thaw consolidation of a deep sand permafrost. Proc. 2nd International Conference on Permafrost, Yakutsk, U.S.S.R., North American Contribution, U.S. National Academy of Sciences, pp. 392-399.

SNODGRASS, M.P. 1971. Waste disposal and treatment in permafrost areas: a bibliography. U.S., Dept. of the Interior, Office of Library Services, Washington, DC, Bibliography Series 22, 29 p.

SOWERS, G.B. and SOWERS, G.F. 1961. Introductory Soil Mechanics and Foundations. (2nd ed.) MacMillan, New York, NY, 386 p.

SPEER, T.L., WATSON, G.H. and ROWLEY, R.K. 1973. Effects of ground-ice variability and resulting thaw settlements on buried warm-oil pipelines. Proc. 2nd International Conference on Permafrost, Yakutsk, U.S.S.R., North American Contribution, U.S. National Academy of Sciences, pp. 746-751.

STANEK, W. 1977. A list of terms and definitions. Appendix to: Muskeg and the Northern Environment in Canada, Univ. of Toronto Press, Toronto, Ont., pp. 367-382.

STEARNS, S.R. 1965. Selected aspects of geology and physiography of the cold regions. U.S. Army, CRREL, Monograph MI-A1, 40 p.

STEARNS, S.R. 1966. Permafrost (perennially frozen ground). U.S. Army, CRREL, Monograph MI-A2, 77 p.

STEHLE, N.S. 1970. Holding strength of piles in ice. U.S. Navy, Naval Facilities Engineering Command, Naval Civil Engineering Laboratory, Port Hueneme, CA, Tech. Rpt. R700, 38 p.

STEINEMANN, S. 1958. Experimentelle Untersuchungen zur Plastizitat von Eis. Beitr. Geol. Karte Schweiz, Geopech. Ser. Hydrol. No. 10, pp. 1-72.

STEPHENSON, D.G. 1977a. Preventing exposed water pipes from freezing. Canada, National Research Council, Division Building Research, Building Research Note 120, 7 p.

STEPHENSON, D.G. 1977b. Insulation to prevent ground freezing. Canada, National Research Council, Division Building Research, Building Research Note 119, 6 p.

STEVENS, A.E. 1974. Seismicity of northern Canada. Bull. Can. Pet. Geol., Vol. 22, No. 4, pp. 387-404.

STEVENS, A.E. and MILNE, W.G. 1974. Study of seismic risk near pipeline corridors in northwestern Canada and eastern Alaska. Can. J. Earth Sci., Vol. 11, No. 1, pp. 147-164.

STEVENS, H.W. 1975. The response of frozen soils to vibratory loads. U.S. Army, CRREL, Tech. Rpt. 265, 103 p.

STRINGER, E.T. 1972. Techniques of climatology. W.H. Freeman, San Francisco, CA, 539 p.

STURTON, A.B., BRETON, R., DAWALIBI, F. and LEMAY, J. 1973. Grounding in the polar plain. Trans. Canadian Electrical Association, Engineering and Operating Division, Vol. 12, Part I, 35 p.

SUTTON, O.G. 1953. Micrometeorology. McGraw-Hill, Toronto, Ont., 333 p.

SWINZOW, G.K. 1964. Tunnelling in permafrost II. U.S. Army, CRREL, Tech. Rpt. TR 91, 18 p.

SWINZOW, G.K. 1966. Tunnelling and subsurface installations in permafrost. Proc. International Conference on Permafrost (1963), Lafayette, IN, U.S. National Academy of Sciences, Publ. 1287, pp. 519-526.

SWINZOW, G.K. 1970. Permafrost tunnelling by a continuous mechanical method. U.S. Army, CRREL, Tech. Rpt. TR 221, 38 p.

SYKES, D.J. 1971. Effects of fire and fire control on soil and water relations in northern forests: a preliminary review. Proc. Fire in the Northern Environment: A Symposium. Univ. of Alaska, Fairbanks, AK, pp. 37-44.

SYKES, J.F. and LENNOX, W.C. 1976. Thaw and seepage in nonlinear elastic porous media. Proc. 1st International Conference on Finite Elements in Water Resources (July), Princeton Univ., Princeton, NJ, Pentech Press, London, England, pp. 3.47-3.67.

SYKES, J.F., LENNOX, C. and CHARLWOOD, R.G. 1974a. Finite element permafrost thaw settlement model. ASCE, J. Geotech. Eng. Div., Vol. 100, No. 11, pp. 1185-1201.

SYKES, J.F., LENNOX, W.C. and UNNY, T.E. 1974b. Two-dimensional heated pipeline in permafrost. ASCE, J. Geotech. Eng. Div., Vol. 100, No. 11, pp. 1203-1214.

TARNOCAI, C. 1973. Soils of the Mackenzie River area. Canada, Dept. of Indian and Northern Affairs, Environmental-Social Program, Northern Pipelines, Rpt. 73-26, 136 p.

TARNOCAI, C. and NETTERVILLE, J.A. 1976. Some characteristics of a pingo in the Simpson Peninsula, N.W.T. Can. J. Earth Sci. Vol. 13, No. 3, pp. 490-492.

TAYLOR, A.E. and JUDGE, A.S. 1974. Canadian Geothermal Data Collection: Northern Wells 1955 to February 1974. Canada, Dept. of Energy, Mines and Resources, Earth Physics Branch, Geothermal Series 1, 171 p.

TAYLOR, A.E. and JUDGE, A.S. 1975. Canadian Geothermal Data Collection: Northern Wells 1974. Canada, Dept. of Energy, Mines and Resources, Earth Physics Branch, Geothermal Series 3, 127 p.

TAYLOR, A.E. and JUDGE, A.S. 1976. Canadian Geothermal Data Collection: Northern Wells 1975. Canada, Dept. of Energy, Mines and Resources, Earth Physics Branch, Geothermal Series 6, 142 p.

TAYLOR, G.S. and LUTHIN, J.N. 1976. Numeric results of coupled heat-mass flow during freezing and thawing. Proc. 2nd Conference on Soil-Water Problems in Cold Regions, Edmonton, Alta., pp. 155-172.

TAYLOR, K.G. and GILL, D. 1973. Environmental alteration and natural revegetation at a mine site in the Northwest Territories, Canada. Proc. International Conference on Land for Waste Management, Ottawa, Ont., pp. 16-25.

TERZAGHI, K. 1952. Permafrost. J. Boston Soc. Civ. Eng., Vol. 39, No. 1, pp. 1-50.

THOMAS, J., FROST, R.R. and HARVEY, R.D. 1973. Thermal conductivity of carbonate rocks. Engineering Geology, Vol. 7, p. 3-12.

THOMAS, J.F.J. 1957. Industrial water resources of Canada: Mackenzie River and Yukon River drainage basins in Canada 1952-53. Canada, Dept. of Mines and Technical Surveys, Mines Branch, Water Survey Rpt. 8, 78 p.

THOMAS, M.K. and BOYD, D.W. 1957. Wind chill in northern Canada. The Canadian Geographer, No. 10, pp. 29-39.

THOMPSON, E.G. and SAYLES, F.H. 1972. Insitu creep analysis of a room in frozen soil. ASCE, J. Soil Mech. Found. Div., No. SM6, pp. 899-915.

THOMPSON, H.A. 1966. Air temperatures in northern Canada with emphasis on freezing and thawing indices. Proc. International Conference on Permafrost (1963), Lafayette, IN, U.S. National Academy of Sciences, Publ. 1287, pp. 272-280.

THOMPSON, H.A. 1967. The climate of the Canadian Arctic. Environment Canada, Atmospheric Environment Service, Toronto, Ont., Reprint from 1967 Canada Year Book, 32 p.

THOMPSON, H.A. 1969. The climate of Hudson Bay. Environment Canada, Atmospheric Environment Service, Toronto, Ont., 24 p.

THOMSON, S. 1966. Icings on the Alaska Highway. Proc. International Conference on Permafrost (1963), Lafayette, IN, U.S. National Academy of Sciences, Publ. 1287, pp. 526-529.

THORNTON, D.E. 1974. Waste impoundment embankments in permafrost regions: the oxidation pond embankment, Inuvik, N.W.T. In: Arctic Waste Disposal, Canada, Dept. of Indian and Northern Affairs, Environmental-Social Committee, Northern Pipelines, Rpt. 74-10, pp. 159-193.

THORNTON, D.E. 1976. Steady-state and quasi-static thermal results for bare and insulated pipes in permafrost. Can. Geotech. J., Vol. 13, No. 2, pp. 161-171.

TICE, A.R., ANDERSON, D.M. and BANIN, A. 1976. The prediction of unfrozen water contents in frozen soils from liquid limit determinations. U.S. Army, CRREL, Rpt. 76-8, 9 p.

TOBIASSON, W. 1971. Utility tunnel experience in cold regions. Amer. Public Works Assoc., Spec. Rpt. 41, pp. 125-138.

TOBIASSON, W. 1973. Performance of the Thule hangar soil cooling systems. Proc. 2nd International Conference on Permafrost, Yakutsk, U.S.S.R., North American Contribution, U.S. National Academy of Sciences, pp. 752-758.

TOBIASSON, W. and JOHNSON, P. 1978. The details behind a typical Alaskan pile foundation. Proc. 2nd International Conference on Permafrost, Edmonton, Alta., Canada, National Research Council, Vol. 1, pp. 891-897.

TOLSTIKHIN, N.I. and TOLSTIKHIN, O.N. 1974. Groundwater and surface water in the permafrost region. Environment Canada, Inland Waters Directorate, Water Resources Branch, Tech. Bull. 97, 30 p. Transl. from Russian (1976).

TROW, W.A. 1955. Frost action on small footings. U.S. Highway Research Board, Bull. 100, pp. 22-27.

TRUPAK, N.G. 1970. Construction of earth dams on permafrost soils. Hydrotechnical Construction (U.S.S.R.), No. 9, pp. 8-11, Transl. by Consultants Bureau, New York, NY, for ASCE.

TSYTOVICH, N.A. 1959. Principles of Geocryology. Part II, Chap. III, pp. 28-79, Canada, National Research Council, Tech. Transl. TT 1239.

TSYTOVICH, N.A. 1960. Bases and foundations on frozen soil. U.S. Highway Research Board, Spec. Rpt. 58, pp. 1-93.

TSYTOVICH, N.A. 1973. The mechanics of frozen ground. Vysshaya Shkola Press, Moscow (In Russian.), Transl. by Scripta Technica (G.K. Swinzow and G.P. Tschebotarioff, ed.), Scripta/McGraw-Hill, New York, NY (1975), 426 p.

TSYTOVICH, N.A. and KRONIK, Ya.A. 1970. Physicomechanical and physicochemical properties of certain cohesive soils used in the construction of dams in the far North. Proc. 1st International Congress of the International Association of Engineering Geologists, UNESCO, Vol. 1, pp. 3-19.

TSYTOVICH, N.A., KRONIK, Ya.A., MARKIN, K.F., AKSENOV, V.I. and SAMUEL'SON, M.V. 1978. Physical and mechanical properties of saline soils. Proc. 2nd International Conference on Permafrost (1973), Yakutsk, U.S.S.R., U.S.S.R. Contribution, U.S. National Academy of Sciences, pp. 238-247.

TSYTOVICH, N.A. and SUMGIN, M.I. 1937. The principles of the mechanics of frozen ground. U.S. Army, CRREL, (SIPRE), Transl. 19 (1959), 432 p.

TSYTOVICH, N.A., UKHOVA, N.V. and UKHOV, S.B. 1972. Prediction of the temperature stability of dams built of local materials on permafrost. U.S. Army, CRREL, Transl. 435, 153 p.

U.S.A., NATIONAL ACADEMY OF SCIENCES. 1976. Problems and priorities in offshore permafrost research. National Research Council, Polar Research Board, Committee on Permafrost, Report by Ad Hoc Study Group on Offshore Permafrost, 52 p.

U.S. ARMY. 1966. Arctic and subarctic construction: terrain evaluation in Arctic and subarctic regions. Tech. Manual TM5-852-8.

U.S. ARMY/AIR FORCE. 1965. Arctic and subarctic construction: surface drainage design for airfields and heliports in Arctic and subarctic regions. Tech. Manual TM5-852-7/AFM 88-19, Chap. 7.

U.S. ARMY/AIR FORCE. 1966a. Arctic and subarctic construction: general provisions. Tech. Manual TM5-852-1/AFM 88-19, Chap. 1.

U.S. ARMY/AIR FORCE. 1966b. Arctic and subarctic construction: site selection and development. Tech. Manual TM5-852-2/AFM 88-19, Chap. 2.

U.S. ARMY/AIR FORCE. 1966c. Arctic and subarctic construction: calculation methods for determination of depths of freeze and thaw in soils. Tech. Manual TM5-852-6/AFM 88-19, Chap. 6.

U.S. ARMY/AIR FORCE. 1967. Arctic and subarctic construction: Structure foundations. Tech. Manual TM5-852-4/AFM 88-19, Chap. 4.

U.S. NAVY. 1955. Arctic engineering. Bureau of Yards and Docks, Washington, DC, Tech. Publ. TP-PW-N, 465 p.

U.S. NAVY. 1967. Design manual NAVFAC DM-9, cold regions engineering. Dept. of the Navy, Naval Facilities Engineering Command, Washington, DC, 192 p.

U.S. NAVY. 1971. Design manual NAVFAC DM-7, soil mechanics, foundations and earth structures. Dept. of the Navy, Naval Facilities Engineering Command, Washington, DC, 323 p.

U.S.S.R. 1960. Technical considerations in designing foundations in permafrost (SN 91-60). Canada, National Research Council, Tech. Transl. TT 1033, 64 p.

U.S.S.R. 1962. Instructions for designing bearing media and foundations in the southern zone of the permafrost region. Canada, National Research Council, Tech. Transl. TT 1298, 77 p.

U.S.S.R. 1964. Guide for design and construction of pile foundations in permafrost (RSN-14-62). Canada, National Research Council, Tech. Transl. TT 1314, 40 p.

U.S.S.R. 1967. Instructions for the design of townsites, factories, buildings and structures in the northern construction-climatic zone (SN 353-66). Canada, National Research Council, Tech. Transl. TT 1547, 100 p.

U.S.S.R. 1969. Handbook for the design of bases and foundations of buildings and other structures on permafrost. Canada, National Research Council, Tech. Transl. TT 1865, 129 p.

U.S.S.R. 1970. Handbook of water utilities, sewers and heating networks designed for settlements in permafrost regions. Canada, Dept. of Indian and Northern Affairs, Northern Science Research Group, Publ. NSRG 70-1, 107 p. (Transl. from the Russian.)

U.S.S.R. 1972. Guide for the application of drilling and blasting method of loosening frozen and perennially frozen ground and moraines. Canada, National Research Council, Tech. Transl. 1877 (1976), 27 p.

U.S.S.R. 1973a. Instructions for the design of bases and foundations on permafrost soils having high ice and salt contents (SN 450-72). Gosstroi, Moscow, 25 p. (In Russian.)

U.S.S.R. 1973b. Handbook for the determination of the physical, thermal and mechanical properties of frozen soils. Gosstroi, Moscow, 191 p. (In Russian.)

VAN EVERDINGEN, R.O. 1974. Groundwater in permafrost regions of Canada. In: Permafrost Hydrology, Proc. of Workshop Seminar, Environment Canada, Canadian National Committee for the International Hydrological Decade, pp. 83-93.

VAN EVERDINGEN, R.O. 1979. Potential interactions between pipelines and terrain in a northern environment. Canada, Dept. of Environment, Inland Waters Directorate, National Hydrology Research Institute, NHRI Paper 8, IWD Tech. Bull. 114, 7 p.

VEILLETTE, J. 1975a. Modified CRREL ice coring augers. Geol. Surv. Can., Paper 75-1, Part A, pp. 425-426.

VEILLETTE, J. 1975b. Helicopter portable drill for high Arctic programs. Geol. Surv. Can., Paper 75-1, Part A, pp. 427-429.

VEILLETTE, J. 1975c. Stabilization of ground temperatures in a shallow borehole. Geol. Surv. Can., Paper 75-1, Part A, pp. 371-372.

VERSCHININ, D.V., DERIAGIN, B.V. and VIRILENKO, N.V. 1960. The non-freezing water in soil. U.S. Army, CRREL, Transl. 30, 10 p.

VIERECK, L.A. 1973a. Wildfire in the taiga of Alaska. J. Quat. Res. Vol. 3, No. 3, pp. 465-495.

VIERECK, L.A. 1973b. Ecological effects of river flooding and forest fires on permafrost in the taiga of Alaska. Proc. 2nd International Conference on Permafrost, Yakutsk, U.S.S.R., North American Contribution, U.S. National Academy of Sciences, pp. 60-67.

VIGDORCHIK, M.E. 1980a. Arctic Pleistocene history and the development of submarine permafrost. Westview Press, Boulder, CO, 286 p.

VIGDORCHIK, M.E. 1980b. Submarine permafrost on the Alaskan continental shelf. Westview Press, Boulder, CO, 118 p.

VINSON, T.S. 1978. Parameter effects on dynamic properties of frozen soils. ASCE, J. Geotech. Eng. Div., Vol. 104, No. GT 10, pp. 1289-1306.

VOITKOVSKIY, K.F. (ed.) 1968. Foundations of structures on frozen soils in Yakutia. Nauka, Moscow, 199 p. (In Russian.)

VORONKOV, O.K., NOZDRIN, G.I. and MIKHAYLOVSKIY, G.V. 1979. Relationships between static and dynamic characteristics of deformability of frozen and thawed rock in rock samples and undisturbed rock masses. U.S. Army, CRREL, Draft Transl. 703, 16 p.

ZARETSKII, Y.K. 1972. Rheological properties of plastic frozen soils and determination of settlement of a test plate with time. J. Soil Mech. Found. Eng. (U.S.S.R.), Vol. 9, No. 2, pp. 81-85, Transl. by Consultants Bureau, New York, NY.

ZARUBIN, N.E. and DZHURIK, V.I. 1975. Seismic properties of frozen soils of the Baikal region. J. Soil mech. Found. Eng. (U.S.S.R.), Vol. 12, No. 3, pp. 4-6, Transl. by Consultants Bureau, New York, NY.

ZELENIN, A.N. 1964. Cutting of soils. U.S. Army, CRREL, Transl. TL 323, 92 p.

ZHIGULSKIY, A.A. 1970. Thermal moisture regime around piles in pre-drilled holes. U.S. Army, CRREL, Transl. 203, 11 p.

ZHILENAS, S.V., MYZNIKOV, Y.N. and TEN, N.A. 1973. Winter placement of moraine material in the dam of the Ust'Khantaisk hydro development. Hydro-technical Construction (U.S.S.R.), No. 3, pp. 232-237, Transl. by Consultants Bureau, New York, NY, for ASCE.

ZOLTAI, S.C. 1972. Palsas and peat plateaus in central Manitoba and Saskatchewan. Can. J. of Forest Res., Vol. 2, No. 3, pp. 291-302.

ZOLTAI, S.C. 1973. Vegetation, surficial deposits and permafrost relationships in the Hudson Bay Lowland. Proc. Symposium on the Physical Environment of the Hudson Bay Lowland, Univ. of Guelph, Guelph, Ont., pp. 17-34.

ZOLTAI, S.C. and PETTAPIECE, W.W. 1973. Studies of vegetation, landform and per-mafrost in the Mackenzie Valley. Canada, Dept. of Indian and Northern Affairs, Environmental-Social Program, Northern Pipelines, Rpt. 73-4, 105 p.

ZOLTAI, S.C. and TARNOCAI, C. 1974. Soils and vegetation of hummocky terrain. Canada, Dept. of Indian and Northern Affairs, Environmental-Social Program, Northern Pipelines, Rpt. 74-5, 86 p.

ZOLTAI, S.C. and TARNOCAI, C. 1975. Perennially frozen peatlands in the western Arctic and subarctic of Canada. Can. J. Earth Sci., Vol. 12, No. 1, pp. 28-43.

BIBLIOGRAPHY—A SELECTED LIST OF CONFERENCE PROCEEDINGS

(1) Proc. International Conference on Permafrost (1963), Lafayette, IN, U.S. National Academy of Sciences, Publ. 1287 (1966), 570 p. (Contains transl. of Soviet papers.)

(2) (a) Proc. 2nd International Conference on Permafrost (1973), Yakutsk, U.S.S.R., North American Contribution, U.S. National Academy of Sciences, 794 p.

    (b) Proc. 2nd International Conference on Permafrost (1973), Yakutsk, U.S.S.R., U.S.S.R. Contribution (F.J. Sanger, ed.), U.S. National Academy of Sciences (1978), 890 p. (Contains transl. of Soviet papers.)

(3) (a) Proc. 3rd International Conference on Permafrost (1978), Edmonton, Alta., Canada, National Research Council, Vol. 1, 992 p., Vol. 2 (1979), 255 p.

    (b) Proc. 3rd International Conference on Permafrost (1978), Edmonton, Alta., Canada, National Research Council, Transl. of Soviet papers (1980), Part I, 400 p., Part II, 430 p.

(4) Proc. Symposium on Cold Regions Engineering (1970), College, AK, Univ. of Alaska, Dept. Civil Eng. (J.L. Burdick, ed.), Vol. 1, 396 p., Vol. 2 (1971), 335 p.

(5) Proc. 2nd International Symposium on Cold Regions Engineering (1976), Fairbanks, AK, Univ. of Alaska, Dept. Civil Eng. (J.L. Burdick and P. Johnson, eds.) (1977), 597 p.

(6) Proc. Conference on Applied Techniques for Cold Environments (1978), Anchorage, AK, ASCE, New York, NY, Vol. 1, 629 p., Vol. 2 (1979), 536 p.

(7) Proc. Symposium on Utilities Delivery in Arctic Regions (1976), Edmonton, Alta., Canada, Environment Canada, Environmental Protection Service, Rpt. EPS-3-WP-77-1 (1977), 596 p.

(8) Proc. 2nd Symposium on Utilities Delivery in Arctic Regions (1979), Edmonton, Alta., Canada, Environment Canada, Environmental Protection Service, Preprint vol., 662 p.

(9) Proc. International Conference on Materials Engineering in the Arctic (1976), St. Jovite, Que. (M.B. Ives, ed.), Am. Soc. for Metals (1977), 331 p.

Index